n

Specialised Stamp Catalogue

Volume 3
Queen Elizabeth II
Pre-decimal Issues

Ninth Edition

Stanley Gibbons Ltd
London and Ringwood

By Appointment to
Her Majesty The Queen
Stanley Gibbons Limited
London Philatelists

Published by **Stanley Gibbons Ltd.**
Publications Editorial, Sales Offices and Distribution Centre:
5 Parkside, Christchurch Road, Ringwood,
Hants BH24 3SH.

© **Stanley Gibbons Ltd 1993**

ISBN 0-85259-358-9

1st edition—August 1970	5th edition—November 1980
2nd edition—October 1971	6th edition—June 1984
3rd edition—February 1976	7th edition—November 1987
Reprinted—October 1976	8th edition—September 1990
Reprinted—April 1977	9th edition—October 1993
4th edition—November 1978	

Item No. 2810 (93)

**Typeset by BPCC Whitefriars Ltd., Tunbridge Wells, Kent
Printed in Great Britain by BPCC Wheatons, Exeter, Devon**

Contents

Stanley Gibbons Holdings Plc.

STANLEY GIBBONS LTD.
399 STRAND, LONDON, WC2R 0LX

Auction and Specialist Stamp Departments. Open Monday to Friday 9.30 a.m. to 5.00 p.m.

Shop. Open Monday to Friday 8.30 a.m. to 6.00 p.m. and Saturday 10 a.m. to 4.00 p.m.

Telephone 071 836 8444. Fax 071 836 7342 for all departments.

STANLEY GIBBONS PUBLICATIONS
5 PARKSIDE, CHRISTCHURCH ROAD, RINGWOOD, HANTS BH24 3SH

Telephone 0425 472363 (24 hour answerphone service) Fax 0425 470247

Publications Shop. Open Monday to Friday 9.00 a.m. to 3.00 p.m.

Publications Mail Order. FREEPHONE 0800 611622. Monday to Friday 8.30 a.m. to 5.00 p.m.

Stanley Gibbons Publications has overseas licensees and distributors for Australia, Austria, Belgium, Canada, Denmark, Finland, France, Germany, Hong Kong, Israel, Italy, Japan, Luxembourg, Netherlands, New Zealand, Norway, Singapore, South Africa, Sweden, Switzerland, United States, West Indies and Caribbean. Please contact the Ringwood address for details.

For details of the Great Britain Philatelic Society write to:
The Great Britain Philatelic Society. Hon. Membership Secretary: Mr D. S. Glover, 10 Rockwood Park, Saint Hill, East Grinstead, W. Sussex RH19 4JX.

Preface

This year, 1993, marks the 40th anniversary of Her Majesty's Coronation. The four stamps issued on that occasion reflected the then current trends in stamp design with the most controversial being the striking full-face 1s. 3d. by Edmund Dulac which was, itself, an echo of his design for the Coronation issue of King George VI.

By the time the sea-change of a new currency had taken place in 1971 the emphasis for new Special Stamps had swung towards pictorial designs and the introduction of new formats. The Wilding low value definitive series, with its echoes of late Victorian and Georgian symbolism, had also been swept away to be replaced by the simplicity of the Machin series.

The decades between these two events are now being increasingly recognised as a period of transition, the study of which is essential to provide an understanding of present and future trends. There was innovation in postal technology, in addition to stamp design, and much attention has been paid in recent years to the introduction of graphite lines and then phosphor bands to assist electronic sorting. Additional information continues to be recorded here and this edition includes an explanation of the narrow phosphor bands which have been found to occur on stamps from booklet panes adjacent to the binding margin. Prices are now provided for those cylinder booklet panes of four which only come with the cylinder numbers partially trimmed. The Wilding section also contains a listing for the recently-discovered 9d. Tudor watermark showing the variety imperforate between stamp and top margin.

The information provided for the Wilding Castle high values has been considerably revised and we are most grateful for permission to use information from the study undertaken by Mr. Ian Hine into the unnumbered plates used to produce the Waterlow and De La Rue printings. Inverted watermarks on these stamps continue to be popular and we have been able to provide some additional information and, for the first time, a listing for the 1958 De La Rue 2s. 6d. showing watermark inverted.

The Machin £sd stamps are less complicated, but the listings of the high values now include the £1 indigo shade, known from a single sheet, the authenticity of which has recently been proved by P.O. analysis.

There are a number of additional errors included in the Special Stamps section including several embossing omitted items and the 1967 Wild Flowers 4d. *se-tenant* block without phosphor bands and with the slate-purple omitted. This is, again, a recent discovery, as is the Postage Due 2d. from the 1954–55 series showing the Tudor Crown watermark sideways Crown to right.

Prices for basic stamps follow those quoted in other Great Britain catalogues published by Stanley Gibbons Ltd., but it is encouraging to see the growth of interest in "specialised" material being reflected in increased prices. In addition to errors and varieties it can be reported that some Wilding cylinder blocks are becoming difficult to find and the demand for stamp booklets of the period is, generally, buoyant.

There is much of interest in these pre-decimal issues of the current reign and we hope that this volume in the award-winning *Great Britain Specialised Catalogue* series will encourage collectors to study the stamps of this fascinating period.

Acknowledgements

In preparing this new edition we would like to thank the members of the Great Britain Philatelic Society who have contacted us with the information on the listings in this catalogue. At the same time we thank the Society's Council for again allowing us to draw on published articles in the *The GB Journal*, in particular, *British Stamp Booklets* by Dr Jean Alexander and the late Mr Leonard F. Newbery.

The views and opinions of active collectors are very welcome and an asset when the time comes to prepare a new catalogue. To those who have given us the benefit of their time and researches we extend our appreciation and thanks.

David J. Aggersberg
Robert H. Oliver

Introductory Notes

The aim of this Catalogue is to classify in specialised form the stamps of Great Britain, to give distinguishing numbers to them and to quote prices which are current with Stanley Gibbons Ltd., at the time of going to press and at which they will supply if in stock.

Detailed Introductory Notes

Before using the catalogue it is important to study the "General Notes" as these explain the technical background of the issues in question. They are to be found at the beginning of the relevant sections.

Arrangement of Lists

The Wilding, Machin £.s.d. and Regional issues are dealt with value by value. The order of listing is as follows:

A. Basic listing of single stamps from sheets, booklets and coils according to paper, phosphor and gum with errors and varieties following in small type.
B. Illustrations of listed cylinder and plate varieties.
C. List of cylinder blocks according to paper, phosphor and gum combinations and priced according to perforation types.
D. Details of constant minor sheet flaws without illustrations and prices but quoting positions on stamps.
E. Information relating to coils.
F. Ancillary data relating to sheet markings, withdrawal dates, and quantities issued or sold.

If there is a deliberate change in the number of phosphor bands this is treated as a separate issue which is then listed in the order shown above.

Booklet panes are listed separately in Sections SB and UB according to paper and gum, with errors and cylinder varieties, and all priced according to perforation types. These are followed by illustrations of cylinder varieties and lists of booklet pane cylinder numbers appear at the end of each listing.

The Special issues (Section W) are listed on the same basis, set by set, with the addition of ancillary information about sheet format, method of printing, a list of the sheet markings, quantities sold and withdrawal dates from information published by the Post Office.

Catalogue Numbering

All *Specialised Catalogue* numbers include a prefix letter or letters which denotes its Section in the Catalogue. This is followed by the related number in the 1993 edition of the *Part I (British Commonwealth) Catalogue.*

Shades, where there is more than one, are denoted by bracketed numbers, e.g. (1) Green, (2) Deep green for No. S25, the Wilding 1½d., with watermark Tudor Crown.

Varieties have a letter identification, e.g. *a*. Watermark inverted; *b*. (short description of cylinder variety) and related varities to item *b*. will be listed as *ba.*, *bb.*, etc.

In Appendix HA the booklets have the same numbers and prefix letters as are used in the *G.B. Concise Catalogue.* Varieties of booklets listed in the *Specialised Catalogue* only are shown with number in brackets, thus "(*a*)".

Prices

Prices quoted in this Catalogue are the selling prices of Stanley Gibbons Ltd., at the time the book went to press. They are for stamps in fine condition for the particular issue, unless otherwise indicated; those of lesser quality may be offered at lower prices. All prices are subject to change without prior notice and no guarantee is given to supply all stamps priced, since it is not possible to keep every catalogued item in stock.

In the case of unused stamps, our prices are for unmounted mint. Prices for used stamps refer to postally used examples.

If a variety exists in more than one *shade* it is priced for the commonest shade and will be worth correspondingly more in a scarcer shade. Except where otherwise stated varieties are priced for single examples and extra stamps required to make up positional blocks would be valued as normals. All *cylinder flaws* and other varieties listed under *booklet panes* are priced for the complete pane.

Cylinder blocks containing varieties are indicated by an asterisk against the price (which includes the cost of the variety).

Cases can exist where a particular stamp shows more than one listed variety. It might, for example, have an inverted watermark as well as a broad phosphor band, both of which are listed but priced separately. It is not practical to cover every possible combination, but the value of such items may be established by adding the difference between the price of the basic stamp and the dearest variety to the catalogue price of the cheapest variety.

The prices quoted for *booklet panes* are for panes with good perforations and complete with the binding margin. Prices for complete booklets are for those containing panes with average perforations as it is unusual for all panes in the booklet to show full perforations on the guillotined sides.

Cylinder blocks are priced according to the type of perforator used. This takes account of the state of the perforations on all four sides of the sheet, not just the corner where the cylinder number appears. Note that a full specification of a cylinder block should quote the basic number of the stamp; cylinder number; with or without dot; perforation type; cream or white paper; gum arabic or PVA, wherever such alternatives exist.

Guarantee

All stamps supplied by Stanley Gibbons Ltd., are guaranteed originals in the following terms:

If not as described, and returned by the purchaser, we undertake to refund the price paid to us in the original transaction. If any stamp is certified as genuine by the Expert Committee of the Royal Philatelic Society, London, or by B.P.A. Expertising Ltd., the purchaser shall not be entitled to make any claim against us for any error, omission or mistake in such certificate.

Consumers' statutory rights are not affected by the above guarantee.

Expertisation

We do not give opinions as to the genuineness of stamps. Expert Committees exist for this purpose and enquiry can be made of the Royal Philatelic Society, 41 Devonshire Place, London W1N 1PE, or B.P.A. Expertising Ltd., P.O. Box 137, Leatherhead, Surrey KT22 0RG. They do not undertake valuations under any circumstances and fees are payable for their services.

Correspondence

Letters should be addressed to the Catalogue Editor, Stanley Gibbons Publications, Parkside, Christchurch Road, Ringwood, Hants BH24 3SH, and return postage is appreciated when a reply is sought. New information and unlisted items for consideration are welcomed.

Please note we do not give opinions as to the genuineness of stamps, nor do we identify stamps or number them by our Catalogue.

To order from this Catalogue

Always quote the *Specialised Catalogue* number, mentioning *Volume 3, 9th Edition*, and where necessary specify additionally the precise item wanted.

National Postal Museum Archive Material

During 1984 and 1985 surplus GB material from the National Postal Museum archives was included in three auction sales. The lots offered were mostly imprimaturs, which were handstamped on the reverse to indicate origin, and specimen overprints. In this catalogue items which are only known from the lots sold at these auctions are included in special entries, under headings clearly indicating their origin. Where items included in these sales had been previously listed a dagger is shown alongside the catalogue price.

Symbols and Abbreviations

†	(after date of issue) date of issue in sheet format, but available earlier from coil or booklet source. See Dates of Issue, under General Notes
†	(in price column) does not exist
—	(in price column) exists, but no market price is known (a blank conveys the same meaning)
*	(against the price of a cylinder block) price includes a listed variety
/	between colours means "on" and the colour following is that of the paper on which the stamp is printed
Cyl.	Cylinder
GA	Gum arabic
mm.	Millimetres
No.	Number
OP	Ordinary and phosphor
Phos.	Phosphor
Pl.	Plate
PVA	Polyvinyl alcohol (gum)
R.	Row (thus "R. 6/4" indicates the fourth stamp from the left in the sixth horizontal row from the top of a sheet of stamps)
Th.	Refers to the Stanley Gibbons "Thirkell" Position Finder. The letters and figures which follow (e.g. Th. E5) pinpoint the position of the flaw on the stamp according to the grid engraved on the Finder

Watermark Illustrations

The illustrations show watermarks as seen from the *front* of the stamp. This is important to remember when classifying sideways watermarks which also exist sideways inverted (i.e. Crown to right).

Quantities Sold

The figures for quantities issued or sold are those published by the Post Office. Some figures for the Regionals, however, came from an article by Mr. E. C. Ehrmann in *Stamp Collecting*.

Items Excluded

In dealing with *varieties* and *minor constant flaws* we record only those for which we can vouch, namely items we have seen and verified for ourselves. It should be recognised, however, that some flaws described as constant may be transient: they may develop in size to be sufficiently noticeable to be worth retouching.

Colour shifts due to faulty registration range from minor shifts to quite spectacular varieties. As it is very difficult to draw a line between major and minor shifts we have not listed any. We likewise exclude: doctor blade flaws; paper creases; partially omitted colours; negative offsets: and misplaced perforations.

We do not quote for traffic light blocks or positional blocks showing various sheet markings other than cylinder blocks, but when available they will be supplied at appropriate prices.

SECTION S
Dorothy Wilding Issues
1952–68. Sheet and Coil Stamps in Photogravure

General Notes

INTRODUCTION. Queen Elizabeth II came to the throne on 6 February, 1952. By contrast with the King George VI series there were five different basic designs from five artists with a common feature consisting of the portrait of the Queen by Dorothy Wilding Ltd. enclosed in an oval. In this portrait the Queen is shown wearing the Crown Jewels, whilst the policy of embodying various emblems representative of the different parts of the Kingdom was continued. These and the intricacies of the Crown Jewels produced many minor varieties and there are probably more varieties and flaws on this issue than on any other issue since the Victorian Line-engraved stamps.

The stamps came out value by value over a period, the first to be issued being the 1½d. and 2½d. which were placed on sale on the 5 December 1952 but it was not until February 1954 that the series was completed. During this period there was an interesting phase when booklets were issued containing panes of King George VI and Queen Elizabeth II stamps.

ARRANGEMENT. This Section takes each value in turn and follows its history through the various watermarks, graphite lines, phosphors, and papers taking in the coils and on page 7 there is a table setting out which values occurred in each state and quoting their catalogue numbers for easy reference. The general arrangement of the catalogue is to show first the basic listing with errors and varieties in small type, followed by illustrations of the listed varieties, a list of the cylinder numbers, a record of the minor constant flaws, coils and finally ancillary information such as sheet markings, withdrawal dates and quantities issued or sold. Booklet panes are dealt with in a similar manner in Section SB. Quantities issued or sold are not given but the numbers of booklets sold are included in Appendix HA.

PRINTERS. All the Wilding issues were printed in photogravure by Harrison & Sons. They were printed on continuous reels of paper "on the web" generally in double pane width, i.e. 480 stamps consisting of two panes (no dot and dot) each of 240 stamps arranged in twenty rows of twelve stamps, the panes being guillotined before issue. However, some printings were made from single cylinders printing sheets of 240 stamps (i.e. no dot panes only). Exceptionally, the 1963 2s. Holiday Booklet (No. NR1) stamps were printed on a sheet-fed machine.

PAPER. For the first ten years the definitives were printed on a creamy paper but starting in April 1962 a whiter paper was gradually introduced. It is always a difficult matter to maintain successive supplies of paper in exactly the same colour and so it is not surprising that there is some variation in the degree of whiteness in the "whiter paper" which sometimes makes it difficult to identify. Sometimes knowledge of the cylinder used can be decisive. The whiter paper does not respond to the chalky test (that is applying silver to see if it will produce a black line) but a true coated chalk-surfaced paper was used for the 2s. Holiday Booklet issued in 1963 which affected the ½d. and 2½d. values in the Crowns watermark.

In 1964 an experimental paper was used for the 3d. non-phosphor Crowns watermark which was slightly thicker. It can be distinguished by the fact that an additional watermark letter "T" lying on its side occurred about four times in the sheet.

Variations can also be found in the thickness of the paper used, a notable example being the 3d. Tudor Crown watermark (No. S67) on thick paper. As weight standards were applied to complete reels only, such differences on individual stamps were within acceptable tolerances.

Paper Fluorescence. Stamps printed on unsurfaced paper may show a varying fluoresence when viewed under a short-wave ultra-violet lamp. This is due to the presence, in the rags used in paper making, of optical brightening agents. Such fluorescent properties are outside the scope of this catalogue.

WATERMARKS

In the Crowns watermark differences in the spacing of the Crowns have been noticed but it is believed that this is due to variations in the dandy roll and does not represent a different version of the watermark.

Errors, or replacement " bits ", occur on most dandy rolls. For example during the period 1964 to 1966 the Crowns watermark can be found with one crown inverted. These errors have been seen on the ½d., No. S2b, and on various commemoratives.

Watermark Varieties. As the Wilding issues are all printed " on the web " inverted watermarks cannot occur on the sheet stamps, but they do occur on 50% of the booklet panes owing to the manner in which the sheets are arranged with some rows having the images inverted on the cylinders. The booklets are guillotined before issue resulting in

1

S Wilding—Notes

some panes with the watermark inverted. Booklets are the only source of inverted watermarks in the Wilding issues.

Until 1961 all stamps with the watermark sideways came only from coils with left side delivery and these all show the top of the watermark pointing to left as seen from the front of the stamp. From 1961 all 2s. booklets on Crowns watermark had the watermark sideways and these, of course, have 50% of the panes with the crowns pointing to left and 50% to right and they are listed both ways.

GUM. Only gum arabic has been used for the Wilding issues as PVA gum was not introduced until the Machin series.

PERFORATION. All stamps are comb perforated 15 × 14 as the King George VI issues
However, the horizontal perforation is very close to the three-quarters mark and so is sometimes described as 14½ × 14. Quite a number of different perforators were used and these are described and illustrated in Appendix G which deals with the perforators employed for all the Harrison issues. The cylinder numbers are listed according to the type of perforator used.
Perforation varieties such as double or misplaced perforations are not listed in this Catalogue.

EXPERIMENTAL GRAPHITE ISSUES. The first Automatic Letter Facing machine (known as ALF) was introduced experimentally at Southampton on 19 December 1957. The machine, which prepares letters for the sorting process, is fed with letters having their long edges parallel but with stamps in any of four possible positions. The letters are reorientated so that the stamps are in one of two possible positions on one long edge. These two positions, together with First and Second Class mail, are separated into stacks, and the stamps are cancelled. Items which cannot be faced, due for example to the absence of a stamp, are rejected to receive manual treatment.
The prototype facing machine looked in the stamp corner for an area of dense printing ink, having the characteristics of a stamp, as a means of stamp detection. This system was inefficient as the machine's performance was influenced by stamp design and the occasional presence of misleading writing on the envelope. However, facing machines were equipped with this method as a secondary means of stamp detection in order to deal with O.H.M.S. and Business Reply items.
To improve the efficiency of facing it was necessary to give these stamps some unmistakable identity. The first attempt used stamps which were printed with electrically conducting vertical black graphite lines on the back under the gum. One line on the 2d., then the printed paper rate, and two lines on the other values. The use of electrically conducting lines was not a complete success as failures were caused by metallic paper fasteners and damp mail.
There were two graphite issues. The first in November 1957 on the ½d., 1d., 1½d., 2d., 2½d. and 3d. sheet stamps with the St. Edward's Crown watermark and also on coils. The second issue came out during 1958-59 on the same values, plus the 4d. and 4½d. in sheets with the Crowns watermark and here there were also coils and booklets.
Stamps showing faked graphite lines are known especially on used samples.

PHOSPHOR-GRAPHITE ISSUES. In November 1959 existing graphite stamps were overprinted on the face with phosphorescent ink which, when exposed to ultra-violet (u.v.) light, releases energy in the form of visible light. The emission of visible light persists for some time after the exposure to u.v. light has ceased. These stamps were originally issued for further experiments at Southampton, November 1959 to February 1960, when the ALF operated with one electrical scanner and one phosphor scanner. Most countries which handle very large quantities of mail have followed the lead of Great Britain in the use of some form of luminescence on stamps to facilitate automatic facing.
The British Post Office uses organic-resin phosphors containing an activator, the choice of activator affecting the optical properties.
Phosphor bands are not always easy to see, especially on used stamps, and it is usually necessary to hold the stamps up to the light at eye level when they become visible as broad bands.
The graphite lined stamps were overprinted with vertical phosphor bands on the face, again one band for the 2d. and two bands for the others. In sheets they appeared on the ½d., 1d., 1½d. and 2d. (in error) with St. Edward's Crown watermark and on the 2d., 2½d., 3d., 4d. and 4½d. with Crowns watermark. The substance used is commercially known as Lettalite B1 (the activator being Parahydroxydiphenyl) and it produces a greenish phosphorescence when reacting with u.v. light in the 2000 to 3000 Angstrom range.
As the phosphor treatment of stamps at Southampton was successful, residual stocks having graphite lines were distributed as normal stock to other areas and a notice was sent to Post Office clerks to say that they should disregard the black lines. This applied also to the 5s. booklet No. H46g (Sept. 1960).

2

PHOSPHOR ISSUES.   The Southampton ALF was converted to scan phosphor only on 6 July 1960 and the $\frac{1}{2}$d. to 4d and 1s.3d. values with Crowns watermark with phosphor bands only were issued on 22 June 1960, the 6d. following on 27 June.   Coils and booklets were issued later.

The same phosphor reacting green was employed but in 1961 this was replaced as an interim measure by Lettalite B2 (Carbazole sulphonic acid being the activator) which reacts blue to u.v. in the 2000–4000 Ångstrom range.   The advantage of this was that it gave a stronger signal.   By this time ALF machines were introduced into other areas and the "blue" phosphor was in use between 1961 and 1966 on the same values as for the "green" phosphor and with the addition of the 4$\frac{1}{2}$d. value.   This period covered the changeover to the whiter paper and also two changes in postal rates so that the 2d., 2$\frac{1}{2}$d. and 3d. were each issued with one and two bands.

With the introduction of address coding and automatic letter sorting, at Norwich in 1965, it became necessary to use a phosphor for stamps which would not interfere with sorting. Thus another change was made, this time to Lettalite B3 (having Terephthalic acid as the activator) which was inert to the u.v. light of wavelength 3650 Ångstroms used in sorting machines but which has a bright visible light output when subjected to 2537 Ångstroms in the facing machine. This reacts violet under the lamp.

Phosphor Band Widths.   There are two widths of the "violet" phosphor bands, the 8 mm. bands, issued in 1965 ($\frac{1}{2}$d., 1d., 1$\frac{1}{2}$d., 2d., 3d., 4d., 6d. and 1s.3d., plus coils and booklets) and the 9·5 mm. bands issued in 1966–67 (1d., 2d., 3d., 4d., 5d., 6d., 7d., 8d., 9d., 10d., 1s., 1s.3d. and 1s.6d. plus coils and booklets). As the bands overlap the stamps it is easier to distinguish these by measuring the space between the bands, this being approximately 12 mm. for the 8 mm. bands and 10·5 mm. for the 9·5 mm. bands. There is the further complication of identifying the 3d. value which has only one band but in the 8 mm. band series this is at the left or right of the stamp whilst in the 9·5 mm. band series it is in the centre. Both the "green" and the "blue" bands normally measure 8 mm.

Phosphor Printed on Both Sides.   Instances have been reported of stamps with phosphor bands on both the front and the back. These can be caused by offsets from normal phosphor bands, but where there is a sharp phosphor impression, these are listed. Offsets, which appear indistinct and weak, are outside the scope of this Catalogue.

Application of Phosphor Bands. The choice of method for applying the phosphor bands is a matter for the printer and three different methods have been used: photogravure, typography and flexography.

To apply bands in photogravure sometimes an additional printing cylinder is brought into use so that it is done in the same operation as printing the stamps. In the case of multicoloured special issues there may not be a spare cylinder available as this would depend upon the colour capacity of the press and the number of colours to be used. The bands may then be applied by typography or photogravure as a separate operation on a sheet-fed press.

Typography was used to apply the bands to cut sheets on the phosphor-graphite issue; and for various later " emergency " printings.

Flexography is a typographic process but using a rubber cylinder (which does not indent the paper) to pick up the impression from a photo-etched inking cylinder. The screen pattern is usually blurred, although some traces of it remain. This method is usually employed for applying bands to stamps already printed " in the web " before being cut into sheets.

Photogravure bands do not indent the paper, are screened (either 150 or 250 lines to the inch, but occasionally occur mixed), extend through the top and bottom sheet margins and cause a glazed appearance on unsurfaced paper, due to the pressure of the cylinder. Bands applied by typography generally indent the paper, as can be seen from the back, are solid and stop short of the edges of the sheet.

It is rather difficult to distinguish with certainty flexography phosphor bands from those printed by photogravure, and for this reason they are not listed separately. Flexography is known to have been used to apply phosphor bands to special issues, and was also used for some printings of the 9·5 mm. violet phosphor series; it may also have been used on earlier definitive issues.

Typographed 6 mm. and 8 mm. Phosphor Bands in Sheets.   For values with the phosphor applied by typography the bands along the left and right margins were only 6 mm. wide, instead of the normal 8 mm. Where these varieties exist they have been listed, the prices being for stamps with the vertical margin attached. Some booklet panes of four from the watermark Crowns issue had the phosphor bands applied by typography. Examples with narrow side bands, similar to those on sheets, have been identified on panes also showing shifted phosphor bands.

Phosphor Reaction.   The "green" phosphor was overprinted by typography on the graphite stamps but in photogravure only on the first phosphor only issue. The "blue" phosphor was normally applied in photogravure but some values also exist with typographic overprint. The "violet" 8 mm. bands are normally applied in photogravure but again some values exist with them typographed, but the 9·5 mm. series exist with them only in photogravure or flexography.

Misplaced Bands on Sheets, Coils and Booklet Panes.   Phosphor bands frequently appear misplaced but such varieties are outside the scope of this Catalogue except where the misplacement affects the number of bands, i.e. one broad instead of two side bands or two narrow bands instead of one centre or side band.

Identification of Phosphor Colours.   Short wave ultra-violet lamps are available to enable collectors to identify the green, blue and violet phosphors. Please refer to the Stanley Gibbons Accessory list for information on these products currently available. Care should be taken when using such lamps as ultra-violet light can damage the eyes.

VARIETIES.   Most of the more prominent varieties are listed and illustrated but we have restricted ourselves to those we have actually seen. Others will be added to future editions as specimens become available for illustration.

The position is always indicated by stating first the cylinder number (and where no full stop is shown this means the " no dot " cylinder, whereas a full stop means the " dot " cylinder) followed by the position indicated first by the horizontal row and then the position in it. Thus "Cyl. 15, R. 10/3" means cylinder 15 no dot, the third stamp in the tenth row down. Where the same cylinder is used on stamps with different watermark, paper or type of phosphor, etc. the varieties on that cylinder will recur, unless corrected by retouching, and these are then listed again with footnotes referring back to its first appearance where it is illustrated.

Unless otherwise stated the prices are for single stamps and extra copies needed to make positional blocks will be charged as normals.

TÊTE-BÊCHE ERRORS.   These derive from booklets due to faulty making-up; this is described in the introductory notes to Appendix HA.

MINOR CONSTANT FLAWS.   These are so numerous that they are merely recorded without illustrations. Their location on the stamp is indicated, where helpful, by reference to the S.G. " Thirkell " Position Finder, an essential tool for identifying flaws. The recording of these flaws, often insignificant in themselves, will prove an aid in identifying a particular cylinder and will also serve to show that the flaw has been considered for listing as a variety but rejected as being too minor. Again we have only recorded what we have actually seen but the picture is necessarily incomplete as we have not been able to view full sheets from every cylinder.

COILS.   Coils are generally printed from double cylinders. In identifying their position the roll number is quoted (this is the number printed on the outer wrapper of the coil which corresponds to the row in the sheet before reeling) but where double cylinders are used only half the coils bearing the roll numbers will contain the variety. Hence there are twelve rolls (vertical delivery) and ten rolls (sideways delivery) from every sheet and varieties will be repeated on every 21st stamp on vertical rolls and on every 25th stamp on sideways delivery rolls.

SHADES.   Intended changes of colour such as the 2d. red-brown and light red-brown, the 6d. reddish purple and deep claret and the 4d. ultramarine and deep ultramarine are given full numbers and some of the more marked shades which were not made by design are shown as alternatives. In some cases, however, there is a whole range of shades which it would be meaningless to attempt to list. The colour descriptions given are based on the Stanley Gibbons Colour Key.

DATES OF ISSUE.   The dates given in bold type in the headings are those on which stamps in normal Post Office *sheets* were first issued, notwithstanding the fact that they may have appeared earlier in booklet form. A dagger is added to the sheet date where stamps were issued at an *earlier* date in booklets or coils. Stamps with inverted or sideways watermarks which appeared either earlier or later than those from ordinary sheets have the dates given after the listing of each item, and for stamps from booklets we have taken the earliest possible dated booklet, i.e. taking into account booklets containing panes with mixed watermarks.

Where there is a change of watermark or type of phosphor or to the whiter paper, the dates given are generally those on which they were first issued by the Supplies Department to Postmasters.

WITHDRAWAL DATE.   All the low value Wilding stamps not previously sold out were withdrawn from issue at the Philatelic Bureaux on 27 February 1970, and were invalidated as from 1 March 1972.

POST OFFICE TRAINING SCHOOL STAMPS.   Examples of most low value stamps exist overprinted with two thick vertical bars. Some values on Tudor Crown watermark paper are also known overprinted " SCHOOL SPECIMEN ". Stamps cancelled with either of these overprints were for use in Post Office Training Schools, and their issue to the public was unauthorised, although most values appear to be quite common.

SHEET MARKINGS. Compared with the King George VI period a wide variety of markings of various kinds have been introduced in Elizabethan issues to facilitate new elements such as registration of multicoloured stamps, ensuring that the cylinders are applied in the correct sequence, aids to registration of perforation, colour dots to ease checking for omission of colours and so on. We give below notes and illustrations of the markings which were used in the Wilding issues and those which apply to other issues are described in the General Notes relating to the other Sections. They are particularly helpful in establishing the position of varieties in the case of marginal blocks and can also help in identifying the type of perforator used or the type of machine employed for printing, etc.

Cylinder Number

Cylinder Number. This always occurs in the left-hand margin opposite Row 18 No. 1. In double pane cylinders the no dot pane is on the left and the dot pane on the right. Booklet cylinder numbers are described in Appendix HA.

Varieties in Cylinder Blocks. Where a cylinder block contains a listed variety the price is adjusted accordingly and bears an asterisk.

"V" shaped
Hand engraved.

" W " shaped Photo etched

Marginal Arrows. These occur against the middle rows of the sheet as an aid to Post Office Clerks when breaking up the sheets. They may be hand engraved or photo-etched. The earlier cylinders were "V" shaped (hand engraved) at the top and bottom of the sheet and "W" shaped (photo-etched) at both sides. Later cylinders were often "W" shaped (photo-etched) at top, bottom and sides but a number of combinations exist. In some cases they are accidentally missing from the cylinder and where these are known this is stated under Sheet Markings. The 2½d. on Crowns watermarked paper, cylinder 55, exists with "V" shaped arrow in the correct position below rows 6/7 and a faint outline to the right, below rows 8/9, where the mark had been placed in error.

Narrow Rule   Wide Rule   Damaged Rule

Marginal Rules. These are the solid bands of colour which appear below the bottom row of the sheet and which used to be called "Jubilee Lines" because they were first introduced in the so-called "Jubilee" issue of 1887. These are invariably co-extensive (with breaks between each stamp) and come in various widths.

Unboxed   Boxed   In Double Box   Black Bar

Perforation Guide Holes. These large circular punched holes occur on all reel-fed printings in various positions as stated in the lists. They are an indication of the type of perforator used and further reference to these is made in Appendix G. They occur unboxed, in a single box and also in double boxes, those illustrated being representative. See also General Notes for Section W. They are liable to be trimmed off almost completely.

Black Bar. This was used alongside the marginal arrows at left on no dot sheets and at right on dot sheets on green and early blue phosphor printings. It was intended for easy recognition of phosphor stocks in the Post Office Supplies Department.

Sheet Numbers. Most sheets are serially numbered in black after printing for checking purposes but the numbers are liable to be placed anywhere in the margins and so are of no use for identifying a position. They are not of much help in establishing whether a sheet occurred early or late in a printing either, as a particular printing was not necessarily numbered from 1 and several machines may have been used.

Checkers Marks. These are small encircled numbers applied with a rubber stamp in a variety of colours. They are applied by Post Office checkers when counting the sheets delivered by the printer. As with sheet numbers they are liable to be placed anywhere in the sheet margins.

Table of Wilding Issues

	½d.	1d.	1½d.	2d. Red-brown	2d. Light red-brown	2d. 2 bands	2½d. Type I	2½d. Type II	2½d. Type II 1 band	2½d. Type I 1 band	3d.	4d. Ultramarine	4d. Deep ultramarine	4½d.	5d.	6d. Reddish purple	6d. Deep claret	7d.	8d.	9d.	10d.	11d.	1s.	1s.3d.	1s.6d.
Tudor Crown	S1	S13	S25	S36	··	··	S50	S51	··	··	S67	S81	··	··	S99	S104	··	S114	S119	S124	S129	S134	S136	S141	S150
St. Edward's Crown	S2	S14	S26	S37	S38	··	S52	S53	··	··	S68	S82	··	··	S100	S105	S106	S115	S120	S125	S130	S135	S137	S142	S151
Graphite. St. Edward's Crown	S3	S15	S27	··	S39	··	··	S54	··	··	S69	··	··	··	··	··	S107	S116	S121	S126	S131	··	S138	S143	S152
Crowns. Cream Paper	S4	S16	S28	··	S40	··	S56	S55	··	··	S70	S83	··	S93	S101	··	S108	S117	S122	S127	S132	··	S139	S144	S153
Crowns. Whiter Paper	S5	S17	S29	··	S41	··	S56b	S57	··	··	S71	S84	S85	S94	S102	··	··	··	··	··	··	··	··	··	··
Crowns. Chalky Paper	S6	··	··	··	··	··	··	S58	··	··	··	··	··	··	··	··	··	··	··	··	··	··	··	··	··
Graphite. Crowns	S7	S18	S30	··	S42	··	··	S59	··	··	S72	S86	··	S95	··	··	··	··	··	··	··	··	··	··	··
Phosphor-graphite	S8	S19	S31	··	S43	··	··	S60	··	··	S73	S87	··	S96	··	··	··	··	··	··	··	··	··	··	··
Green Phosphor	S9	S20	S32	··	S44	··	··	S61	··	··	S74	S88	··	··	··	··	S109	··	··	··	··	··	··	S145	··
Blue Phosphor. Cream Paper	S10	S21	S33	··	S45	S46	··	S62	S63	S64	S75	S89	··	S97	··	··	S110	··	··	··	··	··	··	S146	··
Blue Phosphor. Whiter Paper	S11	S22	S34	··	··	S47	··	S66	S65	··	S76	··	S90	S98	··	··	S111	··	··	··	··	··	··	S147	··
Violet Phosphor. 8 mm.	S12	S23	S35	··	··	S48	··	··	··	··	··	··	S91	··	··	··	S112	··	··	··	··	··	··	S148	··
Violet Phosphor. 9.5 mm.	··	S24	··	··	··	S49	··	··	··	··	S80	··	S92	··	S103	··	S113	S118	S123	S128	S133	··	S140	S149	S154
1 Side Band. Blue Phosphor	··	··	··	··	··	··	··	··	··	··	S77	··	··	··	··	··	··	··	··	··	··	··	··	··	··
1 Side Band. Violet Phosphor	··	··	··	··	··	··	··	··	··	··	S78	··	··	··	··	··	··	··	··	··	··	··	··	··	··
1 Centre Band. Violet Phosphor	··	··	··	··	··	··	··	··	··	··	S79	··	··	··	··	··	··	··	··	··	··	··	··	··	··

Presentation Packs .. .. At end of Section SA

Face Value	Watermark	Further description	Delivery	Stamp No.
½d.	Tudor Crown		V S	S1
½d.	St. Edward's Crown		V S	S2
½d.	St. Edward's Crown	Graphite lines	V	S3
½d.	Crowns	Cream or whiter paper	V S	S6
½d.	Crowns	Graphite lines	V	S7
½d.	Crowns	Green phosphor	V	S9
½d.	Crowns	Blue phosphor, cream or whiter paper	V	S11
½d.	Crowns	Violet phosphor, 8 mm.	V	S12
1d.	Tudor Crown		V S	S13
1d.	St. Edward's Crown		V S	S14
1d.	St. Edward's Crown	Graphite lines	V	S15
1d.	Crowns	Cream or whiter paper	V S	S17
1d.	Crowns	Graphite lines	V	S18
1d.	Crowns	Green phosphor	V	S20
1d.	Crowns	Blue phosphor, cream or whiter paper	V	S22
1d.	Crowns	Violet phosphor, 8 mm.	V	S23
1d.	Crowns	Violet phosphor, 9·5 mm.	V	S24
1½d.	Tudor Crown		V	S25
1½d.	Tudor Crown, sideways		S	S25
1½d.	St. Edward's Crown		V	S26
1½d.	St. Edward's Crown, sideways		S	S26
1½d.	St. Edward's Crown	Graphite lines	V	S27
1½d.	Crowns	Cream paper ..	V	S29
1½d.	Crowns	Whiter paper	S	S29
2d.	Tudor Crown	Red-brown	V	S36
2d.	Tudor Crown, sideways	Red-brown	S	S36
2d.	St. Edward's Crown	Red-brown	V	S38
2d.	St. Edward's Crown, sideways	Red-brown	S	S38
2d.	St. Edward's Crown	Light red-brown	V	S38
2d.	St. Edward's Crown, sideways	Light red-brown	S	S38
2d.	St. Edward's Crown	Graphite lines	V	S39
2d.	Crowns	Cream or whiter paper	V	S41
2d.	Crowns, sideways	Cream or whiter paper	S	S41
2d.	Crowns	Graphite lines	V	S42
2d.	Crowns	Green phosphor	V	S44
2d.	Crowns	Blue phosphor, 1 left band ..	V	S45
2d.	Crowns	Blue phosphor, cream or whiter paper, 2 bands ..	V	S47
2d.	Crowns	Violet phosphor, 8 mm.	V	S48
2d.	Crowns	Violet phosphor, 9·5 mm.	V	S49
2d.	Crowns, sideways	Violet phosphor, 9·5 mm.	S	S49
2½d.	Tudor Crown	Type I..	V	S50
2½d.	Tudor Crown, sideways	Type I..	S	S50
2½d.	St. Edward's Crown	Type I..	V	S52
2½d.	St. Edward's Crown, sideways	Type I..	S	S52
2½d.	St. Edward's Crown	Type II, Graphite lines	S	S54
2½d.	Crowns	Type I. Cream or whiter paper	V	S56
2½d.	Crowns, sideways	Type I. Cream or whiter paper	S	S56
2½d.	Crowns, sideways	Type II. Whiter paper	S	S57
3d.	Tudor Crown		V S	S67
3d.	St. Edward's Crown		V S	S68
3d.	St. Edward's Crown, sideways		S	S68
3d.	St. Edward's Crown	Graphite lines	S	S69
3d.	Crowns	Cream or whiter paper	V	S71
3d.	Crowns, sideways	Cream or whiter paper	S	S71
3d.	Crowns	Graphite lines	V S	S72
3d.	Crowns	Blue phosphor, cream or whiter paper, 2 bands ..	V	S77
3d.	Crowns	Blue phosphor, whiter paper, 1 side band	V	S77
3d.	Crowns	Violet phosphor, 1 side band	V	S80
3d.	Crowns	Violet phosphor, 1 centre band	V	S80
3d.	Crowns, sideways	Violet phosphor, 1 centre band	S	S80
4d.	Tudor Crown	Ultramarine ..	V	S81
4d.	St. Edward's Crown	Ultramarine ..	V S	S82
4d.	Crowns	Ultramarine, cream or whiter paper	V S	S85
4d.	Crowns	Deep ultramarine, whiter paper	V	S85
4d.	Crowns, sideways	Deep ultramarine, whiter paper	S	S85
4d.	Crowns, sideways	Violet phosphor, 9·5 mm.	S	S92
6d.	Tudor Crown		V	S104
6d.	St. Edward's Crown	Reddish purple	V	S106
6d.	St. Edward's Crown	Deep claret ..	V	S106
6d.	Crowns	Cream or whiter paper	V	S108
6d.	Crowns	Violet phosphor, 9·5 mm.	V	S113

PAPER AND WATERMARK

All the following issues are printed on unsurfaced paper, except the ½d. and 2½d. values (Nos. S6 and S58) printed on chalk-surfaced paper.

The illustrations of the watermarks are as seen from the *front* of the stamp. The " Tudor Crown" was in use from 1952 to 1954, the " St. Edward's Crown " from 1955 to 1958 and the Multiple Crowns from 1958 onwards. No Wilding issues appeared on paper without watermark.

Tudor Crown
W.22

St. Edward's Crown
W.23

Crowns
W.24

S1

S2

S3

S4

S5

S6

S7

Portraits of Queen Elizabeth II and National Emblems

(Des. Miss Enid Marx (**S1**), M. C. Farrar-Bell (**S2/3**), G. T. Knipe (**S4**),
Miss Mary Adshead (**S5**), Edmund Dulac (**S6/7**))

(Portrait by Dorothy Wilding Ltd.)

1953–65.   ½d. Orange-red, Type S1

Cat. No.	S.G. No.	Shades	Mint	Used

1953 (AUGUST 31).   WATERMARK TUDOR CROWN, TYPE W.22

S1	515	Orange-red	10	15

a. Watermark inverted (3.54) ..	30	45	
b. Coil join (horiz. pair) ..	1·75		
c. "A" flaw (Vert. coil, Roll 3) ..	3·50		
d. Spot on "d" (Vert. coil, Roll 5)	3·00		
f. Rose flaw (Cyls 1 & 3 Dot, R. 19/12)	2·50		

9

Listed Varieties

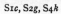

S1c, S2g, S4k

S1d, S2h, S4l

S1f, S2f
Retouched on Crowns
watermark

Cylinder Numbers (Blocks of Six)

Perforation Type B (no dot) and C (dot)

Cyl. No.					No dot	Dot
1	..	..	..	..	.. 5·00	5·00

Perforation Type A

Cyl. No.					No dot	Dot
1	..	..	..	..	.. 1·90	1·90
3	..	..	..	..	.. 2·50	2·50

Minor Constant Sheet Flaws

Cyl. 1   4/4 White smudge at left of upper left rose (Th. B1)
5/6 White spot at end of stem of upper right shamrock (Th. C6)
13/1 Large concealed retouch on Queen's cheek (Th. D3-4)

Cyl. 1.   1/7 Background retouch below upper left rose (Th. B1)
1/10 Orange spot at top right of centre cross in crown (Th. A-B3-4)
15/4 Retouched background between OS of POSTAGE
18/8 Coloured dot in P of POSTAGE

Cyl. 3   4/4 As cyl. 1
5/6 As cyl. 1

Cyl. 3.   18/8 As cyl. 1.

Coils

All coils have the watermark upright and Cylinder A1 or A2 was used.
Vertical delivery printed in continuous reels

Code No.	Number in roll	Face value
AA	240	10/-
G	480	£1
W	960	£2
D	960	£2
Y	1920	£4

Sideways delivery made up from sheets with sheet margin joins

P	480	£1

Sheet Markings

Guide holes: Boxed opposite rows 14/15, at left (no dot) or right (dot)
Others: As given in General Notes

Imprimaturs from the National Postal Museum Archives

Imperforate, watermark Type W.22

Watermark upright
Watermark inverted
Tête-bêche pair

Cat. No.	S.G. No.		Shades	Mint	Used

1955 (DECEMBER 12).† WATERMARK ST. EDWARD'S CROWN, TYPE W.23

S2	540		Orange-red	10	15

  b. Watermark inverted (9.55) ..   15   25
  c. Coil join (horiz, pr.)   ..   ..   1·50
  d. Flaw on shamrock stem (Cyl. 2
      Dot, R. 18/8)   ..   ..   4·00
  e. Major retouch (Cyl. 2 Dot,
      R. 19/2)   ..   ..   ..   5·00
  f. Rose flaw (Cyl. 2 Dot, R. 19/12)   4·00
  g. " A " flaw (Vert. coil, Roll 3) ..   3·50
  h. Spot on " d " (Vert. coil, Roll 5)   3·25
  i. Shamrock flaw (Vert. coil,
      Roll 11)   ..   ..   ..   4·00
  j. " R " flaw (Vert. coil, Roll 11). .   4·00

Listed Varieties

For illustrations of Nos. S2*f*/*h*, see Nos. S1*c*/*d* and S1*f*.

S2*d*, S4*g*

S2*e*, S4*h*

Shows as retouched area
to design edge

S2*i*, S4*m*, S5*g*, S9*b*,
S10*g*, S11*f*

S2*j*, S4*n*, S5*i*, S9*c*, S10*h*,
S11*g*

Cylinder Numbers (Blocks of Six)

Perforation Type B (no dot) and C (dot)

Cyl. No.					No dot	Dot
1	..	..	..	..	.. 2·50	2·50

Perforation Type A

Cyl. No.					No dot	Dot
2	..	..	..	..	.. 1·90	6·00*
3	..	..	..	..	.. 2·50	2·50

Minor Constant Sheet Flaws

Cyl. 1 no dot and dot. As for No. S1, cyl. 1.
Cyls. 2 and 3 no dot and dot. As for No. S1, cyl. 3 except that flaw on 4/4 is retouched on cyl. 3 no dot.
Cyl. 2. 20/2 Retouch by lower right thistle and rose (Th. F5-6).

Coils

All coils have the watermark upright and it is believed that the cylinder numbers used were A3 in double panes as well as cylinder A1 or A2.

Vertical delivery printed in continuous reels

Code No.	Number in roll	Face value
AA	240	10/-
G	480	£1
W	960	£2
D	960	£2
Y	1920	£4

Sideways delivery made up from sheets with sheet margin joins

P	480	£1

Sheet Markings
All the same as for No. S1

Imprimaturs from the National Postal Museum Archives
Imperforate, watermark Type W.23

Watermark upright
Watermark inverted
Tête-bêche pair

Graphite-lined Issues

The graphite lines were printed in black on the back, beneath the gum. Two lines per stamp, except for the 2d. value which only have one line.

S8

Cat. No.	S.G. No.		Shades	Mint	Used

1957 (NOVEMBER 19). WITH GRAPHITE LINES, TYPE S8. WMK. ST. EDWARD'S CROWN

S3	561		Orange-red	20	30

a. "E" flaw (Cyl. 5 No dot, R. 17/9) 3.50
b. Extra stem to thistle (Cyl. 5 No dot, R. 18/10) 3.25

Listed Varieties

S3a, S8b   S3b, S8c

Cylinder Numbers (Blocks of Six)
Single pane cylinders

Cyl. No.	Perforation Type		No dot		Cyl. No.	Perforation Type		No dot
4	B	..	3·00		5	B	..	4·00
4	C	..	3·00		5	C	..	4·00

Minor Constant Sheet Flaw
Cyl. 4 12/8 Orange spot in top thistle (Th. A4)

Coils
All have watermark upright, sheet cylinder 4 having been converted to a 21-row cylinder
Vertical delivery printed in continuous reels

Code No.	Number in roll	Face value
G	480	£1
W	960	£2
Y	1920	£4

Sheet Markings
Guide holes: Boxed opposite rows 14/15, at both sides and unboxed opposite rows 1 and 7/8 at both sides
Others: As given in General Notes

Imprimatur from the National Postal Museum Archives
Imperforate, watermark Type W.23
Watermark upright

Quantity Issued 22,508,400

Cat. No.	S.G. No.	Shades	Mint	Used

1958 (NOVEMBER 25). WATERMARK CROWNS, TYPE W.24
A. Cream Paper

S4	—		Orange-red	15	10

c. Watermark inverted (11.58) .. 30 25
d. Watermark Crown to left (26.5.61) .. .. 1·75 75
e. Watermark Crown to right .. 1·50 75
f. Coil join (horiz. pair) .. .. 1·50
g. Flaw on shamrock stem (Cyl. 2 Dot, R. 18/8) .. .. .. 2·50
h. Major retouch (Cyl. 2 Dot, R. 19/2) .. .. 4·00
k. "A" flaw (Vert. coil, Roll 3) .. 3·00
l. Spot on "d" (Vert. coil, Roll 5) 3·00
m. Shamrock flaw (Vert. coil, Roll 11) .. .. 2·25
n. "R" flaw (Vert. coil, Roll 11).. 2·25

B. Whiter Paper (27 July 1962)†

S5	570		Orange-red	10	10

a. Watermark Crown to left (5.6.62) 10 15
b. Watermark Crown to right .. 10 15
c. Watermark inverted (29.7.62) 40 25
f. Large dot by daffodil (Vert. coil, Roll 4) .. .. .. 2·50
g. Shamrock flaw (Vert. coil, Roll 11) 2·75
h. "d" joined to shamrock (Vert. coil, Roll 11) .. .. .. 2·50
i. "R" flaw (Vert. coil, Roll 11).. 2·50

Cat. No.	S.G. No.		Shades	Mint	Used

C. Chalky Paper   Booklets only (15 July 1963)

S6	570k		Orange-red	2·00	2·25
a. Watermark inverted ..		2·00 2·25			

†The earliest issue was in vertical coils on 30 April 1962.

Listed Varieties

For illustrations of No. S4*g*, see No. S2*d*; for No. S4*h*, see No. S2*e*; for No. S4*k*, see No. S1*c*; for No. S4*l*, see No. S1*d*; for Nos. S4*m*/*n* and S5*g*, S5*i*, see Nos. S2*i*/*j*.

S5*f*, S12*e*   S5*h*, S12*f*

Cylinder Numbers (Blocks of Six)

A. Cream Paper. (No. S4)

Perforation Type B (no dot) and C (dot)   Perforation Type A

Cyl. No.					No dot	Dot	Cyl. No.					No dot	Dot
1 ..	..	..	..	..	2·25	2·25	2 ..	..	..	..	..	2·75	5·00*
3 ..	..	..	..	..	2·25	2·25	3 ..	..	..	..	..	2·75	2·75

B. Whiter Paper. (No. S5).

Perforation Type A

					No dot	Dot							No dot	Dot
1 ..	..	..	..	..	1·60	1·60	3 ..	..	..	..	..		1·60	1·60

Minor Constant Sheet Flaws

Cyl. 1   4/4 White smudge at left of upper left rose (Th. B1)
          5/6 White spot at end of stem of upper right shamrock (Th. C6), rather faint on this cylinder
          13/1 Large concealed retouch on Queen's cheek (Th. D3-4)

Cyl. 1.   1/10 Orange spot at top right of centre cross in crown (Th. A–B3-4)

Cyl. 2.   18/8 Coloured dot in P of POSTAGE (later retouched)
          20/2 Retouch by lower right thistle and rose (Th. F5-6)

Cyl. 3.   5/6 White spot at end of stem of upper right shamrock (Th. C6)

Cyl. 3.   18/8 Coloured dot in P of POSTAGE

Coils

All have watermark upright and cylinder numbers A1, A2 and A3 were used for cream paper printings and numbers A3 and A4 for whiter paper issues.

Vertical delivery printed in continuous reels. Cream or whiter paper.

Code No.	Number in roll	Face value
AA	240	10/-
G	480	£1
W	960	£2
D	960	£2
Y	1920	£4

Sideways delivery made up from sheets with sheet margin joins.   Cream paper

P	480	£1

Sheet Markings

All the same as for No. S1

Imprimaturs from the National Postal Museum Archives

Imperforate, watermark Type W.24. Cream or whiter paper

Watermark upright
Watermark inverted
Tête-bêche pair

Cat. No.	S.G. No.		Shades		Mint	Used

1959 (JUNE 15). WITH GRAPHITE LINES, TYPE S8. WATERMARK CROWNS

This was only issued in booklets and coils. For panes, see Section SB, Nos. SB14/a.

S7	587			Orange-red		6·00	3·00
a. Watermark inverted (4.8.59)		1·25	2·25				

Coils

All have watermark upright, sheet cylinder 4 having been converted to a 21-row cylinder.

Code No.	Number in roll	Face value
W	960	£2
Y	1920	£4

Imprimaturs from the National Postal Museum Archives

Imperforate, watermark Type W.24

Watermark upright
Watermark inverted
Tête-bêche pair

Quantity Issued 4,161,840

1959 (NOVEMBER 18). PHOSPHOR-GRAPHITE ISSUE. WMK. ST. EDWARD'S CROWN

This has two graphite lines, Type **S8**, on the back and two phosphor bands, applied by typography, on the front, which react green under the lamp.

S8	599		Orange-red		4·00	6·00
a. Narrow band at left or right (stamp with vert. margin) ..		6·00				
b. "E" flaw (R. 17/9)		8·00				
c. Extra stem to thistle (R. 18/10)		8·00				

These varieties are as illustrated for Nos. S3*a/b*.

Cylinder Numbers (Blocks of Six)

Single pane cylinder

Cyl. No.	Perf. Type		No dot
5	B	..	27·00
5	C	..	27·00

Sheet Markings

All the same as for No. S3

Imprimatur from the National Postal Museum Archives

Perf. 15 × 14, watermark Type W.24

Watermark upright

Quantity Issued 707,040

Cat. No.	S.G. No.		Shades	Mint	Used

1960 (JUNE 22). TWO PHOSPHOR BANDS REACTING GREEN. WMK. CROWNS

The bands were applied in photogravure.

S9 — Orange-red 1·25 1·00
- a. Watermark inverted (14.8.60) 6·00 6·00
- b. Shamrock flaw (Coil, Roll 11).. 5·00
- c. "R" flaw (Coil, Roll 11) .. 5·00
- d. Coil join (vert. pair) .. .. 6·00
- e. Single broad band £110

For illustrations of Nos. S9b/c see Nos. S2i/j.

Cylinder Numbers (Blocks of Six)

Perforation Type B (no dot) and C (dot)

Cyl. No.   No dot Dot
1 .. .. 9·00 9·00

Minor Constant Sheet Flaws

Cyl. 1   4/4 White smudge at left of upper left rose (Th. B1)
    5/6 White spot at end of stem of upper right shamrock (Th. C6), rather faint on this cylinder
    13/1 Large concealed retouch on Queen's cheek (Th. D3-4)
Cyl. 1.   1/10 Orange spot at top right of centre cross in crown (Th. A–B3-4), later retouched
    19/12 White bulge on upper right sepal of lower right rose (Th. E5-6)

Coils

All have watermark upright and cylinder number A3 was used in double panes.

Vertical delivery printed in continuous reels

Code No.	Number in roll	Face value
G	480	10/-
W	960	£2
Y	1920	£4

Vertical delivery. Made up from sheets with sheet margin joins.
    Y   1920   £4

Sheet Markings

Guide holes: Boxed opposite rows 14/15, at left (no dot) or right (dot)
Black bar: This occurs by the marginal arrows opposite rows 10/11, at left (no dot) or right (dot). These also occur in the central gutter of the booklet sheets.
Others: As given in General Notes

Imprimatur from the National Postal Museum Archives

Imperforate, watermark Type W.24

Watermark upright

1961 (JUNE 5).† TWO PHOSPHOR BANDS REACTING BLUE. WMK. CROWNS

The bands were applied in photogravure on the stamps with upright watermark and by typography on those with watermark sideways.

A. Cream Paper

S10 — Orange-red 20 10
- a. Watermark inverted (3.61) .. 70 90
- b. Watermark Crown to left (14.7.61) .. 10·00 8·00
- c. Watermark Crown to right .. 9·00 8·00
- d. Single broad band (wmk. sideways) .. .. 25·00
- da. Single broad band (wmk. upright or inverted) .. .. 90·00
- g. Shamrock flaw (Coil, Roll 11) .. 2·50
- h. "R" flaw (Coil, Roll 11) .. .. 2·75

B. Whiter Paper (21 June 1965)†

S11   610 Orange-red 10 15
- a. Watermark Crown to left (15.8.62) .. .. 10·00 12·00
- b. Watermark Crown to right .. 10·00 12·00
- c. Watermark inverted (3.6.63) .. 60 60
- d. Single broad band (wmk. sideways) .. .. 32·00
- da. Single broad band (wmk. upright or inverted) .. .. .. 65·00
- f. Shamrock flaw (Coil, Roll 11) .. 2·25
- g. "R" flaw (Coil, Roll 11) .. .. 2·50

Listed Varieties

For illustrations of Nos. S10g and S11f see No. S2i and for S10h and S11g see No. S2j.

Cylinder Numbers (Blocks of Six)
Perforation Type A

	Cream paper. (No. S10)							Whiter paper. (No. S11)		
Cyl. No.					No dot	Dot	Cyl. No.		No dot	Dot
I	..	..	..	..	.. 2·75	2·75	I	.. ..	.. 1·60	1·60

Minor Constant Sheet Flaws
As for No. S9

Coils
All have watermark upright and cylinder number A3 was used in double panes.
Vertical delivery printed in continuous reels. Cream or whiter paper.

Code No.	Number in roll	Face value
G	480	10/–
W	960	£2 (cream paper only)
Y	1920	£4

Sheet Markings
As for No. S9 except that there are no black bars

Imprimaturs from the National Postal Museum Archives
Imperforate, watermark Type W.24. Cream or whiter paper

Watermark upright
Watermark inverted
Tête-bêche pair

Cat. No.	S.G. No.	Shades	Mint	Used

1965 (AUGUST 13). TWO 8 mm. PHOSPHOR BANDS REACTING VIOLET. WMK. CROWNS
The bands were applied by typography on the sheets and in photogravure on the coils.

S12	—		Orange-red	40	35

a.	Narrow band at left or right (stamp with vert. margin)	..	2·50			
b.	Typo. bands omitted*	.. ..	25·00			
c.	Single 8 mm. broad band (typo.)		2·50	e.	Large dot by daffodil (Coil, Roll 4)	3·25
ca.	As c. but 6 mm. band	.. ..	3·00	f.	"d" joined to shamrock (Coil, Roll	
d.	Bands applied photo. (15.10.65)	1·25	50		11)	3·25

*No S12b can be distinguished from a non-phosphor stamp by the fact that this shows a clear impression of the typo. plate with no reaction under the lamp.
For illustrations of Nos. S12e/f, see Nos. S5f/h.

Cylinder Numbers (Blocks of Six)
Perforation Type A

Cyl. No.					No dot	Dot
I	..	..	..	..	.. 4·25	12·00

Minor Constant Sheet Flaws
As for No. S9

Coils
All have the watermark upright and it is believed a new double pane cylinder number A4 was used.
Vertical delivery printed in continuous reels

Code No.	Number in roll	Face value
G	480	10/–
W	960	£2
Y	1920	£4

Sheet Markings
All the same as for No. S1

1953–67.   1d. Ultramarine, Type S1

Cat. No.	S.G. No.	Shades	Mint	Used

1953 (AUGUST 31).   WATERMARK TUDOR CROWN, TYPE W.22

S13	516		Ultramarine		20	20
a. Watermark inverted (3.54)	..	3·75	1·50			
b. Coil join (horiz. pair)	.. ..	2·00				
c. Shamrock flaw (Cyl. 2 No dot, R. 18/2)	.. ..	9·00				

Listed Varieties

S13*c*, S14*d*,
SB22*a*, SB28*a*

White flaw on top shamrock,
later retouched on St.
Edward's Crown watermark

Cylinder Numbers (Blocks of Six)

Perforation Type B (no dot) and C (dot)

Cyl. No.				No dot	Dot
1	..	.. ..	..	.. 2·75	2·75

Perforation Type A

Cyl. No.				No dot	Dot
2	..	.. ..	..	.. 12·00*	3·75

Minor Constant Sheet Flaws

Cyl. 2.   19/8 White flaw between thistle stem and lower right rose (Th. E6)

Coils

Single pane cylinders B1 or B2 were used for the Tudor Crown watermark.   The watermark is always upright.

Vertical delivery printed in continuous reels

Code No.	Number in roll	Face value
AB	240	£1
E	480	£2
X	960	£4
Z	1920	£8

Sideways delivery made up from sheets with sheet margin joins

O	480	£2

Sheet Markings

Guide holes: Boxed opposite rows 14/15, at left (no dot) or right (dot)
Others: As given in General Notes

Imprimaturs from the National Postal Museum Archives

Imperforate, watermark Type W.22

Watermark upright
Watermark inverted
Tête-bêche pair

Cat. No.	S.G. No.		Shades		Mint	Used

1955 (SEPTEMBER 19).†   WATERMARK ST. EDWARD'S CROWN, TYPE W.23

S14	541		Ultramarine		25	15
a. Têtê-bêche (horiz. pair)	..					
b. Watermark inverted (8.55)	..	40	30			
c. Coil join (horiz. pair)	.. ..	2·00				
d. Shamrock flaw (Cyl. 2 No dot,						
R. 18/2)	.. ..	6·00				

†The earliest issue was from E coils in August 1955.

Listed Varieties
For illustration of No. S14*d* see No. S13*c*.

Cylinder Numbers (Blocks of Six)

Perforation Type A

Cyl. No.						No dot	Dot
1	..	..	..	..	..	2·75	2·75
2	..	..	..	..	..	7·00*	2·75
4	..	..	..	..	..	2·75	2·75

Perforation Type B (no dot) or C (dot)

Cyl. No.					No dot	Dot
4	..	..	..	..	3·50	3·50

Minor Constant Sheet Flaws

Cyl. 2	19/8 White flaw between thistle stem and lower right rose (Th. E6)
Cyl. 4	11/9 Blue spot in E of POSTAGE
	19/8 As cyl. 2
4.	14/11 White spur to bottom leaf of shamrock above diadem (Th. A3)

Coils
Single pane cylinders B1 or B2 were again used for the St. Edward's Crown watermark. The watermark is always upright.

Vertical delivery printed in continuous reels

Code No.	Number in roll	Face value
AB	240	£1
E	480	£2
B	960	£4
X	960	£4
Z	1920	£8

Sideways delivery made up from sheets with sheet margin joins

O	480	£2

Sheet Markings
All the same as for No. S13

Imprimaturs from the National Postal Museum Archives

Imperforate, watermark Type W.23

Watermark upright
Watermark inverted
Tête-bêche pair

1957 (NOVEMBER 19). WITH GRAPHITE LINES, TYPE S8. WMK. ST. EDWARD'S CROWN

S15	562		Ultramarine		20	35
a. Flaw on thistle head (Cyls. 7 and 8 No dot, R. 6/1 and Coil Roll 1)	.. ..	4·00				
b. Daffodil stem flaw (Cyls. 7 & 8 No dot, R. 15/2 and Coil, Roll 2)		4·00				
c. Extra stop (Coil, Roll 2)	..	7·50				
d. Stop omitted (Coil, Roll 3)	..	7·50				
e. White flaw on shamrock leaf (Coil, Roll 8)	.. .. ..	5·00				

Listed Varieties

Flaw on top thistle occurs on sheets (Nos. S15a and S19b or coils (Nos. S16n, S18i, S20g and S21g)

S15a, S16n, S18i, S19b, S20g, S21g

| S15b, S19c | S15c
Later retouched | S15d
White stop omitted | S15e |

Cylinder Numbers (Blocks of Six)

Single pane cylinders

Cyl. No.	Perf. Type		No dot
7	B	..	3·00
7	C	..	3·00
8	B	..	7·00
8	C	..	7·00

Coils

Single pane cylinder B4 was used and all have the watermark upright.
Vertical delivery printed in continuous reels

Code No.	Number in roll	Face value
E	480	£2
X	960	£4
Z	1920	£8

Sheet Markings

Guide holes: Boxed opposite rows 14/15, at both sides and unboxed opposite rows 1 and 7/8 at both sides
Others: As given in General Notes

Imprimatur from the National Postal Museum Archives

Imperforate, watermark Type W.23

Watermark upright

Quantity Issued   29,620,080

Cat. No	S.G. No.	Shades	Mint	Used

1959 (MARCH 24).† WATERMARK CROWNS, TYPE W.24

A. Cream Paper

S16   —   Ultramarine   25   10

a. Imperf. (vert. pair from coil) ..		
d. Watermark inverted (11.58) ..	50	40
e. Watermark Crown to left (26.5.61)	1·50	75
f. Watermark Crown to right ..	1·50	75
g. Coil join (horiz. pair)	2·00	
h. Daffodil flaw (Cyl. 5 No dot, R. 10/11)	2·75	
n. Flaw on thistle head (Coil) ..	3·00	

B. Whiter Paper (7 May 1962)

S17   571   Ultramarine   10   10

a. Watermark Crown to left (5.6.62)	60	40
b. Watermark Crown to right ..	60	40
c. Watermark inverted (29.7.62)	15	20
d. Coil join (horiz. pair)	1·75	
e. Daffodil flaw (Cyl. 5 No dot, R. 10/11)	2·50	

Listed Variety

For illustration of No. S16*n*, see No. S15*a*.

S16*h*, S17*e*, S20*c*, S21*e*
Later retouched

Cylinder Numbers (Blocks of Six)

A. Cream Paper (No. S16)

Perforation Type A

Cyl. No.				No dot	Dot
4 ..	..	..	..	.. 2·75	2·75
5 ..	..	..	..	.. 2·75	2·75

Perforation Type B (no dot) and C (**dot**)

Cyl. No.				No dot	Dot
4 ..	..	..	..	.. 3·00	3·00

B. Whiter Paper (No. S17)

Perforation Type A

4 ..	..	..	..	.. 1·60	1·60
5 ..	..	..	..	.. 1·60	1·60

Minor Constant Sheet Flaws

Cyl. 4	11/9 Blue spot on E of POSTAGE
	19/8 White flaw between thistle stem and lower right rose (Th. E6)
Cyl. 4.	14/11 White spur to bottom leaf of shamrock above diadem (Th. A3)
Cyl. 5	3/5 Dark patch below bottom right rose (Th. E5)
	19/8 White flaw between thistle stem and lower right rose (Th. E6)
Cyl. 5.	1/12 Small white flaw on top of top left daffodil (Th. A2)

Coils

Double pane cylinder B1 was used for cream paper printings and cylinder B3 was used for both cream and whiter paper issues with the watermark always upright.

Vertical delivery printed in continuous reels. Cream or whiter paper

Code No.	Number in roll	Face value
AB	240	£1
E	480	£2
B	960	£4
X	960	£4
Z	1920	£8

Sideways delivery made up from sheets with sheet margin joins.   Cream or whiter paper

O	480	£2

Sheet Markings

Guide holes: Boxed opposite rows 14/15, at left (no dot) or right (dot) but in the case of perforation Type F (L)* the boxes remain on both panes but the holes are unboxed above and below the eighth vertical row on the no dot pane only

Others: As given in General Notes

Imprimaturs from the National Postal Museum Archives

Imperforate, watermark Type W.24. Cream or whiter paper

Watermark upright
Watermark inverted
Tête-bêche pair

Cat. No.	S.G. No.		Shades	Mint	Used

1958 (DECEMBER 18).   WITH GRAPHITE LINES, TYPE S8. WATERMARK CROWNS

This was only issued in booklets and coils. For panes, see Section SB, Nos. SB39/a.

S18	588			(1) Ultramarine (coils)	1·00	1·50
a. Watermark inverted (4.8.59) ..	1·25	2·00		(2) Bright ultramarine		
b. Two lines at left or right (7.61)	60	90		(booklets)	2·50	1·75
c. One line at left or right ..	60	90				
d. Three lines	12·00	12·00				
i. Flaw on thistle head (Coil, Roll 1)	6·00					

The misplaced graphite lines (varieties *b/d*) came from Z coils. They were printed after the graphite line experiment had ended to use up residual stock of graphite-lined paper which had been prepared for booklets.

For illustration of No. S18*i*, see No. S15*a*.

Coils

Double pane cylinder B3 was used only for the Z coils with misplaced lines (issued July 1961); other coils were from cylinder B4. The watermark is always upright.

Vertical delivery printed in continuous reels

Code No.	Number in roll	Face value
E	480	£2
X	960	£4
Z	1920	£8

Imprimaturs from the National Postal Museum Archives

Imperforate, watermark Type W.24

Watermark upright
Watermark inverted
Tête-bêche pair

Quantity Issued   12,428,880 including 3,400 Z coils with misplaced lines

Cat. No.	S.G. No.	Shades	Mint	Used

1959 (NOVEMBER 18). PHOSPHOR-GRAPHITE ISSUE. WMK. ST. EDWARD'S CROWN

This has two graphite lines, Type S8, on the back and two phosphor bands on the front, (applied typo.), which react green under the lamp.

S19	600		Ultramarine	6·00	6·00

a. Narrow band at left or right
(stamp with vert. margin) ..   8·00
b. Flaw on thistle head (Cyl. 8,
R. 6/1) ..   ..   9·00

c. Daffodil stem flaw (Cyl. 8,
R. 15/2)   ..   ..   ..   9·00

For illustrations of Nos. S19b/c, see Nos. S15a/b.

Cylinder Numbers (Blocks of Six)
Single pane cylinder

Cyl. No.	Perf. Type		No dot
8	B	..	38·00
8	C	..	38·00

Sheet Markings
All the same as for No. S15

Imprimatur from the National Postal Museum Archives
Perf. 15 × 14, watermark Type W.24

Watermark upright

Quantity Issued   709,680

1960 (JUNE 22). TWO PHOSPHOR BANDS REACTING GREEN. WMK. CROWNS

The bands were applied in photogravure.

S20	—		Ultramarine	1·25	1·25

a. Watermark inverted (14.8.60)   5·00   5·00
b. Single 8mm. broad band (wmk.
upright or inverted) ..   ..   ..   35·00
ba. As b but 6mm. band   ..   ..
c. Daffodil flaw (Cyl. 5 No dot, R.
10/11   ..   ..   5·00
g. Flaw on thistle head (Coil, Roll 1)   5·00

For illustrations of No. S20c, see No. S16h and for No. S20g, see No. S15a.

Cylinder Numbers (Blocks of Six)
Perforation Type B (no dot) and C (dot)

Cyl. No.					No dot	Dot
5 ..	..	..	..	..	9·00	9·00

Minor Constant Sheet Flaws
Cyl. 5   3/5   Dark patch below bottom right rose (Th. E5)
      19/8   White flaw between thistle stem and lower right rose (Th. E6)
Cyl. 5.   1/12   Small white flaw on top of top left daffodil (Th. A2)

Coils
Double pane cylinder B3 was used with the watermark always upright.

Vertical delivery printed in continuous reels

Code No.	Number in roll	Face value
E	480	£2
X	960	£4
Z	1920	£8

Sheet Markings
Guide holes: Boxed opposite rows 14/15, at left (no dot) or right (dot)
Black bar: This occurs by the marginal arrows opposite rows 10/11, at left (no dot) or right (dot), also on
    booklet sheets
Others: As given in General Notes

Imprimatur from the National Postal Museum Archives
Imperforate, watermark Type W.24

Watermark upright

Cat. No.	S.G. No.		Shades		Mint	Used

1961 (JUNE 5).† TWO PHOSPHOR BANDS REACTING BLUE. WMK. CROWNS

The bands were applied in photogravure on the stamps with upright watermark and by typography on those with watermark sideways.

A. Cream Paper

S21	—			Ultramarine	80	80
a. Watermark inverted (3.61)	..	70	70			
b. Watermark Crown to left (14.7.61)		2·00	2·00			
c. Watermark Crown to right	..	2·00	2·00			
d. Single broad band (wmk. sideways)		14·00				
da. Single broad band (wmk. upright or inverted)		50·00				
e. Daffodil flaw (Cyl. 5 No dot, R. 10/11)		3·25				
g. Flaw on thistle head (Coil, Roll 1)		8·00				

B. Whiter Paper (21 June 1965)†

S22	—			Ultramarine	55	55
a. Watermark Crown to left (15.8.62)		2·00	2·00			
b. Watermark Crown to right	..	2·00	2·00			
c. Watermark inverted (3.6.63)	..	70	70			
d. Single broad band (wmk. sideways)		35·00				
da. Single broad band (wmk. upright or inverted)		65·00				

For illustrations of No. S21e, see No. S16h and for No. S21g, see No. S15a.

Cylinder Numbers (Blocks of Six)

A. Cream paper. (No. S21)

Perforation Type B (no dot) and C (dot)

Cyl. No.					No dot	Dot
5 ..	..	..	..	..	5·50	5·50

B. Whiter paper. (No. S22)

Perforation Type A

Cyl. No.					No dot	Dot
4 ..	..	..	..	..	4·75	4·75

Minor Constant Sheet Flaws

Cyl. 4   11/9 Blue spot on E of POSTAGE
          19/8 White flaw between thistle stem and lower right rose (Th. E6)
Cyl. 5   3/5 Dark patch below bottom right rose (Th. E5)
          19/8 As for cyl. 4
Cyl. 5.   1/12 Small white flaw on top of top left daffodil (Th. A2)

Coils

Double pane cylinder B3 was used with the watermark always upright.

Vertical delivery printed in continuous reels. Cream or whiter paper

Code No.	Number in roll	Face value
E	480	£2
X	960	£4
Z	1920	£8

Sheet Markings

As for No. S20 except that there are no black bars

Imprimaturs from the National Postal Museum Archives

Imperforate, watermark Type W.24. Cream or whiter paper

Watermark upright
Watermark inverted
Tête-bêche pair

Cat. No.	S.G. No.	Shades	Mint	Used

1965 (AUGUST 13).   TWO 8 mm. PHOSPHOR BANDS REACTING VIOLET. WMK. CROWNS

The bands were originally applied by typography on sheets and 2s. Booklets and later in photogravure on sheets, coils and booklets.

S23	—		Ultramarine	18·00	8·00
a.	Narrow band at left or right (stamp with vert. margin) ..	60·00			
b.	Bands applied photo. (1966) ..	40	40		
c.	Watermark inverted (9.65) ..	20	30		
d.	Watermark Crown to left (10.65)	1·25	1·25		
e.	Watermark Crown to right ..	1·00	1·00		
f.	Single broad band (wmk. sideways)	10·00			
g.	Phosphor printed on both sides (wmk. sideways)	60·00			

The price quoted for No. S23g is for phosphor applied in photogravure. Similar examples from booklet panes with phosphor applied by typography have been reported.

Cylinder Numbers (Blocks of Six)
Perforation Type A

Bands typo. (No. S23)

Cyl. No.						No dot	Dot
5 ..	..	..	..	..	..	£190	£325

Bands photo. (No. S23b)

Cyl. No.						No dot	Dot
5 ..	..	..	..	..	..	4·25	4·25

Minor Constant Sheet Flaws

Cyl. 5   3/5 Dark patch below bottom right rose (Th. E5)
           19/8 White flaw between thistle stem and lower right rose (Th. E6)
Cyl. 5.   1/12 Small white flaw on top of top left daffodil (Th. A2)

Coils

Double pane cylinder B3 was used with the watermark always upright.   Bands photo.
Vertical delivery printed in continuous reels

Code No.	Number in roll	Face value
E	480	£2
X	960	£4
Z	1920	£8

Sheet Markings

Guide holes: Not known
Others: As given in General Notes

1967 (EARLY).   TWO 9·5 mm. PHOSPHOR BANDS REACTING VIOLET. WMK. CROWNS

The bands were mainly applied in photogravure, but the 2s. booklet had the bands applied by typography of flexography.

S24	611		Ultramarine	10	10
a.	Watermark inverted (2.67) ..	85	85		
b.	Watermark Crown to left (4.67)	35	40		
c.	Watermark Crown to right ..	35	40		
e.	Single broad band (wmk. sideways)	10·00			

Cylinder Numbers (Blocks of Six)
Perforation Type F (L)*

Cyl. No.						No dot	Dot
4 ..	..	..	..	..	..	1·60	1·60

Perforation Type A

Cyl. No.						No dot	Dot
5 ..	..	..	..	..	..	1·60	1·60

Minor Constant Sheet Flaws

Cyl. 4   11/9   Blue spot on E of POSTAGE
           19/8   White flaw between thistle stem and lower right rose (Th. E6)
Cyl. 5   3/5   Dark patch below bottom right rose (Th. E5)
           19/8   As for Cyl. 4
Cyl. 5.   1/12   Small white flaw on top of top left daffodil (Th. A2)

Coils

Double pane cylinder B3 was used with the watermark always upright.
Vertical delivery printed in continuous reels

Code No.	Number in roll	Face value
E	480	£2
X	960	£4
Z	1920	£8

Sheet Markings

Guide holes: Boxed opposite rows 14/15, at left (no dot) or right (dot) but in the case of perforation Type F (L)* the boxes remain on both panes but the holes are unboxed above and double-boxed below the eighth vertical row in the no dot pane only
Others: As given in General Notes

1952–65.   1½d. Green, Type S1

Cat. No.	S.G. No.	Shades	Mint	Used

1952 (DECEMBER 5).   WATERMARK TUDOR CROWN, TYPE W.22

S25   517

b. Imperf. between stamp and top margin £250
c. Watermark inverted (5.53)   .. 25   40
d. Watermark sideways (15.10.54).. 35   60
e. "Butterfly" flaw (Cyl. 6 Dot, R. 19/1) £200
f. Flaw on daffodil stem (Cyl 9 Dot, R. 18/1 .. .. 4·00
g. Extra dot (Cyl. 13 Dot, R. 17/10) 4·50
h. Rose and thistle joined at right (Cyl. 13 Dot, R. 19/1) .. .. 9·00
i. Scratch on neck (Cyl. 13 Dot, R. 20/3) .. .. 5·00
m. Flaw over "O" of "POSTAGE" (Sideways coil, Roll 2) .. .. 5·00
n. Dot over rose (Sideways coil, Roll 10).. .. .. 5·00
o. Daffodil flaw (Sideways coil, Roll 8) .. .. 4·00

(1) Green   10   15
(2) Deep green   1·00   30

Stamps with sideways watermark are from N coils with sideways delivery.

Listed Varieties

S25*e*   S26*g*   S26*i*
(Cyl. 6)   (Cyl. 14)   (Cyl. 15)

The first and later states of the "butterfly" flaw. All on dot panes only.

Of the first thirteen cylinders used, numbered 1 to 15 (with the exception of Nos. 3 and 7 which were not used), the following is a record of the development of the above illustrated flaws:

Cyl. 1. No flaws

Cyls. 2, 4 and 5. Disturbed background

Cyl. 6. This is found in two states. One with disturbed background and the other with a short white flaw as illustrated, the latter being the first of the clear defects in this position

Cyls. 8 to 13. Disturbed background

Cyl. 14. Found in two states, one with disturbed background and the other with a long white flaw as illustrated

Cyl. 15. Also found in two states, one with disturbed background and the other with a larger white flaw as illustrated, the latter only occurring on the St. Edward's Crown watermark

The most plausible explanation of the development of this flaw is that prior to the making of cylinder 2, the multipositive was damaged and imperfectly retouched with the result that cylinders 2, 4 and 5 show an uneven background. Before the making of cylinder 6 the opaque retouching medium appears to have partly peeled off from the multipositive leaving a transparent area which produced the small white flaw on the stamp. This was evidently discovered during the run and the cylinder retouched with the result that we have cylinder 6 with uneven background.

The multipositive was again retouched and this time continued to be used uneventfully for cylinders 8 to 13. After this the retouching medium appears to have peeled off again before making cylinders 14 and 15, each time being discovered and retouched during the printing run. Cylinder 22 is normal, showing no trace of the flaw or a retouch, possibly being from a new multipositive.

Prices are for cylinder blocks of six. The cylinder blocks showing the disturbed background are priced without an asterisk.

Listed Varieties (contd.)

S25*f*, SB41*a*

S25*g*, S26*d*
Later retouched on
St. Edward's Crown
watermark

S25*h*, S26*e*

S25*i*, S26*f*
White vertical line
from ear to shoulder

S25*m*, S26*q*

S25*n*, S26*r*
From sideways delivery N coils

S25*o*, S26*s*

Cylinder Numbers (Blocks of Six)

Perforation Type A

Cyl. No.						No dot	Dot
1	..	..	..	..	..	1·60	1·60
2	..	..	..	..	..	1·60	1·60
4	..	..	..	..	..	1·60	1·60
5	..	..	..	..	..	1·60	1·60
6	..	..	..	..	..	2·40	2·75
8	..	..	..	..	..	2·75	2·75
9	..	..	..	..	..	1·60	7·00*
10	..	..	..	..	..	1·60	1·60
11	..	..	..	..	..	1·60	1·60
12	..	..	..	..	..	1·60	1·60
13	..	..	..	..	..	2·40	12·00*

Perforation Type B (no dot) or C (dot)

Cyl. No.						No dot	Dot
1	..	..	..	..	..	2·50	2·50
2	..	..	..	..	..	4·50	4·50
6	..	..	..	..	..	2·50	2·50
9	..	..	..	..	..	2·50	9·00*

Coils

Printed in continuous reels

Double pane cylinders C1 or C2 were used for the vertical delivery coils and single pane cylinder number C3 for the sideways delivery coils.

	Code No.	Number in roll	Face value
(a) Vertical delivery. Watermark upright			
	L	480	£3
	K	960	£6
(b) Sideways delivery. Watermark sideways			
	N	480	£3

Sheet Markings

Guide holes: Boxed opposite rows 14/15, at left (no dot) or right (dot)

Others: As given in General Notes

Imprimaturs from the National Postal Museum Archives

Imperforate, watermark Type W.22

Watermark upright
Watermark inverted
Tête-bêche pair

Cat. No.	S.G. No.		Shades		Mint	Used
1955 (OCTOBER 11).†		**WATERMARK ST. EDWARD'S CROWN, TYPE W.23**				
S26	542		(1) Green		10	15
			(2) Deep green		40	20

a. Tête-bêche (horiz. pair)	£900	
b. Watermark inverted (8.55) ..	20	25
c. Watermark sideways (7.3.56) ..	15	75
d. Extra dot (Cyl. 13., R. 17/10) ..	4·00	
e. Rose and thistle joined at right (Cyl. 13 Dot, R. 19/1)	4·00	
f. Scratch on neck (Cyl. 13 No dot, R. 20/3)	4·00	
g. "Butterfly" flaw (Cyl. 14 Dot, R. 19/1)	12·00	
h. Bud on rose stem (Cyl. 14 No dot, R. 8/6)	3·00	
i. "Butterfly" flaw (Cyl. 15 Dot. R. 19/1)	5·00	
j. Spot between rose and shamrock (Cyl. 15 No dot, R. 20/3)	3·50	
q. Flaw over "O" of POSTAGE" (Sideways coil, Roll 2)	3·00	
r. Dot over rose (Sideways coil, Roll 10)	3·00	
s. Daffodil flaw (Sideways coil, Roll 8)	3·00	

Stamps with sideways watermark are from N coils with sideways delivery.

Listed Varieties

For illustrations of Nos. S26*d/f* see Nos. S25*g/i*; for Nos. S26*g* and S26*i* see No. S25*e*; and for Nos. S26*q/s* see Nos. S25*m/o*.

S26*h*

S26*j*, S28*e*, S32*b*
Later retouched on whiter paper
with Crowns watermark

Cylinder Numbers (Blocks of Six)
Perforation Type A

Cyl. No.					No dot	Dot	Cyl. No.					No dot	Dot
11 ..	..	..	..	..	1·60	2·10	14 ..	..	..	..	..	1·60	2·10
13 ..	..	..	..	..	1·60	5·00*	15 ..	..	..	..	..	1·60	2·10

See note below No. S25 on the butterfly flaw which occurs on some examples of cylinders 14 and 15 dot. Prices are for normals with disturbed background.

Minor Constant Sheet Flaws

Cyl. 15   17/9   Nick in frame bottom right (Th. G6)
          20/9   Speck opposite left 1 (Th. G1)
Cyl. 15.   1/4   Green dot in lower half ot 1 of left ½ (Th. G1)

Coils
Printed in continuous reels

Double pane cylinders C1 or C2 were again used for the vertical delivery coils and single pane cylinder number C3 for the sideways delivery coil.

Code No.	Number in roll	Face value
(a) Vertical delivery. Watermark upright		
L	480	£3
K	960	£6
(b) Sideways delivery. Watermark sideways		
N	480	£3

Sheet Markings
All the same as for No. S25

Imprimaturs from the National Postal Museum Archives

Imperforate, watermark Type W. 23

Watermark upright
Watermark inverted
Tête-bêche pair

Cat. No.	S.G. No.	Shades	Mint	Used

1957 (NOVEMBER 19). WITH GRAPHITE LINES, TYPE S8. WMK. ST. EDWARD'S CROWN

S27	563	Green	30	1·25

   a. Both lines at left £750   £350
   b. Horiz. pair, one stamp with
         only one line £600
   c. Coil join (horiz. pair)   ..   ..   8·00
   d. Green stroke below " E " (Cyl.
         21 No dot, R. 13/8)   ..   ..   4·00

Nos. S27*a/b* result from a misplacement of the graphite lines.

Listed Variety

Diagonal green stroke below middle " E " of " REVENUE " in bottom margin of stamp

S27*d*, S31*b*

Cylinder Numbers (Blocks of Six)

Single pane cylinder

Cyl. No.	Perf. Type		No dot
2I	B	..	4·00
2I	C	..	4·00

Coils

Sideways delivery made up from sheets with sheet margin joins

Code No.	Number in roll	Face value
N	480	£3

Sheet Markings

Guide holes: Boxed opposite rows 14/15, at both sides and unboxed opposite rows 1 and 7/8, at both sides
Others: As given in General Notes

Quantity Issued 10,506,720

Imprimatur from the National Postal Museum Archives

Imperforate, watermark Type W.23

Watermark upright

Cat. No.	S.G. No.			Shades		Mint	Used
1960 (AUGUST 30).† WATERMARK CROWNS, TYPE W.24							
A. Cream Paper							
S28	—			(1) Green		25	15
a. Watermark inverted (12.58) ..	1·00	40		(2) Deep Green		50	30
b. Watermark Crown to left (26.5.61)	9·00	3·50					
c. Watermark Crown to right ..	9·00	3·50					
d. Coil join (vert. pair)	2·50						
e. Spot between rose and shamrock (Cyl. 15 No dot, R. 20/3) ..	3·00						
B. Whiter Paper (7 May 1962)							
S29	572			(1) Green		10	15
a. Imperf. three sides (horiz, strip of 3)				(2) Deep green		20	25
b. Watermark Crown to left (5.6.62)	7·50	3·50					
c. Watermark Crown to right ..	7·50	3·50					
d. Watermark inverted (18.9.62)	2·50	2·50					
e. Coil join (horiz. pair)	1·75						
g. Thistle flaws (Cyl. 22 Dot, R. 12/1)	3·50						
h. Daffodil flaw (Cyl. 22 Dot, R. 1/12)	3·50						

Listed Varieties

For illustration of No. S28e see No. S26j.

S29g, S34f
White flaws in and
around thistle at upper
left

S29h, S34g
White spot by upper
left daffodil

Cylinder Numbers (Blocks of Six)

A. Cream paper. (No. S28)

Perforation Type A

Cyl. No.					No dot	Dot
15	..	..	..	..	2·75	2·75

B. Whiter paper. (No. S29)

Perforation Type A

Cyl. No.					No dot	Dot
15	..	..	..	..	1·60	1·60
22	..	..	..	..	2·10	2·10

Minor Constant Sheet Flaws

Cyl. 15   13/9   White spur on top left daffodil stem (Th. A2)

Cyl. 15.   1/4   Green dot in lower half of 1 of left ½ (Th. G1)

Coils

Made up from sheets with sheet margin joins. Watermark upright

Code No.	Number in roll	Face value	
L	480	£3	Vertical delivery (Cream paper)
N	480	£3	Sideways delivery (Whiter paper)

Sheet Markings

	Cylinder 15	Cylinder 22
Guide holes:	Boxed opposite rows 14/15, at left (no dot) or right (dot)	Boxed opposite rows 14/15, at left (no dot) or right (dot)
Marginal arrows:	"V" shaped, hand-engraved, at top and bottom; "W" shaped, photo-etched, at both sides	"W" shaped, hand-engraved, at top; "W" shaped, photo-etched at bottom and at both sides
Marginal rule:	At bottom of sheet (1½ mm. wide)	At bottom of sheet (2 mm. wide)
Others:	As given in General Notes	As given in General Notes

Imprimaturs from the National Postal Museum Archives

Imperforate, watermark Type W.24. Cream or whiter paper

Watermark upright
Watermark inverted
Tête-bêche pair

Cat. No.	S.G. No.	Shades	Mint	Used

1959 (AUGUST 4). WITH GRAPHITE LINES, TYPE S8. WATERMARK CROWNS

This was only issued in 3s. Booklets. See Section SB, Nos. SB70/a.

S30	589	Green	90·00	60·00
a. Watermark inverted (4.8.59) .. 40·00 40·00				

Imprimaturs from the National Postal Museum Archives

Imperforate, watermark Type W.24

Watermark upright
Watermark inverted
Tête-bêche pair

Quantity Issued   1,862,400

Cat. No.	S.G. No.	Shades	Mint	Used

1959 (NOVEMBER 18). PHOSPHOR-GRAPHITE ISSUE. WMK. ST. EDWARD'S CROWN

This has two graphite lines, Type S8, on the back and two phosphor bands on the front, applied typo., which react green under the lamp.

S31	601	Green	2·50	5·00

a. Narrow band at left or right
   (stamp with vert. margin)   ..   5·00
b. Green stroke below "E" (Cyl.
   21 No dot, R. 13/8)   ..   ..   6·00

For illustration of No. S31b see No. S27d.

Cylinder Numbers (Blocks of Six)

Single pane cylinder

Cyl. No.	Perf. Type		No dot
21	B	..	18·00
21	C	..	18·00

Sheet Markings

All the same as for No. S27

Imprimatur from the National Postal Museum Archives

Perf. 15 × 14, watermark Type W.24

Watermark upright

Quantity Issued   704,160

1960 (JUNE 22). TWO PHOSPHOR BANDS REACTING GREEN. WMK. CROWNS

The bands were applied in photogravure.

S32	—	Green	1·00	1·00

a. Watermark inverted (14.8.60)   10·00   7·00
b. Spot between rose and sham-
   rock (Cyl. 15 No dot, R. 20/3)..   3·50

For illustration of No. S32b see No. S26j.

Cylinder Numbers (Blocks of Six)

Perforation Type B (no dot) or C (dot)

Cyl. No.					No dot	Dot
15 ..	..	..	..	..	8·00	8·00

Minor Constant Sheet Flaws

Cyl. 15   13/9   White spur on top left daffodil stem (Th. A2)
Cyl. 15.   1/4   Green dot in lower half of 1 of left ½ (Th. G1)

Sheet Markings

Guide holes: Not known
Black bar: This occurs by the marginal arrows opposite rows 10/11, at left (no dot) or right (dot), also on booklet sheets
Others: As given in General Notes

Imprimaturs from the National Postal Museum Archives

Imperforate, watermark Type W.24

Watermark upright
Watermark inverted
Tête-bêche pair

Cat. No.	S.G. No.		Shades	Mint	Used

1961 (JUNE 5).† TWO PHOSPHOR BANDS REACTING BLUE. WMK. CROWNS

The bands were applied in photogravure on the stamps with upright watermark and by typography on those with watermark sideways.

A. Cream Paper

			Shades	Mint	Used
S33	—		Green	65	65
a. Watermark inverted (4.61)	..	9·00	5·00		
b. Watermark Crown to left (14.7.61)		9·00	9·00		
c. Watermark Crown to right	..	9·00	9·00		
d. Single broad band (wmk. sideways)		18·00			
da. Single broad band (wmk. upright or inverted)		50·00			

B. Whiter Paper (Sept. 1964)†

			Shades	Mint	Used
S34	**612**		Green	10	20
a. Watermark Crown to left (15.8.62)		10·00	10·00		
b. Watermark Crown to right	..	10·00	10·00		
c. Watermark inverted (7.64)	..	20·00	10·00		
d. Single broad band (wmk. upright or inverted)		60·00			
e. Single broad band (wmk. sideways)		60·00			
f. Thistle flaws (Cyl. 22 Dot, R. 12/1)		4·00			
g. Daffodil flaw (Cyl. 22 Dot. R. 1/22)		4·00			
h. White bulge on clover (Cyl. 22 No dot, R. 7/2		4·00			

Listed Varieties

For illustrations of Nos. S34*f*/*g*, see Nos. S29*g*/*h*.

S34*h*

Cylinder Numbers (Blocks of Six)

A. Cream paper. (No. S33)
Perforation Type B (no dot) and C (dot)

Cyl. No.				No dot	Dot
15 ..	..	..	..	.. 5·50	5·50

B. Whiter paper. (No. S34)
Perforation Type A

Cyl. No.					No dot	Dot
15 ..	..	..	..	..	1·75	1·75
22 ..	..	..	..	..	2·50	2·50

Minor Constant Sheet Flaws

Cyl. 15   13/9   White spur on top left daffodil stem (Th. A2)
Cyl. 15.   1/4   Green dot on lower half of 1 of left ½ (Th. G1)

Sheet Markings

All the same as for Nos. S28/9

Imprimaturs from the National Postal Museum Archives

Imperforate, watermark Type W.24. Cream or whiter paper

Watermark upright
Watermark inverted
Tête-bêche pair

Cat. No.	S.G. No.	Shades	Mint	Used

1965 (AUGUST 13). TWO 8 mm. PHOSPHOR BANDS REACTING VIOLET. WMK. CROWNS

The bands were applied by typography.

S35	—	Green	1·00	1·00

a.	Narrow band at left or right (stamp with vert. margin) ..	3·00
b.	Single 8 mm. broad band	8·00
ba.	As b but 6 mm. band	8·00
c.	Phosphor printed on both sides..	24·00

Cylinder Numbers (Blocks of Six)

Perforation Type A

		No dot	Dot
Cyl. No.			
15		8·00	8·00

Sheet Markings

All the same as for Cylinder 15 under Nos. S28/9

1953-67. 2d. Red-brown, Type S1

Cat. No.	S.G. No.	Shades	Mint	Used

1953 (AUGUST 31). WATERMARK TUDOR CROWN, TYPE W.22

S36   518   Red-brown   20   15

a. Watermark inverted (3.54)   ..   20·00   14·00
b. Watermark sideways (8.10.54) ..   80   1·25
c. Rose petal flaw (Cyl. 3 No dot, R. 4/8)   ..   ..   12·00
d. "Tadpole" flaw (Cyl. 4 Dot, R. 17/6) ..   ..   12·00
e. Retouched (Cyl. 3 Dot, R. 17/6)   12·00
g. Extra leg to "R" (Sideways coil, Roll 2) ..   ..   3·00
h. Retouched left "2" (Sideways coil, Roll 5) ..   ..   4·00
i. Dot on rose (Sideways coil, Roll 1)   2·50

Stamps with sideways watermark are from T coils with sideways delivery.

Listed Varieties

S36c, S37e

S36d, S37f, S38f
White flaw resembles a
tadpole below thistle

S36e, S37g, S38g, S40d
Later retouched state of
the "tadpole" flaw

S36g, S37l, S38s,
S40i, S41b, S49c

From sideways delivery T coils

Normal

S36h, S37m,
S38t, S40j,
S41c, S49d

S36i, S37k, S38w

Cylinder Numbers (Blocks of Six)
Perforation Type A

Cyl. No.					No dot	Dot	Cyl. No.					No dot	Dot
1	..	..	..	..	..	3·75	3·75	3	..	..	..	..	..	2·75	2·75
2	..	..	..	..	..	3·75	3·75	4	..	..	..	..	..	2·75	2·75

Coils

Double pane cylinder number D1 was used for vertical delivery coils and single pane cylinder D3 for sideways delivery coils.

Printed in continuous reels

Code No.	Number in roll	Face value

(a) Vertical delivery. Watermark upright

R	480	£4
Q	960	£8
V	960	£8

(b) Sideways delivery. Watermark sideways

T	480	£4

Sheet Markings

Guide holes: Boxed opposite rows 14/15, at left (no dot) or right (dot)

Others: As given in General Notes

Sheets are known with the arrows missing at top and bottom from cylinder 2 (no dot)

Imprimaturs from the National Postal Museum Archives

Imperforate, watermark Type W.22

Watermark upright
Watermark inverted
Tête-bêche pair

Cat. No.	S.G. No.	Shades	Mint	Used

1955 (SEPTEMBER 6). WATERMARK ST. EDWARD'S CROWN, TYPE W.23

A. Red-brown

S37	543	Red-brown	20	20

a. Imperf. between pair (from vert.
   coil £1500

b. Imperf. between pair (from sideways wmk. horiz coil £1500

c. Watermark inverted (9.55) .. 10·00 6·00

d. Watermark sideways (31.7.56) .. 20 60

e. Rose petal flaw (Cyl. 3 No dot, R.
   4/8 .. .. 3·00

f. "Tadpole" flaw (Cyl. 4 No Dot,
   R. 17/6) .. .. 4·50

g. Retouched (R. 17/6 on Cyls. 3, 6,
   7 all Dot. Vertical coil, Roll 6) .. 4·00

h. "Tadpole" flaw with shamrock
   flaw (Cyl. 9 Dot, R. 17/6) .. .. 5·00

i. Flaw between shamrock and diadem (Cyl. 7 Dot, R. 1/6) .. .. 4·00

j. White spot by daffodil (Cyl. 9
   Dot, R. 18/8) .. .. 3·00

k. Dot on rose (Sideways coil, Roll 1) 2·50

l. Extra leg to "R" (Sideways coil,
   Roll 2) .. .. 3·00

m. Retouched left "2" (Sideways
   coil, Roll 5) .. .. 3·00

n. Extended stem on daffodil (Sideways coil, Roll 9) .. .. .. 2·75

Stamps with sideways watermark are from T coils with sideways delivery.

Listed Varieties

For illustrations of Nos. S37e/g, see Nos. S36c/e and for Nos. S37k/m, see Nos. S36g/i. No. S37h comprises the variety shown for No. S36d but in addition there is a white flaw to the left of the adjoining shamrock; see also Nos. S40f, S41e and S49e.

S37i, S38j
This was a multipositive flaw which was retouched on other cylinders

S37n, S38u,
S40k, S41d

S37j, S38k

Cat. No.	S.G. No.	Shades	Mint	Used

B. Light red-brown (17 October 1956)

| S38 | 543*b* | | Light red-brown | 20 | 15 |

a. Tête-bêche (horiz pair) £600
c. Imperf. between stamp and top margin £200
d. Watermark inverted (1.57) .. 4·00   2·00
e. Watermark sideways (5.3.57) .. 9·00   5·50
f. "Tadpole" flaw (R. 17/6 on Cyls. 8, 10 and 11 Dot) .. .. .. 3·50
g. Retouched (R. 17/6 on Cyls. 6, 7, 8, 11, 12, 13 & 15 all dot, Vertical coil, Row 6) .. .. 3·00
h. "Tadpole" and shamrock flaws (R. 17/6 on Cyls 9 & 12 Dot .. 5·00
i. "Tadpole" flaw retouched with shamrock flaw (R. 17/6 on Cyls. 14 and 16 Dot.. .. .. .. 5·00
j. Flaw between shamrock and diadem (Cyl. 7 dot, R. 1/6) .. .. 3·00
k. White spot by daffodil (Cyl. 9 Dot, R. 18/8) .. .. 3·00
l. Extended leaf on shamrock (Cyl. 10 No dot, R. 8/6) .. .. .. 2·50
m. "Double trumpet" flaw (Cyl. 10 No dot, R. 11/1) .. .. .. 4·00
n. Dot on shamrock (Cyl. 10 No dot, R. 20/1 .. .. 3·50
o. White flaw on crown (Cyl. 11 No dot, R. 9/11) .. .. 6·00
p. White flaw on shamrock (Cyl. 12 dot, R, 20/3) .. .. 6·00

q. White spot by right thistle (Cyl. 14 Dot, R. 11/10) .. .. .. 7·50
r. Dot over rose stem (Cyl. 14 No dot, R. 1/1) .. .. 4·50
s. Extra leg to "R" (Sideways coil, Roll 2) .. .. 10·00
t. Retouched left "2" (Sideways coil, Roll 5) .. .. 10·00
u. Extended stem on daffodil (Sideways coil, Roll 9) .. .. .. 10·00
w. Dot on rose (Sideways coil, Roll 1) 10·00

Stamps with sideways watermark are from T coils with sideways delivery.

In December 1956 a completely imperforate sheet was noticed by clerks in a Kent post office one of whom purchased it against P.O. regulations. In view of this irregularity we do not consider it properly issued.

Listed Varieties

Tadpole flaws: Nos. S38*f/h* are as Nos. S37*f/h*. The first printings from cylinder 12 show No. S38*h* larger, but on later printings both flaws appear to have been retouched. No. S38*i* is a fourth state which combines the shamrock flaw (small on cyl. 14, larger on cyl. 16) with the retouched state of the tadpole flaw.

For illustrations of Nos. S38*j/k*, see Nos. S37*i/j*, and for Nos. S38*s/w*, see Nos. S36*g/i* and S37*n*.

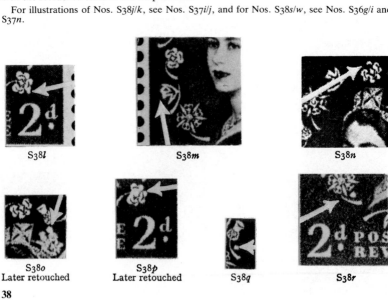

S38*l*   S38*m*   S38*n*

S38*o*   S38*p*   S38*q*   S38*r*
Later retouched   Later retouched

Cylinder Numbers (Blocks of Six)

(a) Red-brown (No. S37)

Perforation Type A

Cyl. No.					No dot	Dot	Cyl. No.						No dot	Dot
3	..	..	..	..	.. 2·75	2·75	7	..	..	..	..	..	2·75	2·75
4	..	..	..	..	.. 2·75	2·75	9	..	..	..	..	..	7·00	7·00
6	..	..	..	..	.. 2·75	2·75								

(b) Light red-brown (No. S38)

Perforation Type A

					No dot	Dot							No dot	Dot
6	..	..	..	..	.. 2·50	2·50	12	..	..	..	..	..	2·40	2·40
7	..	..	..	..	.. 2·50	2·50	13	..	..	..	..	..	2·40	2·40
8	..	..	..	..	.. 2·50	2·50	14	..	..	..	..	..	2·40	2·40
9	..	..	..	..	.. 2·50	2·50	15	..	..	..	..	..	2·40	2·40
10	..	..	..	..	.. 6·00*	2·50	16	..	..	..	..	..	2·40	2·40
11	..	..	..	..	.. 2·40	2·40								

Perforation Type E

| 7 | .. | .. | .. | .. | .. 14·00 | 2·50** | | 9 | .. | .. | .. | .. | .. 14·00 | 2·50** |

**Same price as perforation type A with extension holes in left margin.

Minor Constant Sheet Flaws

Cyl. 7   14/8   White dot above T of POSTAGE

Cyl. 9   20/1   White spur on lower daffodil (Th. G3)

Cyl. 10   14/12   Nick in R of REVENUE

Cyl. 10.   9/6   Dark spot on necklace (Th. E/F3)

Cyl. 16.   20/12   " REVENUE " retouched (Th. G2-5)

Coils

Double pane cylinder number D1 was used for vertical delivery coils of No. S37, cylinder D2 for No. S38; single pane cylinder D3 was used for the sideways delivery coils of No. S37d and cylinders D3 or D4 for No. S38e.

Printed in continuous reels

Code No.	Cat. No.	Number in roll	Face value
(a) Vertical delivery. Watermark upright			
R	S37	480	£4
Q	S37	960	£8
V	S37	960	£8
R	S38	480	£4
Q	S38	960	£8
V	S38	960	£8
(b) Sideways delivery. Watermark sideways			
T	S37d	480	£4
T	S38e	480	£4

Sheet Markings

Guide holes: Boxed opposite rows 14/15, at left (no dot) or right (dot)

Others: As given in General Notes

Imprimaturs from the National Postal Museum Archives

A. Red-brown. Imperforate, watermark Type W.23

Watermark upright
Watermark inverted
Tête-bêche pair

B. Light red-brown. Imperforate, watermark Type W.23

Watermark upright
Watermark inverted
Tête-bêche pair

Graphite-lined Issues

On the 2d. value, Nos. S39, S42/3 the single graphite line normally appeared at the right when viewed from the back. It was printed in black under the gum.

S9

Cat. No.	S.G. No.		Shades	Mint	Used

1957 (NOVEMBER 19). WITH GRAPHITE LINE, TYPE S9. WMK. ST. EDWARD'S CROWN

S39   564   Light red-brown   2·50   1·50
  a. Line at left (as seen from back)   £500   £175
  b. Horiz. pair, one with line
      omitted £1000
  c. Coil join (vert. pair) ..   .. 15·00
  d. Coil join (horiz. pair) ..   .. 10·00

Nos. S39*a/b* result from a misplacement of the line.

Cylinder Numbers (Blocks of Six)

Single pane cylinder

Cyl. No.	Perf. Type		No dot
17	B	..	18·00
17	C	..	18·00

Minor Constant Sheet Flaws

Cyl. 17   11/2   White flaw on tail of left d
          16/1   White flaw in centre of upper left rose (Th. B1)

Coils

Made up from sheets with sheet margin joins

Code No.	Number in roll	Face value	
V	960	£8	Vertical delivery
T	480	£4	Sideways delivery

Sheet Markings:

Guide holes: Boxed opposite rows 14/15, at both sides and unboxed opposite rows 1 and 7/8 at both sides
Others: As given in General Notes

Imprimatur from the National Postal Museum Archives

Imperforate, watermark Type W.23
Watermark upright

Quantity Issued   37,686,480

Cat. No.	S.G. No.		Shades	Mint	Used

1958 (DECEMBER 4).† WATERMARK CROWNS, TYPE W.24)

A. Cream Paper

S40	—		Light red-brown	25	12

a. Imperf. between stamp and top margin	£225	
b. Watermark sideways (3.4.59) ..	1·10	1·10
c. Watermark inverted (10.4.61) ..	80·00	30·00
d. "Tadpole" retouch (R. 17/6 on Cyls. 15 Dot and others)	3·00	
e. "Swan's head" flaw (Cyl. 24 Dot R. 19/10)	3·00	
f. "Tadpole" flaw retouched with shamrock flaw (Cyl. 27 Dot, R. 17/6)	4·00	
i. Extra leg to "R" (Sideways coil, Roll 2)	3·50	
j. Retouched left "2" (Sideways coil, Roll 5)	3·50	
k. Extended stem on daffodil (Sideways coil, Roll 9)	3·50	

B. Whiter Paper (5 September 1963)†

S41	573		Light red-brown	10	10

a. Watermark sideways (27.7.62) ..	25	65
b. Extra leg to "R" (Sideways coil, Roll 2)	3·00	
c. Retouched left "2" (Sideways coil, Roll 5)	3·00	
d. Extended stem on daffodil (Sideways coil, Roll 9)	3·00	
e. "Tadpole" flaw retouched with shamrock flaw (Cyl. 27 Dot, R. 17/6)	3·50	

†No. S40 was issued in November 1958 in V coils and No. S41 appeared on 20 September 1962 in V coils.

Stamps with sideways watermark are from T coils with sideways delivery.

Listed Varieties

Tadpole flaw: No. S40d is as No. S38g. For illustrations of Nos. S40i/j and S41b/c, see Nos. S36g/h; for Nos. S40k and S41d, see No. S37n. For description of Nos. S40f and S41e see below No. S37.

S40e

Cylinder Numbers (Blocks of Six)

A. Cream paper. (No. S40)

Cyl. No. Perforation Type A					No dot	Dot	Cyl. No. Perforation Type A					No dot	Dot
15	..	..	..	..	2·75	2·75	24	..	..	..	..	2·75	2·75
19	..	..	..	..	2·75	2·75	25	..	..	..	..	2·75	2·75
20	..	..	..	..	2·75	2·75	27	..	..	..	..	2·75	2·75
21	..	..	..	..	2·75	2·75	29	..	..	..	..	2·75	2·75
22	..	..	..	..	2·75	2·75	30	..	..	..	..	2·75	2·75
23	..	..	..	..	2·75	2·75							

B. Whiter paper. (No. S41)

Cyl. No. Perforation Type A					No dot	Dot	Cyl. No. Perforation Type A					No dot	Dot
23	..	..	..	..	1·60	1·60	27	..	..	..	..	1·60	1·60
25	..	..	..	..	1·60	1·60	30	..	..	..	..	1·60	1·60

Coils

Double cylinder D2 was used for vertical delivery coils and cylinders D3 and D4 (single pane) for sideways delivery coils.
Printed in continuous reels.   Cream or whiter paper

Code No.   Number in roll   Face value

(a) Vertical delivery. Watermark upright

R	480	£4
Q	960	£8
V	960	£8

(b) Sideways delivery. Watermark sideways

| T | 480 | £4 |

Sheet Markings

Guide holes: Boxed opposite rows 14/15, at left (no dot) or right (dot)
Others: As given in General Notes

Imprimaturs from the National Postal Museum Archives

Imperforate, watermark Type W.24. Cream or whiter paper

Watermark upright
Watermark inverted
Tête-bêche pair

Cat. No.	S.G. No.		Shades	Mint	Used

1958 (NOVEMBER 24).   WITH GRAPHITE LINE, TYPE S9. WATERMARK CROWNS

S42	590		Light red-brown	7·00	3·25
a.	Line at extreme left (as seen from back	£500			
ab.	Horizontal pair, one stamp as S42a and one without line ..	£1750			
b.	Coil join (vert. pair)	20·00			

Cylinder Numbers (Blocks of Six)

Single pane cylinder

Cyl. No.	Perf. Type		No dot
17	B	..	50·00
17	C	..	50·00

Minor Constant Sheet Flaw

Cyl. **17**   11/2   White flaw on tail of left d

Coil

Vertical delivery. Made up from sheets with sheet margin joins

Code No.	Number in roll	Face value
V	960	£8

Sheet Markings

As for No. S39

Imprimatur from the National Postal Museum Archives

Imperforate, watermark Type W.24

Watermark upright

Quantity Issued   48,419,520

1959 (NOVEMBER 18).   PHOSPHOR-GRAPHITE ISSUE. WATERMARK CROWNS

This has one graphite line (Type **S9**), on the back and one phosphor band on the front, applied typo., which reacts green under the lamp.

S43	605			Light red-brown	5·00	3·75
a.	Phosphor printed on both sides	£150				
b.	ERROR. Watermark St. Edward's Crown (3.60) ..	£150	£150			

Cylinder Numbers (Blocks of Six)

Single pane cylinder

Watermark Crowns (No. S43)			Watermark St. Edward's Crown (No. S43b)		
Cyl. No.	Perforation Type	No dot	Cyl. No.	Perforation Type	No dot
17	B	.. 35·00	17	B	.. £975
17	C	.. 35·00	17	C	.. £975

Minor Constant Sheet Flaws

Cyl. 17   11/2 White flaw on tail of left d   ·
        16/1 White flaw in centre of upper left rose (Th. B1) (on St. Edward's Crown wmk. only)

Sheet Markings

As for No. S39

Imprimatur from the National Postal Museum Archives

Perf. 15 × 14, watermark Type W.24

Watermark upright

Quantity Issued   4,509,120 (including both watermarks)

Cat. No.	S.G. No.	Shades	Mint	Used

1960. (JUNE 22). ONE PHOSPHOR BAND AT LEFT REACTING GREEN. WMK. CROWNS

The band was applied in photogravure.

S44	613	Light red-brown	20·00	20·00
a. Coil join (vert. pair) ..	.. 45·00			

Cylinder Numbers (Blocks of Six)

Single pane cylinder

Cyl. No.	Perf. Type		No dot
17	B	..	£130
17	C	..	£150

Minor Constant Sheet Flaws

Cyl. 17   11/2 White flaw on tail of left d

Coil

Vertical delivery. Made up from sheets with sheet margin joins

Code No.	Number in roll	Face value
V	960	£8

Sheet Markings

As for No. S39

Imprimatur from the National Postal Museum Archives

Imperforate, watermark Type W.24

Watermark upright

1961 (JUNE 5). ONE PHOSPHOR BAND AT LEFT REACTING BLUE. WMK. CROWNS

This exists on cream paper only and the phosphor band was applied in photogravure or flexo. See General Notes—Application of Phosphor Bands.

S45	—	Light red-brown	25·00	20·00

Cylinder Numbers (Blocks of Six)

Perforation Type A			Perforation Type B (no dot) and C (dot)		
Cyl. No.		No dot Dot	Cyl. No.		No dot Dot
29	.. £170 £170		29	.. £170 £170	

Minor Constant Sheet Flaw

Cyl. 29. 17/6 There is only a slight shading to the background where the tadpole and shamrock flaws were

Coil

Double pane cylinder D2 was used.

Printed in continuous reels. Vertical delivery with watermark upright

Code No.	Number in roll	Face value
V	960	£8

Sheet Markings

Guide holes: Boxed opposite rows 14/15 at left (no dot) and right (dot)
Others: As given in General Notes

Cat. No.	S.G. No.	Shades	Mint	Used

1961 (OCTOBER 4). TWO PHOSPHOR BANDS REACTING BLUE. WMK CROWNS
A. Cream Paper   Bands typographed

S46	—	Light red-brown	10·00	5·00

a. Imperf. three sides* .. .. ..
b. Narrow band at left or right (stamp with vert. margin) .. 15·00
c. Single 8 mm. broad band (typo.) 20·00
ca. As c. but 6 mm. band .. .. 12·00
d. Bands applied photo. (3.4.62) .. 1·25   1·25
da. Single 8 mm. broad band (photo) 35·00

B. Whiter Paper (5 November 1964)† Bands applied in photogravure

S47	—	Light red-brown	2·75	2·75

a. Single broad band .. .. 75·00

*This comes from the bottom row of a sheet which is imperf. at bottom and both sides. From cyl. 29 no dot with bands applied photo.

†No. S47 appeared earlier from V coils on 21 January 1963.

Cylinder Numbers (Blocks of Six)

Cream paper

Cyl. No.   No dot Dot
Two bands applied typo. (No. S46)
Perforation Type A

Cyl. No.					No dot	Dot
25 ..	..	..	..	..	70·00	†
27 ..	..	..	..	..	†	70·00
29 ..	..	..	..	..	70·00	70·00
30 ..	..	..	..	..	70·00	70·00

Two bands applied photo. (No. S46d)
Perforation Type B (no dot) and C (dot)

29 .. .. 10·00 10·00

Whiter paper

Cyl. No.   No dot Dot
Two bands applied photo. (No. S47)
Perforation Type A

Cyl. No.					No dot	Dot
25 ..	..	..	..	..	20·00	20·00

As the typographed bands were applied on individual sheets and not in the reel, it is possible that the items marked with a dagger may exist.

Minor Constant Sheet Flaw

Dot cyls. 17/6 There remains only a slight disturbance to the background where the tadpole and shamrock flaws were

Coil

Double pane cylinder D2 was used.

Printed in continuous reels. Vertical delivery with watermark upright. Cream or whiter paper.

Code No.	Number in roll	Face value
V	960	£8

Imprimatur from the National Postal Museum Archives

Imperforate, watermark Type W.24. Cream or whiter paper

Watermark upright

Sheet Markings
As for No. S40

Cat. No.	S.G. No.	Shades	Mint	Used

1965 (AUGUST 17). TWO 8 mm. PHOSPHOR BANDS REACTING VIOLET. WMK. CROWNS

The bands were applied in photogravure only.

S48	—	Light red-brown	40	40

Cylinder Numbers (Blocks of Six)
Perforation Type A

Cyl. No.					No dot	Dot
30 ..	..	..	..	..	4·25	4·25

Minor Constant Sheet Flaw

Cyl. 30. 17/6 There remains only a slight disturbance under the thistle of the original tadpole and shamrock flaws

Coil

Double pane cylinder D2 was used.
Printed in continuous reels. Vertical delivery with watermark upright

Code No.	Number in roll	Face value
V	960	£8

Sheet Markings
As for No. S40

1967 (SEPTEMBER).† TWO 9·5 mm. PHOSPHOR BANDS REACTING VIOLET. WMK. CROWNS

The bands were applied in photogravure only.

S49	613*a*	Light red-brown	10	10

a. Watermark Crown to left (6.4.67)   15   60
b. Single broad band (wmk. sideways) .. ..   10·00
c. Extra leg to "R" (Sideways coil, Roll 2) .. ..   3·00
d. Retouched left "2" (Sideways coil, Roll 5) .. ..   3·00
e. "Tadpole" flaw retouched with shamrock flaw (Cyl. 27 Dot R. 17/6) .. ..   4·00

Stamps with sideways watermark are from T coils with sideways delivery.
For illustrations of Nos. S49c/d, see Nos. S36g/h. No. S49e is described below No. S37.

Cylinder Numbers (Blocks of Six)

Perforation Type F (L)*

Cyl. No.					No dot	Dot
25 ..	..	..	..	..	1·60	1·60

Perforation Type A

Cyl. No.					No dot	Dot
27 ..	..	..	..	..	1·60	1·60

Minor Constant Sheet Flaw

Dot panes. 17/6 There remains only a slight disturbance to the background where the tadpole and shamrock flaws were

Coils

Double pane cylinder D2 was used for the vertical delivery coils and cylinder D3 (single pane) for sideways delivery coils.

Printed in continuous reels

Code No.	Number in roll	Face value
(a) Vertical delivery. Watermark upright		
R	480	£4
V	960	£8
(b) Sideways delivery. Watermark sideways		
T	480	£4

Sheet Markings

Guide holes: Boxed opposite rows 14/15, at left (no dot) or right (dot) but in the case of perforation Type F (L)* the boxes remain on both panes but the holes are unboxed above and below the eighth vertical row in the no dot pane only

Others. As given in General Notes.

1952–65. 2½d. Carmine-red, Type S2

Two Types

Type I   In the frontal cross of the diadem, the top line is only half the width of the cross.

Type II   The top line extends to the full width of the cross and there are signs of strengthening in other parts of the diadem.

I   II

Variations in the Multipositives

The original multipositive became damaged and had to be replaced. The original negative consisted of two negatives placed in contact against each other, one for the frame and one for the Queen's head and oval setting. When these two pieces of glass were placed together the position of the two was not exactly the same as when the first multipositive was made, resulting in a slight tilting of the portrait.

The second multipositive (Type B) was used for making cylinder 46 which was employed for No. S53 and the third multipositive (Type C) was used for all later cylinder numbers i.e. Nos. 49 onwards.

Multipositive A was used for the booklets listed under Nos. S53, S55, S57, S59, S61/2 and S65, and, in consequence, stamps from these sections showing multipositive A and upright watermark are worth the same as inverted watermark varieties from booklets

A   B   C

Type A. At the shoulder lines above "E" of "POSTAGE" the line dividing the light from the dark material of the dress, if projected, runs level with the top of the two diagonal lines of the ribbon on the wreath.

Type B. The line runs between the first and second diagonal line of the ribbon.

Type C. The line runs level with the first diagonal line of the ribbon.

These are not listed as separate varieties because the stamps printed from the cylinders made from the three variations in the multipositives differed in other respects. It was, however, a most interesting development which also applied to the 3d. value.

Cat. No.	S.G. No.			Shades	Mint	Used
1952 (DECEMBER 5).		**WATERMARK TUDOR CROWN, TYPE W.22. TYPE I**				
S50	519			Carmine-red	10	15

a. Watermark sideways (15.11.54)   8·00   7·50
b. Broken value circle (Cyl. 8 No dot. R. 20/2)   ..   5·00
c. Extended broken top of diadem (Cyl. 16 Dot, R. 20/5) .. ..   6·00

d. Frame retouch (Sideways coil, Roll 7) ..   ..   12·00

Stamps with sideways watermark are from M coils with sideways delivery.

Listed Varieties

S50*b*   S50*c*   S50*d*, S52*e*, S56*ba*, S56*da*

Cylinder Numbers (Blocks of Six)

Perforation Type A

Cyl. No.					No dot	Dot	Cyl. No.					No dot	Dot
2	..	..	..	..	.. 1·60	1·60	16	..	..	..	..	.. 1·60	1·60
4	..	..	..	..	.. 1·60	1·60	17	..	..	..	..	.. 1·60	1·60
5	..	..	..	..	.. 1·60	1·60	18	..	..	..	..	.. 1·60	1·60
6	..	..	..	..	.. 1·60	1·60	19	..	..	..	..	.. 1·60	1·60
7	..	..	..	..	.. 1·60	1·60	22	..	..	..	..	.. 1·60	1·60
8	..	..	..	..	.. 5·00*	1·60	23	..	..	..	..	.. 1·60	1·60
9	..	..	..	..	.. 1·60	1·60	24	..	..	..	..	.. 1·60	1·60
10	..	..	..	..	.. 1·60	1·60	25	..	..	..	..	.. 2·40	2·40
11	..	..	..	..	.. 1·60	1·60	27	..	..	..	..	.. 1·60	1·60
12	..	..	..	..	.. 1·60	1·60							
13	..	..	..	..	.. 2·40	2·40							

Perforation Type B (no dot) and C (dot)

Cyl. No.					No dot	Dot
14	..	..	..	..	.. 1·60	1·60
15	..	..	..	..	.. 1·60	1·60
14	..	..	..	..	.. 4·00	4·00
24	..	..	..	..	.. 4·00	4·00

Minor Constant Sheet Flaws

Multipositive flaws

No dot   1/4   Red dot over left of crown (Th. A3)
            12/4   Red spot in leaf of shamrock (Th. G1)
            18/1   Diagonal scratch from chin to neck (Th. E3–F4)
Dot   11/9   White spot in R of E R (Cyls. 23. onwards)

Cylinder flaws

Cyl. 2.   16/1   Smudge line across top of REVENUE
Cyl. 8   19/1   Red spot in 1 of fraction
Cyl. 10.   20/1   Extended top of 2 in value

Coils

Single pane cylinder L1 was used for the vertical delivery coils and L3 for the sideways delivery coils.

Printed in continuous reels

Code No.	Number in roll	Face value
(a) Vertical delivery. Watermark upright		
F	960	£10
U	1920	£20
(b) Sideways delivery. Watermark sideways		
M	480	£5

Sheet Markings

Guide holes: Boxed opposite rows 14/15, at left (no dot) or right (dot)
Others: As given in General Notes

Imprimatur from the National Postal Museum Archives

Imperforate, watermark Type W.22

Watermark upright

Cat. No.	S.G. No.	Shades	Mint	Used

1953 (MAY). WATERMARK TUDOR CROWN, TYPE W.22. TYPE II

This issue appeared from booklets only. See Section SB, Nos. SB80/a.

S51	519b		Carmine-red	1·00	70
a.	Watermark inverted (5.53) ..	15	50		

Cat. No.	S.G. No.	Shades	Mint	Used

1955 (SEPTEMBER 28). WATERMARK ST. EDWARD'S CROWN, TYPE W.23. TYPE I

S52   544   Carmine-red   20   15

a. Imperf. between stamp and top margin £250
b. Watermark sideways (23.3.56) 1·25   1·10
c. "b" for "D" in value (Cyl. 30 Dot, R. 19/11) .. .. .. 4·50
d. White flaw below oval (Cyl. 44 Dot, R. 1/4) .. .. 3·75
e. Frame retouch (sideways coil, Roll 7) .. .. 4·00

Stamps with sideways watermark are from M coils with sideways delivery.

Listed Varieties

S52c

S52d

For illustration of No. S52e, see No. S50d

Cylinder Numbers (Blocks of Six)

Perforation Type A

Cyl. No.						No dot	Dot	Cyl. No.						No dot	Dot
22	..	..	..	..	..	2·40	2·40	39	..	..	..	..	..	2·40	2·40
24	..	..	..	..	..	2·40	£450	40	..	..	..	..	..	2·40	2·40
25	..	..	..	..	..	2·40	2·40	42	..	..	..	..	..	2·40	2·40
27	..	..	..	..	..	2·40	2·40	43	..	..	..	..	..	2·40	2·40
30	..	..	..	..	..	2·40	2·40	44	..	..	..	..	..	2·40	2·40
32	..	..	..	..	..	2·40	2·40	45	..	..	..	..	..	32·00	32·00
33	..	..	..	..	..	2·40	2·40								
34	..	..	..	..	..	†	10·00	**Perforation Type E**							
37	..	..	..	..	..	2·40	2·40	32	..	..	..	..	..	10·00	2·40**
38	..	..	..	..	..	2·40	2·40	37	..	..	..	..	..	10·00	2·40**

**Same price as perforation type A with extension holes in left margin.

Minor Constant Sheet Flaws

Multipositive flaws as for No. S50
Cylinder flaw
Cyl. 43 18/5 Red spot on Queen's lip (Th. D3)

Coils

Single pane cylinders L1 or L2 were used for the vertical delivery coils and L3 for the sideways delivery coils.
Printed in continuous reels

	Code No.	Number in roll	Face value
(a) Vertical delivery. Watermark upright			
	F	960	£10
	U	1920	£20
(b) Sideways delivery. Watermark sideways			
	M	480	£5

Sheet Markings

As for No. S50
In cylinder 42, both panes, the marginal arrows at the top and bottom were omitted at first, but added later.

Imprimatur from the National Postal Museum Archives

Imperforate, watermark Type W.23
Watermark upright

Cat. No. S.G. No.	Shades	Mint	Used

1957.† WATERMARK ST. EDWARD'S CROWN, TYPE W.23. TYPE II

S53   544b   Carmine-red   25   40
   a. Tête-bêche (horiz. pair)   .. £750
   d. Imperf. between stamp and top
     margin £300
   e. Watermark inverted (9.55) ..   25   50

Cylinder Numbers (Blocks of Six)
Perforation Type A

Cyl. No.					No dot	Dot
46 ..	..	..	..	..	3·00	3·00

Sheet Markings
As for No. S50

Imprimaturs from the National Postal Museum Archives

Imperforate, watermark Type W.23

Watermark upright
Watermark inverted
Tête-bêche pair

1957 (NOVEMBER 19). WITH GRAPHITE LINES, TYPE S8. WMK. ST. EDWARD'S CROWN. TYPE II

S54   565   Carmine-red   6·00   6·25
   a. Coil join (horiz. pr.) ..   .. 20·00

Cylinder Numbers (Blocks of Six)
Single pane cylinder

Cyl. No.	Perf. Type		No dot
49	B	..	38·00
49	C	..	38·00

Coil
Made up from sheets with sheet margin joins. Sideways delivery

Code No.	Number in roll	Face value
M	480	£5

Sheet Markings
Guide holes: Boxed opposite rows 14/15, at both sides and unboxed opposite rows 1 and 7/8 at both sides
Others: As given in General Notes except that there were no marginal arrows at sides

Imprimatur from the National Postal Museum Archives

Imperforate, watermark Type W.23

Watermark upright

Quantity Issued 20,578,800

Cat. No.	S.G. No.			Shades	Mint	Used

1959 (SEPTEMBER 15).† WATERMARK CROWNS, TYPE W.24

A. Type II Cream Paper

S55 — Carmine-red 50 20

- *a.* Tête-bêche (horiz. pair) ..
- *b.* Imperf. strip of 3 .. .. ..
- *c.* Imperf. between stamp and bottom margin .. .. ..
- *d.* Watermark inverted (11.58) .. 4·00 90
- *e.* State 1. Leaf and extra rose stem flaws (Cyl. 50 Dot, R. 9/4) 5·00
- *ea.* State 2. Extra rose stem. Leaf flaw retouched (Cyl 50 Dot, R. 9/4) .. .. 4·50
- *f.* White emblems (Cyl. 52 No dot, R. 12/4) .. .. .. 5·50

B. Type I. Cream Paper (21 September 1961)

S56 — Carmine-red 2·25 1·00

- *b.* Watermark sideways (10.11.60).. 1·00 50
- *ba.* Imperf. strip of 6 .. .. ..
- *bb.* Frame retouch (Sideways coil, Roll 7) .. .. 5·00

C. Type I. Whiter Paper (30 October 1963)

S56c 574b Carmine-red 15 35

- *d.* Watermark sideways (3.8.62) 20 30
- *da.* Frame retouch (Sideways coil, Roll 7) .. .. 4·00

D. Type II. Whiter Paper (7 May 1962)

S57 574 Carmine-red 10 10

- *a.* Watermark inverted (29.7.62).. 4·00 1·50
- *b.* Imperf. between stamp and top margin .. ..
- *c.* Watermark Crown to left (coils, 9.65 and booklets, 1.7.64) .. 40 75
- *d.* Watermark Crown to right .. 40 75
- *e.* State 2. Extra rose stem. Leaf flaw retouched (Cyl. 50 Dot, R. 9/4) .. .. 4·50
- *f.* Serif to "A" (Cyl. 55 No dot, R. 11/8) .. .. 4·50

E. Type II. Chalky Paper. Booklets only (15 July 1963)

S58 574k Carmine-red 20 45

- *a.* Watermark inverted (15.7.63) 20 60

Imperf. stamps. No. S55b comes from a booklet with watermark upright and No. S56ba is from an M coil with sideways watermark.

Sideways watermark. Nos. S56b, S56d and S57c came from M coils with sideways delivery and Nos. S57c/d are from 2s. Holiday Booklets No. NR2.

Listed Varieties

For illustration of Nos. S56ba and S56da, see No. S50d. No. S56da is known in a second state showing a vertical line adjoining the right-hand frame not filled in with colour.

S55e

State 1. Triangular white flaw adjoining left leaf and extra stem to rose.

State 2. Later printings exist with the leaf flaw retouched (Nos S55ea, S57e, S61c, S62b, S63e).

State 3. Both flaws retouched (S65d).

S55f   Normal
Later retouched

S57f

Cylinder Numbers (Blocks of Six)

Type II. (No. S55) Cream Paper.
Perforation Type A

Cyl. No.					No dot	Dot
50	..	..	..	..	4·25	4·25
51	..	..	..	..	4·25	4·25
52	..	..	..	..	4·25	4·25
53	..	..	..	..	4·25	4·25
54	..	..	..	..	4·25	4·25

Perforation Type B (no dot) and C (dot)

Cyl. No.					No dot	Dot
50	..	..	..	..	6·00	6·00
51	..	..	..	..	6·00	6·00
52	..	..	..	..	5·50	5·50

Type I. (No. S56). Cream Paper
Perforation Type A

					No dot	Dot
42	..	..	..	..	16·00	16·00

Perforation Type B (no dot) and C (dot)
Cream paper

42	..	..	..	..	†	£600

Type II. (No. S57). Whiter Paper
Perforation Type A

					No dot	Dot
50	..	..	..	..	1·60	1·60
51	..	..	..	..	1·60	1·60
52	..	..	..	..	1·60	1·60
53	..	..	..	..	1·60	1·60
54	..	..	..	..	1·60	1·60
55	..	..	..	..	1·60	1·60
56	..	..	..	..	1·60	1·60

Type I. (No. S56c). Whiter Paper
Perforation Type A

					No dot	Dot
42	..	..	..	..	2·25	2·25

Perforation Type A

					No dot	Dot
57	..	..	..	..	1·60	1·60
58	..	..	..	..	1·60	1·60
59	..	..	..	..	1·60	1·60

Perforation Type B (no dot) and C (dot)

51	..	..	..	..	5·00	5·00
52	..	..	..	..	4·25	4·25

Minor Constant Sheet Flaws

Cyl. 42
1/4   Red spot over left of crown (Th. A3)
12/4   Red spot in leaf of shamrock (Th. G1)

Cyl. 42.
4/1   Red and white dots in oval (Th. B2)
5/8   Red dot in thistle (Th. G2)
11/9   White spot in R of E R
14/5   Slight retouch in forehead above Queen's right eye (Th. C2)
16/3   White dot between thistle and leaf (Th. G2)
17/2   Small white flaw on tail of R of E R
18/10   Red dot between Queen's lip and nose (Th. D3). Later partially removed
20/10   White flaw by oval at left (Th. D1–2)

Cyl. 50.
6/10   Background retouched behind P of POSTAGE and R of REVENUE

Cyl. 51.
7/5   Retouch to left of hair (Th. C2)
9/6   White dot at bottom left of R of REVENUE

Cyl. 55.
11/8   Spur on A of POSTAGE (Th. G4)

Coils

Single pane cylinder L2 was used for the vertical delivery coils and cylinders L3 for sideways delivery Type I coils and L5 for Type II coils.

Printed in continuous reels

Code No.	Number in roll	Face value	
(a) Vertical delivery. Watermark upright			
F	960	£10	Type I. Cream or whiter paper
(b) Sideways delivery. Watermark sideways			
M	480	£5	Type I. Cream or whiter paper
M	480	£5	Type II. Whiter paper

Sheet Markings

Guide holes: Boxed opposite rows 14/15, at left (no dot) or right (dot)
Marginal arrows: In Type II these exist hand-engraved at left as well as photo-etched. Also sheets are known with the arrows omitted at bottom. On cylinder 55 the faint outline of the "V" shaped arrow is below rows 8/9 in addition to the etched arrow below vertical rows 6/7.
Others: As given in General Notes

Imprimaturs from the National Postal Museum Archives

Type II. Imperforate, watermark Type W.24. Cream or whiter paper

Watermark upright
Watermark inverted
Tête-bêche pair

Cat. No.	S.G. No.		Shades	Mint	Used
1959 (JUNE 9). WITH GRAPHITE LINES, TYPE S8. WATERMARK CROWNS. TYPE II					
S59	591		Carmine-red	12·00	10·00
a. Watermark inverted (21.8.59)	48·00	45·00			

Cylinder Numbers (Blocks of Six)

Single pane cylinder

Cyl. No.	Perf. Type		No dot
49	B	..	85·00
49	C	..	85·00

Sheet Markings

As for No. S54

Imprimaturs from the National Postal Museum Archives

Imperforate, watermark Type W.24

Watermark upright
Watermark inverted
Tête-bêche pair

Quantity Issued   10,012,800

1959 (NOVEMBER 18). PHOSPHOR-GRAPHITE ISSUE. WATERMARK CROWNS. TYPE II

This has two graphite lines (Type S9), on the back and two phosphor bands on the front, applied typo., which react green under the lamp.

S60	606		Carmine-red	22·00	11·00
a. Narrow band at left or right (stamp with vert. margin)		..	24·00		
b. Single 8 mm. broad band ..		..	£130		
ba. As *b* but 6 mm. band	..	..			

Cylinder Numbers (Blocks of Six)

Single pane cylinder

Cyl. No.	Perf. Type		No dot
49	B	..	£140
49	C	..	£140

Sheet Markings

As for No. S54

Imprimatur from the National Postal Museum Archives

Perf. 15 × 14, watermark Type W.24

Watermark upright

Quantity Issued   689,280

Cat. No.	S.G. No.	Shades	Mint	Used

1960 (JUNE 22). TWO PHOSPHOR BANDS REACTING GREEN. WMK. CROWNS. TYPE II

The bands were applied in photogravure.

S61	—		Carmine-red	1·25	1·25

- *a.* Watermark inverted (14.8.60) .. £140   80·00
- *b.* Single broad band (wmk. upright) 32·00
- *ba.* Single broad band (wmk. inverted) £190
- *c.* State 2. Extra rose stem. Leaf flaw retouched (Cyl. 50 Dot, R. 9/4) .. .. 5·00

For illustration of No. S61*c*, see No. S55*e*.

Cylinder Numbers (Blocks of Six)

Perforation Type B (no dot) and C (dot)

Cyl. No.	No dot	Dot
50	.. 10·00	10·00

Minor Constant Sheet Flaw

Cyl. 50.   6/10 Background retouch behind P of POSTAGE and R of REVENUE

Sheet Markings

Guide holes: Boxed opposite rows 14/15, at left (no dot) or right (dot)
Black bar: This occurs by the marginal arrows opposite rows 10/11, at left (no dot) or right (dot), also on booklet sheets.
Others: As given in General Notes

Imprimaturs from the National Postal Museum Archives

Imperforate, watermark Type W.24

Watermark upright
Watermark inverted
Tête-bêche pair

1961 (JUNE 5). PHOSPHOR BANDS REACTING BLUE. WATERMARK CROWNS.
A. Two Bands (applied photo.). Type II. Cream Paper

S62	—		Carmine-red	6·00	3·00

- *a.* Watermark inverted (3.61) .. £150   75·00
- *b.* Slate 2. Extra rose stem. Leaf flaw retouched (Cyl. 50 Dot, R. 9/4) .. .. 10·00

Cat. No.	S.G. No.					Shades		Mint	Used

B. One Band at left (applied typo.). Type II. Cream Paper (4 October 1961)

S63	—			Carmine-red	2·50 2·50

    a. Band applied photo. (3.11.61) ..   12·00   12·00
    b. Watermark inverted (photo.)
       (3.62) .. ..   30·00   18·00
    c. Error. Two bands (photo.)*   ..   60·00
   ca. Band (photo.) omitted in pair
       with one band at right   ..   £125
    d. Band (typo.) omitted in pair with
       one band at right £160
    e. State 2. Extra rose stem. Leaf
       flaw retouched (Cyl. 50 Dot,
       R.9/4) .. ..   7·00

C. One Band at left (applied typo.). **Type I. Cream Paper** (4 October 1961)

S64	614*b*	Carmine-red	35·00 27·00

    b. Band omitted, in pair with one
       band at right £150
    c. Error. Two bands (typo.)*   ..   70·00

D. One Band at left (applied photo). Type II. Whiter Paper (22 June 1962)

S65	614*a*	Carmine-red	40 75

    a. Band applied typo. .. .. .. £190   75·00
    b. Watermark inverted (3.6.63) .. 30·00   18·00
    d. State 3. Rose stem and leaf flaws
       retouched (Cyl. 50 Dot, R, 9/4) ..   4·00
    e. Error. Two bands (photo.)*   .. £100

   * Two Band Errors. These can be identified by the distance between the bands. This is 12 mm. on No. S62, but 16 mm. on the two band errors, Nos. S63*c*, S64*c* and S65*e*. These three varieties have the narrow left band applied in error over the vertical perforations at each side of the stamp.

E. Two Bands (applied photo.). Type II. Whiter Paper (20 September 1964)

S66	614	Carmine-red	10 40

    a. Bands applied typo. .. .. ..
   ab. Narrow typo. band at left or right
       (stamp with vert. margin) ..
    b. One broad phosphor band
       (photo.) .. .. 10·00

   No. S66 was a reissue of No. S62 but from cylinder 57 and on whiter paper. The shade is slightly more carmine. It was first released in error in the S.E. London area in September 1964 and then put on sale in Birmingham in December 1964 as electronic sorting machines were not in use there at that time. To prepare for the alteration in postal rates on 17 May 1965 when the 2½d. ceased to be the second class mail rate, it was released in the phosphor areas on 3 May 1965 in place of the single band stamps. However, as there was no longer a postal need for this value it was not reprinted.

   For description of Nos. S62*b*, S63*e* and S65*d*, see illustration No S55*e*.

Cylinder Numbers (Blocks of Six)

Two bands (No S62). Type II Cream paper. Perforation Type A

Cyl. No.				No dot	Dot
50 ..	..	..	..	.. 38·00	38·00

One band at left. Type II. Cream paper

Perforation Type A					
Applied typo. (No. S63)					
50 ..	..	..	..	.. 18·00	18·00

Perforation Type B (no dot) or C (dot)					
Applied photo. (No. S63*a*)					
50 ..	..	..	..	.. 85·00	85·00
53 ..	..	..	..	.. 85·00	85·00

One band at left. Type I. Cream paper. Perforation Type A
       Applied typo. (No. S64)

42 ..	..	..	..	.. £225	£225

Type II. Whiter paper. Perforation Type A
   One band. Applied photo. (No. S65)

51	..	..	..	..	..	4·25	4·25
52	..	..	..	..	..	4·25	4·25
54	..	..	..	..	..	4·25	4·25
56	..	..	..	..	..	4·25	4·25
57	..	..	..	..	..	4·25	4·25

One band. Applied typo. (No. S65a)

50	..	..	..	..	..	..	—	—

Two bands. Applied photo. (No. S66)

57	..	..	..	..	..	1·75	1·75

Minor Constant Sheet Flaws

As recorded for Nos. S55/7

Sheet Markings

Guide holes: Boxed opposite rows 14/15, at left (no dot) or right (dot)
Others: As given in General Notes

Imprimaturs from the National Postal Museum Archives

One band at left. Type II. Imperforate, watermark Type W.24. Cream or whiter paper

Watermark upright
Watermark inverted
Tête-bêche pair

1954–67. 3d. Deep lilac, Type S2

Variations in the Multipositives

There are similar variations in the tilt of the portrait in the multipositives used as occurred in the 2½d. value (see notes and illustration at the beginning of the 2½d. list).

The second multipositive, corresponding to Type B, was used for cylinders 25 to 33 and the third multipositive, corresponding to Type C, was employed for cylinders 36 and 37. A fourth multipositive, also Type C, was introduced for cylinders 41 onwards.

Cat. No.	S.G. No.	Shades	Mint	Used

1954 (JANUARY 18). WATERMARK TUDOR CROWN, TYPE W.22

S67	520	Deep lilac	1·00	30

    a. Imperf. between stamp and top
        margin £350
    b. Coil join (horiz. pair)   ..   ..   4·00
    c. Coil join (vert. pair)   ..   ..   6·00

See General Notes under Paper—this stamp exists on very thick paper for this issue. (*Price £50 mint*)

Cylinder Numbers (Blocks of Six)

Perforation Type A			Perforation Type B (no dot) and C (dot)		
Cyl. No.	No dot	Dot	Cyl. No.	No dot	Dot
3	8·00	8·00	3	8·00	8·00

Minor Constant Sheet Flaws

Multipositive flaws
No dot   1/3   White scratch to bottom right of R of large E R (Th. A–B6)
Dot   9/8   Dark patch to left of central cross of tiara (Th. B3)

Coils

Made up from sheets with sheet margin joins. Watermark upright

Code No.	Number in roll	Face value	
C	960	£12	Vertical delivery
S	480	£6	Sideways delivery

Sheet Markings

Guide holes: Boxed opposite rows 14/15, at left (no dot) or right (dot)
Others: As given in General Notes

Imprimatur from the National Postal Museum Archives

Imperforate, watermark Type W.22

Watermark upright

1956 (JULY 17). WATERMARK ST. EDWARD'S CROWN, TYPE W.23

S68	545	Deep lilac	20	15

    a. Tête-bêche (horiz. pair)   ..   £750
    b. Imperf. three sides (pair)   ..   £500
    c. Imperf. between stamp and bot-
        tom margin £300
    d. Watermark inverted (1.10.57). . 60   1·00
    e. Watermark sideways (22.11.57)   14·00   10·00
    f. Coil join (horiz. pair)   ..   ..   2·25
    g. Coil join (vert. pair)   ..   ..   4·50
    h. White flaw over Queen's eye
        (Cyl. 2 Dot, R. 13/7)   ..   ..   5·00

Stamps with sideways watermark are from S coils with sideways delivery.

No. S68*b* comes from a partly perforated booklet pane of six. No complete panes showing this error have been recorded.

Listed Variety

S68*h*

Cylinder Numbers (Blocks of Six)

Perforation Type A

Cyl. No.					No dot	Dot	Cyl. No.					No dot	Dot
2	..	..	..	..	2·50	2·50	10	..	..	..	..	2·50	2·50
3	..	..	..	..	2·50	2·50	15	..	..	..	..	2·50	2·50
4	..	..	..	..	2·50	2·50	16	..	..	..	..	2·50	2·50
5	..	..	..	..	2·50	2·50	17	..	..	..	..	2·50	2·50
9	..	..	..	..	2·50	2·50							

Perforation Type B (no dot) and C (dot)

2	..	..	..	..	6·00	6·00	3	..	..	..	..	6·00	6·00

Perforation Type F (L)

5	..	..	..	..	50·00	†

Minor Constant Sheet Flaws

Multipositive flaws

No dot   1/3   White scratch to bottom right of R of large E R (Tb. A–B6)
Dot   9/8   Dark patch to left of central cross of tiara (Th. B3)

Cylinder flaw

Cyl. 17   17/3 Coloured scratches through E of large E R (Th. A1)

Coils

(a) Made up from sheets with sheet margin joins. Watermark upright

Code No.	Number in roll	Face value	
C	960	£12	Vertical delivery
S	480	£6	Sideways delivery

(b) Printed in continuous reels. Double pane cylinders M1 or M2 were used for the vertical delivery coils and cylinder M9 for the sideways delivery coil.

Code No.	Number in roll	Face value

(a) Vertical delivery. Watermark upright

C	960	£12
U	1920	£24

(b) Sideways delivery. Watermark sideways

S	480	£6

Sheet Markings

Guide holes:
    Perf. Types A, B and C, boxed opposite rows 14/15, at left (no dot) or right (dot)
    Perf. Type F (L), not known

Marginal arrows:
    "V" shaped, hand engraved at top and bottom
    "W" shaped, photo-etched at both sides
    Early printings from cylinder 2 had the "V" shaped arrow omitted from the bottom of the sheet on no dot and
dot panes
    (*Price for positional block showing arrow omitted £15 no dot £25 dot*)
    Marginal rule: These vary in width between 1½ and 2½ mm.
    Others: As given in General Notes

Imprimaturs from the National Postal Museum Archives

Imperforate, watermark Type W.23

Watermark upright
Watermark inverted
Tête-bêche pair

Cat. No.	S.G. No.		Shades	Mint	Used

1957 (NOVEMBER 19). WITH GRAPHITE LINES, TYPE S8. WMK. ST. EDWARD'S CROWN

S69	566		3d. Deep lilac	30	50
a. Coil join (horiz. pair) ..	.	2·00			

Cylinder Numbers (Blocks of Six)

Single pane cylinders

Cyl. No.	Perf. Type		No dot
7	B	..	4·00
7	C	..	4·00
11	B	..	4·00
11	C	..	4·00

Coils

Made up from sheets with sheet margin joins. Watermark upright

Code No.	Number in roll	Face value	
S	480	£6	Sideways delivery

Sheet Markings

Guide holes: Boxed opposite rows 14/15 at both sides and unboxed opposite rows 1 and 7/8, at both sides
Others: As given in General Notes

Imprimatur from the National Postal Museum Archives

Imperforate, watermark Type W.23
Watermark upright

Quantities Issued   91,466,400

Cat. No.	S.G. No.	Shades	Mint	Used

1958 (DECEMBER 8).† WATERMARK CROWNS, TYPE W.24

A. Cream Paper

S70	—	Deep lilac	25	15

   c. Imperf. between stamp and top
     margin £200
   d. Watermark Crown to left (Coils,
     24.10.58 and booklets, 26.5.61)   1·25   75
   e. Watermark inverted (11.58) ..   35   35
   f. Watermark Crown to right
     (Booklets, 26.5.61) .. ..   1·25   65
   g. Spot on "T" of "POSTAGE"
     (Cyl. 37 No dot, R. 19/11) ..   4·00
   h. Phantom "R" (Cyl. 37 No dot,
     below R. 20/12) .. .. ..   25·00
   i. Do. Retouch .. .. ..   8·00
   j. Phantom "R" (Cyl. 41 No dot,
     below R. 20/12) £250
   k. Do. First retouch .. .. ..   10·00
   l. Do. Second or third retouch ..   10·00

B. Whiter Paper (30 April 1962)

S71	575	Deep lilac	10	10

   a. Watermark Crown to left (Coils,
     30.4.62 and booklets, 5.6.62) ..   15   25
   b. Watermark Crown to right (Book-
     lets, 5.6.62)   15   25
   c. Watermark inverted (16.7.62) ..   15   20
   d. Experimental "T" watermark*
     (*marginal block of 6*) .. .. ..   15·00
   e. Serif on "E" (Cyl. 68 Dot, R.
     16/5) .. ..   3·50
   f. Flaw on "E" (R. 14/11 on Cyls. 60
     No dot and others) .. .. ..   3·50
   g. White spur on thistle left of "P"
     (Cyl. 70 No dot, R. 4/2) .. ..   3·00

*In 1964 No. S71 was printed from Cylinder 70 no dot and dot on an experimental paper which is distinguished by an additional watermark letter "T" lying on its side, which occurs about four times in the sheet, usually in the side margins where it is easiest to see. It is difficult to see when it occurs on the stamps themselves. 48,000 sheets were issued.

Variations in the Multipositives. See the notes at the beginning of the 3d. list about the variations in the tilt of the portrait on the different multipositives used.

Tête-bêche. No. S70 exists *tête-bêche*, also separated by gutters. These are from booklet sheets which were not issued.

Imperforate. Examples of No. S71 are known imperforate; these come from uncut booklet sheets which were not issued.

Listed Varieties

S70g

S70h

S71e, S77g

S70j, S74c   S70k

S71f

S71g

An incomplete masking of the stamp image beneath the marginal rule revealed an "R" on cyls. 37 and 41 no dot. It is more noticeable on the latter because of the wider marginal rule. The retouch on cyl. 37 is not easily identified. There is no trace of the "R" but the general appearance of that part of the marginal rule is uneven. However, the retouch can be confirmed in a positional block by the presence of the "Spot on T" variety on R. 19/11, No. S70g.

The "R" on cyl. 41 was retouched three times, the first being as illustrated here (No. S70k) and traces of the "R" can still be seen in the others.

Cylinder Numbers (Blocks of Six)

A. Cream Paper. (No. S70)

Perforation Type A

Cyl. No.					No dot	Dot	Cyl. No.					No dot	Dot
15	..	..	..	..	3·00	3·00	46	..	..	..	..	2·75	2·75
16	..	..	..	..	28·00	28·00	47	..	..	..	..	2·75	2·75
22	..	..	..	..	2·75	2·75	49	..	..	..	..	2·75	2·75
25	..	..	..	..	2·75	2·75	51	..	..	..	..	2·75	2·75
26	..	..	..	..	2·75	2·75	52	..	..	..	..	2·75	2·75
28	..	..	..	..	2·75	2·75	53	..	..	..	..	2·75	2·75
29	..	..	..	..	2·75	2·75	54	..	..	..	..	2·75	2·75
30	..	..	..	..	2·75	2·75	55	..	..	..	..	2·75	2·75
31	..	..	..	..	2·75	2·75	58	..	..	..	..	2·75	2·75
33	..	..	..	..	2·75	2·75	60	..	..	..	..	2·75	2·75
36	..	..	..	..	2·75	2·75	61	..	..	..	..	2·75	2·75
37	..	..	..	..	2·75	2·75	62	..	..	..	..	2·75	2·75
41	..	..	..	..	2·75	2·75	64	..	..	..	..	2·75	2·75

Perforation Type B (no dot) and C (dot)

28	..	..	..	..	..	4·25	4·25	52	..	..	..	..	..	4·50	4·50
41*	..	..	..	..	..	18·00	†	54	..	..	..	..	..	4·50	4·50
51	..	..	..	..	..	4·25	4·25							

Perforation Type H

31	..	..	..	..	..	2·75**	25·00	37	..	..	..	..	..	2·75**	25·00
36	..	..	..	..	..	2·75**	25·00	41	..	..	..	..	..	2·75**	25·00

**Same price as perforation type A with extension holes in left margin.

B. Whiter Paper. (No. S71)

Perforation Type A

Cyl. No.					No dot	Dot	Cyl. No					No dot	Dot
51	..	..	..	..	1·60	†	69	..	..	..	..	1·60	1·60
52	..	..	..	..	1·60	1·60	70	..	..	..	..	1·60	1·60
54	..	..	..	..	1·60	1·60	71	..	..	..	..	1·60	1·60
58	..	..	..	..	1·60	1·60	72	..	..	..	..	1·60	1·60
60	..	..	..	..	1·60	1·60	73	..	..	..	..	1·60	1·60
61	..	..	..	..	1·60	1·60	75	..	..	..	..	1·60	1·60
62	..	..	..	..	1·60	1·60	78	..	..	..	..	1·60	1·60
63	..	..	..	..	1·60	1·60	79	..	..	..	..	1·60	1·60
64	..	..	..	..	1·60	1·60	80	..	..	..	..	1·60	1·60
66	..	..	..	..	1·60	1·60	81	..	..	..	..	1·60	1·60
67	..	..	..	..	1·60	1·60	82	..	..	..	..	1·60	1·60
68	..	..	..	..	1·60	1·60							

*This has been seen Perf. Type B (no dot) and may be an example of No. S74 with phosphor bands omitted.

Minor Constant Sheet Flaws

Multipositive flaws (Cyls. 15, 16 and 22 only)

No dot   1/3   White scratch to bottom right of R of large E R (Th. A–B6)

Dot   9/8   Dark patch to left of central cross of tiara (Th. B3)

Cylinder flaws

Cyl. 46.   20/2   White flaw on leaves of oval at left (Th. E–F1)

Cyl. 52   17/9   White spur to circle around 3d. by D (Th. G6)

Cyl. 52.   18/2   Coloured line from Queen's hair to top of oval (Th. B2)

Cyl. 60.   4/11   Coloured flaw on thistle leaf (Th. G2)

Cyl. 63.   4/11   White flaw on leaf (Th. G2)

Cyl. 69   5/10   White flaw on wreath (Th. F6)

Cyl. 70.   10/4   White flaw above PO of POSTAGE (Th. G3)
  10/11   White flaw on daffodil stem giving appearance of thick stalk (Th. G–H2)
  19/8   Coloured scratch from tiara to oval (Th. C5)

Coils

Printed in continuous reels.   Double pane cylinders M1 or M2 were used for the vertical delivery coils and cylinders M9, M10 and M11 for the sideways delivery coils.   Cylinders M9 and M10 were used on cream paper and M10 and M11 on the whiter paper.

Code No.	Number in roll	Face value

(a) Vertical delivery. Watermark upright. Cream or whiter paper

Code No.	Number in roll	Face value
C	960	£12
U	1920	£24
AC	480	£6
AD	960	£12

(b) Sideways delivery. Watermark sideways. Cream or whiter paper

S	480	£6

Sheet Markings

Guide holes: Boxed opposite rows 14/15, at left (no dot) or right (dot). On the later cylinders there are single " S N " boxes for the guide holes

Marginal arrows: These vary from cylinder to cylinder. The following combinations are known:—
  (a) All hand engraved. "V" shaped at top and bottom; "W" shaped at both sides
  (b) "V" shaped, hand engraved at top and bottom; "W" shaped, photo-etched at both sides
  (c) All photo-etched. "W" shaped at top and bottom and at both sides

Marginal rule: These vary in width from between 1½ and 2½ mm.

Others: As given in General Notes

Imprimaturs from the National Postal Museum Archives

Imperforate, watermark Type W.24. Cream or whiter paper

Watermark upright
Watermark inverted
Tête-bêche pair

Cat. No.	S.G. No.	Shades	Mint	Used

1958 (NOVEMBER 24). WITH GRAPHITE LINES, TYPE S8. WATERMARK CROWNS

S72	592		Deep lilac		50	50
a.	Watermark inverted (4.8.59)		35	60		
b.	Two lines at left (5.61)	..	£375	£350		
c.	Three lines	.. .. ..	32·00	22·00		
d.	One line	.. .. ..	£600	£200		
e.	Coil join (horiz. pair) ..	..	5·00			

The misplaced graphite lines (varieties *b/d*) came from sheets from cyls. 51 no dot and dot printed after the graphite line experiment had ended to use up residual stock of graphite-lined paper.

Examples of No. S72*b* have both graphite lines printed clear of the perforations. Stamps showing lines cutting the perforations are common and worth a fraction of the price of the genuine variety. This applies particularly to cylinder blocks.

Cylinder Numbers (Blocks of Six)

Single pane cylinder

Cyl. No.	Perf. Type		No dot
11	B	..	4·25
11	C	..	4·25

Coils

Printed in continuous reels. Double-pane cylinders M1 or M2 were used. Watermark upright.

Code No.	Number in roll	Face value	
C	960	£12	Vertical delivery

Made up from sheets with sheet margin joins. Watermark upright.

S	480	£6	Sideways delivery

Sheet Markings

As for No. S69

Imprimaturs from the National Postal Museum Archives

Imperforate, watermark Type W.24

Watermark upright
Watermark inverted
Tête-bêche pair

Quantity Issued 57,222,960

1959 (NOVEMBER 18). PHOSPHOR-GRAPHITE ISSUE. WATERMARK CROWNS

This has two graphite lines, Type S8, on the back and two phosphor bands on the front, applied typo., which react green under the lamp.

S73	607		Deep lilac		11·00	8·00
a.	Narrow band at left or right (stamp with vert. margin) ..	16·00				

Cylinder Numbers (Blocks of Six)

Single pane cylinder

Cyl. No.	Perf. Type		No dot
11	B	..	80·00
11	C	..	80·00

Sheet Markings

As for No. S69

Imprimatur from the National Postal Museum Archives

Perf. 15 × 14, watermark Type W.24

Watermark upright

Quantity Issued   4,625,040

Cat. No.	S.G. No.	Shades	Mint	Used

1960 (JUNE 22). TWO PHOSPHOR BANDS REACTING GREEN. WMK. CROWNS

The bands were applied in photogravure.

S74	—	Deep Lilac		1·25	1·25

a. Watermark inverted (14.8.60) ..   1·25   1·25
b. Single broad band (wmk. upright)   30·00
c. Phantom "R" (Cyl. 41 No dot, below R. 20/12) .. .. ..   20·00
d. Single 8 mm. broad band (wmk. inverted).. .. ..
da. As *d* but 6 mm. band   .. ..

For illustrations of No. S74*c*, see No S70*j*.

Cylinder Numbers (Blocks of Six)

Perforation Type B (no dot) and C (dot)

Cyl. No.				No dot	Dot
41 ..	..	..	..	.. 10·00	10·00

Sheet Markings

Guide holes: Not known
Black bar: This occurs by the marginal arrows opposite rows 10/11, at left (no dot) or right (dot), also on booklet sheets
Others: As given in General Notes

1961 (JUNE 5).† PHOSPHOR BANDS REACTING BLUE. WATERMARK CROWNS

The bands were all applied in photogravure on the stamps with upright watermark and by typography on those with watermark sideways.

A. Two Bands. Cream Paper

S75	—	Deep lilac		1·00	1·00

a. Watermark inverted (3.61)   ..   90   90
b. Watermark Crown to left (14.7.61) .. ..   2·00   2·00
c. Watermark Crown to right   ..   2·00   2·00
d. Single broad band (wmk. sideways)   ..   ..   30·00

B. Two Bands. Whiter Paper (24 October 1962)†

S76	615	Deep lilac		60	45

a. Watermark Crown to left (15.8.62) .. ..   1·25   90
b. Watermark Crown to right   ..   2·50   90
c. Watermark inverted (25.9.62) ..   45   70
d. Single broad band on each stamp (horiz. pair) .. ..   75·00

The broad bands on *both* stamps of No. S76*d* prove that the bands were displaced for this issue in addition to No. S77 (see No. S77*fa*).

Cat. No.	S.G. No.	Shades	Mint	Used

C. One Side Band*. Whiter Paper (29 April 1965)

S77   —   Deep lilac (band at left)   2·75   2·50

a.	Band at right	2·75	2·50
ab.	Nos. S77/a (horiz. pair)	7·00	5·00
b.	Watermark Crown to left, band at left (16.8.65)	25·00	15·00
c.	Watermark Crown to left, band at right	22·00	12·00
d.	Watermark Crown to right, band at left	25·00	15·00
e.	Watermark Crown to right, band at right	22·00	12·00
f.	Single broad band (wmk. upright)	35·00	
fa.	Pair, left-hand stamp with phosphor omitted, right hand stamp with one broad band	60·00	
fb.	Single broad band (wmk. sideways)	75·00	
g.	Serif on "E" (Cyl. 68 Dot, R. 16/5)	7·50	

*The one side band stamps were produced by an 8mm. band applied down alternate vertical rows of the sheet over the perforations so that alternate stamps have the band at left (No. S77) or right (No. S77a). In theory the width of the band on a single stamp should be 4mm. but this will vary if the bands have not been perfectly positioned.

For illustration of No. S77g see No. S71e.

Cylinder Numbers (Blocks of Six)

Two bands (No. S75). Cream paper. Perforation Type B (no dot) and C (dot)

Cyl. No.					No dot	Dot	Cyl. No.					No dot	Dot
52 ..	..	..	..	..	8·00	8·00	60 ..	..	..	..	..	8·00	8·00

Whiter paper. Perforation Type A

Two bands. (No. S76)   One side band. (No. S77)

60 ..	..	..	..	..	5·00	5·00	67 ..	..	..	..	..	22·00	22·00
61 ..	..	..	..	..	5·00	5·00	68 ..	..	..	..	..	22·00	22·00
62 ..	..	..	..	..	5·00	5·00	71 ..	..	..	..	..	22·00	22·00
64 ..	..	..	..	..	5·00	5·00	72 ..	..	..	..	..	22·00	22·00
67 ..	..	..	..	..	5·00	5·00							
71 ..	..	..	..	..	5·00	5·00							

Minor Constant Sheet Flaws

Cyl. 52   17/9   White spur to circle around 3d. by D (Th. G6)

Cyl. 52.   18/2   Coloured line from Queen's hair to top of oval (Th. B2)

Cyl. 60.   4/11   Coloured flaw on thistle leaf (Th. G2)

Coils

Double pane cylinders M1 or M2 were used.   Watermark upright.

Two bands. Vertical delivery in continuous reels. Cream or whiter paper

Code No.	Number in roll	Face value
AC	480	£6
AD	960	£12
U	1920	£24

One side band (left or right). Vertical delivery in continuous reels. Whiter paper

AC	480	£6
AD	960	£12
U	1920	£24

Sheet Markings

Guide holes: Boxed opposite rows 14/15, at left (no dot) or right (dot)

Marginal rules: These vary in width between 1 and 2½ mm.

Others: As given in General Notes

Imprimaturs from the National Postal Museum Archives

Two Bands. Imperforate, watermark Type W.24. Cream or whiter paper

Watermark upright
Watermark inverted
Tête-bêche pair

One Side Band. Imperforate, watermark Type W.24. Whiter paper

Watermark sideways
Vertical *tête-bêche* pair with sideways watermark

Cat. No.	S.G. No.		Shades	Mint	Used

1965 (AUGUST 13). PHOSPHOR BANDS REACTING VIOLET. WATERMARK CROWNS

The bands applied in photogravure, except for stamps with sideways watermark where they were applied by typography or flexography.

A. One Side Band*

S78	615c		Deep lilac (band at left)	35	60
a.	Band at right	35	60		
ab.	Nos. S78/a (horiz. pair)	1·00	1·00		
b.	Single broad band (wmk. sideways)	10·00			
ba.	Pair, left-hand stamp with phosphor omitted, right-hand stamp with one broad band (wmk. upright) .. .. (pair)	30·00			
bb.	Single broad band (wmk. upright)	12·00			
c.	Watermark Crown to left, band at left (10.65)	4·50	3·50		
d.	Watermark Crown to left, band at right	4·50	3·50		
e.	Watermark Crown to right, band at left	4·50	3·50		
f.	Watermark Crown to right, band at right	4·50	3·50		
g.	Watermark inverted (band at left) (2.67)†	15·00	12·00		
h.	Watermark inverted (band at right)†	60	60		
ha.	Nos. S78g/h (horiz. pair)	16·00	16·00		
i.	As Nos. S78c/f but phosphor printed on both sides .. (each)	70·00			

B. One 4 mm. Centre Band (8 December 1966)

S79	615e		Deep Lilac	25	40
a.	Watermark sideways (19.6.67) ..	25	60		
b.	Watermark inverted (8.67) ..	90	90		

C. Two 9·5 mm. Bands. Se-tenant Booklets only (November 1967)

S80	—		Deep lilac (Watermark Crown to left)	1·75	1·75
a.	Watermark Crown to right ..	1·50	1·50		
b.	Single broad band (wmk. sideways)	12·00			

*The one side band stamps were produced by an 8 mm. band applied down alternate vertical rows of the sheet over the perforations so that alternate stamps have the band at left (No. S78) or right (No. S78a).   In theory the width of the band on a single stamp should be 4 mm. but this will vary if the bands have not been perfectly positioned.   In addition, one side band stamps with *sideways watermark* were produced by applying a 9·5 mm. band over the perforations but these only came in the April 1967 and October 1967 2s. Booklets (N28p(b) and N30p(b)) *se-tenant* with the 1d. value. As it is not possible to distinguish these from the 8 mm. bands (Nos. S78c/f) *in singles*, the complete panes only are listed under No. SB38.

†Nos. S78g/h only come from the 10s. Booklet of February 1967 (X15p(a/b)).   Each pane comprises two stamps with band at left and four stamps with band at right.

Sideways watermark. Nos. S78c/f come from 2s. Booklets N22p(b), N23p(b), N24p/28p(a), N29p/30p(a), N31p(c) and N32p(c). No. S79a comes from S coils with sideways delivery and Nos. S80/a come from 2s. Booklets N31p(a/b) and N32p(a/b).

Cylinder Numbers (Blocks of Six)

Perforation Type A

One side band. (No. S78)					No dot	Dot	One centre band. (No. S79)					No dot	Dot
Cyl. No.							Cyl. No.						
67 ..	..	..	..	..	4·00	4·00	78 ..	..	..	..	..	2·75	2·75
71 ..	..	..	..	..	4·00	4·00	79 ..	..	..	..	..	2·75	2·75
72 ..	..	..	..	..	4·00	4·00	81 ..	..	..	..	..	2·75	2·75
81 ..	..	..	..	..	4·00	4·00	82 ..	..	..	..	..	2·75	2·75
82 ..	..	..	..	..	4·00	4·00							

Coils

Double pane cylinder M12 was used for the vertical delivery coils and cylinder M11 for the sideways delivery coils.

(a) **One side band.** Vertical delivery printed in continuous reels with the watermark upright

Code No.	Number in roll	Face value
AC	480	£6
AD	960	£12
U	1920	£24

(b) One centre band. Printed in continuous reels

Code No.	Number in roll	Face value

(a) Vertical delivery. Watermark upright

AC	480	£6
AD	960	£12

(b) Sideways delivery. Watermark sideways

S	480	£6

Sheet Markings

Guide holes: Boxed opposite rows 14/15, at left (no dot) or right (dot). Later cylinders show single " SN " box

Marginal arrows: " W " shaped, photo-etched on all four sides

Marginal rules: These vary in width from cylinder to cylinder

Others: As given in General Notes

1953–67.   4d. Ultramarine, Type S3

Cat. No.	S.G. No.	Shades	Mint	Used

1953 (NOVEMBER 2).   WATERMARK TUDOR CROWN, TYPE W.22

S81	521	Ultramarine	3·00	80
a. Coil join (horiz. pair)	7·00			
b. Dotted "R" (Cyl. 1 No dot,				
R. 10/8)	12·00			

Listed Variety

The blue dot is of varying size and was eventually touched out on the St. Edward's Crown watermark.

S81*b*, S82*c*

Cylinder Numbers (Blocks of Six)

Perforation Type A				Perforation Type B (no dot) and C (dot)		
Cyl. No.		No dot	Dot	Cyl. No.	No dot	Dot
1		.. 22·00	22·00	1	.. 25·00	25·00

Minor Constant Sheet Flaws

Cyl. 1   1/4   Retouch on cheek left of ear (Th. D4)
16/9   Scar on neck. This was later the object of a major retouch (see No. S82*d*) but the original flaw is not available for illustrating and listing here

Coil

Made up from sheets with sheet margin joins. Sideways delivery with the watermark upright

Code No.	Number in roll	Face value
H	480	£8

Sheet Markings

Guide holes: Boxed opposite rows 14/15, at left (no dot) or right (dot)
Others: As given in General Notes

Imprimatur from the National Postal Museum Archives

Imperforate, watermark Type W.22

Watermark upright

1955 (NOVEMBER 14).   WATERMARK ST. EDWARD'S CROWN, TYPE W.23

S82	546	Ultramarine	1·40	40
a. Coil join (vert. pair)	3·00			
b. Coil join (horiz. pair)	4·00			
c. Dotted "R" (Cyl. 1 No dot,				
R. 10/8)	7·50			
d. Retouched neck (Cyl. 1 No dot,				
R. 16/9)	6·00			

For illustration of No. S82*c*, see No. S81*b*.

Listed Variety

This is the major retouch of the flaw described in this position on No. S81 under Minor Constant Sheet Flaws. The blue line joining the Queen's neck to the frame is also constant.

S82d, S83c

Cylinder Numbers (Blocks of Six)

Perforation Type A							Perforation Type B (no dot) and C (dot)					
Cyl. No.					No dot	Dot	Cyl. No.				No dot	Dot
1	..	..	..	..	12·00	12·00	1	..	..	..	9·50	9·50
3	..	..	..	..	14·00	14·00						

Minor Constant Sheet Flaws

Cyl. 1 1/4 Retouch on cheek left of ear (Th. D4)
16/9 Scar on neck before retouch as No. S82d

Coils

Made up from sheets with sheet margin joins with the watermark always upright

Code No.	Number in roll	Face value	
A	960	£16	Vertical delivery
H	480	£8	Sideways delivery

Sheet Markings

All as for No. S81

Imprimatur from the National Postal Museum Archives

Imperforate, watermark Type W.23

Watermark upright

Cat. No.	S.G. No.	Shades	Mint	Used
1958 (OCTOBER 29). WATERMARK CROWNS, TYPE W.24				
A. Ultramarine. Cream Paper				
S83 —		Ultramarine	1·50	75
a. Coil join (vert. pair) .. .. 4·00				
b. Coil join (horiz. pair) .. .. 4·00				
c. Retouched neck (Cyl 1 No dot,				
R. 16/9) .. .. 5·00				
d. Imperf. between stamp and top				
margin £300				
B. Ultramarine. Whiter Paper (18 October 1962)				
S84 576		Ultramarine	50	20
a. Coil join (vert. pair) .. .. 2·50				
b. Coil join (horiz. pair) .. .. 2·50				

Cat. No.	S.G. No.	Shades	Mint	Used

C. Deep Ultramarine†. Whiter Paper (28 April 1965)

S85	576a		Deep ultramarine	15	10

   c. Imperf. between stamp and top
      margin £120
   d. Wmk. Crown to left (Coils,
      31.5.65 and booklets, 16.8.65)   45   35
   e. Watermark inverted (21.6.65)   30   30
   f. Watermark Crown to right
      (Booklets, 16.8.65)   45   35

†This "shade" was brought about by making more deeply etched cylinders from a new multipositive, resulting in apparent depth of colour in parts of the design but there is no difference in the colour of the ink. The change was made deliberately and coincided with the change in the first class letter rate from 3d. to 4d. on 17 May 1965.

Listed Varieties

For illustration of No. S83*c*, see No. S82*d*.

Cylinder Numbers (Blocks of Six)

Perforation Type A

(a) Ultramarine

Cream Paper. (No. S83)					No dot	Dot	Whiter Paper. (No. S84)					No dot	Dot
Cyl. No.							Cyl. No.						
1 ..	..	..	..	..	11·00	11·00							
6 ..	..	..	..	..	11·00	11·00							
8 ..	..	..	..	..	11·00	11·00	8 ..	..	..	..	..	4·50	4·50

(b) Deep Ultramarine, Whiter paper. (No. S85)

12 ..	..	..	..	..	2·10	2·10	23 ..	..	..	..	..	2·10	2·10
13 ..	..	..	..	..	2·10	2·10	25 ..	..	..	..	..	2·10	2·10
16 ..	..	..	..	..	2·10	2·10	26 ..	..	..	..	..	2·10	2·10
18 ..	..	..	..	..	2·10	2·10	27 ..	..	..	..	..	2·10	2·10
20 ..	..	..	..	..	2·10	2·10							

Minor Constant Sheet Flaws

Cyl. 1   1/4 Retouch on cheek left of ear (Th. D4)
          10/8 Darker shading to right of and below large R caused by retouching the dot variety
Cyl. 18 18/11 Two patches of retouching by frame at left (Th. C1)

Coils

(a) Ultramarine. Cream or whiter paper
Made up from sheets with sheet margin joins. Watermark upright

Code No.	Number in roll	Face value	
A	960	£16	Vertical delivery
H	480	£8	Sideways delivery

(b) Deep ultramarine
    Printed in continuous reels. It is believed that cylinder P1 was used for the vertical delivery coil and that it was a double pane cylinder but that cylinder P2 was used for the sideways delivery coil and that this was a single pane cylinder.

(a) Vertical delivery. Watermark upright

A	960	£16

(b) Sideways delivery. Watermark sideways

H	480	£8

Sheet Markings

Guide holes: Boxed opposite rows 14/15, at left (no dot) or right (dot)
    On the later cylinders there are double "S O N" boxes for the guide holes
Marginal rules: These vary in width and exist 1 mm., 2 mm. and 2½ mm. wide
Others: As given in General Notes

Imprimatur from the National Postal Museum Archives

Imperforate, watermark Type W.24. Cream or whiter paper

Watermark upright

Cat. No.	S.G. No.	Shades	Mint	Used

1959 (APRIL 29).　WITH GRAPHITE LINES, TYPE S9. WATERMARK CROWNS

S86　　　　593　　　　　　　　　　　Ultramarine　　　　4·00　4·50
a. Two lines at left　　..　　.. £1400

The misplaced graphite lines listed as No. S86*a* result in two lines at left (with the left
line down the perforations) and traces of a third line down the opposite perforations.

Cylinder Numbers (Blocks of Six)

Perforation Type A

	Cyl. No.				No dot	Dot
	6　..	..	..	..	.. 28·00	28·00

Sheet Markings

As for No. S83

Imprimatur from the National Postal Museum Archives

Imperforate, watermark Type W.24

Watermark upright

Quantity Issued　6,891,600

1959 (NOVEMBER 18).　PHOSPHOR-GRAPHITE ISSUE. WATERMARK CROWNS

This has two graphite lines (Type S8) on the back and two phosphor bands on the front,
applied typo., which react green under the lamp.

S87　　　　608　　　　　　　　　　　Ultramarine　　　　12·00　25·00
a. Narrow band at left or right
(stamp with vert. margin)　.. 15·00

Cylinder Numbers (Blocks of Six)

Perforation Type A

	Cyl. No.				No dot	Dot
	6　..	..	..	..	.. £100	85·00

Sheet Markings

As for No. S83

Imprimatur from the National Postal Museum Archives

Perf. 15 × 14, watermark Type W.24

Watermark upright

Quantity Issued　490,560

**1960 (JUNE 22).　TWO PHOSPHOR BANDS REACTING GREEN. WATERMARK
CROWNS**

The bands were applied in photogravure.

S88　　　　—　　　　　　　　　　　Ultramarine　　　　8·00　7·00

Cylinder Numbers (Blocks of Six)

Perforation Type B (no dot) and C (dot)

Cyl. No.					No dot	Dot
8	..	..	..	..	.. 60·00	60·00

Sheet Markings

Guide holes: Boxed opposite rows 14/15, at left (no dot) or right (dot)
Black bar: This occurs by the marginal arrows opposite rows 10/11, at left (no dot) or right (dot)
Others: As given in General Notes

Imprimatur from the National Postal Museum Archives

Imperforate, watermark Type W.24

Watermark upright

Cat. No.	S.G. No.	Shades	Mint	Used

1961 (JUNE 5).   TWO PHOSPHOR BANDS REACTING BLUE. WATERMARK CROWNS

The bands were applied in photogravure on the stamps with upright watermark and by typography on those with watermark sideways.

A. Ultramarine. Cream Paper

S89		616		Ultramarine	3·00	2·50
a.	Broad band in centre ..	.. £175				

B. Deep Ultramarine. Whiter Paper (28 April 1965)

S90		—	Deep ultramarine	60	50
b.	Watermark inverted (21.6.65) ..	85	60		
c.	Watermark Crown to left (16.8.65)	1·75	1·50		
d.	Watermark Crown to right (16.8.65)	1·75	1·50		
e.	Single broad band (wmk. sideways)	60·00			

Cylinder Numbers (Blocks of Six)

(a) Ultramarine. (No. S89)
Perforation Type B (no dot) and C (dot)

Cyl. No.					No dot	Dot	Cyl. No.						No dot	Dot
8	..	..	..	..	22·00	22·00								

(b) Deep ultramarine. (No. S90)
Perforation Type A

						No dot	Dot							No dot	Dot
12	..	..	..	..	..	5·00	5·00	18	..	..	..	..	..	5·00	5·00
13	..	..	..	..	..	5·00	5·00	20	..	..	..	..	..	5·00	5·00

Minor Constant Sheet Flaw

Cyl. 18 18/11 Two patches of retouching by frame at left (Th. C1)

Sheet Markings

As for Nos. S83/5

Cat. No.	S.G. No.		Shades		Mint	Used

1965 (AUGUST 13). TWO 8 mm. PHOSPHOR BANDS REACTING VIOLET. WMK. CROWNS

The bands were applied in photogravure, except for some 2s. Booklets which had them applied by typography.

S91	—		Deep ultramarine	50	50
a. Watermark inverted (9.65)	..	40	40		
b. Wmk. Crown to left (photo.) (1.67)	.. ..	50	50		
c. Wmk. Crown to right (photo.) (1.67)	.. ..	50	50		
d. Single broad band (photo.) (wmk. sideways)	.. ..	12·00			
e. Wmk. Crown to left (typo.) (10.65)	.. ..	14·00			
f. Wmk. Crown to right (typo.) (10.65)	.. ..	14·00			
g. Single broad band (typo.) (wmk. sideways)	.. ..	70·00			
h. Phosphor printed on both sides (wmk. sideways)	.. .. ..				

No. S91 is known with a very wide " phantom " band in addition to the normal two bands. This was probably due to a weak mixture of the phosphor ink, which leaked under the doctor blade. This occurred in the first and second vertical rows in a sheet.

Cylinder Numbers (Blocks of Six)

Perforation Type A

Cyl. No.				No dot	Dot	Cyl. No.					No dot	Dot
18	..	..	..	4·50	4·50	20	..	..	..	..	4·50	4·50

Minor Constant Sheet Flaw

Cyl. 18 18/11 Two patches of retouching by frame at left (Th. C1)

Sheet Markings

As for Nos. S83/5

1967 (EARLY). TWO 9·5 mm. PHOSPHOR BANDS REACTING VIOLET. WMK. CROWNS

The bands were applied in photogravure, except for the 2s. Booklets which had them flexo.

S92	616*a*		Deep ultramarine	15	15
a. Watermark inverted (2.67)	..	25	20		
b. Wmk. Crown to left Booklets, 4.67 and Coils, 24.4.67)	.. ..	15	25		
c. Wmk. Crown to right (Booklets, 4.67)	.. ..	15	25		
e. Single broad band (wmk. sideways)	.. ..	10·00			

Cylinder Numbers (Blocks of Six)

Perforation Type A

Cyl. No.					No dot	Dot	Cyl. No.					No dot	Dot
16	..	..	..	..	2·25	2·25	26	..	..	..	..	2·25	2·25
18	..	..	..	..	2·25	2·25	27	..	..	..	..	2·25	2·25
23	..	..	..	..	2·25	2·25							

Minor Constant Sheet Flaw

Cyl. 18 18/11 Two patches of retouching by frame at left (Th. C1)

Coil

Printed in continuous reels. It is believed that cylinder P2 was used and that it was a single pane cylinder.

Sideways delivery. Watermark sideways

Code No.	Number in roll	Face value
H	480	£8

Sheet Markings

As for Nos. S83/5

1959–66. 4½d. Chestnut, Type S3

Cat. No.	S.G. No.	Shades	Mint	Used

1959 (FEBRUARY 9). WATERMARK CROWNS, TYPE W.24

A. Cream Paper

S93	—	Chestnut	50	50

B. Whiter Paper (29 May 1962)

S94	577	Chestnut	10	15

    a. Phantom frame (Cyl. 8 No dot
below R. 20/12) .. .. ..   5·00

Listed Variety

An incomplete marginal rule revealed a right-angled shaped frame-line on cylinder 8 no dot below R.20/12. Later retouched on No. S98.

S94*a*, S98*c*

Cylinder Numbers (Blocks of Six)

Perforation Type A

Cream paper. (No. S93)

Cyl. No.					No dot	Dot
2	..	..	..	..	6·50	6·50
6	..	..	..	..	4·25	4·25
7	..	..	..	..	4·25	4·25

Whiter paper. (No. S94)

Cyl. No.					No dot	Dot
7	..	..	..	..	1·60	1·60
8	..	..	..	..	1·60	1·60

Minor Constant Sheet Flaws

Multipositive flaw:

No dot   5/6   Pale top half of rose in bottom left corner (Th. F1–2)

Cylinder flaws

Cyl. 2	1/9	White spot on cheek level with mouth (Th. D3)
	1/11	Break in bottom frame line at left corner
	5/5	Three dots to right of curve in S of POSTAGE
	10/8	White dot in laurel oval (Th. E6)
	16/2	Dotted line in bottom right corner (Th. H6)
	19/10	White dot on tail of R of E R
Cyl. 6	5/5	Nick in laurel oval at left (Th. D1)
	16/9	Extra jewel on dress above O of POSTAGE
Cyl. 7	18/6	White flaw in thistle flower (Th. G2)

Sheet Markings

    Guide holes: Boxed opposite rows 14/15, at left (no dot) or right (dot
Others: As given in General Notes

Imprimatur from the National Postal Museum Archives

Imperforate, watermark Type W.24. Cream or whiter paper

Watermark upright

1959 (JUNE 3). WITH GRAPHITE LINES, TYPE S8. WATERMARK CROWNS

S95	594	Chestnut	5·00	4·50

Cylinder Numbers (Blocks of Six)

Perforation Type A

Cyl. No.			No dot	Dot
6	..	..	32·00	32·00

Minor Constant Sheet Flaw

Cyl. 6   5/6 Pale top half of rose in bottom left corner (Th. F1-2)

Sheet Markings

As given for Nos. S93/4

Imprimatur from the National Postal Museum Archives

Imperforate, watermark Type W.24

Watermark upright

Quantity Issued   5,388,480

Cat. No.	S.G. No.	Shades	Mint	Used

1959 (NOVEMBER 18). PHOSPHOR-GRAPHITE ISSUE. WATERMARK CROWNS

This has two graphite lines (Type **S8**), on the back and two phosphor bands on the front, applied typo., which react green under the lamp.

S96	609	Chestnut	28·00	15·00

 a. Narrow band at left or right
   (stamp with vert. margin) .. 42·00
 b. Single broad band .. .. 95·00
 c. Phosphor printed on both sides £130

Cylinder Numbers (Blocks of Six)

Perforation Type A

Cyl. No.					No dot	Dot
6 ..	..	..	..	..	£180	£180

Minor Constant Sheet Flaw

Cyl. 6   5/6 Pale top half of rose in bottom left corner (Th. F1-2)

Sheet Markings

As given for Nos. S93/4

Imprimatur from the National Postal Museum Archives

Perf. 15 × 14, watermark Type W.24

Watermark upright

Quantity Issued   696,000

1961 (SEPTEMBER 13).   TWO PHOSPHOR BANDS REACTING BLUE. WATERMARK CROWNS

A. Cream Paper. Bands by Typography

S97	—	Chestnut	3·00	1·50

 a. Narrow band at left or right
   (stamp with vert. margin) .. 7·50
 b. Single 8 mm. broad band .. .. 8·00
 ba. As *b* but 6 mm. band .. .. 10·00
 c. Bands applied photo. (3.4.62) .. 18·00 10·00

B. Whiter Paper. Bands applied in Photogravure (24 January 1963)

S98	616b	Chestnut	15	25

 a. Bands applied typo. (6.65) .. 1·50 1·50
 ab. Narrow band at left or right
   (stamp with vert. margin) .. 7·00
 b. Single 8 mm. broad band (typo.) 9·00
 ba. As *b* but 6 mm. band .. .. 10·00
 c. Phantom frame (Cyl. 8, below R.
   20/12) .. .. 7·50
 d. Phosphor printed on both sides
   applied typo. .. .. 35·00

For illustration of No. S98*c.*, see No. S94*a.*

Cylinder Numbers (Blocks of Six)

A. Cream Paper

Applied typo. (No. S97)

Perforation Type A

Cyl. No.					No dot	Dot
7	..	..	..	..	22·00	22·00

Applied photo. (No. S97c)

Perforation Type B (no dot) and C (dot)

Cyl. No.					No dot	Dot
7	..	..	..	..	£120	£120

B. Whiter Paper

Applied photo. (No. S98)

Perforation Type A

					No dot	Dot
7	..	..	..	..	3·00	3·00
8	..	..	..	..	2·25	2·25

Applied typo. (No. S98a)

Perforation Type A

					No dot	Dot
8	..	..	..	..	11·00	11·00

Minor Constant Sheet Flaws

Cyls. 7/8   5/6   Pale top half of rose in bottom left corner (Th. F1–2)
Cyl. 7   18/6   White flaw in thistle flower (Th. G2). Later retouched

Sheet Markings

As given for Nos. S93/4 except that the guide holes are in double boxes caused by the original box being inserted the wrong way and so another box was added on each pane, resulting in apparent double boxes

Imprimatur from the National Postal Museum Archives

Imperforate, watermark Type W.24. Cream or whiter paper

Watermark upright

1953–67. 5d. Brown, Type S4

Cat. No.	S.G. No.		Shades	Mint	Used

1953 (JULY 6). WATERMARK TUDOR CROWN, TYPE W.22

S99   522   Brown   90   2·00

   a. Spot by "E" of "POSTAGE"
      (No dot, R. 4/8)   ..   ..   ..   5·00
   b. Spot on daffodil (No dot,
      R. 10/12)   ..   ..   5·00
   c. Neck retouch (Cyl. 1 Dot,
      R. 2/12)   ..   ..   4·50

Listed Varieties

S99/103*a*   S99/103*b*   S99/103*c*

These two varieties occur on the multipositive

Cylinder Numbers (Blocks of Six)

Perforation Type A

Cyl. No.					No dot	Dot
1 ..	..	..	..	..	7·50	7·50

Sheet Markings

Guide holes: Boxed opposite rows 14/15, at left (no dot) or right (dot)
Others: As given in General Notes

Imprimatur from the National Postal Museum Archives

Imperforate, watermark Type W.22

Watermark upright

1955 (SEPTEMBER 21). WATERMARK ST. EDWARD'S CROWN, TYPE W.23

S100   547   Brown   5·00   3·50

   a. Spot by "E" of "POSTAGE"
      (No dot, R. 4/8)   ..   ..   ..   9·00
   b. Spot on daffodil (No dot,
      R. 10/12)   ..   ..   9·00
   c. Neck retouch (Cyl. 1 Dot,
      R. 2/12)   ..   ..   8·00

For illustrations of Nos. S100*a/c*, see Nos. S99*a/c*.

Cylinder Numbers (Blocks of Six)

Perforation Type A

Cyl. No.					No dot	Dot
1 ..	..	..	..	..	35·00	35·00

Sheet Markings

All as for No. S99

Imprimatur from the National Postal Museum Archives

Imperforate, watermark Type W.23

Watermark upright

Cat. No.	S.G. No.	Shades	Mint	Used

1958 (NOVEMBER 10).   WATERMARK CROWNS, TYPE W.24

A. Cream Paper

S101	—	Brown	2·50	60

a. Spot by "E" of "POSTAGE" (No dot, R. 4/8) .. .. .. 6·50
b. Spot on daffodil (No dot, R. 10/12) .. .. 6·50
c. Neck retouch (Cyl. 1 Dot, R. 2/12) .. .. 6·50

B. Whiter Paper (1 May 1963)

S102	578	Brown	25	20

a. Spot by "E" of "POSTAGE" (No dot, R. 4/8) .. .. .. 3·75
b. Spot on daffodil (No dot, R. 10/12) .. .. 3·75
c. Neck retouch (Cyl. 1 Dot, R. 2/12) .. .. 3·50

For illustrations of Nos. S101/2a, S101/2b and S101/2c, see Nos. S99a, S99b and S99c respectively.

Cylinder Numbers (Blocks of Six)

Cream Paper. (No. S101)

Perforation Type A

Cyl. No.					No dot	Dot
1 ..	..	..	..	..	18·00	18·00
2 ..	..	..	..	..	18·00	18·00

Whiter Paper. (No. S102)

Perforation Type A

Cyl. No.					No dot	Dot
1 ..	..	..	..	..	2·75	2·75

Perforation Type F(L)*

1* .. ..
*This is probably No. S103 but with phosphor omitted.

Sheet Markings

All as for No. S99

Imprimatur from the National Postal Museum Archives

Imperforate, watermark Type W.24. Cream or whiter paper

Watermark upright

1967 (JUNE 9).   TWO 9·5 mm. PHOSPHOR BANDS REACTING VIOLET. WMK. CROWNS

The bands were applied in photogravure.

S103	616c	Brown	20	25

a. Spot by "E" of "POSTAGE" (No dot, R. 4/8) .. .. .. 3·50
b. Spot on daffodil (No dot, R. 10/12) .. .. 3·50
c. Neck retouch (Cyl. 1 Dot, R. 2/12) .. .. 3·50

For illustrations of Nos. S103a/c, see Nos. S99a/c.

Cylinder Numbers (Blocks of Six)

Perforation Type A

Cyl. No.					No dot	Dot
1 ..	..	..	..	..	2·40	2·40

Perforation Type F (L)*

Cyl. No.					No dot	Dot
1 ..	..	..	..	..	2·40	2·40

Sheet Markings

Guide holes: Boxed, and also double-boxed, opposite rows 14/15 at left (no dot) or right (dot) but in the case of perforation Type F (L)* the double boxes remain in both panes but the holes are in single boxes at top and bottom of eighth vertical row in the no dot pane only
Others: As given in General Notes

1954-67. 6d. Purple, Type S4

Cat. No.	S.G. No.	Shades	Mint	Used

1954 (JANUARY 18). WATERMARK TUDOR CROWN, TYPE W.22

S104   523   Reddish purple   3·00   60
  a. Imperforate at top and sides
      (pair) ..   ..   ..
  b. Imperf. between stamp and
      bottom margin £250
  c. Coil join (vert. pr.) ..   ..   8·00

Cylinder Numbers (Blocks of Six)

Single pane cylinder

Perforation Type B	Perforation Type C	Perforation Type F (L)
Cyl. No. No dot	Cyl. No. No dot	Cyl. No. No dot
1 .. 22·00	1 .. 22·00	1 .. 22·00

Minor Constant Sheet Flaws

Multipositive flaws used for cylinders 1, 2 and 3

  8/8 Small purple flaw joining C of PENCE to inner frame line
  19/6 Small dark flaw on daffodil stem (Th. G2)
  20/3 Coloured dot in top leaf of thistle (Th. A6)

Coil

Made up from sheets with sheet margin joins. Vertical delivery with the watermark upright

Code No.	Number in roll	Face value
J	480	£12

Sheet Markings

Guide holes:
  Perf. Types B and C, opposite rows 1 and 7/8 at both sides and also boxed opposite rows 14/15 at both
    sides
  Perf. Type F (L), not known
Others: As given in General Notes

Imprimatur from the National Postal Museum Archives

Imperforate, watermark Type W.22

Watermark upright

1955 (DECEMBER 20). WATERMARK ST. EDWARD'S CROWN, TYPE W.23
A. Reddish Purple

S105   548   Reddish purple   4·00   75
  a. Imperforate three sides (pair)   £400
  b. Coil join (vert. pair) ..   .. 18·00
  c. Pink tinted paper†† ..   .. 50·00

B. Deep Claret† (8 May 1958)

S106   548a   Deep claret   3·50   80
  a. Imperforate three sides (pair)..   £400
  b. Coil join (vert. pr.) ..   .. 10·00

  †This was a deliberate change of colour although shade variations exist. See footnote after No.
S108.
  ††This is known from cylinder 1 perforation Type C.

Cylinder Numbers (Blocks of Six)

Single pane cylinders

Reddish Purple. (No. S105)		Deep Claret. (No. S106)	
Cyl. No.	No dot	Cyl. No.	No dot
Perforation Type B		**Perforation Type B**	
1	32·00	2	26·00
2	32·00	3	26·00
Perforation Type C		**Perforation Type C**	
1	28·00	2	24·00
2	28·00	3	24·00
		Perforation Type F (L)	
		3	35·00

Minor Constant Sheet Flaws

Multipositive flaws as shown for No. S104

Coils

Made up from sheets with sheet margin joins. Vertical delivery with the watermark **upright**

Code No.	Number in roll	Face value	
J	480	£12	Reddish purple
J	480	£12	Deep claret

Sheet Markings

All as for No. S104

Imprimatur from the National Postal Museum Archives

A. Reddish Purple. Imperforate, watermark Type W.23

Watermark upright

B. Deep Claret. Imperforate, watermark Type W.23

Watermark upright

Cat. No.	S.G. No.	Shades	Mint	Used

1958 (DECEMBER 23). WATERMARK CROWNS, TYPE W.24

A. Cream Paper

				Shades	Mint	Used
S107	—			Deep claret*	1·25	70
a. Imperforate three sides (pair)..	£450					
b. Imperf. (pair)	£550					
c. Coil join (vert. pr.)	6·00					

B. Whiter Paper (29 June 1962)

			Shades	Mint	Used
S108	579		Deep claret*	25	15
a. Coil join (vert. pr.)	4·00				
b. Spur to frame (Cyl. 10 No dot, R. 17/2)	4·00				

*This colour is unstable and a range of shades exists which also vary according to the colour of the paper. One of the more marked variations is a purple-claret on the cream paper from cylinder 8.

Listed Variety

S108*b*

Cylinder Numbers (Blocks of Six)

A. Cream Paper. (No. S107)

Single pane cylinders

Perforation Type B						Perforation Type C					
Cyl. No.					No dot	Cyl. No.					No dot
2 ..	..	..	..	..	10·00	2 ..	..	..	..	..	10·00
3 ..	..	..	..	..	10·00	3 ..	..	..	..	..	10·00

Double pane cylinders

Perforation Type B (no dot) and C (dot)							Perforation Type A						
Cyl. No.					No dot	Dot	Cyl. No.					No dot	Dot
5 ..	..	..	..	..	16·00	16·00	7 ..	..	..	..	..	10·00	10·00
7 ..	..	..	..	..	10·00	10·00	8 ..	..	..	..	..	10·00	10·00

B. Whiter Paper. (No. S108)

Perforation Type A							Perforation Type F (L)*					
8	..	..	..	..	..	2·75	2·75					
10	..	..	..	..	..	2·75	2·75	10 ..	..	..	..	.. 3·00	3·00
11	..	..	..	..	..	25·00	25·00					

Minor Constant Sheet Flaws

Multipositive flaws on cylinders 2 and 3 as shown for No. S104

A second multipositive was used for cylinder 5 and a third for cylinders 7 onwards.

Coils

(a) Made up from sheets with sheet margin joins. Vertical delivery with the watermark upright

Code No.	Number in roll	Face value	
J	480	£12	Cream paper
J	480	£12	Whiter paper

(b) Printed in continuous reels. Single pane cylinder Q1 was used. Vertical delivery. Watermark upright

J	480	£12	Whiter paper

Sheet Markings

Guide holes:
    Single pane cylinders: Opposite rows 1 and 7/8 at both sides and also boxed opposite rows 14/15 at both sides
    Double pane cylinders:
      Perf. Types A, B and C, boxed opposite rows 14/15, a' left (no dot) or right (dot)
      Perf. Type F (L)*, not known
      On cyl. 10 there are double boxes.
    Others: As given in General Notes
      The marginal rule is damaged in most positions on cyl. 8

Imprimatur from the National Postal Museum Archives

Imperforate, watermark Type W.24. Cream or whiter paper

Watermark upright

Cat. No.	S.G. No.	Shades	Mint	Used

1960 (JUNE 27). TWO PHOSPHOR BANDS REACTING GREEN. WATERMARK CROWNS

The bands were applied in photogravure.

S109	—	Deep claret	2·50	2·00

Cylinders Numbers (Blocks of Six)

Single pane cylinder

Perforation Type B						Perforation Type C					
Cyl. No.					No dot	Cyl. No.					No dot
2	..	..	..	..	20·00	2	..	..	..	..	20·00

Minor Constant Sheet Flaws

Multipositive flaws as shown for No. S104

Sheet Markings

Guide holes: As for Perf. Types B and C on No. S104
Black bar: This occurs by the marginal arrows opposite rows 10/11, at right
Others: As given in General Notes

Imprimatur from the National Postal Museum Archives

Imperforate, watermark Type W.24

Watermark upright

Cat. No.	S.G. No.	Shades	Mint	Used

1961 (JUNE 5). TWO PHOSPHOR BANDS REACTING BLUE. WATERMARK CROWNS

A. Cream Paper. Bands applied in Photogravure

S110	—	Deep claret	4·25	3·00

   a. Bands applied typo   ..   ..

B. Whiter Paper. Bands applied in Photogravure (3 October 1963)

S111	—	Deep claret	50	40

   a. Bands applied typo. £300
  ab. Narrow band at left or right
      (stamp with vert. margin)   ..

Cylinder Numbers (Blocks of Six)

Perforation Type A

Bands applied photo.

	Cream Paper. (No. S110)		No dot	Dot		Whiter Paper. (No. S111)			No dot	Dot
Cyl. No.					Cyl. No.					
7 ..	..	..	30·00	30·00	8 ..	..	..	..	4·50	4·50
					10 ..	..	..	..	4·50	4·50

Bands applied typo.   Whiter Paper (No. S111*a*)

8 ..	..	..	..	..

Sheet Markings

  Guide holes: Boxed opposite rows 14/15, at left (no dot) or right (dot). On cyl. 10 there are double boxes
  Others: As given in General Notes
    The marginal rule is damaged in most positions on cyl. 8

1965 (AUGUST 13). TWO 8 mm. PHOSPHOR BANDS REACTING VIOLET. WMK. CROWNS

  The bands were applied by typography

S112	—	Deep claret	7·00	4·50

   a. Narrow band at left or right
      (stamp with vert. margin)   .. 15·00
   b. Single broad band   ..   .. 45·00

Cylinder Numbers (Blocks of Six)

Perforation Type A.

                          Applied typo.

Cyl. No.				No dot	Dot
8 ..	..	..	..	50·00	50·00

Sheet Markings

  As for No. S111

1967 (EARLY). TWO 9·5 mm. PHOSPHOR BANDS REACTING VIOLET. WMK. CROWNS

  The bands were applied in photogravure only.

S113	617	Deep claret	40	20

Cylinder Numbers (Blocks of Six)

Perforation Type A				No dot	Dot	Perforation Type F (L)*				No dot	Dot
Cyl. No.						Cyl. No.					
10 ..	..	..	..	6·00	6·00	10 ..	..	..	..	4·25	4·25
11 ..	..	..	..	4·25	4·25						

Coils

  Printed in continuous reels. It is believed that cylinder Q1 was used and that it was a single pane cylinder.

              Vertical delivery. Watermark upright

Code No.	Number in roll	Face value
J	480	£12

Sheet Markings

  Guide holes: Boxed opposite rows 14/15 at left (no dot) or right (dot) but in the case of perforation Type F (L)* the boxes remain in both panes but the holes are in single boxes above and below the eighth vertical row in the no dot pane only
  Others: As given in General Notes

1954-67.   7d. Bright green, Type S4

Cat. No.	S.G. No.	Shades	Mint	Used

1954 (JANUARY 18).   WATERMARK TUDOR CROWN, TYPE W.22

S114	524	Bright green	9·00	3·50

Cylinder Numbers (Blocks of Six)

Perforation Type A						Perforation Type B (no dot) and C (dot)					
Cyl. No.				No dot	Dot	Cyl. No.				No dot	Dot
2 ..	..	..	..	.. 65·00	65·00	2 ..	..	..	..	.. 65·00	65·00

Sheet Markings

Guide holes: Double-boxed opposite rows 14/15, at left (no dot) or right (dot)
Others: As given in General Notes

Imprimatur from the National Postal Museum Archives

Imperforate, watermark Type W.22
Watermark upright

1956 (APRIL 23).   WATERMARK ST. EDWARD'S CROWN, TYPE W.23

S115	549	Bright green	48·00	7·50

Cylinder Numbers (Blocks of Six)
Perforation Type A

	Cyl. No.				No dot	Dot
	2 ..	..	..	.. ..	£300	£300

Sheet Markings
As for No. S114

Imprimatur from the National Postal Museum Archives

Imperforate, watermark Type W.23
Watermark upright

1958 (NOVEMBER 26).   WATERMARK CROWNS, TYPE W.24
A. Cream Paper

S116	—	Bright green	2·50	70

B. Whiter Paper (3 July 1962)

S117	580	Bright green	40	20

Cylinder Numbers (Blocks of Six)

Cream Paper. (No. S116)						Whiter Paper. (No. S117)					
Perforation Type A						Perforation Type A					
Cyl. No.				No dot	Dot	Cyl. No.				No dot	Dot
1 ..	..	..	..	.. 18·00	18·00	1 ..	..	..	..	.. 4·25	4·25
2 ..	..	..	..	.. 18·00	18·00	2 ..	..	..	..	.. 4·25	4·25
Perforation Type B (no dot) and C (dot)						Perforation Type F(L)*					
2 ..	..	..	..	.. 18·00	18·00	1* ..	..	..	..	.. £275	£275
						*This is probably No. S118 but with phosphor omitted.					

Sheet Markings

Guide holes: Double-boxed opposite rows 14/15, at left (no dot) or right (dot)
Marginal rule: At bottom of sheet (Cyl. 1, 1½ mm. wide; Cyl. 2, 2 mm. wide)
Others: As given in General Notes

Imprimatur from the National Postal Museum Archives

Imperforate, watermark Type W.24. Cream or whiter paper
Watermark upright

Cat. No.	S.G. No.	Shades	Mint	Used

1967 (FEBRUARY 15).   TWO 9·5 mm. PHOSPHOR BANDS REACTING VIOLET. WMK. CROWNS

The bands were applied in photogravure.

S118	617a	Bright green	60	25

Cylinder Numbers (Blocks of Six)

Perforation Type F (L)*			Perforation Type A		
Cyl. No.	No dot	Dot	Cyl. No.	No dot	Dot
1	7·00	7·00	2	5·00	5·00

Sheet Markings

Guide holes: Double-boxed opposite rows 14/15, at left (no dot) or right (dot) but in the case of perforation Type F (L)* the double boxes remain on both panes but the holes are unboxed above and below the eighth vertical row in the no dot pane only

Marginal rule: At bottom of sheet (Cyl. 1, 1½ mm. wide; Cyl. 2, 2 mm. wide)

Others: As given in General Notes

Imprimatur from the National Postal Museum Archives

Imperforate, watermark Type W.24

Watermark upright

1953-67.   8d. Magenta, Type S5

Cat. No.	S.G. No.	Shades	Mint	Used

1953 (JULY 6).   WATERMARK TUDOR CROWN, TYPE W.22

S119	525	Magenta	1·00	60

Cylinder Numbers (Blocks of Six)

Perforation Type A | Perforation Type B (no dot) and C (dot)

Cyl. No.					No dot	Dot	Cyl. No.					No dot	Dot
3	..	..	..	..	7·50	7·50	3	..	..	..	..	7·50	7·50

Minor Constant Sheet Flaw

Cyl. 3   20/1 Coloured dot between rose at top left and A of POSTAGE (Th. B2)

Sheet Markings

Guide holes: Double-boxed opposite rows 14/15, at left (no dot) or right (dot)
Others: As given in General Notes

Imprimatur from the National Postal Museum Archives

Imperforate, watermark Type W.22

Watermark upright

1955 (DECEMBER 21).   WATERMARK ST. EDWARD'S CROWN, TYPE W.23

S120	550	Magenta	5·50	1·00

Cylinder Numbers (Blocks of Six)

Perforation Type A

Cyl. No.					No dot	Dot
3	..	..	..	..	38·00	38·00

Minor Constant Sheet Flaw

Cyl. 3   20/1 Coloured dot between rose at top left and A of POSTAGE (Th. B2). Later retouched

Sheet Markings

As for No. S119

Imprimatur from the National Postal Museum Archives

Imperforate, watermark Type W.23

Watermark upright

1960 (FEBRUARY 24).   WATERMARK CROWNS, TYPE W.24

A. Cream Paper

S121	—	Magenta	4·00	70

B. Whiter Paper (6 July 1962)

S122	581	Magenta	40	15

a. Diadem flaw (Cyls. 4 No dot,
    R. 18/2)   .. ..   4·00
b. Extra pearl (Cyl. 4 Dot, R. 16/2)   4·00

Listed Varieties

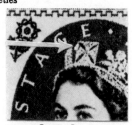

S122a, S123a
Multipostive white flaw on diadem,
lower left of " E " of " POSTAGE "
Exists as a minor flaw on Cyl. 3

S122b, S123b

Cylinder Numbers (Blocks of Six)

Cream Paper. (No. S121)   Whiter Paper. (No. S122)

Perforation Type A   Perforation Type A

Cyl. No.					No dot	Dot		Cyl. No.					No dot	Dot
3	..	..	..	..	.. 27·00	27·00		3	..	..	..	..	.. 7·00*	4·00
								4	..	..	..	..	.. 7·00*	4·00

Perforation Type F(L)*

4*   ..   ..
*This is probably No. S123 but with the phosphor omitted.

Sheet Markings

Guide holes: Unboxed opposite rows 1 and 7/8 and double-boxed opposite rows 14/15, at left (no dot) or right (dot); or double-boxed only opposite rows 14/15, at left (no dot) or right (dot)

Marginal arrows:
" V " shaped, hand engraved at top and bottom of sheet (Cyls. 3 and 4)
" W " shaped, photo-etched at both sides (Cyl. 3) or photo-etched at left and hand engraved at right (Cyl. 4)

Others: As given in General Notes

Imprimatur from the National Postal Museum Archives

Imperforate, watermark Type W.24. Cream or whiter paper

Watermark upright

Cat. No.	S.G. No.	Shades	Mint	Used

1967 (JUNE 28). TWO 9·5 mm. PHOSPHOR BANDS REACTING VIOLET. WMK. CROWNS

The bands were applied in photogravure.

S123	617b		Magenta	20 25
a. Diadem flaw (Cyl. 4 No dot, R. 18/2)	4·00			
b. Extra pearl (Cyl. 4 Dot. R. 16/2)	4·00			
c. Petal joined to frame (Cyl. 4 Dot, R. 13/11)	4·00			

For illustrations of Nos. S123a/b, see Nos. S122a/b.

Listed Variety

S123c

Cylinder Numbers (Blocks of Six)

Perforation Type A   Perforation Type F (L)*

Cyl. No.					No dot	Dot		Cyl. No.					No dot	Dot
4	..	..	..	..	.. 5·00*	2·40		4	..	..	..	..	.. 5·00*	2·40

Sheet Markings

Guide holes: Double-boxed opposite rows 14/15, at left (no dot) or right (dot) but in the case of perforation Type F (L)* the double boxes remain on both panes but the holes are unboxed above and below the eighth vertical row in the no dot pane only

Marginal arrows:
"V" shaped, hand engraved at top and bottom of sheet
"W" shaped, photo-etched at left and hand engraved at right

Others: As given in General Notes

Imprimatur from the National Postal Museum Archives

Imperforate, watermark Type W.24

Watermark upright

1954-66. 9d. Bronze-green, Type S5

Cat. No.	S.G. No.	Shades	Mint	Used

1954 (FEBRUARY 8). WATERMARK TUDOR CROWN, TYPE W.22

S124   526   Bronze-green   22·00   3·00
   a. Frame break at upper right (Cyl.
      1 No dot. R. 8/6)   ..   ..   ..   25·00
   b. Imperf. between stamp and top
      margin* ..   ..
*No. S124*b* was caused by a paper fold.

Listed Variety

         Frame broken at upper right and shading
         below it missing. Later retouched on
         Crowns watermark. A very similar variety
         occurs on Cyl. 2, R. 11/11; see Nos. S126*c*.
         etc.

S124*a*, S125*a*, S126*a*

Cylinder Numbers (Blocks of Six)

Perforation Type A			Perforation Type B (no dot) and C (dot)		
Cyl. No.	No dot	Dot	Cyl. No.	No dot	Dot
1	£140	£140	1	£140	£140

Sheet Markings

   Guide holes: Boxed opposite rows 14/15, at left (no dot) or right (dot)
   Others: As given in General Notes

Imprimatur from the National Postal Museum Archives

   Imperforate, watermark Type W.22

   Watermark upright

1955 (DECEMBER 15). WATERMARK ST. EDWARD'S CROWN, W.23

S125   551   Bronze-green   17·00   2·25
   a. Frame break at upper right
      (Cyl. 1 No dot, R. 8/6) ..   ..   20·00
   For illustration of No. S125*a*, see No. S124*a*.

Cylinder Numbers (Blocks of Six)

Perforation Type A			Perforation Type B (no dot) and C (dot)		
Cyl. No.	No dot	Dot	Cyl. No.	No dot	Dot
1	£110	£110	1	£110	£110

Sheet Markings

   As for No. S124

Imprimatur from the National Postal Museum Archives

   Imperforate, watermark Type W.23

   Watermark upright

1959 (MARCH 24). WATERMARK CROWNS, TYPE W.24

A. Cream Paper

S126   —   Bronze-green   4·00   70
   a. Frame break at upper right
      (Cyl. 1 No dot, R. 8/6) ..   ..   10·00
   b. Broken daffodil (Cyl. 2 No dot,
      R. 7/2) ..   ..   7·00
   c. Frame break at upper right
      (Cyl. 2 No dot, R. 11/11)   ..   8·00
   d. Frame flaw (Cyl. 2 Dot, R. 12/5)   7·50

B. Whiter Paper (4 June 1962)

S127	582		Bronze-green	40 15

   a. Broken daffodil (Cyl. 2 No dot,
     R. 7/2) .. ..   4·50
   b. Frame break at upper right
     (Cyl. 2 No dot, R. 11/11) ..   5·00
   c. Frame flaw (Cyl. 2 Dot, R. 12/5)   4·50

Listed Varieties

For illustration of No. S126*a,* see No. S124*a.*

S126*b,* S127*a,* S128*b*
Stem of daffodil
is broken

S126*c,* S127*b,* S128*c*
A very similar variety to
the one on Cyl. 1, R.8/6
but more pronounced

S126*d,* S127*c,* S128*d*
Flaw on frame
at lower left

Cylinder Numbers (Blocks of Six)

Cream Paper. (No. S126)							Whiter Paper. (No. S127)					
Perforation Type A							Perforation Type A					
Cyl. No.					No dot	Dot	Cyl. No.				No dot	Dot
1 ..	..	..	..	..	27·00	27·00	2 ..	..	..	..	4·25	4·25
2 ..	..	..	..	..	27·00	27·00						

Sheet Markings

   Guide holes: Double-boxed opposite rows 14/15, at left (no dot) or right (dot)
   Others: As given in General Notes

Imprimatur from the National Postal Museum Archives

Imperforate, watermark Type W.24. Cream or whiter paper

   Watermark upright

Cat. No.	S.G. No.		Shades	Mint Used

1966 (DECEMBER 29). TWO 9·5 mm. PHOSPHOR BANDS REACTING VIOLET. WMK. CROWNS

The bands were applied in photogravure.

S128	617*c*		Bronze-green	60 25

   a. Imperf. between stamp and top
     margin £400
   b. Broken daffodil (Cyl. 2 No dot,
     R. 7/2) .. ..   4·50
   c. Frame break at upper right
     (Cyl. 2 No dot, R. 11/11) ..   5·50
   d. Frame flaw (Cyl. 2 Dot, R. 12/5)   4·50

For illustrations of Nos. S128*b/d,* see Nos. S126*b/d.*

Cylinder Numbers (Blocks of Six)

Perforation Type A

Cyl. No.				No dot	Dot
2 ..	..	..	..	5·00	5·00

Sheet Markings

   As for Nos. S126/7

Imprimatur from the National Postal Museum Archives

Imperforate, watermark Type W.24

   Watermark upright

1954-66. 10d. Prussian blue, Type S5

Cat. No.	S.G. No.	Shades	Mint	Used

1954 (FEBRUARY 8). WATERMARK TUDOR CROWN, TYPE W.22

S129	527	Prussian blue	18·00	3·00

Cylinder Numbers (Blocks of Six)

Perforation Type A						Perforation Type B (no dot) and C (dot)					
Cyl. No.				No dot	Dot	Cyl. No.				No dot	Dot
1 ..	..	..	..	.. £125	£125	1 ..	..	..	..	.. £125	£125

Minor Constant Sheet Flaws

Cyl. 1   3/3 White spur on right fork of V of REVENUE
10/12 White flaw on thistle shows as a cut into the left-hand side of the flower (Th. A6)
13/10 White flaw on rim of diadem below emblems (Th. B4)

Sheet Markings

Guide holes: Boxed opposite rows 14/15, at left (no dot) or right (dot)
Others: As given in General Notes

Imprimatur from the National Postal Museum Archives

Imperforate, watermark Type W.22

Watermark upright

1955 (SEPTEMBER 22). WATERMARK ST. EDWARD'S CROWN, TYPE W.23

S130	552	Prussian blue	12·00	2·25

Cylinder Numbers (Blocks of Six)

Perforation Type A

Cyl. No.				No dot	Dot
1 ..	..	..	..	85·00	85·00

Minor Constant Sheet Flaws

Cyl. 1   3/3 White spur on right fork of V of REVENUE
10/12 White flaw on thistle shows as a cut into the left-hand side of the flower (Th. A6)
13/10 White flaw on rim of diadem below emblems (Th. B4)

Sheet Markings

Guide holes: Boxed opposite rows 14/15, at left (no dot) or right (dot)
Others: As given in General Notes

Imprimatur from the National Postal Museum Archives

Imperforate, watermark Type W.23

Watermark upright

1958 (NOVEMBER 18). WATERMARK CROWNS, TYPE W.24

A. Cream Paper

S131	—	Prussian blue	3·25	60

B. Whiter Paper (13 November 1962)

S132	583	Prussian blue	1·00	15

Cylinder Numbers (Blocks of Six)

Cream Paper. (No. S131)						Whiter Paper. (No. S132)					
Perforation Type A						Perforation Type A					
Cyl. No.				No dot	Dot	Cyl. No.				No dot	Dot
1 ..	..	..	..	.. 23·00	23·00	1 ..	..	..	..	.. 7·50	7·50
Perforation Type B (no dot) and C (dot)						Perforation Type F (L)*					
1 ..	..	..	..	.. 23·00	23·00	1* ..	..	..	..	..	..

*This is probably No. S133 but
with the phosphor omitted.

Minor Constant Sheet Flaws

Cyl. 1   3/3 White spur on right fork of V of REVENUE. Later retouched
10/12 White flaw on thistle shows as a cut into the left-hand side of the flower (Th. A6). **Later retouched**
13/10 White flaw on rim of diadem below emblems (Th. B4). Later retouched
14/3 Retouch on Queen's nose (Th. D3)

Sheet Markings

Guide holes: Unboxed opposite rows 1 and 7/8 and boxed opposite rows 14/15, at left (no dot) or right (dot); or boxed only opposite rows 14/15 at left (no dot) or right (dot)
Others: As given in General Notes

Imprimatur from the National Postal Museum Archives

Imperforate, watermark Type W.24. Cream or whiter paper

Watermark upright

Cat. No.	S.G. No.	Shades	Mint	Used

1966 (DECEMBER 30).   TWO 9·5 mm. PHOSPHOR BANDS REACTING VIOLET. WMK. CROWNS

The bands were applied in photogravure.

S133	617d		Prussian blue	80	35
a. Single broad band	..	..	£200		

Cylinder Numbers (Blocks of Six)

Perforation Type A				Perforation Type F (L)*			
Cyl. No.			No dot Dot	Cyl. No.			No dot Dot
1 ..	..	..	..	..	5·50	5·50	1 ..	..	..	..	..	5·50	5·50

Minor Constant Sheet Flaws

Cyl. 1   3/3 White spur on right fork of V of REVENUE. Later retouched
14/3 Retouch on Queen's nose (Th. D3)

Sheet Markings

Guide holes: Boxed opposite rows 14/15, at left (no dot) or right (dot) but in the case of perforation Type F (L)* the boxes remain on both panes but the holes are unboxed above and below the eighth vertical row in the no dot pane only
Others: As given in General Notes

Imprimatur from the National Postal Museum Archives

Imperforate, watermark Type W.24

Watermark upright

1954-55. 11d. Brown-purple, Type S5

Cat. No.	S.G. No.	Shades	Mint	Used

1954 (FEBRUARY 8). WATERMARK TUDOR CROWN, TYPE W.22

S134	528	Brown-purple	30·00	16·00

Cylinder Numbers (Blocks of Six)
Perforation Type B (no dot) and C (dot)

Cyl. No.					No dot	Dot
1 ..	..	..	..	..	£200	£200

Minor Constant Sheet Flaw
Cyl. 1   19/3 White flaw in frame pattern at left by O of POSTAGE (Th. D1)

Sheet Markings
Guide holes: Boxed opposite rows 14/15, at left (no dot) or right (dot)
Others: As given in General Notes

Imprimatur from the National Postal Museum Archives
Imperforate, watermark Type W.22

Watermark upright

1955 (OCTOBER 28). WATERMARK ST. EDWARD'S CROWN, TYPE W.23

S135	553	Brown-purple	40	1·50

Cylinder Numbers (Blocks of Six)

Perforation Type A

Cyl. No.				No dot	Dot
1 ..	..	..	..	4·00	4·00

Perforation Type B (no dot) and C (dot)

Cyl. No.				No dot	Dot
1 ..	..	..	..	4·00	4·00

Minor Constant Sheet Flaw
Cyl. 1   19/3 White flaw in frame pattern at left by O of POSTAGE (Th. D1)

Sheet Markings
Guide holes: Boxed opposite rows 14/15, at left (no dot) or right (dot)
Others: As given in General Notes

Imprimatur from the National Postal Museum Archives
Imperforate, watermark Type W.23

Watermark upright

1953-67. 1s. Bistre-brown, Type S6

Cat. No.	S.G. No.	Shades	Mint	Used

1953 (JULY 6). WATERMARK TUDOR CROWN, TYPE W.22

S136	529	Bistre-brown	1·00	40

Cylinder Numbers (Blocks of Six)

Perforation Type A						Perforation Type B (no dot) and C (dot)		
Cyl. No.					No dot Dot	Cyl. No.		No dot Dot
1	..	..	..	..	8·00 8·00	1	.. ..	13·00 13·00
2	..	..	..	..	22·00 22·00			

Minor Constant Sheet Flaws

Cyl. 1.   3/10 Coloured flaw between left-hand leaves of thistle (Th. B6)
           5/10 Coloured spur to top of lacing at right of value (Th. G5)
Cyl. 2.   3/10 As on Cyl. 1. (multipositive flaw)

Sheet Markings

Guide holes: Boxed opposite rows 14/15, at left (no dot) or right (dot)
Others: As given in General Notes

Imprimatur from the National Postal Museum Archives

Imperforate, watermark Type W.22

Watermark upright

1955 (NOVEMBER 3). WATERMARK ST. EDWARD'S CROWN, TYPE W.23

S137	554	Bistre-brown	15·00	40
a. Thistle flaw (Cyl. 3 Dot, R. 4/5). .	23·00			

Listed Variety

S137*a*, S138*b*, S139*a*

Cylinder Numbers (Blocks of Six)

Perforation Type A

Cyl. No.					No dot Dot	Cyl. No.					No dot Dot
2	..	..	..	..	£100 £100	4	..	..	..	..	£125 £125
3	..	..	..	..	£100 £100						

Minor Constant Sheet Flaws

Cyl. 2.   3/10 Coloured flaw between left-hand leaves of thistle (Th. B6). Later retouched leaving a pale mark
Cyl. 3.   3/10 As on Cyl. 2. but flaw is retouched and appears much smaller (multipositive flaw)
Cyl. 4.   3/10 As for Cyl. 3.
          11/12 Coloured spur to foot of first E of REVENUE

Sheet Markings

As for No. S136

Imprimatur from the National Postal Museum Archives

Imperforate, watermark Type W.23

Watermark upright

Cat. No.	S.G. No.		Shades	Mint	Used

1958 (OCTOBER 30). WATERMARK CROWNS, TYPE W.24

A. Cream Paper

| S138 | — | | Bistre-brown | 3·75 | 80 |

a. Double impression £160
b. Thistle flaw (Cyl. 3 Dot, R. 4/5). . 8·00

B. Whiter Paper (22 July 1962)

| S139 | 584 | | Bistre-brown | 40 | 12 |

a. Thistle flaw (Cyl. 3 Dot, R. 4/5). . 4·50

For illustration of Nos. S138b and S139a, see No. S137a.

Cylinder Numbers (Blocks of Six)

Cream Paper. (No. S138)							Whiter Paper. (No. S139)						
Perforation Type A							Perforation Type A						
Cyl. No.					No dot	Dot	Cyl. No.					No dot	Dot
2 ..	..	..	..	..	26·00	26·00	2 ..	..	..	..	..	4·00	4·00
3 ..	..	..	..	..	26·00	26·00	3 ..	..	..	..	..	4·00	4·00
4 ..	..	..	..	..	26·00	26·00	4 ..	..	..	..	..	4·00	4·00

Minor Constant Sheet Flaws

Multipositive flaw

Dot   3/10 Coloured flaw between left-hand leaves of thistle (Th. B6) now only exists retouched. Cyls. 2. and
3. show as a smudge and Cyl. 4. as a much smaller flaw

Cyl. 4. 11/12 Coloured spur to foot of first E of REVENUE

Sheet Markings

As for No. S136

Imprimatur from the National Postal Museum Archives

Imperforate, watermark Type W.24. Cream or whiter paper

Watermark upright

1967 (JUNE 28). TWO 9·5 mm. PHOSPHOR BANDS REACTING VIOLET. WMK. CROWNS

The bands were applied in photogravure.

| S140 | 617e | | Bistre-brown | 40 | 20 |

Cylinder Numbers (Blocks of Six)

Perforation Type F (L)*

	Cyl. No.				No dot	Dot
	4 ..	..	..	..	4·00	4·00

Minor Constant Sheet Flaws

Cyl. 4.   3/10 Coloured flaw between left-hand leaves of thistle (Th. B6) is now retouched leaving a much
smaller flaw
11/12 Coloured spur to foot of first E of REVENUE

Sheet Markings

Guide holes: Unboxed above and below the eighth vertical row in the no dot pane only. The usual boxes
opposite rows 14/15 remain
Others: As given in General Notes

Imprimatur from the National Postal Museum Archives

Imperforate, watermark Type W.24

Watermark upright

1953-67. 1s.3d. Green, Type S7

Cat. No.	S.G. No.	Shades	Mint	Used

1953 (NOVEMBER 2). WATERMARK TUDOR CROWN, TYPE W.22

S141   530   Green   4·50   2·00
  a. White flaw in Queen's hair
    (Dot, R. 2/9) ..   ..   .. 10·00
  b. " P " flaw (Dot, R. 6/10)   ..   9·00

Listed Varieties

S141*a*, S142*a*, S143*a*, S144*a*   S141*b*, S142*b*, S143*b*, S144*b*
    S145*a*, S146*a*, S147*b*   S145*b*, S146*b*, S147*c*

Cylinder Numbers (Blocks of Six)

Perforation Type A			Perforation Type B (no dot) and C (dot)		
Cyl. No.	No dot	Dot	Cyl. No.	No dot	Dot
1	32·00	32·00	1	32·00	32·00

Sheet Markings
  Guide holes: Boxed opposite rows 14/15, at left (no dot) or right (dot)
  Others: As given in General Notes

Imprimatur from the National Postal Museum Archives
  Imperforate, watermark Type W.22
  Watermark upright

1956 (MARCH 27). WATERMARK ST. EDWARD'S CROWN, TYPE W.23

S142   555   Green   17·00   1·50
  a. White flaw in Queen's hair
    (Dot, R. 2/9) ..   ..   .. 30·00
  b. " P " flaw (Dot, R. 6/10)   .. 27·00
  For illustrations of Nos. S142*a*/*b*, see Nos. S141*a*/*b*.

Cylinder Numbers (Blocks of Six)
Perforation Type A

Cyl. No.	No dot	Dot
1	£110	£110

Sheet Markings
  As for No. S141

Imprimatur from the National Postal Museum Archives
  Imperforate, watermark Type W.23
  Watermark upright

Cat. No.	S.G. No.	Shades	Mint	Used

1959 (JUNE 17). WATERMARK CROWNS, TYPE W.24
A. Cream Paper

S143   —   Green   2·00   75

   a. White flaw in Queen's hair (Cyl. 1
        dot, R. 2/9   ..   ..   7·50
   b. "P" flaw (Cyl. 1, Dot, R. 6/10) ..   7·50

B. Whiter Paper (29 August 1962)

S144   585   Green   25   15

   a. White flaw in Queen's hair
        (Cyl. 1 Dot, R. 2/9)   ..   ..   4·00
   b. "P" flaw (Cyl. 1 Dot, R. 6/10) ..   4·00

For illustrations of Nos. S143*a/b* and S144*a/b*, see Nos. S141*a/b*.

Cylinder Numbers (Blocks of Six)

Cream Paper. (No. S143)			Whiter Paper. (No. S144)		
Perforation Type A			Perforation Type A		
Cyl. No.	Nodot	Dot	Cyl. No.	Nodot	Dot
1	15·00	15·00	1	2·75	2·75
			2	2·75	2·75

Sheet Markings

As for No. S141

Imprimatur from the National Postal Museum Archives

Imperforate, watermark Type W.24. Cream or whiter paper

Watermark upright

1960 (JUNE 22). TWO PHOSPHOR BANDS REACTING GREEN. WATERMARK CROWNS

The bands were applied in photogravure.

S145   —   Green   7·50   5·00

   a. White flaw in Queen's hair
        (Dot, R. 2/9)   ..   ..   ..   12·00
   b. "P" flaw (Dot, R. 6/10)   ..   12·00

For illustrations of Nos. S145*a/b*, See Nos. S141*a/b*.

Cylinder Numbers (Blocks of Six)

Perforation Type B (no dot) and C (dot)

Cyl. No.	Nodot	Dot
1	55·00	55·00

Sheet Markings

Guide holes: Boxed opposite rows 14/15, at left (no dot) or right (dot)
Black bar: This occurs by the marginal arrows opposite rows 10/11, at left (no dot) or right (dot)
Others: As given in General Notes

Imprimatur from the National Postal Museum Archives

Imperforate, watermark Type W.24

Watermark upright

Cat. No.	S.G. No.		Shades	Mint	Used

1961 (JUNE 5).   TWO PHOSPHOR BANDS REACTING BLUE. WATERMARK CROWNS

The bands were applied in photogravure.

A. Cream Paper

S146	—	Green	11·00	4·50

a. White flaw in Queen's hair (Cyl. 1
    Dot, R. 2/9) ..   ..   20·00
b. "P" flaw (Cyl. 1 Dot, R. 6/10) ..   20·00

B. Whiter Paper (21 January 1963)

S147	618	Green	1·75	2·50

a. Single broad band ..   ..   6·50
b. White flaw in Queen's hair
    (Cyl. 1 Dot, R. 2/9) ..   ..   4·00
c. "P" flaw (Cyl. 1 Dot, R. 6/10) ..   4·00

 For illustrations of Nos. S146*a/b* and S147*b/c*, see Nos. S141*a/b*.

Cylinder Numbers (Blocks of Six)

Cream Paper. (No. S146)   Whiter Paper. (No. S147)

Perforation Type A   Perforation Type A

Cyl. No.					No dot	Dot		Cyl. No.					No dot	Dot
1 ..	..	..	..	..	80·00	80·00		1 ..	..	..	..	..	13·00	13·00
								2 ..	..	..	..	..	13·00	13·00

Sheet Markings

As for No. S141

Imprimatur from the National Postal Museum Archives

Imperforate, watermark Type W.24. Cream or whiter paper

Watermark upright

1965 (AUGUST 13).   TWO 8 mm. PHOSPHOR BANDS REACTING VIOLET. WMK. CROWNS

The bands were originally applied by typography.

S148	—	Green	9·00	2·75

a. Narrow band at left or right
    (stamp with vert. margin) ..   15·00
b. Bands applied photo. (1966) ··   5·50   2·75
c. Single broad band (photo.) ..   20·00
d. Single 8 mm. broad band (typo.)   15·00   *da.* As *d* but 6 mm. band ..   ..   22·00

Cylinder Numbers (Blocks of Six)

Perforation Type A

Applied typo. (No. S148)   Applied photo. (No. S148*b*)

Cyl. No.					No dot	Dot		Cyl. No.					No dot	Dot
2 ..	..	..	..	..	65·00	65·00		2 ..	..	..	..	..	38·00	38·00

Sheet Markings

As for No. S141

1967 (EARLY).   TWO 9·5 mm. PHOSPHOR BANDS REACTING VIOLET. WMK. CROWNS

The bands were applied in photogravure only.

S149	—	Green	8·00	4·50

Cylinder Numbers (Blocks of Six)

Perforation Type A

Cyl. No.				No dot	Dot
2 ..	..	..	..	60·00	60·00

Sheet Markings

As for No. S141

1953-66. 1s.6d. Grey-blue, Type S6

Cat. No.	S.G. No.	Shades	Mint	Used

1953 (NOVEMBER 2). WATERMARK TUDOR CROWN, TYPE W.22

S150   531   Grey-blue   11·00   2·75
- *a.* White flaw in Queen's hair below
  diadem (Dot, R. 20/1) ..   ..   20·00
- *b.* White flaw in Queen's hair
  opposite "N" of "REVENUE"
  (Dot, R. 20/2) ..   ..   ..   20·00

Listed Varieties

S150*a*, S151*a*, S152*a*, S153*a*,   S150*b*, S151*b*, S152*b*,
          S154*a*   Later retouched on Crowns
                                                     watermark

Cylinder Numbers (Blocks of Six)

Perforation Type A						Perforation Type B (no dot) and C (dot)			
Cyl. No.				No dot	Dot	Cyl. No.			No dot	Dot
1 ..	..	..	..	.. 80·00	95·00*	1 ..	..	..	.. 80·00	95·00*

Sheet Markings

Guide holes: Boxed opposite rows 14/15, at left (no dot) or right (dot)
Others: As given in General Notes

Imprimatur from the National Postal Museum Archives

Imperforate, watermark Type W.22

Watermark upright

1956 (MARCH 27). WATERMARK ST. EDWARD'S CROWN, TYPE W.23

S151   556   Grey-blue   16·00   1·25
- *a.* White flaw in Queen's hair below
  diadem (Dot, R. 20/1) ..   ..   30·00
- *b.* White flaw in Queen's hair
  opposite "N" of "REVENUE"
  (Dot, R. 20/2) ..   ..   ..   30·00

For illustrations of Nos. S151*a*/*b*, see Nos. S150*a*/*b*.

Cylinder Numbers (Blocks of Six)

Perforation Type A						Perforation Type B (no dot) and C (dot)			
Cyl. No.				No dot	Dot	Cyl. No.			No dot	Dot
1 ..	..	..	..	.. £110	£130*	1 ..	..	..	.. £110	£130*

Sheet Markings

As for No. S150

Imprimatur from the National Postal Museum Archives

Imperforate, watermark Type W.23

Watermark upright

Cat. No.	S.G. No.	Shades	Mint	Used

1958 (DECEMBER 16).   WATERMARK CROWNS, TYPE W.24

A. Cream Paper

S152	—	Grey-blue	10·00	2·50

    a. White flaw in Queen's hair below
       diadem (Cyl 1 Dot, R. 20/1) ..   20·00
    b. White flaw in Queen's hair
       opposite "N" of "REVENUE"
       (Cyl. 1 Dot, R. 20/2)   ..   ..   20·00

B. Whiter Paper (14 November 1962)

S153	586	Grey-blue	5·00	40

    a. White flaw in Queen's hair below
       diadem (Cyl. 1 Dot, R. 20/1) ..   10·00

For illustrations of Nos. S152*a/b* and S153*a*, see Nos. S150*a/b*.

Cylinder Numbers (Blocks of Six)

Cream Paper. (No. S152)   Whiter Paper. (No. S153)

Perforation Type A   Perforation Type A

Cyl. No.					Nodot	Dot	Cyl. No.					Nodot	Dot
1	..	..	..	..	70·00	90·00*	1	..	..	..	..	32·00	38·00*
3	..	..	..	..	70·00	70·00							

Perforation Type B (no dot) and C (dot)

1	..	..	..	..	70·00	90·00*
3	..	..	..	..	70·00	70·00

Sheet Markings

  As for No. S150

Imprimatur from the National Postal Museum Archives

Imperforate, watermark Type W.24. Cream or whiter paper

Watermark upright

1966 (DECEMBER 12).   TWO 9·5 mm. PHOSPHOR BANDS REACTING VIOLET. WMK. CROWNS

  The bands were applied in photogravure.

S154	618*a*	Grey-blue	2·00	1·00

    a. White flaw in Queen's hair below
       diadem (Cyl. 1 Dot, R. 20/1) ..   5·50

For illustration of No. S154*a*, see No. S150*a*.

Cylinder Numbers (Blocks of Six)

Perforation Type A   Perforation Type F (L)*

Cyl. No.					Nodot	Dot	Cyl. No.					Nodot	Dot
1	..	..	..	..	15·00	20·00*	8	..	..	..	..	18·00	18·00

Sheet Markings

  Guide holes: Boxed opposite rows 14/15, at left (no dot) or right (dot) but in the case of perforation Type
  F (L)* the boxes remain on both panes but the holes are unboxed above and below the eighth vertical
  row in the no dot pane only
  Others: As given in General Notes

Imprimatur from the National Postal Museum Archives

Imperforate, watermark Type W.24

Watermark upright

Presentation Packs

SPP1 (issued 1960)   Eighteen values   80·00

The issued pack contained one of each value.   The 1½d. and 11d. were with St. Edward's Crown watermark (Nos. S26 and S135) and the remainder were Crowns watermark all on cream paper, ½d. (No. S4), 1d (S16), 2d. (S40), 2½d. (S55), 3d. (S70), 4d. (S83), 4½d. (S93), 5d. (S101), 6d. (S107), 7d. (S116), 8d. (S121), 9d. (S126), 10d. (S131), 1s. (S138), 1s.3d. (S144), 1s.6d. (S152).

Two forms of the pack exist:
(a) Inscribed "10s 6d" for sale in the U.K. and
(b) Inscribed "$1·80" for sale in the U.S.A.

SPP2 (issued 1960)   Sixteen values   £200

The issued pack contained two of each value of the Phosphor-Graphite experimental issue, ½d. (No. S8), 1d. (S19), 1½d. (S31), 2d (S43), 2½d. (S60), 3d (S73), 4d. (S87), 4½d. (S96). The ½d., 1d. and 1½d. were with St. Edward's Crown watermark and the remainder with Crowns watermark. Although the details printed on the pack erroneously describe the stamps as all having Crowns watermark, the packs usually bear a sticker inscribed "CORRECTION. The ½d, 1d, & 1½d stamps bear the St. Edward Crown Royal Cypher watermark".

Two forms of the pack exist:
(a) Inscribed "3s 8d" for sale in the U.K. and
(b) Inscribed "50c" for sale in the U.S.A.

SECTION SB
Dorothy Wilding Issues
1953–68. Booklet Panes in Photogravure

General Notes

INTRODUCTION. All panes were printed in photogravure by Harrison & Sons. See the detailed notes under Section S for information on printing, paper, gum and phosphor application. Reference to the note, "Booklet and Coil Varieties", at the beginning of Section S describes the panes which were printed from 21-row cylinders. These panes are found with varieties and the cylinder number in either the top or bottom row of the pane.

ARRANGEMENT. The panes are listed in face value order of the stamps they include (for *se-tenant* panes under the lowest denomination). The main listing is followed by errors and varieties in small type.

PERFORATION. Wilding booklet stamps exist in panes of two, four and six and details together with illustrations of the perforation types will be found in Appendix G, section 4. The type abbreviations found above the pane prices refer to the appearance of the binding margin, i.e. I = imperforate, AP = alternate perf., P = perforated and E = extension hole.

BOOKLET ERRORS. Those listed as "Imperf. pane" show one row of perforations either at top or bottom of booklet pane. Those listed as "part perf. pane" have one row of three stamps imperforate on three sides. The tête-bêche errors derive from booklets but these are listed in Section SA.

BOOKLET CYLINDER NUMBERS. These are listed for panes where most of the number is visible. Some panes of four had the number engraved wide of the stamps and such examples are priced in a footnote. Information on the cylinders used is given in most cases. Phosphor cylinder numbers have not been found on Wilding panes. The cylinder numbers being hand-engraved varied slightly as to their position in relation to the stamp so that some were invariably trimmed. A pane showing a complete cylinder number placed away from the stamp will only exist with trimmed perforations on the opposite side.

BOOKLET FLAWS. Cylinder flaws on booklet stamps are listed under the panes in which they occur. Prices are for the variety in a complete pane with its binding margin intact. In cases where a 21-row cylinder has been used both possible positions in the pane are given. When quoting the position on booklet panes no attention is paid to the labels. In a pane of six, stamp 3 would be the third stamp in the row counting from left to right. Again "R. 1/3" refers to row one, third stamp from the left margin. Panes of four from 1s. and 2s. booklets contain panes with a top binding margin and other booklets have panes of six with the binding margin at left.

PHOSPHOR BAND WIDTHS. See notes in Section S; the booklet stamps being similar to those printed in Post Office counter sheets. The 6 mm. bands were printed in typo on panes of four, but these can only be identified when the bands are slightly misplaced. Likewise panes of six showing 8 mm. bands have the 6 mm. band printed *over the first vertical row of perforations at the left*. Major shifts result in stamps from the first column having one 6 mm. wide band and the other four stamps a misplaced band of 8 mm. Such panes are scarce.

MISPLACED BROAD PHOSPHOR BANDS. Panes exist showing phosphor bands misplaced and these are listed where they are known. To qualify the vertical sides of the bands should occur on the stamp and must be clear of the perforation holes. This, in effect, changes the numbers of bands on a single stamp and these have always been popular with collectors. A different kind of error exists where the phosphor cylinder printed one band instead of two but this only occurred on a small printing of the 1d./3d. *se-tenant* panes in 2s. booklets.

PHOSPHOR APPLICATION. It is appropriate to mention here that we do not list separately panes with bands applied in photogravure and flexography. Refer to the notes in Section S under "Phosphor Issues" for information on the types of phosphor employed.

STAMPS OVERPRINTED "SPECIMEN". Panes exist with a handstamped overprint in two sizes. These derive from the National Postal Archive sales mentioned in the Introductory Notes. The handstamp can be found inverted or overlapping the perforations but these are not listed as varieties.

BOOKLET PANE PRICES. The prices quoted are for panes with good perforations all round and with binding margin attached. Panes showing some degree of trimming will be worth less than the published prices in this Catalogue. It should be appreciated that some panes are scarce with full perforations and the prices shown in the Catalogue reflect this. Panes from the 2s. booklets are particularly difficult to find with full perforations on the three sides.

Prices in Appendix HA are for booklets containing panes described as having average perforations (i.e. full perforations on two edges of the pane only).

½d. BOOKLET PANES OF SIX
6 × ½d. Tudor Crown
From 2s. 6d. Booklets F14/34 and 5s. Booklets H6/16

A. Watermark upright
        SB1 (containing No. S1 × 6) (3.54)   2·25

B. Watermark inverted
        SB1a (containing No. S1a × 6) (3.54)   4·50

Booklet Cylinder Numbers

Panes of six (20-row cylinders)

Cyl. No.				No dot	Dot	Cyl. No.				No dot	Dot
E1 ..	..	..	..	12·00	12·00	E4*	..	..	..	10·00	10·00
E2 ..	..	..	..	10·00	10·00						

*The no-dot pane of cylinder E4 originally had a dot inserted in error. This can be distinguished from the true dot cylinder in which the " 4 " is broader and further from the " E ", and the dot is more circular than the erroneous dot.

The erroneous dot was not noticed until the Crowns watermark which exists in three states: I with the erroneous dot; II with dot removed leaving a smudge; and III with smudge removed. These are shown in the following illustration:—

     True dot   I   II   III

½d. BOOKLET PANES OF FOUR
4 × ½d. Tudor Crown
From 1s. Booklet K1/a for use in "E" machines.

A. Watermark upright
                                   Perf. Type P
        SB2 (containing No. S1 × 4) (22.7.54)   4·50

B. Watermark inverted
        SB2a (containing No. S1a × 4) (22.7.54)   6·00

Booklet Cylinder Numbers
Cylinder No. E3 was used, but it does not appear in the finished booklets.

Imprimaturs from the National Postal Museum Archives

Booklet pane of four. Imperforate, watermark Type W.22

Two panes arranged vertically *tête-bêche* with a 12 mm. horizontal gutter margin between

½d. BOOKLET PANES OF TWO

2 × ½d.   Tudor Crown
From 1s. Booklet E1 for use in experimental "D" machines.
Watermark upright

	Perf. Type	
	E	E(½v)
SB3 (containing No. S1 × 2) (2.9.53)	2·25	5·50

Made up from vertical rows 1 and 2 from sheets.

Booklet Cylinder Numbers
Panes of two (from sheets). Perf. Type E

Cyl. No.					No dot	Dot	Cyl. No.					No dot	Dot
1	. .	. .	. .	. .	9·00	9·00	3	. .	. .	. .	. .	9·00	9·00

½d. BOOKLET PANES OF SIX

6 × ½d.   St. Edward's Crown
From 2s.6d. Booklets F34/61, 3s. Booklets M1/10 and 5s. Booklets H17/37

A. Watermark upright

SB4 (Containing No. S2 × 6) (9.55)		2·25
b. Part perf. pane*		
c. White flaw in Queen's hair (R. 1/3 or 2/3) . .		4·00

B. Watermark inverted

SB4a (containing No. S2b × 6) (9.55)		3·25

*Booklet error—see General Notes.

Listed Variety

SB4c, SB7e, SB14b
(Cyl. E4 dot)

Booklet Cylinder Numbers
Panes of six (20/21-row cylinders)

Cyl. No.				No dot	Dot	Cyl. No.				No dot	Dot
E4 *	. .	. .	. .	8·50	8·50	E4 T*	. .	. .	. .	8·50	8·50

*See notes after booklet panes of No. SB1.

The ½d. double pane cylinders E1, E2 and E4 contained 20 rows and the cylinder number always occurred opposite row 18 so that it always appears next to the bottom row of the pane.

Cylinder E4 was later modified by adding another row of 24. In this and later 21-row cylinders, which are printed continuously in the web, the perforated web is cut at every 20th row to make sheets of 480. Consequently on successive sheets the cylinder number appears one row lower and thus a pane can have it adjoining the top or bottom row. Where the cylinder number adjoins the top row of the pane it is designated by the letter "T".

½d. BOOKLET PANES OF FOUR
4 × ½d.   St. Edward's Crown
From 1s. Booklets K2/b for use in " E " machines and 2s. Booklet N1

A. Watermark upright

		Perf. Type	
		AP	P
SB5 (containing No. S2 × 4) (5.7.56)		7·00	5·00

B. Watermark inverted

SB5a (containing No. S2b × 4) (5.7.56)		7·00	5·00

Booklet Cylinder Numbers
Cylinder No. E3 was used, but it does not appear in the finished booklets.

Imprimaturs from the National Postal Museum Archives

Booklet pane of four. Imperforate, watermark Type W.23

Two panes arranged vertically *tête-bêche* with a 12 mm. horizontal gutter margin between

½d. BOOKLET PANES OF TWO
2 × ½d.   St. Edward's Crown
From 1s. Booklet E2 for use in experimental " D " machines.

Watermark upright

		Perf. Type	
		E	E(½v)
SB6 (containing No. S2 × 2) (11.57)		2·75	5·50

Made up from vertical rows 1 and 2 from sheets.

Booklet Cylinder Numbers
Panes of two (from sheets). Perf. Type E

Cyl. No.						No dot	Dot
1	..	..	..	..	..	†	—
3	..	..	..	..	..	9·00	9·00

½d. BOOKLET PANES OF SIX
6 × ½d.   Crowns.   Cream or whiter paper
From 3s. Booklets M9(a)/74, 5s. Booklets H35(a) and H37/74 and 10s. Booklets X1/2

Cream Paper

A. Watermark upright
SB7 (containing No. S4 × 6) (11.58)	3·25
b. Part perf. pane*	£800
c. Dot on left fraction bar (R. 1/1 or R. 2/1) ..	5·00
d. Extended right fraction bar (R. 1/1 or R. 2/1) ..	5·50
e. White flaw in Queen's hair (R. 1/3 or R. 2/3) ..	4·00

B. Watermark inverted
SB7a (containing No. S4c × 6) (11.58)	4·50

Whiter Paper

A. Watermark upright
SB8 (containing No. S5 × 6) (6.62)	3·25
b. Dot on left fraction bar (R. 1/1 or R. 2/1) ..	5·00
c. Extended right fraction bar (R. 1/1 or R. 2/1) ..	5·00

B. Watermark inverted
SB8a (containing No. S5c × 6) (6.62)	3·75

*Booklet error—see General Notes.

Listed Varieties
For illustration of No. SB7e see No. SB4c

SB7c, SB8b,
SB16c, SB17c
(Cyl. E12 no dot)

SB7d, SB8c,
SB16b, SB17b
(Cyl. E12 no dot)

Booklet Cylinder Numbers
Panes of six (21-row cylinders)

Cream paper				Whiter paper					
Cyl. No.		No dot	Dot	Cyl. No.				No dot	Dot
E4* With erroneous dot	..	11·00	10·00	E11	..	..	..	.. 17·00	17·00
E4* No dot with smudge	..	12·00	†	E11 T	..	..	..	.. 17·00	17·00
E4* Smudge removed ..		10·00	†	E12	..	..	..	.. 11·00	11·00
E4 T* With erroneous dot	..	11·00	10·00	E12 T	..	..	..	.. 11·00	11·00
E4 T* No dot with smudge	..	12·00	†						
E4 T* Smudge removed ..		10·00	†						
E11	.. .. ..	7·75	7·75						
E11 T	.. .. ..	7·75	7·75						
E12	.. .. ..	16·00	16·00						
E12 T	.. .. ..	16·00	16·00						

*For explanation see notes below No. SB1.

Specimen overprints from the National Postal Museum Archives
Booklet pane of six. Perf. 15 × 14, watermark Type W.24 inverted

Each stamp handstamped "Specimen" (15 × 2½ mm.)

½d. BOOKLET PANES OF FOUR
4 × ½d. Crowns. Cream paper
From 1s. Booklets K3/a for use in "E" machines and 2s. Booklets N2/3. Perf. Type AP

A. Watermark upright
　　　SB9 (containing No. S4 × 4) (13.8.59)　　　　3·25

B. Watermark inverted
　　　SB9a (containing No. S4c × 4) (13.8.59)　　　3·25

Booklet Cylinder Numbers
Cylinder No. E3 was used, but it does not appear in the finished booklets.

Specimen overprints from the National Postal Museum Archives
Booklet pane of four. Perf. 15 × 14, watermark Type W.24 inverted

Each stamp handstamped "Specimen" (13 × 2 mm.)

½d. BOOKLET PANES OF FOUR. SIDEWAYS WATERMARK
4 × ½d. Crowns. Cream or whiter paper
From 2s. Booklets N4/20

Cream Paper

		Perf. Type		
		I	I(½v)	AP
A. Watermark Crown to left				
SB10 (containing No. S4d × 4) (26.5.61)		8·00	16·00	5·50
B. Watermark Crown to right				
SB10a (containing No. S4e × 4) (26.5.61)		8·00	16·00	5·50

Whiter Paper

A. Watermark Crown to left
> SB11 (containing No. S5a × 4) (5.6.62)   5·50   15·00   3·00

B. Watermark Crown to right
> SB11a (containing No. S5b × 4) (5.6.62)   5·50   15·00   3·00

Booklet Cylinder Number

Cylinder No E13 was used, but it was partly or completely trimmed off. (*Price for pane showing "E", from £40*).

Imprimaturs from the National Postal Museum Archives

Booklet pane of four. Imperforate, watermark Type W.24

Two panes arranged vertically *tête-bêche* with a 12 mm. horizontal gutter margin between

Specimen overprints from the National Postal Museum Archives

Booklet pane of six. Perf. 15 × 14, watermark Type W.24

Each stamp handstamped "Specimen" (13 × 2 mm.)

SB12   SB13

SE-TENANT PANES OF FOUR FROM HOLIDAY BOOKLETS
Crowns watermark. Chalky paper. 3 × ½d. with 2½d. from 2s. Booklet NR1/1a

A. Watermark upright

	Perf. Type		
	I	I(½v)	AP
SB12 (containing No. S6 × 3, S58) (15.7.63)	12·00	20·00	7·50
b. Screen damage on 2½d.	†	†	20·00

B. Watermark inverted

	I	I(½v)	AP
SB12a (containing No S6a × 3, S58a) (15.7.63)	12·00	20·00	7·50
ab. Daffodil flaw on ½d.	†	†	22·00
ac. Daffodil trumpet flaw on ½d.	†	†	18·00

Listed Varieties

SB12b
Later retouched

SB12ab
Bottom left stamp of pane
(2½d. to right)

SB12ac
Upper right
stamp of pane

Whiter paper. Crowns sideways watermark
Pair of ½d. with pair of 2½d. from 2s. Booklet NR2

A. Watermark Crown to left

	Perf. Type		
	I	I(½v)	AP
SB13 (containing Nos. S5a × 2, S57c × 2) (1.7.64)	2·50	10·00	1·25
b. Comma flaw (R. 1/2)	10·00	†	†
c. Spot to right of d (R. 1/1)	9·00	†	†
d. Rose flaw (R. 1/2)	†	†	10·00
e. "P" for "D" (R. 2/1)	†	†	10·00
f. Wreath flaw (R. 2/1)	†	†	7·50
g. White spot above 2 (R. 2/1)	†	†	7·50

B. Watermark Crown to right
    SB13a (containing Nos. S5b × 2, S57d × 2)

(1.7.64)	2·50	10·00	1·25
ab. Rose stem flaw (R. 1/2)	†	†	8·00
ac. Frame flaw (R. 1/2)	†	†	6·00
ad. White spot by daffodil (R. 1/1)	†	†	6·00

Listed Varieties

SB13b
Right stamp of pane

SB13c
Left stamp of pane

SB13d
Upper right stamp
of pane

SB13e
Left stamp of pane

SB13f
Left stamp of pane

SB13g
Left stamp of pane

SB13ab
Upper right
stamp of pane

SB13ac
Upper right
stamp of pane

SB13ad
Upper left stamp
of pane

Booklet Cylinder Numbers
Panes of four (20-row single pane cylinder of 480 stamps).
    Cylinder numbers are not known from Booklets NR1/1a but the following exists from the Holiday Booklet NR2 on whiter paper

Cyl. Nos.   No dot
  E14 (½d.), J15 (2½d.)   .. .. 40·00

Imprimaturs from the National Postal Museum Archives

Se-tenant booklet panes of four. Imperforate, watermark Type W.24

Two panes as No. SB12 arranged vertically *tête-bêche* with binding margin at top and bottom
Two panes as No. SB13 arranged vertically *tête-bêche* with binding margin at top and bottom

½d. BOOKLET PANES OF SIX WITH GRAPHITE LINES
6 × ½d. Crowns. Graphite lines as Type **S8**, shown above No. S3 on page 12.
From 3s. Booklets M13g/15g, M19g/21g and 5s. Booklets H39g, H43g and H46g

A. Watermark upright
    SB14 (containing No. S7 × 6) (4.8.59)   35·00
      b. White flaw in Queen's hair (R. 1/3 or 2/3) .. 38·00

B. Watermark inverted
> SB14a (containing No. S7a × 6) (4.8.59) .. 11·00

Listed Variety
> For illustration of No. SB14b, see No. SB4c.

Booklet Cylinder Numbers

Panes of six (21-row cylinder)

Cyl. No.					No dot	Dot	Cyl. No.					No dot	Dot
E4	..	..	..	..	45·00	45·00	E4 T	..	..	..	..	45·00	45·00

½d. BOOKLET PANES OF SIX WITH TWO PHOSPHOR BANDS REACTING GREEN
6 × ½d.   Crowns.   Two phosphor bands applied in photogravure
From 3s. Booklets M25p, M28p/29p and M37p(a) and 5s. Booklet H46p

A. Watermark upright
> SB15 (containing No. S9 × 6) (14.8.60)   15·00

B. Watermark inverted
> SB15a (containing No. S9a × 6) (14.8.60)   35·00

Booklet Cylinder Numbers

Panes of six (21-row cylinder)

Cyl. No.				No dot	Dot	Cyl. No.				No dot	Dot
E11	..	..	..	28·00	28·00	E11 T	..	..	..	28·00	28·00

½d. BOOKLET PANES OF SIX WITH TWO PHOSPHOR BANDS REACTING BLUE
6 × ½d.   Crowns.   Two phosphor bands applied in photogravure.   Cream or whiter paper
From 3s. Booklets M33p, M36p, M37p(b), M38p/39p, M43p/47p, M49p/53p, M55p/61p, M64p/74p, and 5s. Booklets H49p, H51p/52p and H54p/74p

Cream Paper

A. Watermark upright
> SB16 (containing No. S10 × 6) (3.61)   3·50
>   b. Extended right fraction bar (R. 1/1 or 2/1)   ..   5·00
>   c. Dot on left fraction bar (R. 1/1 or 2/1)   ..   ..   5·50
>   d. One broad band on each stamp   ..   ..   ..

B. Watermark inverted
> SB16a (containing No. S10a × 6) (3.61)   6·00

Whiter Paper

A. Watermark upright
> SB17 (containing No. S11 × 6) (3.6.63)   4·00
>   b. Extended right fraction bar (R. 1/1 or 2/1)   ..   5·50
>   c. Dot on left fraction bar (R. 1/1 or 2/1) ..   ..   6·00
>   d. One broad band on each stamp £400

B. Watermark inverted
> SB17a (containing No. S11c × 6) (3.6.63)   7·50
>   ab. One broad band on each stamp £400

Listed Varieties
> For illustrations of Nos. SB16b/c and SB17b/c, see Nos. SB7c/d

Booklet Cylinder Numbers

Panes of six (21-row cylinder)

	Cream paper							Whiter paper			
Cyl. No.				No dot	Dot	Cyl. No.				No dot	Dot
E12	..	..	..	12·00	12·00	E12	..	..	..	14·00	14·00
E12 T	..	..	..	12·00	12·00	E12 T	..	..	..	14·00	14·00

Specimen overprints from the National Postal Museum Archives

Booklet pane of six. Perf. 15 × 14, watermark Type W.24 upright

Each stamp handstamped "Specimen" (13 × 2 mm.)
Each stamp handstamped "Specimen" (15 × 2½ mm.)

½d. BOOKLET PANES OF FOUR WITH TWO PHOSPHOR BANDS REACTING BLUE. SIDEWAYS WATERMARK

4 × ½d.   Crowns.   Two phosphor bands applied by typography.   Cream or whiter paper
From 2s. Booklets N4p, N8p/10p, N12p/20p

Cream Paper

A. Watermark Crown to left

	Perf. Type		
	I	I(½v)	AP
SB18 (containing No. S10*b* × 4) (14.7.61)	50·00	70·00	35·00
b. One broad band on each stamp	£180	—	£100

B. Watermark Crown to right

SB18a (containing No. S10*c* × 4) (14.7.61)	50·00	70·00	35·00
ab. One broad band on each stamp	—	—	£100

Whiter Paper

A. Watermark Crown to left

	Perf. Type		
	I	I(½v)	AP
SB19 (containing No. S11*a* × 4) (15.8.62)	50·00	75·00	40·00
b. One broad band on each stamp	—	—	£130

B. Watermark Crown to right

SB19a (containing No. S11*b* × 4) (15.8.62)	50·00	75·00	40·00
ab. One broad band on each stamp	—	—	£130

A few examples of pane Nos. SB18/18a are known with a band measuring 9.3 mm. over the centre perforations and two side bands. Two examples have also been seen of the same panes with the normal 8 mm. band over the centre perforations but with the gap to one side band only 10.6 mm. instead of the normal 12 mm. It is assumed that this side band was also wider than normal. These comments also apply to the 1½d. panes, Nos. SB74/74a.

Booklet Cylinder Numbers
Panes of four (20-row single pane cylinder of 480 stamps)
In the 2s. Booklets the cylinder numbers were partly or completely trimmed off, but No. E13 was the cylinder used. (*Price for pane showing "E", from £*55).

Imprimaturs from the National Postal Museum Archives

Booklet pane of four. Imperforate, watermark Type W.24

Two panes arranged vertically *tête-bêche*

Specimen overprints from the National Postal Museum Archives

Booklet pane of four. Perf. 15 × 14, watermark Type W.24

Each stamp handstamped "Specimen" (13 × 2 mm.)

1d. BOOKLET PANES OF SIX
6 × 1d.   Tudor Crown
From 5s. Booklets H7/16

A. Watermark upright
SB20 (containing No. S13 × 6) (3.54)	12·00
b. Hair flaw (R. 1/1)	16·00

B. Watermark inverted
SB20a (containing No. S13*a* × 6) (3.54)	35·00
ab. Extended leaf on shamrock (R. 2/1)	40·00

Listed Varieties

This is a multipostive flaw
from booklet panes.
All watermarks and phosphors.
(Cyls. F3, F4 and F10
from the no dot pane)

SB20*b*, SB26*d*   SB20*ab*, SB26*ad*, SB30*ac*, SB31*ac*, SB39*ac*,
(Cyl. F4 no dot)   SB40*ac*, SB41*ab*, SB42*ab*, SB49*ab*, SB54*ab*

Booklet Cylinder Numbers

Panes of six from 5s. Booklets

Cyl. No.					No dot	Dot
F4 ..	..	..	..	..	20·00	22·00*

*Contains the dot in serif flaw (R. 1/3).

1d. BOOKLET PANES OF FOUR

4 × 1d.   Tudor Crown
From 1s. Booklet K1/a for use in "E" machines.

A. Watermark upright

	Perf. Type P
SB21 (containing No. S13 × 4) (22.7.54)	7·00

B. Watermark inverted

SB21a (containing No. S13a × 4) (22.7.54)	20·00

Booklet Cylinder Numbers

Cylinder No. F7 was used, but it does not appear in the finished booklets.

Imprimaturs from the National Postal Museum Archives

Booklet pane of four. Imperforate, watermark Type W.22

Two panes arranged vertically *tête-bêche* with a 12 mm. horizontal gutter margin between

1d. BOOKLET PANES OF TWO

2 × 1d.   Tudor Crown
From 1s. Booklet E1 for use in experimental "D" machines.
Watermark upright

		Perf. Type		
	I	I(½v)	E	E(½v)
SB22 (containing No. S13 × 2) (2.9.53)	2·10	5·50	2·10	—
a. Shamrock flaw (as on No. S13c)	†	†	10·00	†

Made up from vertical rows 1 and 2 from sheets.

Booklet Cylinder Numbers

Panes of two (from sheets)

Cyl. No.	Perf. Type I		Cyl. No.	Perf. Type E	
	No dot	Dot		No dot	Dot
1	10·00	10·00	2	10·00	10·00

SB23

1d. SE-TENANT WITH PRINTED LABELS—"MINIMUM INLAND PRINTED PAPER RATE 1½d."
3 × 1d.   Tudor Crown
From 2s.6d. Booklet F15

A. Watermark upright
	SB23 (containing S13 × 3) (3.54)		£150
	b. "RATE" and "1½d." 16 mm. apart (on cyl. pane)		£225
	c. Dot in serif (R. 1/3)		£160

B. Watermark inverted
	SB23a (containing S13a × 3) (3.54)	£150

In the label inscription the distance between " RATE " and " 1½d." is usually 15 mm. However, on the cylinder pane of No. SB23, F5 dot and F6 no dot and dot only, the right-hand label shows a spacing of 16 mm.

Listed Variety

SB23c, SB24ba, SB24c, SB25b, SB26b, SB29b, SB30e, SB31b, SB41b, SB42b, SB49b, SB54b

Dot in serif of " 1 ". Right-hand stamp

This is a multipositive flaw which is found only in booklet panes, stamp 3 in either the first or second horizontal rows; all watermarks and phosphors on the dot cylinder panes F3, F4 and F10 also on the ordinary panes from cylinders F3, F4, F5, F6, F9 and F10. On cylinder F3 dot the flaw exists as a retouched state leaving the dot as a blemish and later the mark was removed. The later state occurs only in the position R. 2/3 and is not listed separately. Note that the flaw is present on all panes of six (R. 1/3) with cylinder number in bottom position.

Booklet Cylinder Numbers
Panes with printed labels from 2s.6d. Booklet F15

Cyl. No.						No dot	Dot
F5	..	..	..	..	..	†	£750
F6	..	..	..	..	..	£200	£200

SB24

1d. SE-TENANT WITH PRINTED LABELS—"PLEASE POST EARLY IN THE DAY"
3 × 1d.   Tudor Crown
From 2s.6d. Booklets F16/25

A. Watermark upright
 SB24 (containing S13 × 3) (4.54)   18·00
  b. Modified setting .. ..   24·00
  ba. Do. Dot in serif (R. 1/3) .. ..   30·00
  c. Dot in serif (R. 1/3) .. ..   24·00

B. Watermark inverted
 SB24a (containing S13a × 3) (4.54)   24·00
  ab. Modified setting .. ..   30·00
 In the modified setting the distance between " IN THE " is 1 mm. and this is only found on the majority of the Jan. 1955 edition (Booklet F25).   The normal spacing is 1½ mm.

Booklet Cylinder Numbers
 Panes with printed labels from 2s.6d. Booklets F16/25
 Cyl. No.   No dot Dot
  F6 .. .. 40·00 40·00
  F6 (modified setting) .. .. 48·00 48·00
 From cylinder F6 onwards the labels were printed in photogravure instead of typography.

SB25, SB29

1d. SE-TENANT WITH PRINTED LABELS—"PACK YOUR PARCELS SECURELY" (1st label), "ADDRESS YOUR LETTERS CORRECTLY" (2nd label) and "AND POST EARLY IN THE DAY" (3rd label)
3 × 1d.   Tudor Crown
From 2s.6d. Booklet F26/34

A. Watermark upright
 SB25 (containing No. S13 × 3) (1.55)   30·00
  b. Dot in serif (R. 1/3) .. ..   35·00
  c. Daffodil flaw (R. 1/1) .. ..   35·00

B. Watermark inverted
 SB25a (containing No. S13a × 3) (1.55)   30·00

Listed Variety

SB25c, SB29c
(Cyl. F6 no dot)

Booklet Cylinder Numbers

Panes with printed labels from 2s.6d. Booklets F26/34

Cyl. No.						No dot	Dot
F6	..	..	..	..	..	50·00	50·00

Imprimaturs from the National Postal Museum Archives

Booklet pane with printed labels. Imperforate, watermark Type W.22

Two panes as No. SB25 arranged *tête-bêche*

1d. BOOKLET PANES OF SIX

6 × 1d.   St. Edward's Crown
From 3s. Booklets M1/9 and 5s. Booklets H17/36

A. Watermark upright

SB26 (containing No. S14 × 6) (8.55)	3·25
b. Dot in serif (R. 2/3, F3 dot))	7·00
c. "Dew drop" (R. 1/1 or 2/1)	6·00
d. Hair flaw (R. 1/1)	7·00

B. Watermark inverted

SB26a (containing No. S14*b* × 6) (8.55)	5·00
ab. Spot on "d" (R. 1/1 or 2/1)	9·00
ac. White flaw by rose (R. 1/2 or 2/2)	9·00
ad. Extended leaf on shamrock (R. 1/1 or 2/1) ..	8·00
ae. Rose flaw (R. 1/1 or 2/1)	8·00

Listed Varieties

For illustrations of No. SB26*b*, see No. SB23*c*, for No. SB26*d*, see No. SB20*b* and for No. SB26*ad*, see No. SB20*ab*.

SB26*c*, SB30*d*, SB39*b* Later retouched on Crowns and phosphor (Cyl. F3 dot)	SB26*ab*, SB30*ab*, SB31*ab*, SB39*ab*, SB40*ab* (Cyl. F3 dot)	SB26*ac* (Cyl. F3 dot)	SB26*ae*, SB30*ad*, SB39*ad*, SB40*ad* (Cyl. F3 no dot)

Booklet Cylinder Numbers

Panes of six

Cyl. No.		Cat. No		No dot	Dot
F3 ..	..	SB26 ..	..	12·00	13·00*
F3 T	..	SB26 ..	..	12·00	12·00
F4 ..	..	SB26 ..	..	10·00	11·00*

Cylinder F3 contained 21 rows so that cylinder numbers adjoin either the top (T) or the bottom row. It was used in all 5s. Booklets H31/36. Cylinder F4 was a 20-row cylinder and used for the 5s. Booklets H17/30.

1d. BOOKLET PANES OF FOUR

4 × 1d.   St. Edward's Crown
From 1s. Booklets K2/*b* for use in "E" machines and 2s. Booklet N1

A. Watermark upright

	Perf. Type	
	AP	P
SB27 (containing No. S14 × 4) (5.7.56)	6·50	5·00
b. Spur to shamrock (R. 2/1)	9·00	†

B. Watermark inverted

SB27a (containing No. S14*b* × 4) (5.7.56)	6·50	5·00

Listed Variety

SB27*b*, SB32*b*
Later retouched on Crowns wmk.

Booklet Cylinder Numbers
Cylinder Nos. F7 and F8 were used, but they do not appear in the finished booklets.

Imprimaturs from the National Postal Museum Archives

Booklet pane of four. Imperforate, watermark Type W.23

Two panes arranged vertically *tête-bêche* with a 12 mm. horizontal gutter margin between

1d. BOOKLET PANES OF TWO
2 × 1d. St. Edward's Crown
From 1s. Booklet E2 for use in experimental "D" machines.

Watermark upright

	Perf. Type	
	E	E($\frac{1}{2}$v)
SB28 (containing No. S14 × 2) (11.57)	3·25	5·00
a. Shamrock flaw (as on No. S14*d*)	7·50	†

Made up from vertical rows 1 and 2 from sheets.

Booklet Cylinder Numbers
Panes of two (from sheets). Perf. Type E

Cyl. No.						No dot	Dot
1 ..	..	..	..	..	..	6·00	6·00

1d. SE-TENANT WITH PRINTED LABELS—"PACK YOUR PARCELS SECURELY" (1st label), "ADDRESS YOUR LETTERS CORRECTLY" (2nd label) and "AND POST EARLY IN THE DAY" (3rd label)
3 × 1d. St, Edward's Crown
From 2s.6d. Booklets F34/52

A. Watermark upright

SB29 (containing No. S14 × 3) (8.55)	10·00
b. Dot in serif (R. 1/3)	12·00
c. Daffodil flaw (R. 1/1)	12·00

B. Watermark inverted

SB29a (containing No. S14*b* × 3) (8.55)	10·00

Listed Varieties
For illustration of No. SB29*b* see No. SB23*c* and for No. SB29*c* see No. SB25*c*.

Booklet Cylinder Numbers
Panes with printed labels from 2s.6d. Booklets F34/52

Cyl. No.				No dot	Dot
F6	..	..	..	22·00	22·00
F9	..	..	..	35·00	35·00

Cylinder F6 was used for the 2s.6d. Booklets F34/40 and part of F41/52 and F9 for 2s.6d. Booklets F41/52. Both cylinders were 20-row.

Imprimaturs from the National Postal Museum Archives

Booklet pane with printed labels. Imperforate, watermark Type W.23

Two panes as No. SB29 arranged *tête-bêche*

1d. BOOKLET PANES OF SIX

6 × 1d.   Crowns. Cream or whiter paper
From 3s. Booklets M9(b)/(c), M10/74, 4s.6d. Booklets L59/65, 5s. Booklets H35(b)/(c), H36(a) and H37/74 and 10s. Booklets X1/14

Cream Paper

A. Watermark upright

SB30 (containing No. S16 × 6) (11.58)	3·25
b. Imperf. pane*	
c. Part perf. pane*	
d. "Dew drop" (R. 1/1 or 2/1)	6·50
e. Dot in serif (R. 2/3)	7·75

B. Watermark inverted

SB30a (containing No. S16d × 6) (11.58)	3·25
ab. Spot on "d" (R. 1/1 or 2/1)	7·00
ac. Extended leaf on shamrock (R. 1/1 or 2/1) ..	6·50
ad. Rose flaw (R. 1/1 or 2/1)	6·50

Whiter Paper

A. Watermark upright

SB31 (containing No. S17 × 6) (29.7.62)	3·25
b. Dot in serif (R. 2/3)	7·50

B. Watermark inverted

SB31a (containing No. S17c × 6) (29.7.62)	5·25
ab. Spot on "d" (R. 1/1 or 2/1)	8·00
ac. Extended leaf on shamrock (R. 1/1) or 2/1) ..	7·50

*Booklet errors—See General Notes.

Listed Varieties

For illustrations of No. SB30d see No. SB26c; for Nos. SB30ab and SB31ab see No. SB26ab; for Nos. SB30ac and SB31ac see No. SB20ab and for No. SB30ad see No. SB26ae.

On the cream paper the dot in serif flaw (Cyl. F3 dot) was removed by retouching but a smudged state exists. For illustration of No. SB30e, see No. SB23c. On whiter paper the flaw exists from Cyl. F10 dot.

Booklet Cylinder Numbers

Panes of six (21-row cylinders)

Cyl. No.	Cream paper			No dot	Dot	Cyl. No.	Whiter paper			No dot	Dot
F3	.. ..			8·00	9·00*	F3	.. ..			19·00	19·00
F3 T	.. ..			8·00	8·00	F3 T	.. ..			19·00	19·00
F10	.. ..			13·00	14·00*	F10	.. ..			8·00	9·00*
F10 T	.. ..			13·00	13·00	F10 T	.. ..			8·00	8·00

Specimen overprints from the National Postal Museum Archives

Booklet pane of six. Perf. 15 × 14, watermark Type W.24

Each stamp handstamped "Specimen" (13 × 2 mm.) wmk. upright
Each stamp handstamped "Specimen" (15 × 2½ mm.) wmk. inverted

1d. BOOKLET PANES OF FOUR

4 × 1d.   Crowns.   Cream paper
From 1s. Booklets K3/a for use in "E" machines and 2s. Booklets N2/3. Perf. Type AP

A. Watermark upright

SB32 (containing No. S16 × 4) (13.8.59)	3·75
b. Spur to shamrock (R. 2/1)	6·00

B. Watermark inverted

SB32a (containing No. S16d × 4) (13.8.59)	3·75

Listed Variety

For illustration of No. SB32b see No. SB27b.

Booklet Cylinder Numbers

Cylinder No. F8 was used, but it does not appear in the finished booklets.

Imprimaturs from the National Postal Museum Archives

Booklet pane of four. Imperforate, watermark Type W.24

Two panes arranged vertically *tête-bêche* with a 12 mm. horizontal gutter margin between

Specimen overprints from the National Postal Museum Archives

Booklet pane of four. Perf. 15 × 14, watermark Type W.24 upright

Each stamp handstamped "Specimen" (13 × 2 mm.)

1d. BOOKLET PANES OF FOUR WITH SIDEWAYS WATERMARK

4 × 1d.   Crowns.   Cream or whiter paper
From 2s. Booklets N4/20

Cream paper

A. Watermark Crown to left

	Perf. Type		
	I	I(½v)	AP
SB33 (containing No. S16e × 4) (26.5.61)	10·00	22·00	6·50

B. Watermark Crown to right

SB33a (containing No. S16f × 4) (26.5.61)	10·00	22·00	6·50

Whiter Paper

A. Watermark Crown to left

SB34 (containing No. S17a × 4) (5.6.62)	8·50	19·00	4·25

B. Watermark Crown to right

SB34a (containing No. S17b × 4) (5.6.62)	8·50	19·00	4·25

Booklet Cylinder Numbers

Cylinder No. F12 was used, but it was partly or completely trimmed off. *(Price for pane showing "F" from £26).*

Specimen overprints from the National Postal Museum Archives

Booklet pane of four. Perf. 15 × 14, watermark Type W.24

Each stamp handstamped "Specimen" (13 × 2 mm.)

SB35, SB37, SB45, SB47,
SB50, SB52, SB55, SB57

SB36, SB38, SB46, SB48,
SB51, SB53, SB56, SB58

1d. AND 3d. SE-TENANT BOOKLET PANES OF FOUR. SIDEWAYS WATERMARK
Pair of 1d with pair of 3d. Crowns, Whiter paper
From 2s. Booklets N21/27

Panes SB35 and SB37   Panes of four with 1d. at left
Panes SB36 and SB38   Panes of four with 1d. at right

A. Watermark Crown to left

		Perf. Type	
	I	I(½v)	AP
SB35 (containing Nos. S17a × 2, S71a × 2)			
(16.8.65)	9·00	18·00	7·50
SB36 (containing Nos. S71a × 2, S17a × 2)			
(16.8.65)	9·00	18·00	7·50
a. Thistle flaw on 1d. (R. 2/2)	†	24·00	†

B. Watermark Crown to right

	I	I(½v)	AP
SB37 (containing Nos. S17b × 2, S71b × 2)			
(16.8.65)	9·00	18·00	7·50
SB38 (containing Nos. S71b × 2, S17b × 2)			
(16.8.65)	9·00	18·00	7·50
a. " R " flaw on 1d. (R. 2/2)	†	†	10·00

These panes are on paper with a slight gloss.

Listed Varieties

SB36a, SB46c, SB51d, SB56a, SB56ba
Large white flaw to right of left thistle.
Occurs on bottom right stamp of pane with
3d. at left

SB38a, SB48c, SB53d, SB58a, SB58ba
Flaw on " P " which appears as " R " and
occurs on bottom right stamp of pane with
3d. at left

Booklet Cylinder Numbers
Panes of four (20-row single pane cylinder of 480 stamps).
From *se-tenant* pane booklets on whiter paper

Cyl. Nos.   No dot
  F13 (1d.), K22 (3d.)   ..   .. 35·00

1d. BOOKLET PANES OF SIX WITH GRAPHITE LINES
6 × 1d.   Crowns.   Graphite lines as Type **S8**
From 3s. Booklets M13g/15g, M19g/21g and 5s. Booklets H39g, H43g and H46g

A. Watermark upright

SB39 (containing No. S18 × 6) (4.8.59)	10·00
b. " Dew drop " (R. 1/1 or 2/1)	15·00

B. Watermark inverted

SB39a (containing No. S18a × 6) (4.8.59)	12·00
ab. Spot on " d " (R. 1/1 or 2/1)	17·00
ac. Extended leaf on shamrock (R. 1/1 or 2/1) ..	16·00
ad. Rose flaw (R. 1/1 or 2/1)	16·00

Listed Varieties
For illustrations of No. SB39b see No. SB26c; for Nos. SB39ab/ad see Nos. SB26ab, SB20ab
and SB26ae.

Booklet Cylinder Numbers

Panes of six (21-row cylinder)

Cyl. No.				No dot	Dot		Cyl. No.				No dot	Dot
F3 ..	..	..	..	.. 25·00	25·00	|	F3 T	..	..	..	.. 25·00	25·00

1d. BOOKLET PANES OF SIX WITH TWO PHOSPHOR BANDS REACTING GREEN
6 × 1d.   Crowns.   Two phosphor bands applied in photogravure
From 3s. Booklets M25p, M28p/29p and M37p(*a*) and 5s. Booklet H46p

A. Watermark upright

SB40 (containing No. S20 × 6) (14.8.60)	15·00	
b. One broad band on each stamp	£250	

B. Watermark inverted

SB40a (containing No. S20a × 6) (14.8.60)	35·00
ab. Spot on "d" (R. 1/1 or 2/1)	40·00
ac. Extended leaf on shamrock (R. 1/1 or 2/1) ..	40·00
ad. Rose flaw (R. 1/1 or 2/1)	40·00
ae. One broad band on each stamp	£250

Listed Varieties
For illustrations of Nos. SB40*ab*/*ad* see Nos. SB26*ab*, SB20*ab* and SB26*ae*.

Booklet Cylinder Numbers
Panes of six (21-row cylinder)

Cyl. No.				No dot	Dot		Cyl. No.				No dot	Dot
F3 ..	..	..	..	40·00	40·00		F3 T	..	..	..	40·00	40·00

1d. BOOKLET PANES OF SIX WITH TWO PHOSPHOR BANDS REACTING BLUE
6 × 1d.   Crowns.   Two phosphor bands applied in photogravure.   Cream or whiter paper
From 3s. Booklets M33p, M36p, M37p(*b*), M38p/9p, M43p/7p, M49p/53p, M55p/61p, M64p/74p, 4s.6d. Booklets L59p/60p(*a*), L61p(*a*), L62p(*a*) and 5s. Booklets H49p, H51p/2p, H54p/74p

Cream Paper

A. Watermark upright

SB41 (containing No. S21 × 6) (3.61)	5·00
b. Dot in serif (R. 2/3)	7·50
c. One broad band on each stamp	

B. Watermark inverted

SB41a (containing No. S21a × 6) (3.61)	5·00
ab. Extended leaf on shamrock (R. 1/1 or 2/1) ..	7·50
ac. One broad band on each stamp	

Whiter Paper

A. Watermark upright

SB42 (containing No. S22 × 6) (3.6.63)	4·50
b. Dot in serif (R. 2/3)	10·00
c. One broad band on each stamp	

B. Watermark inverted

SB42a (containing No. S22c × 6) (3.6.63)	4·50
ab. Extended leaf on shamrock (R. 1/1 or 2/1) ..	7·50
ac. One broad band on each stamp	

Listed Varieties
For illustrations of Nos. SB41*b* and SB42*b* see No. SB23*c*; for Nos. SB41*ab* and SB42*ab* see No. SB20*ab*.

Booklet Cylinder Numbers
Panes of six (21-row cylinders).

	Cream paper							Whiter paper				
Cyl. No.				No dot	Dot		Cyl. No				No dot	Dot
F10	..	..	..	15·00	15·00*		F10	..	..	..	12·00	12·00*
F10 T	..	..	..	15·00	15·00		F10 T	..	..	..	12·00	12·00

Specimen overprints from the National Postal Museum Archives

Booklet pane of six. Perf. 15 × 14, watermark Type W.24 inverted

Each stamp handstamped "Specimen" (13 × 2 mm.)
Each stamp handstamped "Specimen" (15 × 2½ mm.)

1d. BOOKLET PANES OF FOUR WITH TWO PHOSPHOR BANDS REACTING BLUE. SIDEWAYS WATERMARK

4×1d. Crowns. Two phosphor bands applied by typography. Cream or whiter paper
From 2s. Booklets N4p, N8p/10p, N12p/20p

Cream Paper

A. Watermark Crown to left

	Perf. Type		
	I	I($\frac{1}{2}$v)	AP
SB43 (containing No. S21b × 4) (14.7.61)	12·00	24·00	8·00
b. One broad band on each stamp	—	—	60·00

B. Watermark Crown to right

SB43a (containing No. S21c × 4) (14.7.61)	12·00	24·00	8·00
ab. One broad band on each stamp	—	—	60·00

Whiter Paper

A. Watermark Crown to left

SB44 (containing No. S22a × 4) (15.8.62)	12·00	24·00	8·00
b. One broad band on each stamp	£150	—	£140

B. Watermark Crown to right

SB44a (containing No. S22b × 4) (15.8.62)	12·00	24·00	8·00
ab. One broad band on each stamp	£150	—	£140

Booklet Cylinder Numbers

Panes of four (20-row single pane cylinder of 480 stamps).
In the 2s. Booklets the cylinder numbers were partly or completely trimmed off, but No. F12 was the cylinder used. (*Price for pane showing* "F", *from* £30).

Imprimaturs from the National Postal Museums Archives

Booklet pane of four. Imperforate, watermark Type W.24

Two panes arranged vertically *tête-bêche*

Specimen overprints from the National Postal Museum Archives

Booklet pane of four. Perf. 15 × 14, watermark Type W.24

Each stamp handstamped " Specimen " (13 × 2 mm.)

1d. AND 3d. SE-TENANT BOOKLET PANES OF FOUR WITH PHOSPHOR BANDS REACTING BLUE. SIDEWAYS WATERMARK

Pair of 1d. (two bands) with pair of 3d. (1 side 8 mm. blue band). Crowns. Whiter paper
From 2s. Booklets N21p/22p(a) and N23p(a)

Panes SB45 and SB47 Panes of four with 1d. at left
Panes SB46 and SB48 Panes of four with 1d. at right

A. Watermark Crown to left

	Perf. Type		
	I	I($\frac{1}{2}$v)	AP
SB45 (containing Nos. S22a × 2, S77b × 2) (16.8.65)	45·00	65·00	42·00
SB46 (containing Nos. S77c × 2, S22a × 2) (16.8.65)	45·00	65·00	42·00
a. One broad band on each stamp	—	—	—
b. Broad band on 1d. and no bands on 3d. ..	—	—	—
c. Thistle flaw on 1d. (R. 2/2)	†	70·00	†

B. Watermark Crown to right

SB47 (containing Nos. S22b × 2, S77d × 2) (16.8.65)	45·00	65·00	42·00
a. One broad band on each stamp..	†	†	—
SB48 (containing Nos. S77e × 2, S22b × 2) (16.8.65)	45·00	65·00	42·00
a. One broad band on each stamp	—	—	—
b. Broad band on 1d. and no bands on 3d. ..	—	—	—
c. " R " flaw on 1d. (R. 2/2)	†	†	45·00

Listed Varieties

For illustrations of Nos. SB46c and SB48c see Nos. SB36a and SB38a.

The following illustration shows how the *se-tenant* stamps with one phosphor band on 3d. are printed and the arrows indicate where the guillotine falls. The result gives 1d. stamps with two bands and 3d. stamps with one band, either at left or right.

The stamps were printed sideways, as indicated by the position of the watermark.

Booklet Cylinder Numbers

Panes of four (20-row single pane cylinder of 480 stamps).
From *se-tenant* pane booklets on whiter paper

Cyl. Nos.   No dot
  F13 (1d.), K22 (3d.)   .. .. 80·00

1d. BOOKLET PANES OF SIX WITH TWO 8 mm. PHOSPHOR BANDS REACTING VIOLET

6 × 1d. Crowns. Two phosphor bands applied in photogravure
From 4s.6d. Booklets L60p(b), L61p(b) and L62p(b)/65p(a) and 10s. Booklet X15p(a)

A. Watermark upright
        SB49 (containing No. S23b × 6) (9.65)   3·25
          b. Dot in serif (R. 2/3) .. .. 6·50

B. Watermark inverted
        SB49a (containing No. S23c × 6) (9.65)   3·75
          ab. Extended leaf on shamrock (R. 1/1 or 2/1) .. 6·75

Listed Varieties

For illustrations of Nos. SB49b and SB49ab see Nos. SB23c and SB20ab.

Booklet Cylinder Numbers

Panes of six (21-row cylinder). Bands photo.

Cyl. No.				No dot	Dot	Cyl. No.				No dot	Dot
F10	..	..	..	12·00	12·00*	F10 T	..		..	12·00	12·00

1d. AND 3d. SE-TENANT BOOKLET PANES OF FOUR WITH 8 mm. PHOSPHOR BANDS REACTING VIOLET. SIDEWAYS WATERMARK

Pair of 1d. (two bands) with pair of 3d. (1 side 8 mm. violet band). Crowns.
From 2s. Booklets N22p(b), N23p(b)/28p(a), N29p, N30p(a), N31p(c) and N32p(c)

Panes SB50 and SB52 Panes of four with 1d. at left
Panes SB51 and SB53 Panes of four with 1d. at right

A. Watermark Crown to left

	Perf. Type		
	I	I(½v)	AP
SB50 (containing Nos. S23d × 2, S78c × 2) (10.65)	12·00	20·00	10·00
SB51 (containing Nos. S78d × 2, S23d × 2) (10.65)	12·00	20·00	10·00
a. One broad band on each stamp	45·00	—	40·00
b. Broad band on 1d. and no bands on 3d. ..	45·00	†	40·00
c. Phosphor bands printed on both back and front	—	—	£200
d. Thistle flaw on 1d. (R. 2/2)	†	24·00	†

B. Watermark Crown to right

	I	I(½v)	AP
SB52 (containing Nos. S23e × 2, S78e × 2) (10.65)	10·00	18·00	10·00
SB53 (containing Nos. S78f × 2, S23e × 2) (10.65)	10·00	18·00	10·00
a. One broad band on each stamp	45·00	—	40·00
b. Broad band on 1d. and no bands on 3d	45·00	—	40·00
c. Phosphor bands printed on both back and front	—	—	£200
d. "R" flaw on 1d. (R. 2/2)	†	†	15·00

These panes are printed on paper with a slight gloss.

Listed Varieties

For illustrations of Nos. SB51*d* and SB53*d* see Nos. SB36*a* and SB38*a*.

Booklet Cylinder Numbers

Panes of four (20-row single pane cylinder of 480 stamps).
From *se-tenant* pane booklets. Bands printed in typo. or flexo.

Cyl. Nos.		No dot
F13 (1d.), K22 (3d.)	.. ..	35·00

1d. BOOKLET PANES OF SIX WITH TWO 9·5 mm. PHOSPHOR BAND REACTING VIOLET

6 × 1d. Crowns. Two phosphor bands applied in photogravure
From 4s.6d. Booklets L65p(*b*)/71p and 10s. Booklets X15p(*b*) and X16p/17p

A. Watermark upright

SB54 (containing No. S24 × 6) (2.67)	3·00
b. Dot in serif (R. 2/3)	7·00

B. Watermark inverted

SB54a (containing No. S24*a* × 6) (2.67)	3·50
ab. Extended leaf on shamrock (R. 1/1 or 2/1) ..	7·00

Listed Varieties

For illustrations of Nos. SB54*b* and SB54*ab* see Nos. SB23*c* and SB20*ab*.

Booklet Cylinder Numbers

Panes of six (21-row cylinder)

Cyl. No.					No dot	Dot	Cyl. No.					No dot	Dot
F10..	..	..	..	..	10·00	10·00*	F10 T	..	..	..	..	10·00	10·00

1d. AND 3d. SE-TENANT BOOKLET PANES OF FOUR WITH 9·5 mm. PHOSPHOR BANDS REACTING VIOLET. SIDEWAYS WATERMARK

Pair of 1d. (two bands) with pair of 3d. (two 9·5 mm. violet bands). Crowns
From 2s. Booklets N31p(*a*/*b*) and N32p(*a*/*b*)

Panes SB55 and SB57   Panes of four with 1d. at left
Panes SB56 and SB58   Panes of four with 1d. at right

A. Watermark Crown to left

	I	Perf. Type I(½v)	AP
SB55 (containing Nos. S24*b* × 2, S80 × 2)			
(11.67)	7·50	12·00	4·75
a. As SB55 but 1 band on 3d.	£160	—	£150
SB56 (containing Nos. S80 × 2, S24*b* × 2)			
(11.67)	7·50	12·00	4·75
a. Thistle flaw on 1d (R. 2/2)	†	18·00	†
b. As SB56 but 1 band on 3d.	£160	—	£150
ba. Do. with thistle flaw	†	—	†
c. One broad band on each stamp	60·00	85·00	48·00
d. Broad bands on 1d. and no bands on 3d. ..	50·00		40·00

B. Watermark Crown to right

	I	Perf. Type I(½v)	AP
SB57 (containing Nos. S24*c* × 2, S80*a* × 2)			
(11.67)	7·50	12·00	4·75
a. As SB57 but 1 band on 3d	£160	—	£150
SB58 (containing Nos. S80*a* × 2, S24*c* × 2)			
(11.67)	7·50	12·00	4·75
a. "R" flaw on 1d. (R. 2/2)	†	†	7·50
b. As SB58 but 1 band on 3d	£160	—	£150
ba. Do. with "R" flaw	†	†	£160
c. One broad band on each stamp	60·00		48·00

Part of the October 1967 2s. Booklets (N30p(*a*)) had 8 mm. bands and part 9·5 mm. bands (N30p(*b*)) which had only a single line band on the 3d. value at right or left as listed above. As these bands are applied across the perforations and are liable to shift, it is not possible to distinguish the 3d. one-band 9·5 mm. bands from the 8 mm. bands of Nos. SB50, etc. *in singles*, and hence these are not listed as varieties under the 3d. value. Two examples of the April 1967 2s. Booklet (N28p(*b*)) are also known with a single 9·5 mm. band on the 3d.

Listed Varieties

For illustrations of the cylinder flaws, see Nos. SB36*a* and SB38*a*.

Booklet Cylinder Numbers
    Panes of four (20-row single pane cylinder of 480 stamps). From *se-tenant* pane booklets. Bands typo. or flexo.

Cyl. Nos.		No dot
F13 (1d.), K22 (3d.)	.. ..	20·00

1½d. BOOKLET PANES OF SIX
6 × 1½d. Tudor Crown
From 2s. 6d. Booklets F1/36 and 5s. Booklets H1/17

A. Watermark upright

SB59 (containing No. S25 × 6) (5.53)		2·50
b. Extra jewel (R. 1/1)		7·00
c. Extra bud on daffodil stem (R. 2/1)		7·50

B. Watermark inverted

SB59a (containing No. S25c × 6) (5.53)		3·00
ab. Imperf. pane*		

    *Booklet error.—This pane of six stamps is completely imperf. (cf. General Notes).

Listed Varieties

SB59*b*, SB62*c*   SB59*c*
Multipositive flaw
on Tudor and Edward Crown
watermarks

Booklet Cylinder Numbers
Panes of six (20-row cylinders)

Cyl. No.					No dot	Dot	Cyl. No.				No dot	Dot
G2	..	..	..	..	12·00	12·00	G6	..	..	..	20·00	20·00
G3	..	..	..	..	12·00	12·00						

1½d. BOOKLET PANES OF FOUR
4 × 1½d. Tudor Crown
From 1s. Booklet K1/*a* for use in " E " machines.

A. Watermark upright

	Perf. Type P
SB60 (containing No. S25 × 4) (22.7.54)	4·00
b. Rose petal flaw (R. 1/1)	8·00

B. Watermark inverted

SB60a (containing No. S25c × 4) (22.7.54)	5·00

Listed Variety

SB60*b*, SB63*b*, SB67*b*

Booklet Cylinder Numbers
    Cylinder No. G5 was used, but it does not appear in the finished booklets.

Imprimaturs from the National Postal Museum Archives

Booklet pane of four. Imperforate, watermark Type W.22

Two panes arranged vertically *tête-bêche* with a 12mm. horizontal gutter margin between

1½d. BOOKLET PANES OF TWO

2 × 1½d. Tudor Crown
From 1s. Booklet E1 for use in experimental " D " machines.
Watermark upright

	Perf. Type		
	I	E	E(½v)
SB61 (containing No. S25 × 2) (2.9.53)	2·00	2·00	5·50
a. Flaw on daffodil stem (as on No. S25*f*)	†	8·00	†

Made up from vertical rows 1 and 2 from sheets.

Booklet Cylinder Numbers

Panes of two (from sheets)

	Perf. Type				Perf. Type	
	I	E			E	
Cyl. No.	No dot	Dot	Cyl. No.		No dot	Dot
2	9·00	9·00	6		9·00	9·00
			9		9·00	9·00
			12		9·00	9·00

1½d. BOOKLET PANES OF SIX

6 × 1½d. St. Edward's Crown
From 2s. 6d. Booklets F33(*b*) and F34/52, 3s. Booklets M1/11 and 5s. Booklets H17/31

A. Watermark upright
     SB62 (containing No. S26 × 6) (8.55)   1·90
        b. " Rabbit's ears " (R. 2/2)   ..   ..   4·50
        c. Extra jewel (R. 1/1 or 2/1)   ..   ..   4·00
        d. Large dot by daffodil (R. 1/1)   ..   ..   ..   5·00
        e. Major retouch around emblems (R. 2/2)   ..   15·00
        f. Flaw on rose at right (R. 1/2)   ..   ..   ..   5·00

B. Watermark inverted
     SB62a (containing No. S26*b* × 6) (8.55)   3·00
        ab. Flaw on rose at top left (R. 1/2 or 2/2) ..   ..   5·50

Listed Varieties

For illustration of No. SB62*c* see No. SB59*b*

SB62*b*
Two white dots extending
upwards from shamrock at
left appearing as rabbit's
ears (Cyl. G7 no dot)

SB62*d*
(Cyl. G7)

SB62*e* Normal
Major retouch affecting a
pair with weak shading in
the emblems. (Cyl. G7 dot)

SB62*f*
(Cyl. G10 dot)

SB62*ab*
White flaw on rose
at top left
(Cyl. G10 dot)

Booklet Cylinder Numbers
Panes of six (G6 and G7 20-row cylinders, others 21-row cylinders)

Cyl. No.					No dot	Dot	Cyl. No.				No dot	Dot
G6 ..	..	..	..	..	9·00	9·00	G9 T	..	..	..	.. 12·00	12·00
G7 ..	..	..	..	..	11·00	11·00	G10	..	..	..	.. 18·00	18·00
G9 ..	..	..	..	..	12·00	12·00	G10 T	..	..	..	.. 18·00	18·00

1½d. BOOKLET PANES OF FOUR
4 × 1½d. St. Edward's Crown
From 1s. Booklet K2/*b* for use in " E " machines and 2s. Booklet N1

A. Watermark upright

	Perf. Type	
	AP	P
SB63 (containing No. S26 × 4) (5.7.56)	7·50	5·00
b. Rose petal flaw (R. 1/1)	†	7·00

B. Watermark inverted

SB63a (containing No. S26*b* × 4) (5.7.56)	7·50	5·00

Listed Variety
For illustration of No. SB63*b* see No. SB60*b*.

Booklet Cylinder Numbers
Cylinder No. G5 was used, but it does not appear in the finished booklets.

Imprimaturs from the National Postal Museum Archives
Booklet pane of four. Imperforate, watermark Type W.23

Two panes arranged vertically *tête-bêche* with a 12mm. horizontal gutter margin between

1½d. BOOKLET PANES OF TWO
2 × 1½d. St. Edward's Crown
From 1s. Booklet E2 for use in experimental " D " machines.

Watermark upright

	Perf. Type	
	E	E(½v)
SB64 (containing No. S26 × 2) (11.57)	3·25	5·00

Made up from vertical rows 1 and 2 from sheets

Booklet Cylinder Numbers
Panes of two (from sheets)

					Perf. Type E	
Cyl. No.					No dot	Dot
13 ..	..	..	..	..	—	†
14 ..	..	..	..	..	7·00	7·00

1½d. BOOKLET PANES OF SIX
6 × 1½d.   Crowns. Cream or whiter paper
From 3s. Booklets M9/74 and 10s. Booklets X1/9

Cream Paper

A. Watermark upright
       SB65 (containing No. S28 × 6) (12.58)   6·50
         b. Dot on thistle (R. 1/3 or 2/3)   . .   . .   . .   10·00

B. Watermark inverted
       SB65a (containing No. S28a × 6) (12.58)   6·50

Whiter Paper

A. Watermark upright
       SB66 (containing No. S29 × 6) (18.9.62)   14·00
         b. Dot on thistle (R. 1/3 or 2/3)   . .   . .   . .   18·00

B. Watermark inverted
       SB66a (containing No. S29d × 6) (18.9.62)   18·00

Listed Variety

SB65*b*, SB66*b*
Dot on thistle
Retouched on cream paper (Cyl. G15 dot)

Booklet Cylinder Numbers
Panes of six (21-row cylinders)

| Cream paper | | | | | | Whiter paper | | | | | |
Cyl. No.				No dot	Dot	Cyl. No.				No dot	Dot
G10	..	..	..	..	12·00	12·00	G15	..	..	..	..	24·00	24·00
G10 T	..	..	..	..	12·00	12·00	G15 T	..	..	..	..	24·00	24·00
G11	..	..	..	..	10·00	10·00	G16	..	..	..	..	32·00	32·00
G11 T	..	..	..	..	10·00	10·00	G16 T	..	..	..	..	32·00	32·00
G15	..	..	..	..	10·00	10·00						
G15 T	..	..	..	..	10·00	10·00						

Specimen overprints from the National Postal Museum Archives

Booklet pane of six. Perf. 15 × 14, watermark Type W.24 upright

Each stamp handstamped "Specimen" (13 × 2 mm.)

1½d. BOOKLET PANES OF FOUR
4 × 1½d.   Crowns. Cream paper
From 1s. Booklet K3/a for use in "E" machines and 2s. Booklets N2/3. Perf. Type AP

A. Watermark upright
       SB67 (containing No. S28 × 4) (13.8.59)   3·75
         b. Rose petal flaw (R. 1/1)   . .   . .   7·00

B. Watermark inverted
       SB67a (containing No. S28a × 4) (13.8.59)   6·50

Listed Variety
For illustration of No. SB67*b* see No. SB60*b*.

Booklet Cylinder Numbers
Cylinder No. G5 was used, but it does not appear in the finished booklets.

Imprimaturs from the National Postal Museum Archives

Booklet pane of four. Imperforate, watermark Type W.24

Two panes arranged vertically *tête-bêche* with a 12mm. horizontal gutter margin between

Specimen overprints from the National Postal Museum Archives

Booklet pane of four. Perf. 15 × 14, watermark Type W.24 inverted

Each stamp handstamped "Specimen" (13 × 2 mm.)

1½d. BOOKLET PANES OF FOUR WITH SIDEWAYS WATERMARK
4 × 1½d. Crowns. Cream or whiter paper
From 2s. Booklets N4/20

Cream Paper

A. Watermark Crown to left

	I	Perf. Type I(½v)	AP
SB68 (containing No. S28b × 4) (26.5.61)	40·00	55·00	38·00

B. Watermark Crown to right
SB68a (containing No. S28c × 4) (26.5.61)	40·00	55·00	38·00

Whiter Paper

A. Watermark Crown to left
SB69 (containing No. S29b × 4) (5.6.62)	38·00	50·00	30·00

B. Watermark Crown to right
SB69a (containing No. S29c × 4) (5.6.62)	38·00	50·00	30·00

Booklet Cylinder Numbers

Cylinder No. G17 was used, but it was partly or completely trimmed off. (*Price for pane showing* "G", *from £45*).

Specimen overprints from the National Postal Museum Archives

Booklet pane of four. Perf. 15 × 14, watermark Type W.24

Each stamp handstamped "Specimen" (13 × 2 mm.)

1½d. BOOKLET PANES OF SIX WITH GRAPHITE LINES
6 × 1½d. Crowns. Graphite lines as Type **S8**
From 3s. Booklets M13g/15g and M19g/21g

A. Watermark upright
SB70 (containing No. S30 × 6) (4.8.59)	£475

B. Watermark inverted
SB70a (containing No. S30a × 6) (4.8.59)	£225

Booklet Cylinder Numbers

Panes of six (21-row cylinder)

Cyl. No.				No dot	Dot		Cyl. No.					No dot	Dot
G11 ..	..	..	..	.. £550	£550		G11 T	..	..	..	..	£550	£550

Imprimaturs from the National Postal Museum Archives

Booklet pane of six. Imperforate, watermark Type W.24

Two panes as No. SB70 arranged *tête-bêche*

1½d. BOOKLET PANES OF SIX WITH TWO PHOSPHOR BANDS REACTING GREEN
6 × 1½d. Crowns. Two phosphor bands applied in photogravure
From 3s. Booklets M25p, M28p/29p and M37p(a)

A. Watermark upright
SB71 (containing No. S32 × 6) (14.8.60)	15·00

B. Watermark inverted
SB71a (containing No. S32a × 6)(14.8.60)	50·00

Booklet Cylinder Numbers

Panes of six (21-row cylinders)

Cyl. No.				No dot	Dot		Cyl. No.				No dot	Dot
G11	..	..	..	.. 40·00	40·00		G11 T	..	..	..	.. 40·00	40·00

1½d. BOOKLET PANES OF SIX WITH TWO PHOSPHOR BANDS REACTING BLUE

6 × 1½d. Crowns. Two phosphor bands applied in photogravure. Cream or whiter paper
From 3s. Booklets M33p, M36p, M37p(*b*), M38p/9p, M43p/7p, M49p/53p, M55p/61p and
M64p/74p

Cream Paper

A. Watermark upright

    SB72 (containing No. S33 × 6) (4.61)　　　　5·50

    b. One broad band on each stamp .. .. ..　£250

B. Watermark inverted

    SB72a (containing No. S33a × 6) (4.61)　　　48·00

    ab. One broad band on each stamp .. .. ..　£250

Whiter Paper

A. Watermark upright

    SB73 (containing No. S34 × 6) (7.64)　　　20·00

    b. One broad band on each stamp .. .. ..　£325

B. Watermark inverted

    SB73a (containing No. S34c × 6) (7.64)　　£100

    ab. One broad band on each stamp .. .. ..　£325

    ac. Phosphor displaced with marginal stamps showing

         a left and centre band, others with 8 mm. band in

         centre .. ..

Booklet Cylinder Numbers
Pane of six (21-row cylinders)

Cream paper						Whiter paper				
Cyl. No.				No dot	Dot	Cyl. No.				No dot Dot
G15	..	..	..	.. 15·00	15·00	G16	..	..	..	.. 45·00 45·00
G15 T	..	..	..	.. 15·00	15·00	G16 T	..	..	..	.. 45·00 45·00

1½d. BOOKLET PANES OF FOUR WITH TWO PHOSPHOR BANDS REACTING BLUE. SIDEWAYS WATERMARK

4 × 1½d. Crowns. Two phosphor bands applied by typography. Cream or whiter paper
From 2s. Booklets N4p, N8p/10p, N12p/20p

Cream Paper

	Perf. Type		
	I	I(½v)	AP
A. Watermark Crown to left			
SB74 (containing No. S33b × 4) (14.7.61)	55·00	70·00	40·00
b. One broad band on each stamp	65·00	—	55·00
B. Watermark Crown to right			
SB74a (containing No. S33c × 4) (14.7.61)	55·00	70·00	40·00
ab. One broad band on each stamp	65·00	—	55·00

Whiter Paper

	I	I(½v)	AP
A. Watermark Crown to left			
SB75 (containing No. S34a × 4) (15.8.62)	55·00	70·00	40·00
b. One broad band on each stamp	—	—	—
B. Watermark Crown to right			
SB75a (containing No. S34b × 4) (15.8.62)	55·00	70·00	40·00
ab. One broad band on each stamp			

Examples on cream paper are known where the centre band measures 9.3 mm. wide instead
of the normal 8 mm. The broad band varieties were caused by the incorrect position of the
normal bands. It is probable that the 9.3 mm. wide band was accidental and affected one row on
the phosphor cylinder.

Booklet Cylinder Numbers
Panes of four (20-row single pane cylinder of 480 stamps)

    In the 2s. Booklets the cylinder numbers were partly or completely trimmed off, but No. G17 was
the cylinder used. (*Price for pane showing "G", from £65*).

Imprimaturs from the National Postal Museum Archives

Booklet pane of four. Imperforate, watermark Type W.24

Two panes arranged vertically *tête-bêche*

Specimen overprints from the National Postal Museum Archives

Booklet pane of four. Perf. 15 × 14, watermark Type W.24

Each stamp handstamped "Specimen" (13 × 2 mm.)

2d. RED-BROWN BOOKLET PANES OF SIX
6 × 2d.   Tudor Crown
From 5s. Booklets H8/16

A. Watermark upright
SB76 (containing No. S36 × 6) (3.54)   20·00

B. Watermark inverted
SB76a (containing No. S36a × 6) (3.54)   £200

Booklet Cylinder Numbers
Panes of six (20-row cylinder)

Cyl. No.		No dot	Dot
H1	.. ..	40·00*	38·00

*Includes retouched face variety (R. 2/1). Two states exist showing as a small retouch to left of ear and in state two the retouched area includes the forehead and cheek. Same price for either state included in the cylinder pane with upright watermark.

2d. RED-BROWN BOOKLET PANES OF SIX
6 × 2d. St. Edward's Crown
From 5s. Booklets H17/25

A. Watermark upright
SB77 (containing No. S37 × 6) (9.55)   15·00

B. Watermark inverted
SB77a (containing No. S37c × 6) (9.55)   90·00

Booklet Cylinder Numbers
Panes of six (20-row cylinder)

Cyl. No.		No dot	Dot
H1	.. ..	60·00*	55·00

*Includes the second state of the retouched face variety (R. 2/1).

2d. LIGHT RED-BROWN BOOKLET PANES OF SIX
6 × 2d.   St. Edward's Crown
From 2s. 6d. Booklets F53/61 and 5s. Booklets H26/31

A. Watermark upright
SB78 (containing No. S38 × 6) (1.57)   12·00
   b. Imperf. pane* .. ..
   ba. Part perf. pane* .. ..
   c. Daffodil flaw (R. 1/3 or 2/3) .. .. .. 15·00
   d. Shamrock flaw (R. 1/3 or 2/3) .. .. 30·00
   e. Bud on thistle stem (R. 1/3 or 2/3) .. 17·00
   f. White flaw on thistle (R. 1/1 or 2/1) .. 15·00
   g. Daffodil stem flaw (R. 2/2) .. .. .. 16·00

B. Watermark inverted
SB78a (containing No. S38d × 6) (1.57)   25·00
   ac. "D" for "P" (R. 1/2 or 2/2) .. .. .. 32·00
   ad. Spot after "2" (R. 1/2 or 2/2) .. .. 32·00
   ae. "Dew drop" (R. 1/2 or 2/2) .. .. .. 28·00
   af. Diadem flaw (R. 1/3 or 2/3) .. .. .. 28·00
   ag. White flaw at top of thistle (R. 1/2 or 2/2) .. 28·00
   ah. Accent on first "2" and spot on shamrock (R. 1/3 or 2/3) .. .. 28·00
   aha. Retouched state. Spot on shamrock (R. 1/3 or 2/3) .. .. 28·00

*Booklet error—see General Notes.

Listed Varieties

SB78c
Later retouched
(Cyl. H6 no dot)

SB78d
Later retouched
(Cyl. H6 no dot)

SB78e, SB79b
Later retouched
(Cyl. H6 dot)

SB78f
(Cyl. H6 dot)

SB78g
Later retouched
(Cyl. pane H6 and on
ordinary pane)

SB78ac, SB79ab
(Cyl. H6 dot)

SB78ad, SB79ac
(Cyl. H6 no dot)

SB78ae
Later retouched
(Cyl. H6 no dot)

SB78af
Later retouched
(Cyl. H6 dot)

SB78ag
Later retouched
(Cyl. H6 no dot)

SB78ah
The flaw on value
was later
retouched but the
spot on shamrock
remained.
(Cyl. H6 dot)

Booklet Cylinder Numbers

Panes of six (21-row cylinder)

Cyl. No.						No dot	Dot
H6 ..	..	..	..	..	..	42·00	42·00
H6T	..	..	..	..	..	42·00	42·00

Early printings of the Cyl. H6 pane show a white dot below the daffodil stem at left (R. 1/2). This was later removed by retouch. *Cylinder No.* H6 *with variety price* £55.

2d. LIGHT RED-BROWN BOOKLET PANES OF SIX

6 × 2d.   Crowns.   Cream paper
From 10s. Booklets X1/2

A. Watermark upright

SB79 (containing No. S40 × 6) (10.4.61)		30·00
b. Bud on thistle stem (R. 1/3 or 2/3)		32·00

B. Watermark inverted

SB79a (containing No. S40c × 6) (10.4.61)		£325
ab. "D" for "P" (R. 1/2 or 2/2)		£400
ac. Spot after "2" (R. 1/2 or 2/2)		£375

Listed Varieties

For illustration of No. SB79*b*, see No. SB78e and for Nos. SB79*ab/ac* see Nos. SB78*ac/ad*.

Booklet Cylinder Numbers

Panes of six (21-row cylinder). Cream paper

Cyl. No.				No dot	Dot	Cyl. No.				No dot	Dot
H6 ..	••	..	..	.. 70·00	70·00	H6 T	••	••	••	.. 70·00	70·00

All stamps in the 2½d. panes show the frontal cross of the diadem with the top line extending the full width of the cross (Type II).

2½d. BOOKLET PANES OF SIX

6 × 2½d.   Tudor Crown.
From 2s.6d. Booklets F1/34, 3s.9d. Booklets G1/10 and 5s. Booklets H1/16

A. Watermark upright

SB80 (containing No. S51 × 6) (5.53)		6·00
b. Jewels flaw (R. 2/2)		8·00

B. Watermark inverted

SB80a (containing No. S51a × 6) (5.53)		3·25
ab. "R" flaw (R. 1/1)		6·00

Listed Varieties

SB80*ob*
(Cyl. J1 or J3 no dot)

SB80*ab*, SB81*ad*
(Cyl. J5 no dot)

Booklet Cylinder Numbers

Panes of six (20-row cylinders)

Cyl. No.				No dot	Dot	Cyl. No.				No dot	Dot
J1 ..	••	..	••	.. 16·00	16·00	J5 ..	••	••	••	.. 18·00	18·00
J3 ..	••	..	••	.. 16·00	16·00						

2½d. BOOKLET PANES OF SIX
6 × 2½d. St. Edward's Crown
From 2s.6d. Booklets F34(c) and (e) and F35/61, 3s.9d. Booklets G9(a) and G10(a)/21 and 5s.
Booklets H17/36

A. Watermark upright

SB81 (containing No. S53 × 6) (9.55)		2·40
b. Imperf. pane*		£900
d. "Swan's head" (R. 1/1 or 2/1)		8·00
e. Wreath flaw (R. 1/3 or 2/3)		7·00
f. Damaged "P" (R. 1/3 or 2/3)		7·00
g. Dot by shamrock (R. 1/1 or 2/1)		5·50
h. Forehead retouch R. 1/2 or 2/2)		5·00
i. White flaw below thistle (R. 1/2 or 2/2)		7·00

B. Watermark inverted

SB81a (containing No. S53e × 6) (9.55)		2·40
ac. Part perf. pane*		
ad. "R" flaw (R. 1/1)		8·00
ae. Dotted "R" (R. 1/3 or 2/3)		8·00
af. Spur to "1" (R. 1/1 or 2/1)		6·00

Listed Varieties
For illustration of No. SB81ad, see No. SB80ab.

SB81d, SB82d
Top of figure 2 is extended
and curled (Cyl. J8 no dot)

SB81e, SB82e
(Cyl. J9 no dot)

SB81f, SB82f
Red flaw almost obliterates the
loop on "P". St. Edward's
and Crown wmks., (Cyl. J8 dot)

SB81g
Retouched later
(Cyl. J9 dot)

SB81h, SB82g
(Cyl. J9 no dot)

SB81i, SB82h
(Cyl. J8 no dot)

SB81ae
Later retouched on Crowns
wmk. (Cyl. J9 no dot)

SB81af, SB82ac SB85ab
(Cyl. J9 dot)

Booklet Cylinder Numbers

Panes of six (J5 20-row cylinder, others 21-row cylinders)

Cyl. No.					No dot	Dot	Cyl. No.					No dot	Dot
J5	..	..	..	..	10·00	10·00							
J6	..	..	..	..	10·00	10·00	J8 T	..	..	..	..	9·00	9·00
J6 T	..	..	..	..	10·00	10·00	J9	..	..	..	..	9·00	9·00
J8	..	..	..	..	9·00	9·00	J9 T	..	..	..	..	9·00	9·00

2½d. BOOKLET PANES OF SIX

6 × 2½d.   Crowns.   Cream or whiter paper
From 5s. Booklets H36(b)/(c), (e) and H37/74 and 10s. Booklets X3/9

Cream Paper

A. Watermark upright

SB82 (containing No. S55 × 6) (11.58)		7·00
d. "Swan's head" (R. 1/1 or 2/1)	.. .. ..	14·00
e. Wreath flaw (R. 1/3 or 2/3) ..	.. .. ..	12·00
f. Damaged "P" (R. 1/3 or 2/3)	.. .. ..	12·00
g. Forehead retouch (R. 1/2 or 2/2)	.. .. ..	12·00
h. White flaw below thistle (R. 1/2 or 2/2) ..	..	12·00

B. Watermark inverted

SB82a (containing No. S55d × 6) (11.58)		20·00
ac. Spur to "1" (R. 1/1)	.. ..	25·00

Whiter Paper

A. Watermark upright

SB83 (containing No. S57 × 6) (29.7.62)		3·75
b. Imperf. pane*	.. ..	£1100

B. Watermark inverted

SB83a (containing No. S57a × 6) (29.7.62)	25·00

*Booklet error—see General Notes.

Listed Varieties

For illustrations of Nos. SB82d/f, see Nos. SB81d/f, for Nos. SB82g/h, see Nos. SB81h/i and for No. SB82ac see No. SB81af.

Booklet Cylinder Numbers

Panes of six (21-row cylinders)

Cream paper							Whiter paper						
Cyl. No					No dot	Dot	Cyl. No.					No dot	Dot
J6	..	..	..	..	24·00	24·00	J13	..	..	..	..	12·00	12·00
J6 T	..	..	..	..	24·00	24·00	J13 T	..	..	..	..	12·00	12·00
J8	..	..	..	..	32·00	32·00	J14	..	..	..	..	15·00	15·00
J8 T	..	..	..	..	32·00	32·00	J14 T	..	..	..	..	15·00	15·00
J9	..	..	..	..	18·00	18·00							
J9 T	..	..	..	..	18·00	18·00							
J13	..	..	..	..	18·00	18·00							
J13 T	..	..	..	..	18·00	18·00							

Specimen overprints from the National Postal Museum Archives

Booklet pane of six. Perf. 15 × 14, watermark Type W.24 inverted

Each stamp handstamped "Specimen" (15 × 2½ mm.)

2½d. BOOKLET PANES OF FOUR

4 × 2½d.   Crowns.   Chalky paper
From 2s. Booklet NR1/1a

A. Watermark upright

	Perf. Type		
	I	I(½v)	AP
SB84 (containing No. S58 × 4) (15.7.63)	3·50	9·00	2·25

B. Watermark inverted

SB84a (containing No. S58a × 4) (15.7.63)	3·50	9·00	2·25

Booklet Cylinder Numbers
Panes of four (20-row single pane cylinder of 480 stamps).
Cylinder numbers are not known from Booklets NR1/1a.

Imprimaturs from the National Postal Museum Archives

Booklet pane of four. Imperforate, watermark Type W.24

Two panes arranged vertically *tête-bêche*

2½d. BOOKLET PANES OF SIX WITH GRAPHITE LINES
6 × 2½d.   Crowns.   Graphite lines as Type **S8**
From 5s. Booklets H39g, H43g and H46g

A. Watermark upright
SB85 (containing No. S59 × 6) (21.8.59)   60·00
   b. Forehead retouch (R. 1/2 or 2/2) .. .. ..   70·00

B. Watermark inverted
SB85a (containing No. S59a × 6) (21.8.59)   £275
   ab. Spur to " 1 " (R. 1/1 or 2/1) £300

Listed Varieties
For illustration of No. SB85*b*, see No. SB81*h* and for No. SB85*ab*, see No. SB81*af*.

Booklet Cylinder Numbers

Panes of six (21-row cylinders)

Cyl. No.				No dot	Dot	Cyl. No.				No dot	Dot
J6 ..	..	..	..	£225	£225	J9 ..	..	..	..	£225	£225
J6 T	..	..	..	£225	£225	J9 T	..	..	..	£225	£225

2½d. BOOKLET PANES OF SIX WITH TWO PHOSPHOR BANDS REACTING GREEN
6 × 2½d.   Crowns.   Two phosphor bands applied in photogravure
From 5s. Booklet H46p

A. Watermark upright
SB86 (containing No. S61 × 6) (14.8.60)   55·00
   b. One broad band on each stamp £200

B. Watermark inverted
SB86a (containing No. S61a × 6) (14.8.60)   £750
   ab. One broad band on each stamp £1100

Booklet Cylinder Numbers

Panes of six (21-row cylinder)

Cyl. No.				No dot	Dot	Cyl. No.				No dot	Dot
J13 ..	..	..	..	£120	£120	J13 T	..	..	..	£120	£120

2½d. BOOKLET PANES OF SIX WITH TWO PHOSPHOR BANDS REACTING BLUE
6 × 2½d.   Crowns.   Two phosphor bands applied in photogravure.   Cream paper
From 5s. Booklets H49p, H51p/52p and H54p

A. Watermark upright
SB87 (containing No. S62 × 6) (3.61)   55·00

B. Watermark inverted
SB87a (containing No. S62a × 6) (3.61)   £800

Booklet Cylinder Numbers

Panes of six (21-row cylinders)

Two bands. Cream paper

Cyl. No.				No dot	Dot	Cyl. No.				No dot	Dot
J13 ..	..	..	..	£120	£120	J13 T	..	..	..	£120	£120

Specimen overprints from the National Postal Museum Archives

Booklet pane of six. Perf. 15 × 14, watermark Type W.24 upright

Each stamp handstamped " Specimen " (13 × 2 mm.)

2½d. BOOKLET PANES OF SIX WITH ONE PHOSPHOR BAND AT LEFT REACTING BLUE
6 × 2½d.   Crowns.   Band at left applied in photogravure.   Cream or whiter paper
From 5s. Booklets H55p/74p

Cream Paper

A. Watermark upright
        SB88 (containing No. S63 × 6) (3.62)   55·00

B. Watermark inverted
        SB88a (containing No. S63*b* × 6) (3.62)   £200

Whiter Paper

A. Watermark upright
        SB89 (containing No. S65 × 6) (3.6.63)   22·00
            b. Two narrow phosphor bands on each stamp but
                one band on stamps 3 and 6 ..   ..   £300

B. Watermark inverted
        SB89a (containing No. S65*b* × 6) (3.6.63)   £120
            ab. Two narrow phosphor bands on each stamp but
                one band on stamps 3 and 6 ..   ..   —

Booklet Cylinder Numbers
    Pane of six (21-row cylinders)

One band. Cream paper	No dot	Dot						No dot	Dot
J13	£150	£150	**|**	J13 T	..	..	.. ..	£150	£150

One band. Whiter paper									
J13	40·00	40·00	**|**	J13 T	..	..	..	40·00	40·00
J14	40·00	40·00	**|**	J14 T	..	..	..	40·00	40·00

Specimen overprints from the National Postal Museum Archives
    Booklet pane of six. Perf. 15 × 14, watermark Type W.24 upright
    Each stamp handstamped "Specimen" (15 × 2½ mm.)

3d. BOOKLET PANES OF SIX
6 × 3d.   St. Edward's Crown
From 3s. Booklets M1/10, 4s.6d. Booklets L1/17 and 5s. Booklets H32/36

A. Watermark upright
        SB90 (containing No. S68 × 6) (1.10.57)   3·25
            b. White dot on laurel leaf (R. 1/2 or 2/2) ..   ..   6·50

B. Watermark inverted
        SB90a (containing No. S68*d* × 6) (1.10.57)   6·50

Listed Variety

SB90*b*
(Cyl. K2 no dot)

Booklet Cylinder Numbers

Panes of six (K8 20-row cylinder, others 21-row cylinders)

Cyl. No.					No dot	Dot	Cyl. No.					No dot	Dot
K1	..	..	..	..	14·00	14·00	K7	..	..	..	..	14·00	14·00
K1 T				..	14·00	14·00	K7 T	..	..	..	..	14·00	14·00
K2	..	..	..	..	14·00	14·00	K8 T	..	..	..	..	14·00	14·00
K2 T				..	14·00	14·00							

K8 was engraved in the middle of the sheet by row 11 and only occurs at the top of the pane.

3d. BOOKLET PANES OF FOUR

4 × 3d.   St. Edward's Crown
From 2s. Booklet N1. Perf. Type AP

A. Watermark upright
    SB91 (containing No. S68 × 4) (22.4.59)   6·50

B. Watermark inverted
    SB91a (containing No. S68d × 4) (22.4.59)   20·00

Booklet Cylinder Numbers
Cylinder numbers did not appear in the finished booklets, but it is known that K12 and one other cylinder were used.

Imprimaturs from the National Postal Museum Archives

Booklet pane of four. Imperforate, watermark Type W.23

Two panes arranged vertically *tête-bêche* with a 12 mm. horizontal gutter margin between

3d. BOOKLET PANES OF SIX

6 × 3d.   Crowns.   Cream or whiter paper
From 3s. Booklets M10/74, 4s.6d. Booklets L8/58, 5s. Booklets H36(d)/(e) and H37/74 and 10s. Booklets X1/14

Cream Paper

A. Watermark upright
    SB92 (containing No. S70 × 6) (11.58)   3·50
      b. Imperf. pane* £850
      c. Part perf. pane*   ..   ..

B. Watermark inverted
    SB92a (containing No. S70e × 6) (11.58)   3·50
      ab. Long tailed " R " (R. 1/1)   ..   ..   7·50
      ac. Background retouch (R. 1/1)   ..   ..   ..   7·50
      ad. Part perf. pane*   ..   ..

Whiter Paper

A. Watermark upright
    SB93 (containing No. S71 × 6) (16.7.62)   1·60

B. Watermark inverted
    SB93a (containing No. S71c × 6) (16.7.62)   2·75
      ab. Long tailed " R " (R. 1/1)   ..   ..   6·00
      ac. Background retouch (R. 1/1)   ..   ..   ..   5·00

*Booklet errors—see General Notes.

Listed Varieties

SB92*ab*, SB93*ab*,
SB97*ab*, SB99*ab*,
SB100*ab*
(Cyl. K15 no dot)

SB92*ac*, SB93*ac*, SB97*ac*,
SB99*ac*, SB100*ac*
Retouched area of fine dots behind
Queen's head (Cyl. K15 no dot)

Booklet Cylinder Numbers

Panes of six (K13, K15 and K16 20-row cylinders, others 21-row cylinders)

	Cream paper							Whiter paper			
Cyl. No.				No dot	Dot	Cyl. No.				No dot	Dot
K7 ..	..	..	..	18·00	18·00	K15 ..	..	..	..	12·00	12·00
K7 T	..	..	..	18·00	18·00	K16 ..	..	..	..	28·00	28·00
K13 ..	..	..	..	10·00	10·00	K18 ..	..	..	..	7·50	7·50
K15 ..	..	..	..	18·00	18·00	K18 T	..	..	..	7·50	7·50
K17 ..	..	..	..	10·00	10·00	K20 ..	..	..	..	7·50	7·50
K17 T	..	..	..	10·00	10·00	K20 T	..	..	..	7·50	7·50
K18 ..	..	..	..	10·00	10·00	K21 ..	..	..	..	—	—
K18 T	..	..	..	10·00	10·00	K21 T	..	..	..	—	—
K20 ..	..	..	..	10·00	10·00						
K20 T	..	..	..	10·00	10·00						

Specimen overprints from the National Postal Museum Archives

Booklet pane of six. Perf. 15 × 14, watermark Type W.24 upright

Each stamp handstamped "Specimen" (13 × 2 mm.)
Each stamp handstamped "Specimen" (15 × 2½ mm.)

3d. BOOKLET PANES OF FOUR
4 × 3d. Crowns. Cream paper
From 2s. Booklets N2/3. Perf. Type AP

A. Watermark upright
      SB94 (containing No. S70 × 4) (2.11.60)   4·25

B. Watermark inverted
      SB94a (containing No. S70e × 4) (2.11.60)   4·25
      ab. Break in bottom ribbon (R. 1/2) .. .. .. 7·50

Listed Variety

SB94*ab*

Booklet Cylinder Numbers

Cylinder No. K14 was used, but it does not appear in the finished booklets.

Specimen overprints from the National Postal Museum Archives

Booklet pane of four. Perf. 15 × 14, watermark Type W.24 inverted

Each stamp handstamped "Specimen" (13 × 2 mm.)

3d. BOOKLET PANES OF FOUR WITH SIDEWAYS WATERMARK
4 × 3d. Crowns. Cream or whiter paper
From 2s. Booklets N4/20 and NX1

Cream Paper

		Perf. Type	
	I	I(½v)	AP
A. Watermark Crown to left			
SB95 (containing No. S70d × 4) (26.5.61)	7·00	12·00	5·00
B. Watermark Crown to right			
SB95a (containing No. S70f × 4) (26.5.61)	7·00	12·00	5·00

Whiter Paper

A. Watermark Crown to left			
SB96 (containing No. S71a × 4) (5.6.62)	5·00	9·00	2·50
B. Watermark Crown to right			
SB96a (containing No. S71b × 4) (5.6.62)	5·00	9·00	2·50

Booklet Cylinder Numbers

Cylinder No. K19 was used, but it was partly or completely trimmed off. (*Price for pane showing* "K", *from £30*).

Imprimaturs from the National Postal Museum Archives

Booklet pane of four. Imperforate, watermark Type W.24

Two panes arranged vertically *tête-bêche* with a 12 mm. horizontal gutter margin between

Specimen overprints from the National Postal Museum Archives

Booklet pane of four. Perf. 15 × 14, watermark Type W.24

Each stamp handstamped "Specimen" (13 × 2 mm.)

3d. BOOKLET PANES OF SIX WITH GRAPHITE LINES
6 × 3d.   Crowns.   Graphite lines as Type **S8**
From 3s. Booklets M13g/15g, M19g/21g, 4s.6d. Booklets L11g, L15g/16g, L18g/19g and 5s. Booklets H39g, H43g and H46g

A. Watermark upright
SB97 (containing No. S72 × 6) (4.8.59)   4·75

B. Watermark inverted
SB97a (containing No. S72a × 6) (4.8.59)   6·00
ab. Long tailed "R" (R. 1/1)   ..   ..   10·00
ac. Background retouch (R. 1/1)   ..   ..   ..   9·00

Listed Varieties
For illustrations of Nos. SB97ab/ac, see Nos. SB92ab/ac.

Booklet Cylinder Numbers
Panes of 6 (K7 21-row cylinder, others 20-row cylinders)

Cyl. No.					No dot	Dot	Cyl. No.					No dot	Dot
K7 ..	..	..	..	..	17·00	17·00	K13 ..	..	..	..	..	27·00	27·00
K7 T	..	..	..	..	17·00	17·00	K15 ..	..	..	..	..	21·00	21·00

3d. BOOKLET PANES OF SIX WITH TWO PHOSPHOR BANDS REACTING GREEN
6 × 3d.   Crowns.   Two phosphor bands applied in photogravure
From 3s. Booklets M25p, M28p/9p and M37p(*a*), 4s.6d. Booklets L21p, L24p and L27p(*a*) and 5s. Booklet H46p

A. Watermark upright
SB98 (containing No. S74 × 6) (14.8.60)   12·00

B. Watermark inverted
SB98a (containing No. S74a × 6) (14.8.60)   12·00

See No. S74*d* for the broad band variety.

Booklet Cylinder Numbers
Panes of six (21-row cylinders)

Cyl. No.					No dot	Dot	Cyl. No.					No dot	Dot
K17 ..	..	..	..	..	22·00	22·00	K17 T	..	..	..	..	24·00	24·00

3d. BOOKLET PANES OF SIX WITH PHOSPHOR BANDS REACTING BLUE
6 × 3d.   Crowns.   Two phosphor bands applied in photogravure.   Cream or whiter paper
From 3s. Booklets M33p, M36p, M37p(*b*), M38p/9p, M43p/7p, M49p/53p, M55p/61p, M64p/74p, 4s.6d. Booklets L25p, L27p(*b*), L28p, L30p/42p, L44p/56p and 5s. Booklets H49p, H51p/2p and H54p/74p

Cream Paper

A. Watermark upright
SB99 (containing No. S75 × 6) (3.61)   6·00

B. Watermark inverted
SB99a (containing No. S75a × 6) (3.61)   6·00
ab. Long tailed "R" (R. 1/1)   ..   ..   10·00
ac. Background retouch (R. 1/1)   ..   ..   ..   10·00

Whiter Paper

A. Watermark upright
SB100 (containing No. S76 × 6) (25.9.62)   5·00

B. Watermark inverted
SB100a (containing No. S76c × 6) (25.9.62)   5·00
ab. Long tailed " R " (R. 1/1) .. ..   9·00
ac. Background retouch (R. 1/1) .. .. ..   9·00

Listed Varieties
For illustrations of Nos. SB99ab/ac and SB100ab/ac, see Nos. SB92ab/ac.

Booklet Cylinder Numbers
Panes of six (K15 20-row cylinder, others 21-row cylinders). Two bands.

	Cream paper							Whiter paper			
Cyl. No.				No dot	Dot	Cyl. No.				No dot	Dot
K15 ..	..	..	..	.. 15·00	15·00	K15	..	..	..	.. 15·00	15·00
K18 ..	..	..	..	.. 25·00	25·00	K18	..	..	..	.. 15·00	15·00
K18 T	..	..	..	.. 25·00	25·00	K18 T	..	..	..	.. 15·00	15·00
						K20	..	..	..	.. 15·00	15·00
						K20 T	..	..	..	.. 15·00	15·00

Specimen overprints from the National Postal Museum Archives

Booklet pane of six. Perf. 15 × 14, watermark Type W.24 upright

Each stamp handstamped "Specimen" (13 × 2 mm.)
Each stamp handstamped "Specimen" (15 × 2½ mm.)

**3d. BOOKLET PANES OF FOUR WITH TWO PHOSPHOR BANDS REACTING BLUE.
SIDEWAYS WATERMARK**
4 × 3d. Crowns. Two phosphor bands applied by typography. Cream or whiter paper
From 2s. Booklets N4p, N8p/10p, N12p/20p

Cream Paper

A. Watermark Crown to left

	Perf. Type		
	I	I(½v)	AP
SB101 (containing No. S75b × 4) (14.7.61)	10·00	20·00	7·00
b. One broad band on each stamp	—	—	70·00

B. Watermark Crown to right
SB101a (containing No. S75c × 4) (14.7.61)	10·00	20·00	7·00
ab. One broad band on each stamp	—	—	70·00

Whiter Paper

A. Watermark Crown to left
SB102 (containing No. S76a × 4) (15.8.62)	6·00	12·00	4·00

B. Watermark Crown to right
SB102a (containing No. S76b × 4) (15.8.62)	6·00	12·00	4·00

Booklet Cylinder Numbers
Cylinder No. K19 was used, but it was partly or completely trimmed off. (*Price for pane showing* "K", *from* £35).

Imprimaturs from the National Postal Museum Archives

Booklet pane of four. Imperforate, watermark Type W.24

Two panes arranged vertically *tête-bêche*

Specimen overprints from the National Postal Museum Archives

Booklet pane of four. Perf. 15 × 14, watermark Type W.24

Each stamp handstamped "Specimen" (13 × 2 mm.)

SB103

3d. BOOKLET PANES OF SIX WITH 8 mm. PHOSPHOR BANDS REACTING VIOLET
2 × 3d. (band at left) and 4 × 3d. (band at right).   Crowns.   Phosphor bands applied in photogravure
From 10s. Booklet X15p(*a/b*)

A. Watermark upright
            SB103 (containing Nos. S78 × 2, S78*a* × 4)
            (2.67)   8·50

B. Watermark inverted
            SB103a (containing Nos. S78*g* × 2, S78*h* × 4)
            (2.67)   30·00

Booklet Cylinder Numbers
Panes of six (21-row cylinder)
            One side band

Cyl. No.				No dot	Dot
K18 ..	..	..	..	.. 27·00	27·00
K18 T	..	..	..	.. 27·00	27·00

3d. BOOKLET PANES OF SIX WITH 4 mm. PHOSPHOR BANDS REACTING VIOLET
6 × 3d. (centre band).   Crowns.   The centre phosphor bands were applied in photogravure using a mixed screen.
From 10s. Booklets X16p/17p

A. Watermark upright
            SB104 (containing No. S79 × 6) (8.67)   4·00

B. Watermark inverted
            SB104a (containing No. S79*b* × 6) (8.67)   7·00

Booklet Cylinder Numbers
    Panes of six (21-row cylinder)
            One centre band

Cyl. No.					No dot	Dot
K18	..	..	..	..	.. 16·00	16·00
K18T	..	..	..	..	.. 16·00	16·00

4d. DEEP ULTRAMARINE BOOKLET PANES OF SIX
6 × 4d. Crowns
From 4s.6d. Booklets L59/65, 6s. Booklets Q1/23 and 10s. Booklets X10/14

A. Watermark upright

SB105 (containing No. S85 × 6) (21.6.65)		3·75
b. Imperf. pane*		£650
c. Part perf. pane*		
d. Line through diadem (R. 1/1 or 2/1)		5·50
e. Dot below top frame (R. 1/1 or 2/1)		4·75
f. "Y" flaw (R. 1/2 or 2/2)		4·75

B. Watermark inverted

SB105a (containing No. S85*e* × 6) (21.6.65)		3·75
ab. Retouch over "4" (R. 1/1 or 2/1)		4·50

Listed Varieties

SB105*d*
Later retouched (Cyl. N1 no dot)

SB105*e*, SB107*c*,
SB109*b*, SB111*b*
(Cyl. N1 dot)

SB105*f*, SB107*d*, SB109*c*, SB111*c*
Multipositive flaw from panes showing
N1, N2 (T), N3 also without cylinder no.

SB105*ab*, SB107*ab*,
SB109*ab*, SB111*ab*
(Cyl. N1 no dot)

Booklet Cylinder Numbers (Deep ultramarine)
Panes of six (21-row cylinders N1/2 or 20-row cylinder N3)

Cyl. No.					No dot	Dot	Cyl. No.				No dot	Dot
N1 ..	..	..	..	..	12·00*	10·00	N1 T	..	..	..	.. 10·00	10·00
N2 ..	..	..	..	..	10·00	10·00	N2 T	..	..	..	.. 12·00*	10·00
N3 ..	..	..	..	..	17·00*	15·00						

Specimen overprints from the National Postal Museum Archives
Booklet pane of six. Perf. 15 × 14, watermark Type W.24 inverted

Each stamp handstamped "Specimen" (13 × 2 mm.)

4d. BOOKLET ULTRAMARINE BOOKLET PANES OF FOUR. SIDEWAYS WATERMARK
4 × 4d. Crowns
From 2s. Booklets N21/27

A. Watermark Crown to left

	Perf. Type		
	I	I(½v)	AP
SB106 (containing No. S85*d* × 4) (16.8.65)	3·50	10·00	2·50

B. Watermark Crown to right

SB106a (containing No. S85*f* × 4) (16.8.65)	3·50	10·00	2·50

Some panes are on paper with a slight gloss.

Booklet Cylinder Numbers

Panes of four (20-row single pane cylinder of 480 stamps)
Sideways watermark

Cyl. No.	No dot
N4 (Wmk. Crown to left) ..	10·00
N4 (Wmk. Crown to right) ..	10·00

4d. DEEP ULTRAMARINE BOOKLET PANES OF SIX WITH TWO PHOSPHOR BANDS REACTING BLUE

6 × 4d. Crowns. Two phosphor bands applied in photogravure.
From 4s.6d. Booklets L59p, L60p(*a*)/(62p(*a*) excl. (*b*) nos. and 6s. Booklets Q1p/3p, Q4p(*a*)/8p(*a*) excl. (*b*) nos.

A. Watermark upright

SB107 (containing No. S90 × 6) (21.6.65)		4·50
b. Part perf. pane*	.. ..	
c. Dot below top frame (R. 1/1 or 2/1)	.. ..	7·00
d. "Y" flaw (R. 1/2 or 2/2)	.. ..	7·00

B. Watermark inverted

SB107a (containing No. S90*b* × 6) (21.6.65)	10·00
ab. Retouch over "4" (R. 1/1 or 2/1)	14·00

*Booklet error—see General Notes.

Listed Varieties

For illustrations of Nos. SB107*c/d* and SB107*ab*, see Nos. SB105*e/f* and SB105*ab*.

Booklet Cylinder Numbers

Panes of six (21-row cylinder)

Cyl. No.					No dot	Dot		Cyl. No.				No dot	Dot
N1 ..	..	..	..	..	18·00*	15·00		N1 T	..	..	..	15·00	15·00

Specimen overprints from the National Postal Museum Archives

Booklet pane of six. Perf. 15 × 14, watermark Type W.24 inverted

Each stamp handstamped "Specimen" (13 × 2 mm.)

4d. DEEP ULTRAMARINE BOOKLET PANES OF FOUR WITH TWO PHOSPHOR BANDS REACTING BLUE. SIDEWAYS WATERMARK

4 × 4d. Crowns. Two phosphor bands applied by typography
From 2s. Booklets N21p, N22p(*a*) and N23p(*a*)

A. Watermark Crown to left

	Perf. Type		
	I	I(½v)	AP
SB108 (containing No. S90*c* × 4) (16.8.65)	16·00	22·00	11·00
b. One broad band on each stamp	—	—	—

B. Watermark Crown to right

SB108a (containing No. S90*d* × 4) (16.8.65)	16·00	22·00	11·00
ab. One broad band on each stamp	—	—	—

Booklet Cylinder Numbers

Panes of four (20-row single pane cylinder of 480 stamps).
Sideways watermark

Cyl. No.	No dot
N4 (Wmk. Crown to right) ..	32·00

4d. DEEP ULTRAMARINE BOOKLET PANES OF SIX WITH TWO 8 mm. PHOSPHOR BANDS REACTING VIOLET

6 × 4d. Crowns. Two phosphor bands applied in photogravure.
From 4s. 6d. Booklets L60p(*b*), L61p(*b*) and L62p(*b*)/65p(*a*), 6s. Booklets Q4p(*b*)/8p(*b*) excl. (*a*) nos. and Q9p/20p and 10s. Booklet X15p(*a*)

A. Watermark upright

SB109 (containing No. S91 × 6) (9.65)	3·50
b. Dot below top frame (R. 1/1 or 2/1)	6·00
c. "Y" flaw (R. 1/2 or 2/2)	6·00

B. Watermark inverted

SB109a (containing No. S91*a* × 6) (9.65)	3·50
ab. Retouch over "4" (R. 1/1 or 2/1)	6·00

Listed Varieties

For illustrations of Nos. SB109*b/c* and SB109*ab*, see Nos. SB105*e/f* and SB105*ab*.

Booklet Cylinder Numbers

Panes of six (21-row cylinders N1 and N2 or 20-row cylinder N3)

Cyl. No.					No dot	Dot	Cyl. No.					No dot	Dot
N1	..	..	..	..	12·00*	9·00	N1 T	..	..	..	..	9·00	9·00
N2	..	..	..	..	9·00	9·00	N2 T	..	..	..	..	12·00*	9·00
N3	..	..	..	..	24·00*	20·00							

4d. DEEP ULTRAMARINE BOOKLET PANES OF FOUR WITH TWO 8 mm. PHOSPHOR BANDS REACTING VIOLET. SIDEWAYS WATERMARK

4 × 4d.   Crowns.   Two phosphor bands applied in photogravure or typography
From 2s. Booklets N22p(*b*), N23p(*b*)/28p(*a*), N29p, N30p(*a*), N31p(*b*) and N32(*b*)

A. Watermark Crown to left

	Perf. Type		
	I	I($\frac{1}{2}$v)	AP
SB110 (containing No. S91*b* × 4) (1.67)	4·50	10·00	3·00
b. One broad band on each stamp	50·00	—	40·00
c. Bands typo. (10.65)	75·00	—	70·00
d. Do. One broad band on each stamp	—	—	—

B. Watermark Crown to right

SB110a (containing No. S91*c* × 4) (1.67)	4·50	10·00	3·00
ab. One broad band on each stamp	50·00	—	40·00
ac. Bands typo. (10.65)	75·00	—	70·00
ad. Do. One broad band on each stamp	—	—	—
ae. Phosphor bands printed on both back and front	—	†	†

Some panes are on paper with a slight gloss.

Booklet Cylinder Numbers

Panes of four (20-row single pane cylinder of 480 stamps). Sideways watermark

	Photo. bands				Typo. bands		
Cyl. No.			No dot	Cyl. No.			No dot
N4 (Wmk. Crown to left)			22·00	N4 (Wmk. Crown to left)			†
N4 (Wmk. Crown to right)			22·00	N4 (Wmk. Crown to right)			—

4d. DEEP ULTRAMARINE BOOKLET PANES OF SIX WITH TWO 9·5 mm. PHOSPHOR BANDS REACTING VIOLET

6 × 4d.   Crowns.   Two phosphor bands applied in photogravure
From 4s.6d. Booklets L65p(*b*)/71p, 6s. Booklets Q21/27p and 10s. Booklet X15p(*b*), X16p/17p

A. Watermark upright

SB111 (containing No. S92 × 6) (2.67)	2·50
b. Dot below frame (R. 1/1 or 2/1)	4·00
c. "Y" flaw (R. 1/2 or 2/2)	4·00

B. Watermark inverted

SB111a (containing No. S92a × 6) (2.67)	2·50
ab. Retouch over "4" (R. 1/1 or 2/1)	4·00

Listed Varieties

For illustrations of Nos. SB111*b/c* and SB111*ab*, see Nos. SB105*e/f* and SB105*ab*.

Booklet Cylinder Numbers

Panes of six (21-row cylinders)

Cyl. No.					No dot	Dot	Cyl. No.					No dot	Dot
N1	..	..	..	..	12·00*	8·00	N1 T	..	..	..	..	8·00	8·00
N2	..	..	..	..	8·00	8·00	N2 T	..	..	..	..	12·00*	8·00
N2 (Wmk. inverted)	..	..					N2 T (Wmk. inverted)	..	..			50·00	50·00

Cylinder panes showing watermark inverted (Cyl. No. N2) come from Booklet X17p.

4d. DEEP ULTRAMARINE BOOKLET PANES OF FOUR WITH TWO 9·5 mm. PHOSPHOR BANDS REACTING VIOLET. SIDEWAYS WATERMARK
4 × 4d.   Crowns.   Two phosphor bands applied by flexography
From 2s. Booklets N28p(*b*), N30p(*b*), N31p(*a*), N31p(*c*), N32p(*a*) and N32p(*c*)

A. Watermark Crown to left

	I	Perf. Type I(½v)	AP
SB112 (containing No. S92*b* × 4) (4.67)	3·50	7·00	2·50
b. One broad band on each stamp	50·00	—	40·00

B. Watermark Crown to right

SB112a (containing No. S92*c* × 4) (4.67)	3·50	7·00	2·50
ab. One broad band on each stamp	50·00	—	40·00

Booklet Cylinder Numbers
Panes of four (20-row single pane cylinder of 480 stamps).
Sideways watermark
Cyl. No.   No dot
    N4 (Wmk. Crown to right) .. .. .. 18·00

SECTION T
Dorothy Wilding Issues
1955–68. High Values. Recess-printed

General Notes

CROWNS WATERMARK. The Crowns are slightly smaller than in the low values.

PAPER. The stamps are all on unsurfaced paper except the 2s. 6d., No. T6 which is on chalky paper.

Bradbury, Wilkinson printings are found with a degree of fluorescence when viewed under a short-wave u.v. lamp. This is due to the use of optical brightening agents in the rags used for paper making.

Stamps printed by Waterlow and De La Rue tend to curl from top to bottom while Bradbury, Wilkinson printings curl at the sides.

PERFORATION. All stamps in this Section are comb perforated 11 × 12 and the sheet perforation is always Type A.

PLATE NUMBERS. All plates were made from the original Waterlow Die. All stamps were printed from double plates producing left and right panes which were guillotined to make Post Office sheets of 40 (4 × 10). Plate numbers were used both by Waterlow and De La Rue but they appeared between the panes and were trimmed off. The Bradbury, Wilkinson plate numbers appear below stamps 3/4 in the bottom margin, the whole numbers on the left pane and the "A" numbers on the right pane. All three printers used rotary sheet-fed machines.

Bradbury, Wilkinson Plate No.

DE LA RUE PLATE DOTS. De La Rue printed on paper with St. Edward's Crown watermark and with Crowns watermark and as a control to distinguish the two papers during the change-over period, dots were inserted in the bottom margin below the first stamp in the bottom row.

In the case of the 2s.6d. the first printings on St. Edward's Crown paper were without dot, but later a single dot appeared on this paper, whilst early printings of stamps on the Crowns paper had two dots.

In the 10s. the dots are 7 mm. from the design and 5 mm. apart and in the other values they are 6 mm. from the design and 2½ mm. apart.

The number of sheets printed with double dots were:—

2s.6d.	93,630	10s.	37,510
5s.	60,158	£1	18,660

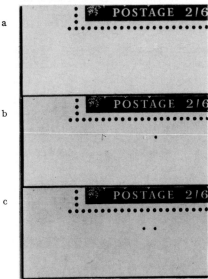

a. No dot   b. One dot   c. Two dots

145

DISTINGUISHING THE WORK OF THE THREE PRINTERS.   Waterlow printed the stamps up to 31 December 1957 and then De La Rue held the contract until 31 December 1962, after which all printings were made by Bradbury, Wilkinson. The following characteristics will help to distinguish their work:—

Paper

Waterlow	De La Rue	Bradbury, Wilkinson
(*a*) Wmk. W.**23** Creamy	(*a*) Wmk. W.**23** Light cream	(*a*) Wmk. W.**24** Whiter
(*b*) Wmk. W.**23** Light cream	(*b*) Wmk. W.**24** Light cream	(*b*) Wmk. W.**24** Chalky
(From Feb., '57)	(*c*) Wmk. W.**24** Whiter	(2s.6d. only)
	(From 1962)	(*c*) No wmk. White

Shades

	Waterlow	De La Rue
2s.6d.	Blackish brown	More chocolate
5s.	Rose-carmine	Lighter red, less carmine
10s.	Ultramarine	More blue
£1	Black	Less intense

The shade variations result in part from the differences in paper.

Gutters. The width of gutters between the stamps varies, particularly the horizontal, as follows:—

Waterlow	De La Rue
3.8 to 4.0 mm.	3.4 to 3.8 mm.

Later De La Rue plates were less distinguishable in this respect.

Perforation. The vertical perforation of the Bradbury, Wilkinson is 11.9 to 12 as against 11.8 for the De La Rue.

Impression. The individual lines of the De La Rue impression are cleaner and devoid of the whiskers of colour of Waterlow's, and the whole impression is lighter and softer. The Bradbury, Wilkinson stamps are generally more deeply engraved than the De La Rue, showing more of the diadem detail and heavier lines on the Queen's face.

Waterlow Sheet Markings

   Perforation Markings.   As a check for the alignment of the perforations the following marks occur between the stamps in the Waterlow printings only:—

   (*a*) 3 mm. cross in the centre of the sheet
   (*b*) 2½ mm. vertical lines in centre at top and bottom of sheet
   (*c*) 2½ mm. horizontal lines in centre at each side of sheet

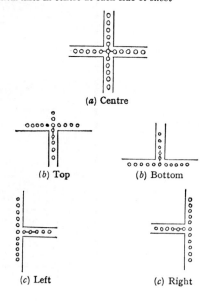

(*a*) Centre

(*b*) Top   (*b*) Bottom

(*c*) Left   (*c*) Right

Perforation Pin-holes. Coloured circles appear at left and right with a pin-hole through them opposite row six at left and right, although one is usually trimmed off.

Pin-hole   Corner trim mark

Corner Trim Marks. These occur in the corners but naturally one or both sides may be trimmed off.

De La Rue Sheet Markings

Guide Marks. The only markings on De La Rue sheets are the guide marks which appear in the side margins between rows 5 and 6 which also serve to distinguish the left and right panes. Their position varies with each value and also in some cases in format between the different plates used from time to time. The circles or crosses also have pin-holes.

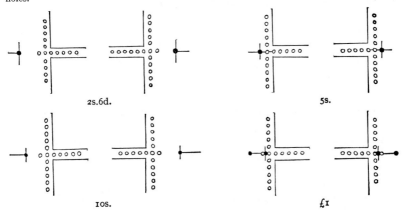

2s.6d.   5s.

10s.   £1

St. Edward's Crown Watermark
    2s. 6d., 5s., 10s., Type 1. £1 Type 1a

Multiple Crowns Watermark
    2s. 6d., Types 1, 2, 2a, 2b, 2c, 4. 5s. Types 1, 2c, 2d, 3. 10s. Types 1, 2, 2d. £1 Types 1, 1b, 2, 4a.

Specialists recognise four basic types of guide marks which are described as seen from left panes. Reverse for right.
    Type 1 Horizontal "T" shaped mark with spot at intersection
        a As above but dot added to left extremity of horizontal arm
        b As above but with "target" added between the two dots
The "target" mark is small, circular with open centre which was pierced by the perforating machine.

    Type 2 This is as type 1 but with the addition of a "target" between the horizontal "T" and stamp
        a As type 2 but intersection dot to right of cross over point
        b As type 2 but intersection dot to left of cross over point
        c As type 2 but no dot
        d As type 2c but "target" *joined* to "T"

    Type 3 This is as type 1 but "target" is added first followed by "T"

    Type 4 "Target" centred on "T" and without dot at intersection
        a As type 4 but arms partly erased (south and east arms erased left pane; north and west arms for right pane).

Bradbury, Wilkinson Sheet Markings

Guide Holes. These appear in a coloured circle opposite row 6, at left on left-hand panes and at right on right-hand panes.

Lay Dots. On the 2s. 6d. plates 1/1A to 7/7A small "lay" dots appear in the top sheet margin, above the first vertical row on the left-hand pane and on the right-hand pane above the fourth vertical row. Only one copy of the 5s. is known but examples may exist on the other values. These were guide marks to check any movement of the plate.

Guide hole   Guide cross

Guide Crosses. These occur in the region of rows 5 and 6 at right on left-hand panes and at left on right-hand panes. However, these do not appear on all plates, being omitted for instance on plates 8/8A, 9/9A of the 2s. 6d. and 4/4A of the 5s.

TINTED SHEET MARGINS. Some sheets show a background wash or tint of the colour in which the stamps are printed. This is an indication of a new state of a plate or a plate that has been rechromed. The explanation for this is that in wiping off the excess ink from the surface of the plate a small amount may be left at the edge of the plate and this will continue until the plate is sufficiently smooth for the surface to be thoroughly wiped clean of ink. These marginal tints stop short of the edge of the sheet as the extremities of the plate do not come into contact with the inking roller.

DATES OF ISSUE. Where a change of watermark or paper occurs the date given is generally that on which the stamps were first issued by the Supplies Department to Postmasters.

POST OFFICE TRAINING SCHOOL STAMPS. All values of the Waterlow printings exist overprinted with thick vertical bars and stamps from the other printings with thin vertical bars. These were supplied to Post Office Training Schools, and their issue to the public was unauthorised.

"CANCELLED" OVERPRINT. Nos. T5, T17 and T24 come overprinted "CANCELLED" (size 40 × 5 *mm*) as part of the test programme carried out by the Forensic Department of the Post Office.

The values overprinted "CANCELLED" (size 24 × 3*mm*) from the De La Rue archive are listed below No. T2.

WITHDRAWAL DATES. It is known that the following went off sale at the Philatelic Bureau in the months shown:

Mar. 1968   £1 No. T24
Nov. 1968   2s.6d. No. T6
Nov. 1968   5s. No. T12
Jan. 1969   2s.6d. No. T5
Mar. 1970   10s. No. T18

The **2s.6d., 5s., 10s. and £1** no watermark, white paper (Nos. T7, T13, T19 and T25) were all withdrawn on 15 May 1970.

All 2s. 6d., 5s. and 10s. stamps were invalidated as from 1 March 1972.

T1. Carrickfergus Castle

T2. Caernarvon Castle

T3. Edinburgh Castle

T4. Windsor Castle

(Des. Lynton Lamb. Portrait by Dorothy Wilding, Ltd.)

1955–68. 2s.6d., Type T1

Cat. No.	S.G. No.	Shades	Mint	Used

1955 (SEPTEMBER 23). WATERMARK ST. EDWARD'S CROWN, TYPE W.23

(a) Waterlow Printings

T1	536	Black-brown	10·00	2·00
a. Re-entry (R. 2/2) .. .. 40·00				

(b) De La Rue Printings (17 July 1958)

T2	536a	Black-brown	30·00	2·50

  a. Watermark inverted .. .. † —
  b. With one plate dot in bottom
    margin (R. 10/1) .. .. .. 65·00

Imprimatur from the National Postal Museum Archives

No. T1 imperforate, watermark Type W.23

Watermark upright

Cancelled Overprints from the De La Rue Archives

Nos. T2, T9, T15 and T21 overprinted "CANCELLED" (24 × 3mm) .. *Set of four* £600.

The overprint was handstamped in violet and impressions vary slightly in position.
  The above were from surplus registration sheets used by the printer for colour matching. They were placed on the market in 1990.

Plates. Plates numbered 47001, 47145 and 47316, each double pane, are known to have been used by Waterlow. These plates were later destroyed and it is possible that others could have been created. The De La Rue plates were made using the original Waterlow dies. No plate numbers were found on the issued sheets, but from study of the stamps it is likely that there were six double pane plates.

Listed Variety

T*1a*

The doubling occurs down the left-hand margin

Cat. No.	S.G. No.	Shades	Mint	Used

1959 (JULY 22). WATERMARK CROWNS, TYPE W.24

(a) De La Rue Printings

A. Light Cream Paper

T3	—	Black-brown	12·00	75

a. With two plate dots in bottom
margin (R. 10/1) .. .. 25·00

B. Whiter Paper (13 July 1962)

T4	595	Black-brown	10·00	75

a. Watermark inverted .. ..
No. T4*a*. Probably no more than five used examples exist.

(b) Bradbury, Wilkinson Printings

A. Whiter Paper (1 July 1963)

T5	595a	Black-brown	50	30

a. Watermark inverted .. £800 75·00
b. Weak entry (Pl. 5A, R.5/4 or
6/4) .. .. 7·50

c. Re-entry (Pl. 9A, R. 8/4) .. 7·50
d. Re-entry (Pl. 9, R. 10/2) .. 5·00

B. Chalky Paper (30 May 1968)

T6	595k	Black-brown	50	1·10

a. Re-entry (Pl. 9A, R. 8/4) .. 7·00

b. Re-entry (Pl. 9, R. 10/2) .. 5·00

Imprimatur from the National Postal Museum Archives

No. T6 imperforate, watermark Type W.24
Watermark upright

Listed Varieties

T5*b*

Lines of shading weak
or omitted at base of
collar, on dress and at
foot of background
Occurs on R. 5/4 and 6/4
(the illustration is of
R. 6/4)

T5*c*, T6*a*

Re-entry shows in the
form of brown dots over
battlements
The re-entry on Nos.
T5*d* and T6*b* occurs in
the same place but is
less marked

Plates Numbers (Blocks of Four)

Bradbury, Wilkinson Printings

Whiter Paper. (No. T5)

Pl. No.			Pl. No.			Pl. No.			Pl. No.		
1	..	22·00	1A	..	22·00	6	..	4·50	6A	..	4·50
2	..	22·00	2A	..	22·00	7	..	4·00	7A	..	4·00
3	..	22·00	3A	..	22·00	8	..	3·50	8A	..	3·50
4	..	£300	4A	..	£500	9	..	3·00	9A	..	3·00
5	..	8·50	5A	..	8·50						

Chalky Paper. (No. T6)

Pl. No.			Pl. No.		
9	..	3·00	9A	..	3·00

A "trial" perforation exists on plates 5 and 6, of which 21,000 sheets were reported to come
with double extension holes in the side margins.

Minor Constant Flaws

On Plate 9 there are a number of faint scratch marks in the top and bottom margins and
these are particularly noticeable on the chalky paper. They occur in the top margin on
R. 10/3 and in the bottom margin on R. 1/1, 1/2, 2/1, 3/3, 3/4, 7/2, 7/4 and 8/2.
Plates 8A, 10 and 10A all show evidence of progressive wear around the guide hole. On
plates 10 and 10A this takes the form of a crack extending from the guide hole towards
the stamps. Plate 13A R. 1/2 shows a 2 cm. long scratch on the left-hand side of the bottom margin.

Cat. No.	S.G. No.	Shades	Mint	Used
1968 (JULY 1). NO WATERMARK. WHITE PAPER				
Bradbury, Wilkinson Printings				
T7	759	Black-brown	40	50

Plate Numbers (Blocks of Four)

Pl. No.			Pl. No.			Pl. No.			Pl. No.		
10	..	3·00	10A	..	3·00	12	..	2·00	12A	..	2·00
11	..	3·00	11A	..	3·00	13	..	2·00	13A	..	2·00

Imprimatur from the National Postal Museum Archives

No. T7 imperforate

No watermark

1955–68. 5s., Type T2

Cat. No.	S.G. No.		Shades	Mint	Used

1955 (SEPTEMBER 23). WATERMARK ST. EDWARD'S CROWN, TYPE W.23

(a) Waterlow Printings

T8	537		Rose-carmine	40·00	3·50
a. Re-entry (R. 8/1)	..	.. 80·00			

(b) De La Rue Printings (30 April 1958)

T9	537a		Rose-carmine	75·00	6·50

Listed Variety

T8a

Major re-entry showing doubling of vertical lines of background above the diadem, and in the diadem along the left edge of the frontal cross, both sides of the side cross and the diagonals

Imprimatur from the National Postal Museum Archives

No. T8 imperforate, watermark Type W.23

Watermark upright

Plates. It is known that a double pane plate numbered 46726 was used by Waterlow. De La Rue created a further four plates, all double pane. Plate numbers did not occur on the issued sheets.

1959 (JUNE 15). WATERMARK CROWNS, TYPE W.24

(a) De La Rue Printings

A. Light Cream Paper

T10	—		Scarlet-vermilion	40·00	2·00
a. Watermark inverted	..	..			
b. With two plate dots in bottom margin (R. 10/1)	..	.. 80·00			

Twelve used, but no mint, examples have been reported of No. T10a.

B. Whiter Paper (7 May 1962)

T11	596		Scarlet-vermilion	40·00	2·00

(b) Bradbury, Wilkinson Printings

Whiter Paper (3 September 1963)

T12	596a		(1) Red	2·50	70
a. Watermark inverted	..	.. £225	50·00	(2) Brownish red	
b. Printed on the gummed side	.. £750		(Plates 3, 4)	1·00	60

Plate Numbers (Blocks of Four)
Bradbury, Wilkinson Printings. (No. T12)

Pl. No.		Pl. No.			Pl. No.			Pl. No.		
1	.. 45·00	1A	.. 45·00		3	..	5·00	3A	..	5·00
2	.. 45·00	2A	.. 45·00		4	..	7·50	4A	..	7·50

Cat. No.	S.G. No.	Shades	Mint	Used

1968 (APRIL 10). NO WATERMARK. WHITE PAPER
Bradbury, Wilkinson Printings

T13	760	Brownish red	1·00	1·00

Plate Numbers (Blocks of Four)

Pl. No.		Pl. No.			Pl. No.			Pl. No.		
4	.. 5·00	4A	.. 5·00		6	..	6·00	6A	..	6·00
5	.. 5·00	5A	.. 5·00							

Imprimatur from the National Postal Museum Archives

No. T13 imperforate
No watermark

1955–68. 10s., Type T3

Cat. No.	S.G. No.	Shades	Mint Used

1955 (SEPTEMBER 1). WATERMARK ST. EDWARD'S CROWN, TYPE W.23

(a) Waterlow Printings

T14   538   (1) Ultramarine   95·00   11·00
   a. Weak entry (R. 1/2)   ..   .. £125   20·00   (2) Pale ultramarine   95·00   11·00

(b) De La Rue Printings (25 April 1958)

T15   538a   Dull ultramarine   £150   19·00
   a. Weak frame (R. 4/1) £175

Listed Varieties

Other weak frames
have been found on
this design in different
positions but always
on the right-hand side
of the stamp

T14a   T15a, T17a

Weak entry to right of lower panel
gives ragged appearance

Minor Sheet Flaws

In rows 8, 9 and 10 there are blue marks on the extremity of the white letters and figures of " POSTAGE " and value which are more marked on the bottom two rows. These may not be fully constant but could be helpful for purposes of identification.

Imprimatur from the National Postal Museum Archives

No. T14 imperforate, watermark Type W.23

Watermark upright

Plates. It is known that Waterlow used a double pane plate numbered 46728. De La Rue are stated to have created three more, but study of the stamps suggests that four were made.

1959 (JULY 21). WATERMARK CROWNS, TYPE W.24

(a) De La Rue Printings

A. Light Cream Paper

T16   —   Blue   55·00   6·00
   a. With two plate dots in bottom
      margin (R. 10/1)   ..   ..   90·00

B. Whiter Paper (30 April 1962)

T17   597   Blue   35·00   5·00
   a. Weak frame (R. 4/1) ..   ..   50·00

(b) Bradbury, Wilkinson Printings

Whiter Paper (16 October 1963)

T18   597a   Bright ultramarine   2·50   3·00
   a. Watermark inverted ..   ..   — £650
No. T18a. Three used examples have been confirmed.

Plate Numbers (Blocks of Four)

Bradbury, Wilkinson Printings. (No. T18)

Pl. No.		Pl. No.		Pl. No.		Pl. No.	
1	.. 50·00	1A	.. 50·00	2	.. 14·00	2A	.. 14·00

1968 (APRIL 10).   NO WATERMARK. WHITE PAPER
Bradbury, Wilkinson Printings

T19	761	Bright ultramarine	5·00	5·50

Plate Numbers (Blocks of Four)

Pl. No.		Pl. No.	
2	.. 25·00	2A	.. 25·00

Imprimatur from the National Postal Museum Archives

No. T19 imperforate

No watermark

1955–67.   £1, Type T4

Cat. No.	S.G. No.	Shades	Mint	Used

1955 (SEPTEMBER 1).   WATERMARK ST. EDWARD'S CROWN, TYPE W.23

(a) Waterlow Printings

T20	539	Black	£160	28·00

(b) De La Rue Printings (28 April 1958)

T21	539a	Black	£275	50·00

Minor Re-entries

Waterlow Printings

1/2 Slight doubling (Th. B1 and D–F1)
4/4 Slight doubling (Th. B1)
5/2 Slight doubling (Th. B1 and D–E1)
6/1 Slight doubling (Th. A–C13)
7/1 Slight doubling (Th. A–C13)
Other minute signs of doubling of left frame line occur on R. 7/2 and of right frame line on R. 1/1, 2/1 3/3, 4/1, 4/2 and 9/2.

Imprimatur from the National Postal Museum Archives

No. T20 imperforate, watermark Type W.23

Watermark upright

Plates. It is known that the double pane plate used by Waterlow was numbered 46727. A further two plates were created by De La Rue. No plate numbers appeared on the issued sheets.

1959 (JUNE 23). WATERMARK CROWNS, TYPE W.24
(a) De La Rue Printings
A. Light Cream Paper

T22	—		Black	95·00 14·00
a.	With two plate dots in bottom margin (R. 10/1) £140			

B. Whiter Paper (30 April 1962)

T23	598		Black	85·00 12·00
a.	Watermark inverted .. .. — £1500			

No. T23*a*. No more than three or four examples, all used, have been reported.

(b) Bradbury, Wilkinson Printings
Whiter Paper (14 November 1963)

T24	598a		Black	10·00 5·00
a.	Watermark inverted .. .. — £2000			

Plate Numbers (Blocks of Four)
Bradbury, Wilkinson Printings. (No. T24)

Pl. No.		Pl. No.	
1	.. 50·00	1A	.. 50·00

1967 (DECEMBER 4). NO WATERMARK. WHITE PAPER
Bradbury, Wilkinson Printings

T25	762		Black	4·00 4·00

Plate Numbers (Blocks of Four)

Pl. No.		Pl. No.	
1	.. 20·00	1A	.. 20·00

Imprimatur from the National Postal Museum Archives
No. T25 perf. 11 × 12

No watermark

Presentation Pack

TPP1 (issued 1960)	Four values	£450

The issued pack contained one of each value in the De La Rue printing with Crowns watermark on the light cream paper (Nos. T3, T10, T16 and T22).

Three forms of the pack exist:
(a) Inscribed "$6·50" for sale in the U.S.A. (*Price* £550)
(b) Without price for sale in the U.K.
(c) With "£1.18s." for sale at 1960 Festival Hall, Int. Stamp Exhibition

SECTION U

Machin £.s.d. Issues

1967-70. Sheet and Coil Stamps in Photogravure

General Notes

INTRODUCTION. In February 1965, after twelve years of the Wilding portrait issue, the Queen granted permission for the preparation of studies for a new definitive series. Designs from several artists were submitted and Arnold Machin was eventually selected. His preferred approach, with the aim of emulating the simplicity of the Penny Black of 1840, was to present the Queen's head in profile by the medium of a plaster cast or plaque. He progressively worked upon this cast through most of 1966, for instance by adding a corsage at the Queen's request, until he was satisfied that his aim had been fulfilled. Photographs were taken of the cast in various conditions of light, of which one was finally approved. The first version came to be used for values with a solid background, but it was found to be unsatisfactory for other values with a light or gradated background. Accordingly an earlier version of the cast was also selected which gave an improved sculptured appearance to the image. There were small differences between these two casts, which, as is explained under Machin Heads on page 158, led to two different series of Head Types. Of the original casts used by Arnold Machin, one is in the National Postal Museum and the other is said to have been lost. The first three values, 4d., deep sepia, 1s. and 1s.9d., of the sterling Machin definitives appeared on 5 June 1967. The remaining values were issued in stages during the following thirteen months and the low value series was completed on 1 July 1968, although subsequent changes of stamp colours and variations in the number of phosphor bands on some values introduced further additions to the basic series. Uniquely this was the first definitive issue to be printed on paper without watermark, thus eliminating some of the factors which complicated the listing for previous issues.

PRINTERS. All the low value Machin issues £.s.d. were printed in photogravure by Harrison & Sons. They were printed on continuous reels of paper "on the web" generally in double pane width, i.e. 480 stamps consisting of two panes (no dot and dot) each of 240 stamps arranged in twenty rows of twelve stamps, the panes being guillotined before issue. The 10d., 1s.6d., 1s.9d. and part of the 1s. printings were made from single cylinders printing sheets of 240 stamps (i.e. no dot panes only).

The phosphor bands were applied at the same operation. The bi-coloured 1s.6d. and 1s.9d. were printed by the three-colour (including the phosphor cylinder) Halley machine and the remainder by the two-colour Timson machine. The multi-value coils and se-tenant panes from the £1 "Stamps for Cooks" booklet were printed by the five-colour Thrissel machine.

MASTER NEGATIVES and MULTIPOSITIVES. The process of preparing a new Machin definitive photogravure cylinder started with a master negative from photographs (sometimes referred to as master positives) of one of the two casts of the Queen's head in profile. Further master negatives are taken as needed and there is evidence that these can be retouched. The next step is the transfer of the image on this master negative by means of a step-and-repeat camera onto a photographic plate known as a multipositive, This is normally rather larger than the pane size of 200 or double pane size of 400. This multipositive of the head and background is then combined with a second multipositive for the face value, added to the previously screened carbon tissue. The relative positioning of these two multipositives is not always uniformly precise and can result in tiny variations of distance between head and value digits described under Machin Heads in these notes. Finally this carbon tissue forms the medium by means of which each new cylinder is etched. After an application of a thin layer of chrome the cylinder is ready for use.

PAPER. Unwatermarked chalk-surfaced paper was used for all values. Exceptionally, examples of all four panes from the £1 "Stamps for Cooks" booklet and the 3d. and 10d. from sheets exist on uncoated paper. It does not respond to the chalky test (that is applying silver to see if it will produce a black line) and may be further distinguished from the normal chalk-surfaced paper by the fibres which clearly show on the surface, resulting in the printing impression being rougher, and by the screening dots which are not so evident.

Paper Thickness. Variation in the thickness of paper sometimes occurs in the making and is undetected where the finished reel conforms to the prescribed weight. Within the reel there may be sections where the paper is unusually thick or thin. A particular example is the 2s. booklet of March 1970 which is known with panes UB15 and UB18 on very thick paper. This has an effect on the thickness of the booklet and could cause jamming in the vending machine. Such varieties are not listed. Certain coil issues were on translucent paper, the design showing clearly on the back of the stamps.

GUM. Polyvinyl alcohol (PVA) was introduced by Harrison & Sons in place of gum arabic in 1968. It is almost invisible except that a small amount of pale yellowish colouring matter was introduced to make it possible to see that the stamps had been gummed. Although this can be distinguished from gum arabic in unused stamps there is, of course, no means of detecting it in used copies. Where the two forms of gum exist on the same value they are listed separately.

It should be further noted that gum arabic is normally shiny in appearance, and that, normally, PVA has a matt appearance. However, depending upon the qualities of the paper ingredients and the resultant absorption of the gum, occasionally, PVA has a slightly shiny appearance, and in cases of severe under-gumming gum arabic may appear matt. In such cases it is sometimes impossible to be absolutely sure which gum has been used except by testing the stamps with a very expensive infra-red spectrometer. Chemical tests unfortunately destroy the stamps. Therefore, whilst very shiny gum is gum arabic it does not follow that all matt gum is PVA. A few late printings of stamps originally issued on PVA were made on gum arabic paper, either in error or to use up stocks.

Paper treated with gum arabic is passed over a fracture bar before printing to reduce its tendency to curl. This results in a "crazy paving" appearance, often visible under magnification, not present on PVA.

The term PVA is used because it is generally accepted, but the official abbreviation is PVAl to distinguish it from PVAc, polyvinyl acetate, another adhesive which has not so far been used for stamps, although it does occur on postal stationery. De La Rue use the term PVOH, polyvinyl hydroxyl, to describe the same adhesive.

MACHIN HEADS. Basically two master negatives were used for preparing the multipositive for each value comprising (a) head with background and (b) value. The portrait negative used for the initial releases had a three-dimensional effect only in the 1od. and 1s. values where a light background was used. On the other values, for which a different portrait master negative was used, the darker background merged with the outline and much of the relief effect was lost.

Beginning with coils and booklets in March 1968 a modified portrait negative was used giving greater contrast at those points where it had been lost. Thus there are three clearly different portraits; the original Head A with a flatter bust, Head B with a curved "shadow" and Head C the three-dimensional version from the light background stamps.

These differences are listed and, for ease of reference, appear in tabulated form, together with details of the phosphor screens, at the beginning of the catalogue list.

As a result of the combination of two master negatives described above the position of the value in relation to the frame varies from one multipositive to another. The 2d. Types I and II show an extreme case of this, where the change was made deliberately. Taking the 4d. for example the distance to the left frame varies from 0·9 mm. on the early sheet cylinders to 1·2 mm. on the multi-value coils, while the spacing to the bottom is normally 0·9 mm. but decreases to 0·6 mm. in the £1 "Stamps for Cooks" booklet.

PHOSPHOR BANDS. See the General Notes for Section S for a detailed description of these. The Machin definitives were normally issued with "violet" phosphor bands only. Most values have appeared with the phosphor omitted in error and these are listed separately.

The 1s. 6d. (No. U29) was issued as an experiment in 1969 with violet phosphor incorporated into the coating.

PHOSPHOR SCREENS. The phosphor bands were applied in photogravure, some of the cylinders having a 150-line screen and others a 250-line screen. The absence of a screen on parts of a printing is due to the cylinder becoming clogged.

The phosphor screen used for the single centre band on the 3d., 4d. sepia and 4d. vermilion booklet panes of six is unique in having a mixed screen. Continuous 21-row cylinders are normally produced from two pieces of carbon tissue, thus giving two joins. On this particular phosphor cylinder, the pieces of carbon tissue had different screens. Thus four types of booklet panes can be found—(1) 150 screen; (2) screen join 150/250; (3) 250 screen; (4) screen join 250/150. It is calculated that out of 100 panes the proportions are 67 150 screen, 14 250 screen and 19 screen joins.

It is not easy to distinguish the different screens but we include them in the following check list of the Machin Head Types.

PERFORATION. Harrisons used the same 15 × 14 comb perforation as for the previous Wilding definitives. A number of different perforators were used for both sheets and booklets and these are described and illustrated in Appendix G. The cylinder numbers are listed and priced according to the type of perforator used.

BOOKLET PANES. In Section UB we list separately the booklet panes and the varieties on them and priced according to perforator types. See General Notes to that Section.

COIL VARIETIES. See the General Notes for Section S for detailed notes on these.

SHADES. There are numerous shades in these issues and we have restricted our listing to the most marked ones and related them to the cylinder number blocks where possible.

DATES OF ISSUE. The dates given are those announced by the Post Office, except in the case of dates for changes of gum or in the number of phosphor bands when we have quoted either the dates of release by the Philatelic Bureau or the earliest dates known. As in Section S the dates given in bold type in the headings are those on which stamps first appeared in sheet form. Where a date is followed by a dagger it means that the stamp appeared earlier in coils or booklets as indicated in footnotes.

FIRST DAY COVERS. They are listed after the Presentation Pack but we only quote for official covers, prepared and issued by the Post Office, cancelled by "FIRST DAY OF ISSUE" circular postmarks.

PRESENTATION PACKS. See General Notes under Section W.

"UNPRINTED STAMPS". Widely trimmed sheet margins may produce the effect of unprinted stamps as illustrated above. The blank paper has the phosphor bands printed as on the normal stamps. In the Machin and Regional issues they come from either the left or right-hand margins; in the special issues they are known from the top of the sheet.

INVALIDATION. All £.s.d. Machin definitives were withdrawn from sale on 25 November 1971, and were, with the exception of the £1 value, invalidated as from 1 March 1972. They ceased to be valid in Guernsey and Jersey from 1 October 1969 when these islands each established their own independent postal administrations and introduced their own stamps.

SHEET MARKINGS. Reference should be made to the descriptions of sheet markings given in the General Notes for Section S, as most of these apply to this Section and the information given there is not repeated here. In the case of the 1s.6d. and 1s.9d. bicoloured Machin definitives reference should be made to the descriptions of sheet markings given in Section W as many of them also apply to these two values. Additional information to that provided in Sections S and W is given here.

Cylinder Numbers. In the Machin definitives ½d. to 1s. values they appear in the left-hand margin opposite Row 18 No. 1 in the style as illustrated in Section S. In the case of the 1s.6d. and 1s.9d. values the cylinder numbers appear boxed in the left-hand margin opposite Row 19 No. 1 in the style as illustrated in Section W.

Phosphor Cylinder Numbers. As with the Special issues in Section W, phosphor cylinder numbers were introduced during 1970, "Ph 1" appearing on the Machin issues. It only occurs on the dot panes and appears in the right-hand margin and therefore not on the cylinder block. Moreover it is not synchronised with the ink cylinders and so can appear anywhere in the margin, and the "1" is often trimmed off. Its existence is recorded under the sheet markings.

Varieties in Cylinder Blocks. Where a cylinder block contains a listed variety the price is adjusted accordingly and bears an asterisk.

Marginal Arrows. In the Machin definitives these are "W" shaped (photo-etched) at top, bottom and sides, unless otherwise stated.

Perforation Guide Holes. A number of different styles of guide hole box have been used for the Machin definitives and these are fully illustrated as for Sections S and W.

In addition to guide hole boxes of one type or another opposite rows 14/15 (used for perforation Type A), the earlier cylinders of nearly all the values from ½d. to 1s. also show a single "traffic light" type box above and below the eighth vertical row in the no dot panes. This latter type would only be used in conjunction with perforation Type F (L)* and it is illustrated here to explain its presence on the sheets. When Type F (L)* is used the circular central part of the box is either partly or completely removed.

CHECK LIST OF MACHIN HEADS AND PHOSPHOR SCREENS

For fuller explanations see General Notes.

Head A	Head B
Flatter base	Curved shadow

Head C

Three-dimensional effect with light background

Abbreviations

Phosphor bands: 1C = one centre; 1L = one left side; 1R = one right side
Booklet panes: s/t = stamps *se-tenant*; s/t labels = stamps *se-tenant* with labels
Coils: MV = multi-value; S = sideways delivery; V = vertical delivery

Face Value	Cat. No.	Description	Phosphor Bands	Gum	Head	Screen	Sheet Cylinders	Sources Booklet Panes	Coils
½d.	U 1		2	PVA	A	150	2, 3	—	—
1d.	U 2		2	PVA	A	150	2	—	—
	U 2		2	PVA	B	150	4, 6	6	V
	U 2		2	PVA	B	250	—	s/t, 6 s/t 15 s/t	—
	U 3		1C	PVA	B	250	—	6 s/t	—
	U 4		1C	GA	B	250	—	—	MV
2d.	U 5	Type I	2	PVA	A	150	1	—	—
	U 6	Type II	2	PVA	B	150	5, 6	—	V
	U 6	,,	2	PVA	B	250	—	—	V, S
	U 7	,,	1C	GA	B	250	—	—	MV
3d.	U 8		1C	GA	A	150	1	—	V
	U 8		1C	GA	A	250	—	—	S
	U 8		1C	GA	B	250	—	—	MV
	U 9		1C	PVA	A	150	1, 3, 4	—	—
	U 9		1C	PVA	A	250	—	—	S
	U 9		1C	PVA	B	150	—	6	—
	U 9		1C	PVA	B	Join	—	6	—
	U 9		1C	PVA	B	250	—	6	—
	U10		2	PVA	A	150	3, 4	—	V
	U10		2	PVA	B	150	—	—	V
	U10		2	PVA	B	250	—	4 s/t	—
4d.	U11	Sepia	2	GA	A	150	4, 8	6	V
	U11	,,	2	GA	A	250	—	—	S
	U11	,,	2	GA	B	250	14	—	—
	U12	,,	2	PVA	A	150	4, 10, 12, 13	6	—
	U12	,,	2	PVA	B	250	14, 15	4	—
	U13	,,	1C	PVA	A	150	4, 12, 13	6	V
	U13	,,	1C	PVA	A	Join	—	6	—
	U13	,,	1C	PVA	A	250	—	6	S
	U13	,,	1C	PVA	B	250	14, 15	4, 4 s/t labels 6 s/t	—

Face Value	Cat. No.	Description	Phosphor Bands	Gum	Head	Screen	Sheet Cylinders	Sources Booklet Panes	Coils
4d.	U14	Vermilion	1C	PVA	A	150	4, 10, 13	6	V
	U14	,,	1C	PVA	A	Join	—	6	—
	U14	,,	1C	PVA	A	250	—	6	S
	U14	,,	1C	PVA	B	150	—	6	—
	U14	,,	1C	PVA	B	Join	—	6	—
	U14	,,	1C	PVA	B	250	15, 16, 17	4, 4 s/t labels, 6, 15	S
	U15	,,	1C	GA	B	250	—	—	MV
	U15	,, Feb/Mar	1C	GA	A	150	—	6	—
	U15	,, '69 6s. &	1C	GA	A	Join	—	6	—
	U15	,, May '69 10s.	1C	GA	A	250	—	6	—
	U16	,,	1L	PVA	B	250	—	6 s/t, 15 s/t	—
	U16A	,,	1R	PVA	B	250	—	15 s/t	—
5d.	U17		2	PVA	A	150	1	—	—
	U17		2	PVA	B	150	7, 10, 15	6	V
	U17		2	PVA	B	250	11, 13	15, 15 s/t	S
6d.	U18		2	PVA	A	150	2, 3, 4, 5	—	—
	U18		2	PVA	B	150	—	—	V
	U18		2	PVA	B	250	—	—	V
7d.	U19		2	PVA	B	150	3, 4	—	—
8d.	U20	Vermilion	2	PVA	A	150	2	—	—
	U21	Turquoise-blue	2	PVA	B	150	3	—	—
9d.	U22		2	GA	A	150	2	—	—
	U23		2	PVA	A	150	2	—	—
10d.	U24		2	PVA	C	150	1	—	—
	U24		2	PVA	C	250	1	—	—
1s.	U25		2	GA	C	150	3, 11	—	—
	U26		2	PVA	C	150	11	—	—
	U26		2	PVA	C	250	11	—	—
1s.6d.	U27		2	GA	A	150	2A–2B, 3A–2B	—	—
	U27 (3)	Phosphor omitted	—	GA	A	—	5A–2B	—	—
	U28		2	PVA	A	150	3A–2B, 5A–2B	—	—
	U28		2	PVA	A	250	3A–1B	—	—
	U29	"All-over" phos.	—	PVA	A	—	5A–2B	—	—
1s.9d.	U30		2	GA	A	150	1A–1B	—	—
	U31		2	PVA	A	250	1A–1B	—	—

INDEX TO COIL STAMPS

Face Value	Phosphor Bands	Gum	Head	Further description	Delivery	See stamp No.
1d.	2	PVA	B	.. ..	V	U2
2d.	2	PVA	B	Type II	V S	U6
3d.	1C	GA	A	.. ..	V S	U8
3d.	1C	PVA	A	.. ..	S	U9
3d.	2	PVA	A	.. ..	V	U10
3d.	2	PVA	B	.. ..	V	U10
4d.	2	GA	A	Deep olive-brown	V S	U11
4d.	1C	PVA	A	Deep olive-brown	V S	U13
4d.	1C	PVA	A	Bright vermilion	V S	U14
4d.	1C	PVA	B	Bright vermilion	S	U14
5d.	2	PVA	B	.. ..	V S	U17
6d.	2	PVA	B	.. ..	V	U18
2×2d. +3d. +1d. +4d.	1C	GA	B	Multi-value coil. 4d. Bright vermilion	S	U32

PAPER AND WATERMARK

All the following issues are printed on chalk-surfaced paper, except for the uncoated errors, and are without watermark.

U1
Value at left

U2
Value at right

Queen Elizabeth II

(Des. after plaster cast by Arnold Machin)

½d., Type U1 (1968)

Cat. No.	S.G. No.	Shades	Mint	Used
1968 (FEBRUARY 5). TWO 9·5 mm. PHOSPHOR BANDS. PVA GUM. HEAD A				
U1	723	Orange-brown	10	20

  a. Phosphor omitted .. .. 30·00
  b. Dot in 1 of ½ (Cyl. 3 No dot,
        R. 20/2) .. .. 2·50

Listed Variety

U1*b*

Cylinder Numbers (Blocks of Six)

Perforation Type A

Cyl. No.				No dot	Dot
2	..	..	..	1·90	1·90
3	..	..	..	3·75*	3·00

  *Includes variety U1*b*.

Minor Constant Sheet Flaws

Cyl. 2. 5/12 Small retouch at base of Queen's hair (Th. E4–5)
           9/5 Dark horizontal strip of shading behind Queen's neck (Th. F5–6)
Cyl. 3 12/9 Dark patch below Queen's chin (Th. E2–3)

A number of stamps from cylinder 2 dot display irregularities of the background in the form of dark patches and lines. This is most prominent on R. 9/5 recorded above; others occur on R. 2/2, 7/6, 8/6, 9/11, 10/1, 13/2–5, 14/5, 17/4–5, and 18/1.

Sheet Markings

Guide holes: In double "S O N" box opposite rows 14/15, at left (no dot) or right (dot). In addition a single "traffic light" type box appears above and below the eighth vertical row in the no dot pane only. (These would only be used in conjunction with perforation Type F (L)*).

Others: As given in General Notes

Sold Out 10.2.70.

1d., Type U1 (1968-70)

Cat. No.	S.G. No.	Shades	Mint	Used

1968 (FEBRUARY 5).

A. Two 9·5 mm. Phosphor Bands. PVA Gum

U2   724

  a. Imperf. (coil strip)* £750

  b. Uncoated paper ('70)** .. .. 65·00

  c. Phosphor omitted .. .. .. 1·00

  d. Phosphor omitted on front but printed on the gummed side ..

  e. One broad phosphor band .. 2·00

  f. Left-hand band omitted .. .. 30·00

  g. Neck retouches (Cyl. 4 No dot, R. 20/3) .. .. 3·00

  h. Flaw by Queen's chin (Vertical coil) .. .. 3·50

  i. Thick "1 D" (Vertical coil) .. 10·00

  j. Flaw by Queen's chin (Vertical coil) .. .. 3·50

  s. Optd. "Specimen" (14 mm.) .. £150

(A) Head A

(1) Light olive   50   10

(B) Head B

(2) Yellowish olive   10   10

(3) Greenish olive   10   10

B. One 4 mm. Centre Phosphor Band. PVA Gum.
Se-tenant Booklet pane only (16 September 1968)

U3   725   Yellowish olive (Head B)   25   30

C. One 4 mm. Centre Phosphor Band. Gum Arabic.
Multi-value coil only (27 August 1969)

U4   725Eg   Yellowish olive (Head B)   25

  a. Dark vert. line (Roll 7 etc.) .. 2·50

*No. U2a occurs in a vertical strip of four, top stamp perforated on three sides, bottom stamp imperf. three sides and the two middle stamps completely imperf.

**Uncoated paper. No. U2b comes from the *se-tenant* pane of 15 in the £1 "Stamps for Cooks" Booklet (see No. UB2ab); see also General Notes.

No. U3 only comes from the 10s. Booklet of September 1968 (XP6). It also occurs with the phosphor omitted but since a single stamp would be difficult to distinguish from No. U2c it is only listed when in a complete *se-tenant* booklet pane (see No. UB3a).

No. U4 only comes from the multi-value coil strip which is listed as No. U32.

Listed Varieties

U2g

U2h

U4a
This is Roll 7 but a similar variety occurs on Roll 3 and it may occur on others.

Normal U2i

U2j

Cylinder Numbers (Blocks of Six)

Two bands. Perforation Type A

Cyl. No.		No dot	Dot
2 (Shade 1) (Head A) ..	..	4·75	4·75
4 (Shade 2) (Head B) ..	..	1·10	1·10
6 (Shade 3) (Head B) ..	..	1·10	1·10

Minor Constant Sheet Flaws

Cyl. **2.**   5/11 Small flaw at back of Queen's collar (Th. F5)

Cyl. 4   6/9 White flaw at top of Queen's hair (Th. B3)

Cyl. 6.   11/7 Horizontal line of coloured dots across Queen's shoulder (Th. F3–5)
       12/10 Vertical lines of coloured dots through Queen's forehead and cheek (Th. B2, C2–3 and D2)

Coils

Two bands.   Vertical delivery printed in continuous reels from double pane cylinder B1 Head B

Code No.	Number in roll	Face value
E	480	£2
X	960	£4
Z	1920	£8

One centre band. Multi-value coil, see No. U32.

Sheet Markings

Guide holes:
     Cyl. 4, in single "SN" box opposite rows 14/15, at left (no dot) or right (dot)
     Cyls. 2 and 6, in double "SON" box opposite rows 14/15, at left (no dot) or right (dot)

Marginal arrows:
     Cyls. 2 and 6, "W" shaped, photo-etched at top, bottom and sides
     Cyl. 4, "W" shaped, hand engraved at top, bottom and sides

Marginal rule:
     Cyl. 2, at bottom of sheet, 2 mm. wide
     Cyls. 4 and 6, at bottom of sheet, 2½ mm. wide

Others: As given in General Notes

2d., Type U1 (1968-69)

Two Types

I   II

Type I. Value spaced away from left side of stamp (Cyls. 1 no dot and dot)

Type II. Value closer to left side from new multipositive (Cyls. 5 no dot and dot onwards). The portrait appears in the centre, thus conforming to the other values.

Cat. No.	S.G. No.		Shades	Mint	Used

1968 (FEBRUARY 5).   TYPE I.   TWO 9·5 mm. PHOSPHOR BANDS.   PVA GUM. HEAD A

U5   726   Lake-brown   10   15
   a. Phosphor omitted ..   ..   ..   25·00

Cylinder Numbers (Blocks of Six)
Perforation Type A

Cyl. No.					No dot	Dot
1	..	..	..	..	1·40	1·40

Minor Constant Sheet Flaws
Cyl. 1   3/11 Small white spot in band of diadem (Th. C5)
        8/8 Dark spot by emblems at rear of diadem (Th. B5)
      12/9 Retouching in Queen's hair just by ear (Th. C–D4)

Sheet Markings
   Guide holes: In double " S O N " box opposite rows 14/15, at left (no dot) or right (dot)
   Others: As given in General Notes

1969 (FEBRUARY).†   CHANGE TO TYPE II.   HEAD B
A. Two 9·5 mm. Phosphor Bands. PVA Gum

U6   727   Lake-brown   15   15
   a. Phosphor omitted   ..   ..   1·00
   b. One broad phosphor band   ..   20·00

B. One 4 mm. Centre Phosphor Band. Gum Arabic.
Multi-value coil only (27 August 1969)
U7   728   Lake-brown   40   50
   †No. U6 was issued on 4 April 1968 in sideways delivery coils, and on 19 March 1969 in vertical delivery coils.
   No. U7 only comes from the multi-value coil strip which is listed as No. U32.

Cylinder Numbers (Blocks of Six)
Two bands. Perforation Type A

Cyl. No.					No dot	Dot
5	..	..	..	..	2·50	1·60
6	..	..	..	..	1·90	1·60

Minor Constant Sheet Flaws
Cyl. 5.   6/8 Dark area above 2 (Th. F1)
        8/1 Small flaw on Queen's shoulder (Th. F3)
      10/1 Coloured line through Queen's nose and upper lip (Th. C–D2)
      10/3 Dark area below Queen's chin (Th. E2)
      19/5 Retouch to background to left of diadem (Th. A2–3). There are two states of this
Cyl. 6.   18/4 Small retouch at top of Queen's neck and vertical scratch extending to her dress (Th. E3–G3).
          Several states exist

Coils
   Two bands.   Printed in continuous reels from double pane cylinders D2 (vertical) or single pane D1 (sideways)

Code No.	Number in roll	Face value	
T	480	£4	Sideways delivery
V	960	£8	Vertical delivery

   One centre band. Multi-value coil, see No. U32.

Sheet Markings
   Phosphor cylinder number: "Ph 1" found on a later printing of cyl. 6 dot, right margin (*price £15 in block of* 6).
   Guide holes: In double "S O N" box opposite rows 14/15, at left (no dot) or right (dot). In addition a single "traffic light" type box appears above and below the eighth vertical row in the no dot pane only (These would only be used in conjunction with perforation Type F (L)*).
   Others: As given in General Notes

3d., Type U1 (1967-69)

Cat. No.	S.G. No.		Shades	Mint	Used

1967 (AUGUST 8). ONE 4 mm. CENTRE PHOSPHOR BAND

A. Gum Arabic

U8   729

a. Imperf (vertical pair)	£475
b. Phosphor omitted	1·25
c. Spot on nose (Sideways coil, Roll 10)	3·00
d. Gash on diadem (Multi-value coil, Roll 1)	3·50

(A) Head A
(1) Violet   10   10
(2) Bluish violet (sideways coils) 1·00   25

(B) Head B
(1) Violet (multi-value coils)   50   15

B. PVA Gum (12 March 1968)

U9   729Ev

a. Phosphor omitted	1·25
b. Spot on nose (Sideways coil, Roll 10)	3·00

(A) Head A
(1) Violet   10
(2) Bluish violet (sideways coils) 28·00

(B) Head B
(1) Violet (booklets)   2·00

No. U8 is known pre-released on 7 August at Bournemouth, Hyde (Cheshire), in South London and at Torquay.

Listed Varieties

U8c, U9b
From sideways delivery coils

U8d
Occurs in sideways delivery multi-value GS and GL coils on every fifth 3d. stamp

Cylinder Numbers (Blocks of Six)

	Gum Arabic				PVA Gum			
	Perforation Type A				Perforation Type A			
Cyl. No.			No dot	Dot	Cyl. No.		No dot	Dot
1	.. .. ..	14·00	16·00	1	.. ..	1·60	1·60
	Perforation Type F (L)*				3	.. ..	1·75	1·75
1	.. ..	1·75	1·75	4	.. ..	4·00	4·00
					Perforation Type F(L)*			
					1	.. ..	†	—

There are two states of cyl. 1 no dot: (a) " 1 " is hatched, the bottom part lacks colour and the serifs are short (gum arabic printings); (b) " 1 " is solid and the serifs are long (gum arabic perf. type F(L)* and PVA).

Cylinder blocks from the no dot pane of Cylinder 3 show a phantom " 3 ", slightly smaller and just below and to the right of the normal cylinder number. This occurred on part of the printing.

Minor Constant Sheet Flaws

Cyl. 1   1/9 Vertical scratch on Queen's neck (Th. E3–4)
          3/9 Pale patch in background around D of value
          7/1 Small white flaw inside cross of diadem (Th. B5)

Cyl. 1.   1/4 Small retouch on Queen's neck below ear (Th. D4). PVA only
          1/7 White scratch in Queen's hair below diadem at right (Th. C5). PVA only
         4/11 Small retouch on Queen's neck (Th. E3)
         12/4 Retouch at front of Queen's collar (Th. G3)
         19/6 Small retouch by Queen's mouth (Th. D3)

Cyl. 3.   8/3 Scratch on Queen's temple (Th. C3)
         12/7 Retouch on Queen's neck below necklace (Th. F4)
         16/4 Flaw on Queen's shoulder (Th. F4). Later retouched

Coils

Printed in continuous reels from double pane cylinder M1 (vertical) or single pane M2 (sideways). Head A

Gum Arabic.

Code No.	Number in roll	Face value	
S	480	£6	Sideways delivery
AC	480	£6	Vertical delivery
AD	960	£12	do.
U	1920	£24	do.

PVA Gum

S*	480	£6	Sideways delivery

*Stamps from this coil can be distinguished from all other PVA centre-band stamps in singles. The coil stamps have Machin Head Type A and 250-line phosphor screen. The sheet stamps have Head Type A and 150-line screen, whilst the booklet stamps have Head Type B.

For the multi-value coil, see No. U32

Sheet Markings

Guide holes:
Perf. Type A, in double "S O N" box opposite rows 14/15, at left (no dot) or right (dot). In addition a single "traffic light" type box appears above and below the eighth vertical row in the no dot pane from cyl. 1 (latter only used in conjunction with perforation Type F (L)*).
Perf. Type F (L)*, boxed above and below the eighth vertical row in the no dot pane only. The usual "S O N" boxes opposite rows 14/15 remain.

Others: As given in General Notes

Cat. No.	S.G. No.	Shades		Mint	Used
1969 (AUGUST 20).† CHANGE TO TWO 9·5 mm. PHOSPHOR BANDS. PVA GUM					
U10	730	Violet			
a. Uncoated paper*	£900		(A) Head A	30	30
b. One broad phosphor band ..	2·00		(B) Head B	50	20

*Uncoated paper—see General Notes.

†Issued on 6.4.68 in 2s. Booklets dated May 1968, on 26 September 1968 in vertical delivery coils.

Cylinder Numbers (Blocks of Six)

Perforation Type A

Cyl. No.				No dot	Dot
3 (Head A)	..	..	..	3·25	3·25
4 (Head A)	..	..	..	5·50	5·50

The note about the phantom "3" mentioned under No. U9 also applies here and the whole of the printing was affected.

Minor Constant Sheet Flaws

Cyl. 3.   8/3   Scratch on Queen's temple (Th. C3)
     12/7   Retouch on Queen's neck below necklace (Th. F4)

Coil

Vertical delivery printed in continuous reels from double pane cylinders M1 (Head A) or M4 (Head B)

Code No.	Number in roll	Face value
AD	960	£12

Sheet Markings

Guide holes: In double "S O N" box opposite rows 14/15, at left (no dot) or right (dot)
Others: As given in General Notes

4d., Type U1 (1967-70)

Cat. No.	S.G. No.	Shades	Mint	Used

1967 (JUNE 5).   TWO 9·5 mm. PHOSPHOR BANDS

A. Gum Arabic

U11   731/*Ea*

a. Phosphor omitted. Shade (1)	..	1·00		
ab. Phosphor omitted. Shade (2)	..	1·25		
b. One broad phosphor band	..	35·00		
c. Right-hand band omitted ..	..	45·00		

(A) Head A
(1) Deep sepia	10	10
(2) Deep olive-brown	10	15

(B) Head B
(2) Deep olive-brown	£1800

B. PVA Gum (22 January 1968)

U12   731Ea*v*

a. One broad phosphor band	..	2·00	
b. Phosphor omitted	.. ..	1·00	
c. White patch (Cyl. 13 No dot, R. 20/12)	.. .. ..	3·75	
d. Nick in hair (Cyl. 15 Dot, R. 16/5)	.. ..	3·50	

(A) Head A
(2) Deep olive-brown	10	
(3) Deep olive-sepia	10	10

(B) Head B
(2) Deep olive-brown	10	10
(3) Deep olive-sepia	10	10

No. U11 (1) in shades of washed out grey are colour changelings which we understand are caused by the concentrated solvents used in modern dry-cleaning methods.

No. U11 (1) is known pre-released on 25 May at Gravesend.

Listed Varieties

U12*c*, U13*b*, U14*e*
White patch over
eye and hair

U12*d* U13*c*, U14*f*
Reported as
being later retouched

Cylinder Numbers (Blocks of Six)

Gum Arabic

Cyl. No.			No dot	Dot
Perforation Type F (L)*				
(a) Shade (1) Deep sepia				
4 (Head A)	..	..	4·50	4·50
8 (Head A)	..	..	4·00	4·00
(b) Shade (2) Deep olive-brown				
4 (Head A)	..	..	9·00	9·00
8 (Head A)	..	..	9·00	9·00
Perforation Type A				
14 (Head B)	..	..	—	—

PVA Gum

Cyl. No.			No dot	Dot
(a) Shade (2) Deep olive-brown				
Perforation Type F (L)*				
4 (Head A)	..	..	18·00	12·00
Perforation Type A				
4 (Head A)	..	..	8·00	8·00
10 (Head A)	..	..	2·50	2·50
12 (Head A)	..	..	2·75	2·75
13 (Head A)	..	..	14·00	14·00
14 (Head B)	..	..	1·50	1·50
15 (Head B)	..	..	60·00	60·00
(b) Shade (3) Deep olive-sepia				
Perforation Type A				
14 (Head B)	..	..	2·75	2·75
15 (Head B)	..	..	60·00	60·00

Stamps from cylinder 12 show traces of screening dots within the white area of the face value. Cylinder 15 has the number close to the stamp resulting in the dot often being removed by the perforations. The dot pane has a tiny dot on the horizontal rule below R. 20/1 whilst in the no dot pane the marginal rule below R. 20/1 is damaged and there is a line in the margin below R. 20/2.

Minor Constant Sheet Flaws

Cyl. 4. 1/1 Nick in neck (Th. F5)
       1/13 Nick in neck (Th. F5)
       2/9 Dark flaw in Queen's hair (Th. C4)
       20/8 Scar on Queen's forehead (Th. C2–3)
Cyl. 8 18/12 Diagonal line through back of Queen's hair (Th. C5)
Cyl. 8. 9/9 White spot in band of diadem (Th. B3–4)
       15/3 Diagonal coloured line on Queen's shoulder and dress (Th. F–G4)
       15/5 Prominent retouch on Queen's neck just below jawline (Th. E3–4)
Cyl. 10 18/12 As Cyl. 8
Cyl. 10. 3/4 Coloured flaw on Queen's shoulder (Th. F3)
       3/6 Two coloured flaws on Queen's shoulder (Th. F3)
       10/8 Pale patch in background to left of Queen's throat (Th. E2)
       11/7 Dark flaw at back of Queen's neck, just above necklace (Th. E4)
       12/5 Dark flaw on Queen's shoulder, just below necklace (Th. F3)
       15/3 As Cyl. 8
       15/5 As Cyl. 8
       19/2 Dark coloured vertical line in lower right-hand stamp margin (Th. G7)
Cyl. 12 18/12 As Cyl. 8
Cyl. 12. 15/3 As Cyl. 8
       15/5 As Cyl. 8
Cyl. 13 9/12 Large area of retouching behind Queen's head (Th. C5–6 and D5–6)
      18/12 As Cyl. 8
Cyl. 13. 15/3 As Cyl. 8
       15/5 As Cyl. 8 but more prominent
Cyl. 14 6/11 Vertical white scratch on Queen's neck (Th. E–F4)
      18/7 White flaw at back of Queen's dress (Th. F5)

Coils

Printed in continuous reels from double pane cylinder P3 (vertical) or single pane P1 (sideways). Head A

Gum Arabic. Shade (2) Deep olive-brown

Code No.	Number in roll	Face value	
H	480	£8	Sideways delivery
A	960	£16	Vertical delivery

Sheet Markings

Guide holes:
    Perf. Type A, in double " S O N " box opposite rows 14/15, at left (no dot) or right (dot). In addition a single " traffic light " type box appears above and below the eighth vertical row in the no dot pane only (latter only used in conjunction with perforation Type F (L)*).
    Perf. Type F (L)*, boxed above and below the eighth vertical row in the no dot pane only. The usual " S O N " boxes opposite rows 14/15 remain.

Others: As given in General Notes

Cat. No.	S.G. No.	Shades		Mint	Used

1968 (SEPTEMBER 16). CHANGE TO ONE 4 mm. CENTRE PHOSPHOR BAND. PVA GUM

				Mint	Used
U13	732		(A) Head A		
b.	White patch (Cyl. 13 No dot, R. 20/12)	4·00	(2) Deep olive-brown	10	10
c.	Nick in hair (Cyl. 15 Dot, R. 16/5)	3·75	(B) Head B		
			(2) Deep olive-brown	12	10
			(3) Deep olive-sepia	15	10

For illustrations of Nos. U13b/c see Nos. U12c/d.

No. U13 also occurs with the phosphor omitted but since a single stamp would be indistinguishable from No. U12b it is only listed when in a complete *se-tenant* booklet pane (see No. UB3a).

Cylinder Numbers (Blocks of Six)

Perforation Type A

(a) Shade (2) Deep olive-brown

Cyl. No.				No dot	Dot
4 (Head A)	..	..	..	1·75	1·75
12 (Head A)	..	..	..	1·75	1·75
13 (Head A)	..	..	..	50·00	40·00
14 (Head B)	..	..	..	2·00	2·00
15 (Head B)	..	..	..	2·00	2·00

(b) Shade (3) Deep olive-sepia

Cyl. No.				No dot	Dot
14 (Head B)	..	..	..	2·50	2·50
15 (Head B)	..	..	..	2·40	2·40

The notes, concerning cylinders 12 and 15, under No. U12 also apply here.

Minor Constant Sheet Flaws

Cyl. 4. 1/1   Nick in neck (Th. F5)
         1/13 Nick in neck (Th. F5)
         2/9   Coloured flaw in Queen's hair (Th. C4)
         19/1 Flaw on lower rim of Queen's diadem shows as "missing pearls" (Th. C5)
         20/8 Scar on Queen's forehead (Th. C2–3)
Cyl. 12   18/12 Diagonal line through back of Queen's hair (Th. C5)
Cyl. 12. 15/3 Diagonal coloured line on Queen's shoulder and dress (Th. F–G4)
          15/5 Prominent retouch on Queen's neck just below jawline (Th. E3–4)
Cyl. 13   9/12 Large area of retouching behind Queen's head (Th. C5–6 and D5–6)
          18/12 As Cyl. 12
Cyl. 13. 15/3 As Cyl. 12
          15/5 As Cyl. 12, but more prominent
Cyl. 15. 5/12 Two small white dots on Queen's shoulder (Th. F–G4). Later retouched
          17/12 White scratch in background above value, extending to Queen's shoulder. Later retouched
                but flaw still shows on Queen's shoulder

Coils

Printed in continuous reels from double pane cylinder P3 (vertical) or single pane P5 (sideways). Head A

Code No.	Number in roll	Face value	
H	480	£8	Sideways delivery
A	960	£16	Vertical delivery

Sheet Markings

Guide holes: As for perf. Type A under Nos. U11/12
Others: As given in General Notes

Cat. No.	S.G. No.	Shades	Mint	Used

1969 (JANUARY 6).   CHANGE OF COLOUR. ONE 4 mm. CENTRE PHOSPHOR BAND

A. PVA Gum

U14	733	Bright vermilion		
a. Tête-bêche (horiz. pair) ..	£2500	(A) Head A	10	10
b. Uncoated paper ('70)** ..	6·00	(B) Head B	10	10
c. Phosphor omitted	1·25			
d. Red nick in D (Cyl. 4 Dot, R.				
1/4)	3·50			
e. White patch (Cyl. 13 Dot, R.				
20/12)	4·50			
f. Nick in hair (Cyl. 15 Dot, R.				
16/5)	3·50			
g. Imperf. between stamp and top				
margin	90·00			
h. Error. Two bands*	45·00			
s. Opt. "Specimen" (14 mm.) ..	30·00			

B. Gum Arabic. (20 February 1969)

U15	733Eg	Bright vermilion		
a. Phosphor omitted	£600	(A) Head A (booklets)	20·00	
b. Diagonal scratch in background		(B) Head B (multi-value coil)	10	
(Multi-value coil)	6·00			

**Uncoated paper. No. U14b comes from the £1 "Stamps for Cooks" Booklet (see Nos. UB16ab and UB17ab); see also General Notes.

Nos. U14 and U16/A from the £1 " Stamps for Cooks " Booklet (ZP1) show slight differences compared with stamps from normal sheets and all other booklets. The main stem of the " 4 " is thicker and it is only 0·6 mm. from its foot to the base of the design compared with 0·9 mm. on stamps from sheets and all other booklets. Also, the cross-bar of the " 4 ", normally opposite the point of the Queen's gown, is lower on the £1 booklet stamps. See under " Machin Heads " in General Notes.

*No. U14h comes from "Method" pane UB17a which has the central phosphor bands printed over the vertical perforations at each side.

No. U15B comes from the multi-value coil strip, issued 27 August 1969, which is listed as No. U32 and U15A from the February and part of March 1969 6s. Barn Owl and Jay Booklets (QP46/7) and also part of May 1969 10s. Mary Kingsley Booklets (XP8).

Listed Varieties

For illustrations of Nos. U14e/f, see Nos. U12c/d.

U14d
Believed later retouched

U15b

Cylinder Numbers (Blocks of Six)

PVA Gum. Perforation Type A

Cyl. No.				No dot	Dot	Cyl. No.				No dot	Dot
4 (Head A)	..	..	..	1·40	1·40	15 (Head B)	..	..	..	1·50	1·50
10 (Head A)	..	..	..	1·40	1·40	16 (Head B)	..	..	..	4·25	4·25
13 (Head A)	..	..	..	1·40	1·40	17 (Head B)	..	..	..	1·50	1·50

The note about the cylinder number being close to the stamp on Cylinder 15 mentioned under No. U12 also applies here.

Minor Constant Sheet Flaws

Cyl. 4.   1/1 Nick in neck (Th. F5)
          1/13 Nick in neck (Th. F5)
          19/1 Flaw on lower rim of Queen's diadem shows as "missing pearls" (Th. C5)
          20/8 Scar on Queen's forehead (Th. C2–3)

Cyl. 10 18/12 Diagonal line through back of Queen's hair (Th. C5)

Cyl. 10. 15/3 Diagonal coloured line on Queen's shoulder and dress (Th. F–G4)
          15/5 Prominent retouch on Queen's neck just below jawline (Th. E3–4)

Cyl. 13   9/12 Large area of retouching behind Queen's head (Th. C5–6 and D5–6)
          18/12 As Cyl. 10

Cyl. 13. 15/3 As Cyl. 10
          15/5 As Cyl. 10., but more prominent

Cyl. 15. 17/12 Scratch on Queen's shoulder at left (Th. F3)

Cyl. 17   4/7 Small coloured spot in band of diadem (Th. B4)
          7/3 Small retouch on Queen's shoulder (Th. F3)
          18/4 Small flaw in band of diadem (Th. B4)

Cyl. 17. 19/10 White scratch at back of Queen's shoulder (Th. F5)

Coils

PVA Gum. Printed in continuous reels from double pane cylinder P3 (vertical) or single pane P5 (Head A) and P7 (Head B) (sideways)

Code No.	Number in roll	Face value	
H	480	£8	Sideways delivery Head A or Head B
A	960	£16	Vertical delivery Head A

Gum Arabic. Multi-value coil, see No. U32.

Sheet Markings

Guide holes: As for perf. Type A under Nos. U11/12

Others: As given in General Notes

Cat. No.	S.G. No.	Shades	Mint	Used

1969 (JANUARY 6)

A. One Side Phosphor Band at Left*. PVA Gum. Head B
From 10s. Booklets XP7/12 and £1 Booklet ZP1

U16   734   Bright vermilion   1·40   1·60
  b. Uncoated paper ('70)**   ..   £150
  c. One broad phosphor band   ..   £125
  d. Phosphor omitted on front but
    printed at left on the gummed
    side   ..   ..   ..
  s. Optd. " Specimen " (14 mm.) ..   £150

B. One Side Phosphor Band at Right*. PVA Gum. Head B
From £1 Booklet ZP1 only (1 December 1969)

U16A   734Eb   Bright vermilion   2·00   3·00
  b. Uncoated paper ('70)**   ..   £150
  c. Phosphor omitted on front but
    printed at right on the gummed
    side   ..   ..
  s. Optd. " Specimen " (14 mm.) ..   £150

*The one side band stamps were produced by applying a 9·5 mm. band over the vertical perforations between the 4d. and its adjoining stamp in the booklet panes. In theory the width of the band on a single stamp should be 4¾ mm. but this will vary if the band has not been perfectly positioned.

**Uncoated paper. Nos. U16b and U16Ab came from the *se-tenant* pane of 15 in the £1 " Stamps for Cooks " Booklet (see No. UB2ab.); see also General Notes.

No. U16 also occurs with the phosphor omitted but since a single stamp would be indistinguishable from No. U14c it is only listed when in a complete *se-tenant* booklet (see No. UB4a).

No. U16Ac came from the *se-tenant* pane No. UB2ad of which three examples are believed to exist.

See note after No. U15 describing the differences between 4d. stamps in the £1 Booklet (ZP1) and those in sheets and all other booklets.

5d., Type U1 (1968-'70)

Cat. No.	S.G. No.			Shades	Mint	Used

1968 (JULY 1). TWO 9·5 mm. PHOSPHOR BANDS. PVA GUM.

U17   735
- *a.* Imperforate (pair)† £100
- *ab.* Imperf. between stamp and top margin .. ..
- *b.* Uncoated paper ('70)** .. .. 13·00
- *c.* Two bands and phosphor coating (Cyl. 15) £300
- *d.* Phosphor omitted. Shade (1) .. 1·25
- *da.* Phosphor omitted. Shade (2) .. 2·00
- *db.* Right-hand band omitted .. ..
- *e.* Phosphor omitted on front but printed on the gummed side ..
- *f.* One broad phosphor band .. 35·00
- *g.* Neck retouch (Cyls. 7, 10, 11, 13 No dot. R. 18/1 and cyl. 15, R. 19/1) .. .. 2·50
- *h.* Scratch severing neck (Cyl. 13 No dot, R. 19/4) .. .. 12·00
- *s.* Optd. "Specimen" (14 mm.) .. 45·00

(A) Head A
(1) Royal blue 10 10

(B) Head B
(2) Deep blue 10 12

†No. U17a comes from the original state of cylinder 15 which is identifiable by the screening dots in the gutters (see note after cylinder number list). This must not be confused with imperforate stamps from cylinder 10, a large quantity of which was stolen from the printers early in 1970. Examples of No. U17 in *tête-bêche* pairs were not issued.

**Uncoated paper. No. U17b comes from the £1 " Stamps for Cooks " Booklet (see Nos. UB2ab and UB20ab and b); see also General Notes.

No. U17c is thought to result from the issue, in error, of stamps on phosphor-coated paper, intended for experiments only. Examples were purchased from various sources in 1972.

No. U17 from the £1 "Stamps for Cooks" Booklet (ZP1) and cylinders 7, 10 and 11 (no dot and dot panes) show slight differences compared with stamps from cylinder 1 (no dot and dot) and all other booklet panes. The " 5D " is slightly thicker and is positioned fractionally lower than on stamps from cylinder 1 and all other booklet panes. See under " Machin Heads " in the General Notes.

No. U17 is known postmarked at Trafalgar Square (London) on 29 June and at Dorking and Guildford on 30 June 1968.

Listed Varieties

This variety is due to damage on the multipositive. Cyl. 1 is normal and the most marked retouch is on cyl. 11. Cyl. 15 was formed by moving up one row of the multipositive (which is 28 rows by 31 columns) and the variety occurs on 19/1. All on no dot panes.

U17g

U17h

173

Cylinder Numbers (Blocks of Six)

Perforation Type A

Cyl. No.			No dot	Dot	Cyl. No.			No dot	Dot
1 (Shade 1) (Head A)	..	..	1·25	1·25	11 (Shade 2) (Head B)	..	..	6·50*	5·00
7 (Shade 2) (Head B)	..	..	3·25*	1·50	13 (Shade 2) (Head B)	..	..	£550*	£350
10 (Shade 2) (Head B)	..	..	3·25*	1·50	15 (Shade 2) (Head B)	..	..	4·00*	2·25

Cyl. 15 dot has a smudge so that it looks like "151".

Original printings of cylinder 15 (no dot and dot) had screening dots extending through the gutters of the stamps and into the margins of the sheet. Later the cylinder was cleaned and re-chromed.

Minor Constant Sheet Flaws

Cyl. 1		
	7/1	Coloured spot in band of diadem (Th. C5)
	7/5	Short white flaw in Queen's hair (Th. C4)
	12/2	White flaw in band of diadem (Th. B4)
Cyl. 1.	1/11	Pale patch in background below top bar of 5 (Th. G1)
	20/4	White spot in band of diadem (Th. C5)
Cyl. 7.	18/2	Scratch on Queen's shoulder (Th. F4)
Cyl. 7.	1/10	White flaw on Queen's forehead (Th. C3)
	14/12	Small retouch on Queen's shoulder (Th. G4)
Cyl. 10	15/8	Coloured flaw below Queen's earring (Th. D4)
	18/2	Scratch on Queen's shoulder (Th. F4)
	20/5	Two diagonal scratches on Queen's neck (Th. E3–4, F4 and G4)
	20/6	Retouch on Queen's neck (Th. E4)
Cyl. 13	5/6	White flaw in Queen's hair (Th. C3)
	12/4	White ring flaw on Queen's forehead (Th. C2)
	13/3	Flaw on Queen's shoulder (Th. G3)
	14/5	Necklace flaw (Th. E4)
	18/2	Coloured flaw on Queen's neck (Th. F5)
Cyl. 15	16/8	Coloured flaw below Queen's earring (Th. D4)
	19/2	Scratch on Queen's shoulder (Th. F4)
Cyl. 15.	1/10	Scratch on Queen's nose (Th. C2)

Coils

Printed in continuous reels from double pane cylinder S1 (vertical) or single pane S2 (sideways). Head B

Code No.	Number in roll	Face value	
AF	480	£10	Sideways delivery
AE	960	£20	Vertical delivery

Sheet Markings

Phosphor cylinder number "Ph 1" found on the later printings of cyl. 15 dot, right margin (*price £22 block of 6*).
Guide holes: In double "S O N" box (or "S O" box cyl. 10) opposite rows 14/15, at left (no dot) or right (dot). In addition a single "traffic light" type box appears above and below the eighth vertical row in the no dot pane only. (These would only be used in conjunction with perforation Type F (L)*).
Others: As given in General Notes.

6d., Type U1 (1968)

Cat. No.	S.G. No.	Shades	Mint	Used

1968 (FEBRUARY 5). TWO 9·5 mm. PHOSPHOR BANDS. PVA GUM

U18   736

a. Phosphor omitted. Shade (1) ..   4·50
ab. Phosphor omitted. Shade (3) ..   10·00
b. Hair flaws (Cyl. 2 No dot, R. 18/1)   4·25
c. Background retouch (Cyl. 2 Dot, R. 11/1) ..   ..   4·00
d. Diadem flaw (Cyl. 3 No dot, R. 2/3) ..   ..   3·75
e. Two spots in front of neck (Vert. coil, Roll 12) (Head B (1))   ..   12·00
f. Retouch above "6 D" (Vert. coil) (Head B (1)) ..   ..   ..   12·00
g. One broad phosphor band   ..

(A) Head A

	Mint	Used
(1) Bright reddish purple *(shades*	20	20
(2) Bright magenta	2·00	50
(3) Claret	50	40

(B) Head B (coils)

	Mint	Used
(1) Bright reddish purple	10·00	5·00
(3) Claret	80·00	35·00

Listed Varieties

U18b
Two coloured lines crossing base of diadem, one extending in curves through the hair

U18c
Large circular retouch above value

U18d
Coloured flaw in band of diadem

U18e
Two spots in front of neck

U18f

Cylinder Numbers (Blocks of Six)

Perforation Type A

(a) Shade (1) Bright reddish purple

Cyl. No.				No dot	Dot
2	..	..	..	6·00*	4·75
3	..	..	..	2·40	2·40
4	..	..	..	38·00	38·00
5	..	..	..	2·40	2·40

(b) Shade (2) Bright magenta

Cyl. No.					No dot	Dot
3	..	..	..	..	27·00	27·00

(c) Shade (3) Claret

					No dot	Dot
5	..	..	..	..	5·25	5·25

Minor Constant Sheet Flaws

Cyl. 2.   2/4   White flaw in band of diadem (Th. B4)
        4/4   Coloured line in band of diadem (Th. B3–4)
        4/11   Small retouch on Queen's collar (Th. G4)
        10/11   Vertical flaws in Queen's hair and in band of diadem (Th. B–C4)
Cyl. 3   13/5   Two small white flaws on Queen's neck above necklace (Th. F3)
        19/9   Small coloured dot in band of diadem (Th. B3)
Cyl. 3.   5/3   Line of white dashes on Queen's collar (Th. G3–4)
        11/5   Small retouch on Queen's collar (Th. G4)
Cyl. 4   11/10   Small background retouch left of Queen's forehead (Th. B2)
Cyl. 5   18/1   White tail below "D"

Coil

Vertical delivery printed in continuous reels from cylinder Q2.   Head B

Code No.	Number in roll	Face value
J	480	£12

Sheet Markings

Phosphor cylinder number: "Ph 1" found on a later printing from cyl. 5 dot, right margin (*price £140, block of 6*).

Guide holes: In double "S O N" box opposite rows 14/15, at left (no dot) or right (dot. In addition a single "traffic light" type box appears above and below the eighth vertical row in the no dot pane only (These would only be used in conjunction with perforation Type F (L)*.)

Others: As given in General Notes

7d., Type U2 (1968)

Cat. No.	S.G. No.	Shades	Mint	Used
1968 (JULY 1). TWO 9·5 mm. PHOSPHOR BANDS. PVA GUM. HEAD B				
U19	737	Bright emerald	40	30
a. Phosphor omitted	.. .. 45·00			

No. U19 is known postmarked at Dorking and at Guildford on 30 June 1968.

Cylinder Numbers (Blocks of Six)

Perforation Type A

Cyl. No.					No dot	Dot
3	..	..	..	..	4·00	4·00
4	..	..	..	..	12·00	9·00

Minor Constant Sheet Flaws

Cyl. 3   8/6 Flaw in background by Queen's collar (Th. F5)
         12/6 Dark flaw on jewel in band of diadem (Th. C5)

Sheet Markings

Phosphor cylinder number: "Ph 1" found on all sheets from cyl. 4 dot, right margin (*Price £35, block of 6*)

Guide holes: in single hand engraved box opposite rows 14/15, at left (no dot) or right (dot)

Marginal arrows: "W" shaped, hand engraved at top, bottom and sides on cyl. 3, photo-etched on cyl. 4

Others: As given in General Notes

8d., Type U2 (1968–9)

1968 (JULY 1). TWO 9·5 mm. PHOSPHOR BANDS. PVA GUM. HEAD A

U20   738   Bright vermilion   15   30
   a. Phosphor omitted £400

   No. U20 is known postmarked at Dorking and at Guildford on 30 June 1968.

Cylinder Numbers (Blocks of Six)

Perforation Type A

Cyl. No.					No dot	Dot
2	..	..	..	..	2·25	2·25

Sheet Markings

   Guide holes: In double " S O N " box opposite rows 14/15, at left (no dot) or right (dot). In addition a single " traffic light " type box appears above and below the eighth vertical row in the no dot pane only. (These would only be used in conjunction with perforation Type F (L)*.)

   Others: As given in General Notes

1969 (JANUARY 6). CHANGE OF COLOUR. TWO 9·5 mm. PHOSPHOR BANDS. PVA GUM. HEAD B

U21   739   Light turquoise-blue   45   50
   a. Phosphor omitted ..   ..   ..   50·00
   b. Missing pearls (Cyl. 3 No dot,
        R. 19/2)   ..   ..   ..   4·00

Listed Variety

U21*b*

Cylinder Numbers (Blocks of Six)

Perforation Type A

	Cyl. No.					No dot	Dot
	3	..	..	..	..	7·00*	5·00

Minor Constant Sheet Flaw

Cyl. 3. 19/2 White flaw by Queen's mouth (Th. D2)

Sheet Markings

   Guide holes: In single " S N " box opposite rows 14/15, at left (no dot) or right (dot). In addition a single " traffic light " type box appears above and below the eighth vertical row in the no dot pane only. (These would only be used in conjunction with perforation Type F (L)*.)

   Others: As given in General Notes.

9d., Type U2 (1967-68)

Cat. No.	S.G. No.	Shades	Mint	Used

1967 (AUGUST 8). TWO 9·5 mm. PHOSPHOR BANDS. HEAD A

A. Gum Arabic

U22   740   Myrtle-green   50   30
   a. Phosphor omitted ..   ..   ..   16·00
   b. Dots below necklace (Cyl. 2
      Dot, R. 9/6) ..   ..   3·75

B. PVA Gum (29 November 1968)

U23   740Ev   Myrtle-green   50
   a. Phosphor omitted   ..   ..   18·00

No. U22 is known pre-released on 7 August at Bournemouth and Torquay.

Listed Variety

U22b

Cylinder Numbers (Blocks of Six)

	Gum Arabic			PVA Gum		
Cyl. No.		No dot	Dot	Cyl. No.		No dot	Dot
Perforation Type F (L)*							
2	.. ..	5·00	5·00				
Perforation Type A				Perforation Type A			
2	.. ..	28·00	25·00	2	.. ..	5·00	5·00

Cylinder 2 has the number close to the stamp resulting in the dot often being removed by the perforations. The no dot cylinder can be distinguished by a horizontal line below R. 20/2, although this may be trimmed off if the margin is narrow.

Minor Constant Sheet Flaws

Cyl. 2   2/7 Coloured line in gutter above stamp (Th. above A4–6)
         3/12 Retouch on Queen's shoulder (Th. F4)
         6/2 Pale area on Queen's shoulder (Th. F4). Retouched on PVA
         6/7 Dark patches on Queen's neck (Th. E–F3). Less noticeable on PVA
         7/3 Dark spot over D of value (Th. F6)

Cyl. 2.   6/10 Coloured line across Queen's shoulder and dress (Th. F–G4)
         8/11 Retouch on Queen's forehead (Th. B–C2)
         10/4 Coloured spot at rear of diadem (Th. C5)
         14/8 Two white flaws on Queen's neck by hair (Th. D–E4). Retouched on PVA
         14/11 Retouch on Queen's neck by necklace (Th. E4)
         15/11 Retouch on Queen's dress at front (Th. G3)
         19/10 Retouch on Queen's shoulder (Th. F4)

Sheet Markings

Phosphor cylinder number: "Ph 1" found on a later printing from cyl. 2 dot, right margin (*Price £925 block of* 6)
Guide holes:
    Perforation Type A, in double "S O N" box opposite rows 14/15, at left (no dot) or right (dot). In addition a single "traffic light" type box appears above and below the eighth vertical row in the no dot pane only (latter only used in conjunction with perforation Type F (L)*).
    Perforation Type F (L)*, boxed above and below the eighth vertical row in the no dot pane only. The usual "S O N" boxes opposite rows 14/15 remain
Others: As given in General Notes

10d., Type U1 (1968)

Cat. No.	S.G. No.	Shades	Mint	Used

1968 (JULY 1). TWO 9·5 mm. PHOSPHOR BANDS. PVA GUM. HEAD C

U24   741   Drab   45   50
  a. Uncoated paper ('69)* ..   .. 23·00
  b. Phosphor omitted   ..   .. 40·00
  c. Neck flaw (Cyl 1, R. 2/12)   .. 3·75

  *Uncoated paper—see General Notes.
  No. U24 is known postmarked at Dorking and at Guildford on 30 June 1968.

Listed Variety

Flaw comprises dark spots surrounded by white
" halo " caused by lack of screening dots

        U24*c*

Cylinder Number (Block of Six)
Single pane cylinder
Perforation Type F (L)

Cyl. No.					No dot
1	..	..	..	..	5·50

Minor Constant Sheet Flaw
Cyl. 1   20/5 Coloured flaw in Queen's hair (Th. B3)

Sheet Markings
  Guide holes: Through marginal arrow above vertical rows 6/7 and below vertical row 10
  Others: As given in General Notes

1s., Type U1 (1967-68)

1967 (JUNE 5). TWO 9·5 mm. PHOSPHOR BANDS. HEAD C

A. Gum Arabic

U25   742/E*a*
  a. Phosphor omitted ..   ..   ..   60·00
  b. Background retouches (Cyl. 3
     No dot, R. 20/5) ..   ..   ..   4·50

(1) Light bluish violet	40	30
(2) Pale bluish violet	60	30

B. PVA Gum (26 April 1968)

U26   742Ea*v*
  a. Phosphor omitted   ..   ..   3·50

Pale bluish violet	50

No. U25(1) is known pre-released on 25 May at Gravesend.

Listed Variety

Retouching extends from behind the Queen's neck to the base of the design where it is most noticeable. There are also minor retouches on the Queen's shoulder and on her dress

U25*b*

Cylinder Numbers (Blocks of Six)

Gum Arabic
Double pane cylinder
Perforation Type F (L)*
Shade (1) Light bluish violet

Cyl. No.				No dot	Dot
3	..	..	..	.. 4·00	4·00

Single pane cylinder
Perforation Type F (L)
Shade (2) Pale bluish violet

Cyl. No.				No dot
11	..	..	..	.. 5·50

PVA Gum
Single pane cylinder
Perforation Type F (L)

Cyl. No.				No dot
11	..	..	..	.. 4·50

Minor Constant Sheet Flaws

Cyl. 3   1/10 Retouch in background above diadem (Th. A5)
        2/2 Light diagonal line extending from lowest point of Queen's hair to bottom right-hand corner (E5 through to G6)
        2/3 White spot in background left of Queen's shoulder (Th. G2)
        9/12 White spot in background to right of Queen's necklace (Th. E5)
        11/11 Coloured spot in band of diadem (Th. B4)
        17/2 As 11/11 but Th. B3
        18/12 Coloured spot in hyphen of value
        19/10 Coloured scratch through Queen's neck and background below portrait
        20/4 Horizontal scratch through Queen's neck and into background at right
Cyl. 3.   1/8 White spot in background at top of stamp (Th. A4)
        7/8 Coloured flaw in Queen's hair to right of earring (Th. D4)
        8/4 Coloured flaw in Queen's hair (Th. B3)
        9/7 Retouch to background to right of Queen's ear (Th. D5)
        19/8 Coloured spot in background above diadem emblems (Th. B5)
Cyl. 11   7/8 Coloured spot by band of diadem, also small spot in background at rear of diadem (Th. B4 and C5)
        7/9 Diagonal coloured line in background behind Queen's neck (Th. F5)
        15/4 Disturbed area in background at rear of diadem (Th. C–D5)
        16/9 Diagonal coloured scratches extending the depth of the stamp behind the Queen's portrait
        18/7 Diagonal coloured scratch about 10 mm. long at left of Queen's portrait
        19/2 White flaw in Queen's hair to right of ear (Th. D4)

UA Machin—1s.

Sheet Markings

Guide holes:
Perforation Type F (L)*, boxed above and below the eighth vertical row in the no dot pane only. In addition double "S O N" box appears opposite rows 14/15, at left (no dot) or right (dot). (These would only be used in conjunction with perforation Type A.)
Perforation Type F (L), through marginal arrow above vertical rows 6/7 and below vertical row 10

Others: As given in General Notes

1s.6d., Type U1 (1967-69)

Cat. No.	S.G. No.		Shades	Mint	Used

1967 (AUGUST 8).   TWO 9·5 mm. PHOSPHOR BANDS.   HEAD A

A. Gum Arabic

U27   743
 a. Greenish blue omitted   ..   £100
 b. Phosphor omitted. Shade (1)   6·00
 c. Retouch on dress (Cyl. 2A, R. 7/12) ..   ..   5·50
 d. Neck retouch (Cyl. 2A, R. 19/4)   5·00
 e. Neck retouch (Cyl. 2A, R. 20/3)   5·00

(1) Greenish blue and deep blue   50   30
(2) Prussian blue and indigo (phosphor omitted)   11·00

B. PVA Gum (28 August 1968)

U28   743Ev
 a. Greenish blue omitted   ..   80·00
 b. Imperf. top margin ..   ..   ..   80·00
 c. Phosphor omitted. Shade (1)   ..   14·00
 d. One broad phosphor band   ..   10·00
 e. Greenish blue omitted and broad phosphor band   ..   ..   95·00

(1) Greenish blue and deep blue   60
(2) Prussian blue and indigo   1·50   75

No. U27 is known pre-released on 7 August at Bournemouth and Torquay.

Listed Varieties

U27c

U27d

U27e

Cylinder Numbers (Blocks of Four)

Single pane cylinders.
Perforation Type A

Cyl. Nos.

No dot

Gum Arabic

2A (deep blue)—2B (greenish blue)   ..   ..   5·50
3A (deep blue)—2B (greenish blue)   ..   ..   12·00
5A (indigo)—2B (Prussian blue) (phosphor omitted) £140

PVA Gum

3A (deep blue)—2B (greenish blue)   ..   ..   6·00
3A (indigo)—1B (Prussian blue)   ..   ..   16·00
5A (indigo)—2B (Prussian blue)   ..   ..   9·00

Minor Constant Sheet Flaws

Cyls. 2A–2B 3/12 Coloured spot in band of diadem (Th. B4)
            7/8 Coloured spots on Queen's collar (Th. G3)
            14/1 Coloured spot on Queen's shoulder (Th. F4–5)
            17/3 Coloured spot on Queen's temple (Th. C3)
            18/4 Coloured spot on Queen's shoulder (Th. F5)
            20/2 Pale patch on Queen's neck (Th. E3–4)
            20/7 Retouch on Queen's neck (Th. E4)
Cyls. 3A–2B 3/12 As for cyls. 2A–2B
Cyls. 5A–2B 19/1 Retouch on Queen's shoulder (Th. F5)

Sheet Markings

Cylinder numbers: Boxed, opposite R. 19/1
Guide holes: In single " traffic light " type box opposite rows 14/15, at both sides
Colour register marks: Opposite rows 3/4 and 17/18, at both sides
Autotron marks (solid): Deep blue and greenish blue opposite rows 7/8, left margin
Colour designations: " G1 " (greenish blue) opposite rows 7/8 and " G2 " (deep blue) opposite rows 5/6 both
    reading up in right margin
Traffic lights (boxed): Deep blue and greenish blue opposite row 19, right margin
Others: As given in General Notes

Cat. No.	S.G. No.	Shades	Mint	Used

**1969 (DECEMBER 10). CHANGE TO PHOSPHORISED PAPER. PVA GUM.
HEAD A**

U29	743b		Prussian blue and indigo	75	90

a. Prussian blue omitted £225

No. U29 was an experimental issue and the small printing represented approximately three months normal issue. After the supply was exhausted No. U28 again became the normal issue.

Cylinder Numbers (Block of Four)

Single pane cylinders.

Cyl. Nos. (No dot)   Perf. Type A

5A (indigo)—2B (Prussian blue) ..   ..   8·00

Minor Constant Sheet Flaws

Cyls. 5A–2B   12/5 Two white spots on Queen's dress (Th. G3)
            19/1 Retouch on Queen's shoulder (Th. F5)

Sheet Markings

All the same as for Nos. U27/8

1s.9d., Type U1 (1967-70)

1967 (JUNE 5). TWO 9·5 mm. PHOSPHOR BANDS. HEAD A

A. Gum Arabic

U30	744		(1) Dull orange and black	40	30

a. Phosphor omitted   ..   .. 25·00   (2) Bright orange and black   1·50   50

B. PVA Gum (16 November 1970)

U31	744Ev		Bright orange and black	40

No. U30 is known pre-released on 25 May at Gravesend.
The bright orange shade occurs on whiter paper and may be due to this.

Cylinder Numbers (Blocks of Four)

Single pane cylinders

Cyl. Nos. (No dot)							Perforation Type A	
							Gum Arabic	PVA Gum
1A (black)—1B (dull orange)	..	..	..	..	..	..	9·00	†
1A (black)—1B (bright orange)	..	..	..	..	..	..	18·00	16·00

Minor Constant Sheet Flaws

Cyls. 1A–1B   4/6 White spot in Queen's ear (Th. D4)
            5/7 Coloured spots on Queen's upper lip (Th. D2)
            5/10 White patch in Queen's hair (Th. B4)
            8/1 Coloured flaw on Queen's neck (Th. E4)
            13/1 Retouch on Queen's shoulder (Th. F3–4)
            20/1 Pale patch in Queen's hair (Th. C4)

Sheet Markings

Cylinder numbers: Boxed, opposite R. 19/1
Guide holes: In single " traffic light " type box opposite rows 14/15, at both sides
Colour register marks: Opposite rows 3/4 and 17/18, at both sides
Autotron marks (solid): Black and orange opposite rows 7/8, left margin
Colour designations: " G1 " (orange) opposite rows 7/8 and " G2 " (black) opposite rows 5/6 both reading up
    in right margin
Traffic lights (boxed): Black and orange opposite row 19, right margin
Others: As given in General Notes

Multi-value Coil Strip (1969)

Cat. No.	S.G. No.		Shades	Mint	Used

1969 (AUGUST 27). STRIP OF FIVE (2d.+2d.+3d.+1d.+4d. SE-TENANT) EACH WITH ONE 4 mm. CENTRE PHOSPHOR BAND. GUM ARABIC. HEAD B

U32	725m		1d. Light olive (No. U4), 2d. lake-brown (No. U7×2), 3d. violet (No. U8) and 4d. bright vermilion (No. U15) ..		1·25

No. U32 was issued in strips from stamp vending machines taking a shilling or a five pence piece. Complete coils only were available from the Philatelic Bureau at Edinburgh.

For listed varieties, see Nos. U4a, U8d and U15b.

A new type of perforation was adopted for these coils. The paper was drawn, gum upwards, over a cylinder containing short points pushing up pimples from the undersurface which were then shaved off.

It is understood that gum arabic was used for these coils, as also for the next decimal multi-value coil, because it is more brittle than PVA and facilitates the clean removal of the perforations.

Coils

Sideways delivery printed in continuous reels from cylinders B5–D3–M3–P6

Code No.	Number in roll	Face value
GS	1500 (300 strips)	£15
GL	3000 (600 strips)	£30

Presentation Pack

UPP1 (issued 5 March 1969)		Fourteen values	6·00
a. With German text	.. ..	45·00	

The issued Pack contained one each of the low value definitive stamps (½d. to 1s.9d.). The 4d. and 8d. were in the changed colours (Nos. U14 and U21 respectively).

UPP 1 also exists with a Japanese insert card.

First Day Covers

On official covers prepared and issued by the Post Office and stamps franked with circular "FIRST DAY OF ISSUE" postmarks.

UFC1 (5.6.67)	4d, 1s, 1s. 9d	1·40
UFC2 (8.8.67)	3d, 9d, 1s. 6d	1·40
UFC3 (5.2.68)	½d, 1d, 2d, 6d	75
UFC4 (1.7.68)	5d, 7d, 8d, 10d	1·10
UFC5 (1.12.69) "Stamps for Cooks" pane stamps, four covers		20·00*

There was no F.D.C. service for the 4d. red and 8d. turquoise-blue values.

*The price is for covers with complete panes with recipe attached. The Milk Marketing Board issued a special handstamp cancellation reading "Visit the Stamps for Cooks Exhibition, Milk Marketing Board, Thames Ditton, Surrey".

SECTION UB
Machin £.s.d. Issues
1967–70. Booklet Panes in Photogravure

General Notes

INTRODUCTION. All panes were printed in photogravure by Harrison & Sons. See the detailed notes under Section U for information on printing, paper and gum. Reference to the note, " Booklet and Coil Varieties ", at the beginning of Section S describes the panes which were printed from 21-row cylinders. These panes are found with varieties and the cylinder number in either the top or bottom row of the pane. In this Section the panes of six of the 1d., 3d., 4d. (both colours) and 5d. were printed from 21-row cylinders.

BOOKLET ERRORS. Those listed as " Part perf. pane " have one row of three stamps imperforate on three sides.

Booklet Cylinder Number

BOOKLET CYLINDER NUMBERS. These are listed for the panes of six only and the other panes had cylinder numbers engraved so that they did not occur in the finished booklet. The cylinders employed are recorded for reference. The cylinder numbers being hand-engraved varied as to their position in relation to the stamp so that some were invariably trimmed. A pane which shows a complete cylinder number placed away from the stamp will only exist with badly trimmed perforations on the opposite side.

BOOKLET FLAWS. Cylinder flaws on booklet stamps are listed under the panes in which they occur and not under the sheet stamps as in Section S. The flaws are priced in panes since this is the preferred method of collecting wherever possible. In consequence when checking varieties on single stamps it will be necessary to look at the lists of the sheet and coil stamps as well as the booklet panes.

When quoting the position on booklet panes no attention is paid to the labels. Therefore a flaw on the first stamp in the pane No. UB13 (4d.(2) and pair of labels) will be described as being on " R. 1/1 ". Since this Catalogue is primarily concerned with stamps we do not list flaws which sometimes occur in the wording of the labels from booklet panes.

BOOKLET PANE PRICES. The prices quoted are for panes with good perforations all round with binding margin. Prices for complete booklets in Appendix H are for booklets with average perforations.

CHECKLIST OF MACHIN £.s.d. BOOKLET PANES

UB No.	Face Value	Phos. Bands	Gum	Head	Size of Pane	Further description	Page
1	1d.	2	PVA	B	6	Yellowish olive	187
2	6 × 1d. 3 × 4d. 3 × 4d. 3 × 5d.	2 1L 1R 2	PVA	B	15	"Baked Stuffed Haddock" recipe	187
3	4 × 1d. 2 × 4d.	1C 1C	PVA	B	6	4d. in sepia	188
4	4 × 1d. 2 × 4d.	2 1L	PVA	B	6	4d. in bright vermilion	189
5	2 × 1d. 2 × 3d.	2 2	PVA	B	4	1d. at left	190
5a	2 × 1d. 2 × 3d.	2 2	PVA	B	4	1d. at right	190
6	3d.	1C	PVA	B	6	Violet	190
7	4d.	2	GA	A	6	Deep sepia	191
8	4d.	2	GA	A	6	Deep olive-brown	191
9	4d.	2	PVA	A	6	Deep olive-brown	191
10	4d.	2	PVA	B	4	Deep olive-brown	192
11	4d.	1C	PVA	A	6	Deep olive-brown	192
12	4d.	1C	PVA	B	4	Deep olive-sepia	192
13	4d.	1C	PVA	B	4	Deep olive sepia, including 2 labels	193
14 (A)	4d.	1C	PVA	A	6	Bright vermilion	193
14 (B)	4d.	1C	PVA	B	6	Bright vermilion	193
14 (b)	4d.	1C	GA	A	6	Bright vermilion	193
15	4d.	1C	PVA	B	4	Bright vermilion	194
16	4d.	1C	PVA	B	15	"Stuffed Cucumber" and "Method" recipe ..	194
17	4d.	1C	PVA	B	15	"Method" for Braised Shoulder of Lamb recipe ..	195
18	4d.	1C	PVA	B	4	Bright vermilion, including 2 labels	196
19	5d.	2	PVA	B	6	Deep Blue	196
20	5d.	2	PVA	B	15	"Method" for Cream of Potato Soup recipe ..	197

1d. BOOKLET PANES OF SIX

6 × 1d. (two bands). Head B.
Shade (2) Yellowish olive
From 4s.6d. Booklets LP45/59 and 10s. Booklets XP4/5

UB1 (containing No. U2 × 6) (25.3.68)		1·40
a. Part perf. pane*		
b. Imperf. pane*		£3750
c. Phosphor omitted		25·00

*Booklet error—see General Notes.

Booklet Cylinder Numbers

Panes of six (21-row cylinders)

Pane No.	Cyl. No.	Perf. Type I No dot	Dot	Pane No.	Cyl. No.	Perf. Type I No dot	Dot
UB1	F1	48·00	48·00	UB1	F3	3·00	3·00
UB1	F1 T	48·00	48·00	UB1	F3 T	3·00	3·00

In the above and all other 21-row cylinders, which are printed continuously in the web, the perforated web is cut at every 20th row to make sheets of 480. Consequently on successive sheets the cylinder number appears one row lower and thus a pane can have it adjoining the top or bottom row. Where the cylinder number adjoins the top row of the pane it is designated by the letter " T ".

Examples of Cyl. No. pane F1 (lower position) are known with forged cylinder number.

UB2

" STAMPS FOR COOKS " SE-TENANT BOOKLET PANE WITH RECIPE LABEL

Pane of fifteen comprising 6 × 1d. (two bands) with 3 × 4d. (one side band at left), 3 × 4d. (one side band at right), 3 × 5d. and *se-tenant* recipe label. Head B
" Baked Stuffed Haddock " recipe from £1 " Stamps for Cooks " Booklet ZP1

A. Stapled

UB2 (containing Nos. U2 × 6, U16 × 3, U16A × 3, U17 × 3) (1.12.69)		30·00
b. Phosphor omitted		£350
c. One broad phosphor band on each stamp, except first vertical row which has phosphor omitted		£600
d. Mole on cheek (R. 1/2)		35·00
s. Optd. " Specimen " (14 mm.)		£1900

B. Stitched

UB2a (containing Nos. U2 × 6, U16 × 3,
U16A ×3, U17 × 3)   8·50
  ab. Uncoated paper* £900
  ac. Phosphor omitted £150
  ad. Phosphor omitted from front, but shown on
    gummed side £2000
  ae. Mole on cheek (R. 1/2)   ..   ..   12·00
  ag. One broad phosphor band on each stamp except
    for first vertical row which has phosphor
    omitted £600
  uh. As *ug* but phosphor omitted from first two ver-
    tical rows and broad band at left on rows
    containing 5d., 1d., 4d., ...
  uj. Broad band at right on first row at left and
    phosphor omitted from vertical rows 1d., 5d.,
    1d., 4d.   ..   ..

*Uncoated paper—see General Notes for Section U.

Listed Varieties

UB2d, UB2ae(1d.)

Booklet Cylinder Numbers
In the £1 Booklet (ZP1) the cylinder numbers were always trimmed off, however, the cylinders known to have been used were F7(1d.), N8(4d.) and R5(5d.).

UB3

1d. AND 4d. SEPIA SE-TENANT BOOKLET PANES OF SIX
4 × 1d. (centre band) with vertical pair 4d. sepia (centre band).   Head B
From 10s. Booklet XP6

	I	Perf. Type I(½v)	P
UB3 (containing Nos. U3 × 4, U12 × 2) (16.9.68)	3·75	14·00	5·00
a. Phosphor omitted	30·00	60·00	38·00
b. Centre band on second and third vert. rows and missing phosphor on first row (2 × 1d.)			
c. Centre band on first and second vert. rows and missing phosphor on third row (2 × 4d.)			

Booklet Cylinder Numbers
Se-tenant pane of six (20-row cylinder)
One centre band

Pane No.	Cyl. Nos.	Perf. Type	
		I	P
		No Dot	No Dot
UB3	F4 (1d.), N5 (4d.)	20·00	22·00

UB4

1d. AND 4d. BRIGHT VERMILION SE-TENANT BOOKLET PANES OF SIX

4 × 1d. (two bands) with vertical pair 4d. bright vermilion (one left side band).   Head B
From 10s. Booklets X P7/12

	Perf. Type P
UB4 (containing Nos. U2 × 4, U16 × 2) (6.1.69)	3·25
a. Phosphor omitted	£190

Booklet Cylinder Numbers
Se-tenant pane of six (20-row cylinder)
Two bands

Pane No.	Cyl. Nos.	Perf. Type P
		No dot
UB4	F4 (1d.), N5 (4d.)	8·00

UB5   UB5a

1d. AND 3d. SE-TENANT BOOKLET PANES OF FOUR
Pair 1d. (two bands) with pair 3d. (two bands).   Head B
From 2s. Booklets NP27/9

Pane UB5   Pane of four with 1d. at left
Pane UB5a   Pane of four with 1d. at right

	I	Perf. Type I(½v)	AP
UB5 (containing Nos. U2 × 2, U10 × 2) (6.4.68)	6·00	£110	2·75
b. One broad phosphor band on each stamp .. .. 15·00		—	12·00
c. Phosphor omitted .. .. 75·00		—	50·00
UB5a (containing Nos. U2 × 2, U10 × 2) (6.4.68)	6·00	14·00	2·75
ab. One broad phosphor band on each stamp .. .. 15·00		28·00	12·00
ac. Phosphor omitted .. .. 65·00		£100	50·00

Booklet Cylinder Numbers
Se-tenant panes of four
In the 2s. Booklets (NP27/9) the cylinder numbers were always trimmed off, but cylinders F2 and K3 were used.

3d. BOOKLET PANES OF SIX
6 × 3d. (centre band).   PVA gum.   Head B
From 10s. Booklets XP4/5

UB6 (containing No. U9 × 6) (25.3.68)   22·00
  a. Phosphor omitted   ..   ..

Booklet Cylinder Numbers
Panes of six (21-row cylinder)

Pane No.	Cyl. No.		No dot	Dot	Pane No.	Cyl. No.		No dot	Dot
UB6	K2	.. ..	50·00	50·00	UB6	K2T	.. ..	50·00	50·00

190

4d. DEEP OLIVE-BROWN BOOKLET PANES OF SIX

6 × 4d. (two bands).   Gum Arabic.   Head A
(a) Shade (1) Deep sepia
From 6s. Booklets QP28/32

UB7 (containing No. U11 × 6) (21.9.67)	8·50	
a. Phosphor omitted	22·00	

(b) Shade (2) Deep olive-brown
From 6s. Booklets QP33/6

UB8 (containing No. U11 × 6) (1.68)	9·00
a. Part perf. pane*	£550
b. Phosphor omitted	26·00
*Booklet error—see General Notes.	

6 × 4d. (two bands).   PVA gum.   Head A
From 4s.6d. Booklets LP45/6, 6s. Booklets QP37/40 and 10s. Booklets XP4/5

UB9 (containing No. U12 × 6) (25.3.68)	1·10
a. One 9·5 mm. phosphor band	£160
b. Phosphor omitted	20·00
c. Patch on cheek (R. 1/2 or 2/2)	5·50

Listed Variety

UB9*c*, UB11*b*
From 10s. Booklet

Booklet Cylinder Numbers
Panes of six (21-row cylinders)
     Gum Arabic

Pane No.	Cyl. No				No dot	Dot
(a) Shade (1) Deep sepia						
UB7	N1	..	..	..	20·00	20·00
UB7	N1 T	..	..	..	20·00	20·00
(b) Shade (2) Deep olive-brown						
UB8	N1	..	..	..	20·00	20·00
UB8	N1 T	..	..	..	20·00	20·00

     PVA Gum

Pane No.	Cyl. No.				No dot	Dot
UB9	N1	..	..	..	6·00	6·00
UB9	N1 T	..	..	..	6·00	6·00
UB9	N2	..	..	..	4·50	4·50
UB9	N2 T	..	..	..	4·50	4·50

4d. DEEP OLIVE-BROWN BOOKLET PANES OF FOUR
4 × 4d. (two bands).   PVA gum.   Head B
From 2s. Booklets NP27/31

	I	Perf. Type I(½v)	AP
UB10 (containing No. U12 × 4) (6.4.68)	3·00	10·00	1·40
a. One broad phosphor band on each stamp	18·00	28·00	14·00
b. Phosphor omitted	18·00	50·00	10·00
c. Dot on "D" (R. 1/2)	14·00	†	—
ca. Retouched state	4·50	†	—

Listed Variety

Later retouched and shows as a pale triangular patch on Nos. UB10, 12 and 15.

UB10c

Booklet Cylinder Numbers
In the 2s. Booklets (NP27/31) the cylinder numbers were always trimmed off, however, the cylinder known to have been used was N3.

4d. DEEP OLIVE-BROWN BOOKLET PANES OF SIX
6 × 4d. (centre band).   Head A
From 4s.6d. Booklets LP47/8, 6s. Booklets QP41/5 and 10s. Booklet XP6

UB11 (containing No. U13 × 6) (16.9.68)	1·60
a. Part perf. pane*	£450
b. Patch on cheek (R. 1/2 or 2/2)	6·00

No. UB11 also occurs with the phosphor omitted but since a single pane would be indistinguishable from No. UB9b it is only listed there.

*Booklet error—see General Notes.

Booklet Cylinder Numbers
Panes of six (21-row cylinders)

Pane No.	Cyl. No.			No dot	Dot	Pane No.	Cyl. No.			No dot	Dot
UB11	N1	..	..	5·00	5·00	UB11	N2	..	..	5·00	5·00
UB11	N1 T	..	..	5·00	5·00	UB11	N2 T	..	..	5·00	5·00

4d. DEEP OLIVE-SEPIA BOOKLET PANES OF FOUR
4 × 4d. (centre band).   Head B
From 2s. Booklets NP31a/33

	I	Perf. Types I(½v)	AP	P
UB12 (containing No. U13 × 4) (16.9.68)	20·00	30·00	1·50	1·50
a. Phosphor omitted	*	*	*	50·00
b. Dot on "D" retouched	22·00	†	—	

*Phosphor omitted errors exist from these booklets in Perf. Types I and AP, but the panes are identical with No. UB10b.

Booklet Cylinder Numbers
In the 2s. Booklets (NP31/3) the cylinder number was always trimmed off, however, the cylinder known to have been used was N3.

UB13, UB18

4d. DEEP OLIVE-SEPIA SE-TENANT WITH PRINTED LABELS

2 × 4d. (centre band). with two labels.   Head B
" £4,315 FOR YOU AT AGE 55 " (1st label) and " SEE OTHER PAGES " (2nd label)
from 2s. Booklets NP30/3

	I	Perf. Types I(½v)	AP	P
UB13 (containing No. U13 × 2) (16.9.68)	2·50	9·00	75	1·50
a. Phosphor omitted	55·00	—	45·00	†
b. Damaged pearls in crown (R. 1/2)				

Listed Variety

UB13b, UB18b

Booklet Cylinder Numbers
In the 2s. Booklets (NP30/3) the cylinder number was always trimmed off, however, the cylinder known to have been used was N6.

4d. BRIGHT VERMILION BOOKLET PANES OF SIX
6 × 4d. (centre band).   PVA gum.
From 4s.6d. Booklets LP49/59, 6s. Booklets QP46/55 and 10s. Booklets XP7/12

UB14 (containing No. U14 × 6) (6.1.69)	
(A) Head A	90
(B) Head B	1·25
a. Phosphor omitted	20·00
b. Gum arabic (Head A)	£120
ba. Gum arabic (Head A). Phosphor omitted ..	—

Booklet Cylinder Numbers
Panes of six (21-row cylinders)

Pane No.	Cyl. No.	No dot	Dot		Pane No.	Cyl. No.		No dot	Dot
UB14 (A)	N1 (Head A)	4·75	4·75		UB14 (A)	N2 (Head A)	..	4·50	4·50
UB14 (A)	N1 T	4·75	4·75		UB14 (A)	N2 T	..	4·50	4·50
UB14b	N1 (gum arabic)	£225	£225		UB14 (B)	N7 (Head B)	..	6·50	6·50
UB14b	N1 T (gum arabic)	£225	£225		UB14 (B)	N7 T	..	6·50	6·50

Stamps from booklet cylinder N7 show screening dots within the face value and in the margins.

4d. BRIGHT VERMILION BOOKLET PANES OF FOUR
4 × 4d. (centre band).   PVA gum.   Head B
From 2s. Booklets NP34/45

		Perf. Types		
	I	I(½v)	AP	P
UB15 (containing No. U14 × 4) (3.3.69)	2·75	12·00	£600	80
a. Phosphor omitted	50·00	£130	†	45·00
b. Dot on "D" retouched	5·00	†	—	—

Booklet Cylinder Numbers
In the 2s. Booklets (NP34/45) the cylinder number was always trimmed off, however, the cylinder known to have been used was N3.

UB16

4d. BRIGHT VERMILION BOOKLET PANE OF FIFTEEN WITH RECIPE LABEL
15 × 4d. (centre band).   Panes of fifteen *se-tenant* with recipe label.   PVA gum.   Head B
" Stuffed Cucumber " recipe and " Method " from £1 " Stamps for Cooks " Booklet ZP1
A. Stapled

UB16 (containing No. U14 × 15) (1.12.69)		15·00
b. Broken necklace (R. 1/1)		18·00
c. Tail on 4 (R. 1/4)		20·00
s. Opt. "Specimen" (14 mm.)		£400

B. Stitched

UB16a (containing No. U14 × 15)		2·50
ab. Uncoated paper ('70)*		£150
ac. Phosphor omitted		£100
ad. Broken necklace (R. 1/1)		4·50
ae. Tail on 4 (R. 1/4)		6·50

194

UB17

"Method" only for Braised Shoulder of Lamb from £1 "Stamps for Cooks" Booklet ZP1

A. Stapled

UB17 (containing No. U14 × 15) (1.12.69)   15·00
  b. Broken necklace (R. 1/1) .. ..   18·00
  c. Spot over eye (R. 2/2) .. ..   20·00
  s. Opt. "Specimen" (14 mm.) £400

B. Stitched

UB17a (containing No. U14 × 15)   2·50
  ab. Uncoated paper ('70)* £130
  ac. Phosphor omitted £110
  ad. Broken necklace (R. 1/1) .. ..   4·50
  ae. Spot over eye (R. 2/2) .. ..   6·00
  af. Two narrow bands on each stamp £300

*Uncoated paper—see General Notes for Section U.
The note below No. U15, describing No. U14h, also applies to pane UB17af.

Listed Varieties

UB16b, UB16ad,
UB17b, UB17ad

UB16c, UB16ae

UB17c, UB17ae
Later retouched on
UB17 and exists re-
touched only on UB16

Booklet Cylinder Numbers
  In the £1 Booklet (ZP1) the cylinder number was always trimmed off, however, the cylinder known to have been used was N9.

4d. BRIGHT VERMILION SE-TENANT WITH PRINTED LABELS

2 × 4d. (centre band). PVA gum. Head B
" £4,315 FOR YOU AT AGE 55 " (1st label) and " SEE OTHER PAGES " (2nd label)
from 2s. Booklets NP34/45

	I	Perf. Types I(½v)	AP	P
UB18 (containing No. U14 × 2) (3.3.69)	3·25	15·00	£700	1·00
a. Phosphor omitted	90·00	£140	†	70·00
b. Damaged pearls in crown (R. 1/2)				

Booklet Cylinder Numbers

In the 2s. Booklets (NP34/45) the cylinder number was always trimmed off, however, the cylinder known to have been used was N6.

For illustration of No. UB18b, see No. UB13b.

5d. BOOKLET PANES OF SIX

6 × 5d. (two bands). Head B
From 5s. Booklets HP26/38 and 10s. Booklets XP6/12

UB19 (containing No. U17 × 6) (27.11.68)	1·10
a. Imperf. pane*	£450
b. Part perf. pane*	£400
c. Phosphor omitted	20·00
ca. Third and fourth phosphor bands from left omitted	£120
d. White flaw on diadem (R. 1/2 or 2/2)	4·25
e. Scratch through hair (R. 1/1 or 2/1)	5·50

*Booklet errors—see General Notes.
No. UB19ca is known with cylinder number R3T, see also No. U17db.

Listed Varieties

UB19d   UB19e

Booklet Cylinder Numbers

Panes of six (21-row cylinders)

Pane No.	Cyl. No.				No dot	Dot	Pane No.	Cyl. No.				No dot	Dot
UB19	R2	..	..	..	3·50	3·50	UB19	R3	..	..	..	4·00	4·00
UB19	R2 T	..	..	..	3·50	3·50	UB19	R3 T	..	..	..	4·00	4·00

Method

Dice potatoes. Thinly slice onion and celery. Fry vegetables v. gently in butter (in saucepan) for 10 mins. Do not allow to brown. Add water, salt and pepper. Bring to boil. Cover pan and simmer v. gently for 45 mins. Rub through sieve (or liquidise) and return to pan. Mix cornflour to smooth paste with a little of the cold milk. Stir in remainder. Add to Soup and bring to boil, stirring. Simmer 5 mins. Ladle into 4 warm soup bowls. Sprinkle with parsley. Serves 4.

UB20

5d. BOOKLET PANE OF FIFTEEN WITH RECIPE LABEL

15 × 5d. (two bands). Panes of fifteen *se-tenant* with recipe label. PVA gum. Head B " Method " only for Cream of Potato Soup from £1 " Stamps for Cooks " Booklet ZP1

A. Stapled

UB20 (containing No. U17 × 15) (1.12.69)	25·00	
b. Uncoated paper ('70)*	£200	
c. White flaw below collar (R. 1/2)	28·00	
d. Flaw on shoulder (R. 1/2)	28·00	
s. Opt. " Specimen " (14 mm.)	£500	

B. Stitched

UB20*a* (containing No. U17 × 15)	2·50	
ab. Uncoated paper ('70)*	£225	
ac. Phosphor and recipe omitted		
ad. One broad band on each stamp	£600	
ae. Phosphor omitted	£150	
af. White flaw below collar (R. 1/2)	4·50	
ag. Flaw on shoulder (R. 1/2)	4·50	

*Uncoated paper—see General Notes for Section U.

Listed Varieties

UB20*c*, UB20*af*

UB20*d*, UB20*ag*

Booklet Cylinder Numbers

In the £1 Booklet (ZP1) the cylinder number was always trimmed off, however, the cylinder known to have been used was R6 for UB20.

SECTION UC

Machin £.s.d. Issues

1969. High Values. Recess-printed

General Notes

INTRODUCTION. The four high values, in similar design to the low values, were issued on 5 March, 1969 thus completing the Machin definitive series.

PRINTERS. The Machin high values were recess-printed by Bradbury, Wilkinson & Co. Ltd. on rotary sheet-fed machines.

PAPER. Unwatermarked lightly coated paper was used for all values. Several types of coated paper appear to have been used and generally there is only a slight response to the chalky test. Variations in the thickness of the paper also exist. Shades are known but it is probable that they are due to the variations in the coating and thickness of the paper rather than to the use of different inks.

GUM. Only PVA gum was used for the Machin high values.

Diagram showing the printer's sheet
comprising four Post Office panes, the
method of perforation, and the positions of the
plate numbers and perforation guide holes

SHEET DETAILS. The printer's sheets comprised 160 stamps in four panes of 40 each arranged in five rows of eight stamps (see diagram above), the sheet being guillotined into four before issue.

Perforation. All values are comb perforated 12. The printer's sheet was perforated as a complete sheet with perforation Type A*; therefore, the characteristics of each individual pane are different as is clearly shown in the diagram above. Perforator Type A* is described in Appendix G.

Plate Numbers. See the General Notes for Section T for an illustration of these. Each printer's sheet produces four plate numbers comprising a "whole number" and "A", "B" and "C" numbered panes and these appear below stamp 7 in the bottom row of each pane, as shown in the diagram above. The arrangement of the panes is the same for all plates of all the values.

Guide hole and plugged impression

Perforation Guide Holes. The Machin high values have a single guide hole opposite the first row of stamps, in the left-hand margin of the "whole" number panes and in the right-hand margin of the "A" plates as shown in the diagram of the printer's sheet. Additionally for plate 2 of the 2s. 6d., and 5s., and plate 1 of the 10s., there are " blind " perforation guide holes slightly below the punched holes.

The punched holes are usually heavily rimmed with colour and may be either partly or completely trimmed off. The appearance of the " blind " holes ranges from a thin outline to being completely coloured in.

U3.   Queen Elizabeth II
(Des. after plaster cast by Arnold Machin)

1969. Type U3

Cat. No.	S.G. No.	Shades	Mint	Used

1969 (MARCH 5). 2s.6d. BROWN

UC1	787	Brown	50	30

Plate Numbers (Blocks of Four)

Pl. No.				Pl. No.				Pl. No.			
2	..	..	5·00	3	..	..	5·00	6	..	..	7·50
2A	..	..	5·00	3A	..	..	5·00*	6A	..	..	7·50
2B	..	..	5·00	3B	..	..	5·00	6B	..	..	7·50
2C	..	..	5·00	3C	..	..	5·00	6C	..	..	35·00

*This contains the recorded minor constant flaw.

Minor Constant Flaw

Pl. 3A 5/8 Dot to right of Queen's eye (Th. D–E4)

Quantities Printed.   Pl. 2/2C 7,840,000; Pl. 3/3C 27,200,000; Pl. 6/6C 9,360,000

1969 (MARCH 5). 5s. CRIMSON-LAKE

UC2	788	Crimson-lake	2·25	60

Plate Numbers (Blocks of Four)

Pl. No.				Pl. No.			
2	..	..	13·00	3	..	..	13·00
2A	..	..	13·00	3A	..	..	13·00
2B	..	..	13·00	3B	..	..	13·00
2C	..	..	13·00	3C	..	..	13·00

Quantities Printed.   Pl. 2/2C 8,480,000; Pl. 3/3C 15,200,000

1969 (MARCH 5). 10s. DEEP ULTRAMARINE

UC3	789	Deep ultramarine	7·00	7·50

Plate Numbers (Blocks of Four)

Pl. No.				Pl. No.			
1	..	..	40·00	1B	..	..	40·00
1A	..	..	40·00	1C	..	..	40·00

Quantities Printed.   Pl. 1/1C 8,880,000

Cat. No.	S.G. No.	Shades	Mint	Used
1969 (MARCH 5).	**£1 BLUISH BLACK**			
UC4	—	(1) Bluish black	3·00	1·60
		(2) Indigo	£675	

The indigo shade, from plate 3B, was due to a faulty ink mix and has been confirmed by analysis.

Plate Numbers (Blocks of Four)

Pl. No.				Pl. No.			
3	..	..	25·00	4	..	..	35·00
3A	..	..	25·00	4A	..	..	35·00
3B	..	..	25·00	4B	..	..	35·00
(3C)*	..	..	†	4C	..	..	35·00

*This plate number block is not known as there was a fault on the plate and only the left half of this pane was issued.

New plates were made for the decimal £1 in 1970, but in single pane settings of 100 (10 × 10) in place of the plates of four panes each of 40 (8 × 5). Plate blocks of four from Plate 3 of the decimal issue (No. UC11 in Vol. 4 of this catalogue) can easily be distinguished from Plate 3 blocks of the pre-decimal issue as they show part of the "TOTAL SHEET VALUE" inscription in the margin opposite R. 9/10.

However, specialists may also recognise single stamps by studying the background shading under a strong magnifying glass, particularly in the top left and bottom right corners. The pre-decimal issue has thicker horizontal lines of shading whilst the decimal issue has thicker vertical lines, each caused by the direction in which the transfer roller was rocked, both plates being produced by the conventional process of rocking in impressions from the die. (Illustrations taken from top left corner)

UC4
Pre-decimal issue
Thicker horizontal lines

UC11
Decimal issue
Thicker vertical lines

Quantities Printed. Pl. 3/3C 3,760,000; Pl. 4/4C 2,800,000

Presentation Pack

UPP2 (issued 5 March 1969)   Four values   18·00
  a. With German text   ..   ..   45·00
   The issued Pack contained one each of Nos. UC1/4.
UPP2 also exists with a Japanese insert card.

First Day Cover

UFC6 (5.3.69)   2s. 6d., 5s., 10s., £1   15·00

SECTION W
Special Issues (1953–70)

General Notes

SPECIAL ISSUES. Until 1966 it had been the policy of the Post Office to restrict commemorative issues to celebrating particular events, such as anniversaries or exhibitions, conferences and festivals, etc. The introduction of the Landscape series in May 1966 heralded a new departure as this was followed by pictorial sets showing British Birds, Paintings, Bridges, Cathedrals, etc. and Technological Achievements. These cannot be described as being commemorative stamps, yet it is obviously convenient and logical for them to be listed here and so we have headed this Section Special Issues.

SE-TENANT COMBINATIONS. *Se-tenant* means " joined together ". Some sets include stamps of different design arranged *se-tenant* as blocks or strips and, in mint condition, these are usually collected unsevered as issued. Where such combinations exist, the individual stamps are priced normally as mint and used singles.

PRINTERS. All the £.s.d. special issues were printed in photogravure by Harrison & Sons with the exception of the 1964 2s.6d. Shakespeare and 1966 2s.6d. Westminster Abbey which were recess-printed by Bradbury, Wilkinson & Co. and the 1969 Post Office Technology and 1970 Commonwealth Games issues which were printed by De La Rue & Co. by lithography.

Generally, the double-sized stamps were printed on continuous reels of paper "on the web" in double pane width, i.e. 240 stamps consisting of two panes (no dot and dot) each of 120 stamps arranged in twenty rows of six stamps, the panes being guillotined before issue. However, the higher values were often printed in single panes, either on reel or sheet-fed machines. After the listing of each issue we give the sheet arrangement and state whether printed in the reel or in sheets.

QUEEN'S PORTRAIT. The portrait from the photograph by Dorothy Wilding Ltd. was used from the 1953 Coronation to the 1966 Westminster Abbey issues. This was replaced on the 1966 Landscapes to 1967 Christmas by the profile coinage design by Mrs. Mary Gillick, adapted by David Gentleman. The third, and final, change was made on the 1968 Bridges issue with the introduction of a design from a plaster cast by Arnold Machin. The Machin head can be distinguished from the Gentleman adaptation of the Gillick profile by two, instead of one, laurel leaves on top of the Queen's head.

PAPER. The same type of paper as for the definitive issues was used up to the 1960 General Letter Office issue and thereafter chalk-surfaced paper was used.

SCREEN. The 200-line screen as used for the Wilding definitives was employed up to the 1960 Europa issue but thereafter Harrisons used a finer 250-line screen.

WATERMARKS. These are illustrated in Section SA and were used as follows:

Tudor Crown	1953 Coronation issue
St. Edward's Crown	1957 World Scout Jubilee and Inter-Parliamentary Union and 1958 Commonwealth Games
Crowns	All later issues until 1967 Wild Flowers and British Discovery and Invention
No watermark	1967 Paintings and Sir Francis Chichester and all issues from 1967 Christmas onwards

The watermark normally appears sideways on upright designs. On certain stamps, the 2½d. and 3d. 1962 Productivity Year, and the 1963 Freedom from Hunger and Paris Postal Conference issues, the watermark is normally inverted. These stamps were printed " on the web " and for technical reasons the paper had to be re-reeled and, to save time and expense, it was decided to print on the paper wound in the reverse direction to normal, thus resulting in the watermark being inverted. A large proportion of the printing for the 1967 Wild Flowers 9d. was similarly treated. Other inverted watermark varieties on commemorative issues are normally from sheet-printed issues where the paper has been accidentally fed the wrong way and these are often quite scarce.

GUM. The distinction between gum arabic and PVA gum is explained in the General Notes relating to Section UA. It is sufficient to state here that gum arabic was used for all commemorative stamps up to the 1967 Christmas issue and thereafter Harrisons and De La Rue only used PVA gum.

PERFORATION. Harrisons used the same 15 × 14 comb perforation as for the Wilding definitives but some of the upright designs are perforated 14 × 15. The 1964 2s.6d. Shakespeare and 1966 2s.6d. Westminster Abbey were comb perforated 11 × 12 by Bradbury, Wilkinson and the 1969 Post Office Technology and 1970 Commonwealth Games issues were comb perforated 13½ × 14 by De La Rue. Harrisons have used a number of different perforators in the commemorative issues and these are illustrated and described in Appendix G. The cylinder numbers are listed and priced according to the type of perforator used.

202

PHOSPHOR BANDS. See the General Notes for Section S for a detailed description of these. In the special issues they were applied as follows:

"Blue": From 1962 N.P.Y. to 1965 Salvation Army and 1965 I.T.U. Generally 8 mm. but occasionally 9·5 mm. bands.

"Violet" 8 mm. bands: Other 1965 issues to 1966 Christmas.

"Violet" 9·5 mm. bands: 1967 E.F.T.A. to 1970 Christmas.

From 1962 until the 1967 Wild Flowers set the special issues appeared both with and without phosphor bands. From the 1967 British Paintings set onwards it was intended that all special issues should appear only with phosphor bands. However, it is quite common practice for sheets to be issued with the phosphor accidentally omitted and these are listed as varieties.

Methods of Application. All three methods, photogravure, flexography and typography were utilised to apply the phosphor bands to £.s.d. special issues (for the characteristics of each method see Section S Notes).

In the light of considerable research it now appears that from 1962 until 1969 the bands were applied either by flexography or photogravure, the only exceptions being the two special issues printed by De La Rue which had the bands applied by typography. These two issues used a slightly different substance known as SA, sulphanilic acid being the activator.

It is known that the first phosphor issue, 1962 National Productivity Year set, had the bands printed on the web by flexography and the following reel-fed issues used the same process or photogravure. Flexography was used for the few sheet-fed issues. Since 1970 Harrisons have only used photogravure to apply the bands, and phosphor cylinder numbers were introduced.

Some difficulty can arise in distinguishing between phosphor bands applied by photogravure and those printed by flexography. The latter often do not run to the bottom of the sheet or show a break in the bottom margin. They also show, in some instances, a vertical split in the centre of the band.

In some instances the cylinders or stereos used to apply the bands were made-up with a narrow band at one side or both sides, of the sheet. These narrow bands vary in size, as do the normal bands, but most are 6 mm. wide. Where such varieties occur they are included, listing being for a single stamp with vertical margin attached.

PHOSPHOR CYLINDER NUMBERS. Starting with the 1970 Anniversaries issue cylinder numbers were introduced on the phosphor cylinders as an additional check on tracing errors in applying the bands.

CYLINDER VARIETIES AND MINOR CONSTANT FLAWS. We have only listed or recorded those we have actually seen and know to be constant in the position given. Others have been reported and may be added in future editions as specimens become available for inspection. To pinpoint the position of the flaws we give the reference according to the S.G. "Thirkell" Position Finder where this is appropriate. Please note that for designs which lack outer frame lines the position finder should be placed over the outside of the perforation. For further information see the General Notes to Section S under **"Varieties"** and **"Varieties in Cylinder Blocks"**.

Flaws on Phosphor Issues. In the recorded lists of flaws on stamps which come both ordinary and phosphor, "O" means that the flaw occurs only on the ordinary stamp, "P" phosphor only and "OP" on ordinary and phosphor.

MULTICOLOURED STAMPS. Colour descriptions are taken from the traffic lights to identify the colours of the cylinder numbers and also missing colour errors. Where colours are superimposed one over another, the colours that result will be different from those described. So far as possible we have followed the normal practice giving the colours starting first with the most prominent one in the centre of the stamp and then moving outwards, usually ending with the colours of the inscriptions, background and Queen's head.

PRESENTATION PACKS. Special Packs comprising slip-in cards with printed commemorative inscriptions and descriptive notes on the back and with protective covering, were introduced in 1964 with the Shakespeare issue. These are listed and priced.

Issues of 1968–69 (British Paintings to the Prince of Wales Investiture) were also issued in packs with text in German for sale through the Post Office's German Agency and these are also listed.

Subsequently, the packs sold in Germany, Japan and the Netherlands were identical to the normal English version with the addition of a separate printed card in German, Japanese or Dutch. These are noted where they exist.

REPRINTED INSERT CARDS. In 1988 permission was granted to a British stamp dealer by the Post Office to reproduce, from an original, 1,000 sets of the Dutch insert cards for the 1969 Ships to the 1970 Literary Anniversaries issues.

"SPECIMEN" AND "CANCELLED" STAMPS. The former practice of distributing these ceased during the reign of King George VI but occasionally such overprints were applied to Elizabethan Special Issues for advance publicity or exhibition purposes and these are listed.

Various issues of 1964, 1965 and 1966 are known overprinted "CANCELLED", usually without gum. These were for use in trials carried out by the Forensic Department of the Post Office, and should not have reached the general public.

Issues of 1969/70 are known with "CANCELLED" applied with a violet *rubber* handstamp (26 × 3½ mm.), generally across a corner of the stamps. This practice was introduced in an attempt to defeat the postal use of the stamps prior to their first day of issue and which could be obtained from advance publicity material distributed to shops supplied by the Post Office Agency in West Germany. When it was realised that the use of the rubber handstamp created material of a collectable nature the practice was discontinued but the following are known to exist, Nos. W159/69 and W171/97. The Machin 1969 high values, Nos. U33/6 were similarly obliterated. Later stamps were cancelled by a red pen line across the corner. Such publicity material is outside the scope of this catalogue.

WITHDRAWAL DATES. The earlier commemorative issues were left on sale until exhaustion and definite withdrawal dates are not always known, but starting with 1963 Red Cross issue the Post Office announced a standard practice to keep commemorative stamps on sale at the Philatelic Bureau for twelve months from date of issue unless sold out before. All £.s.d. stamps were invalidated as from 1 March 1972.

QUANTITIES. Up to the end of the 1962 issues (N.P.Y.) it is believed that stamps were sold to exhaustion except where a definite withdrawal date was announced, and so the printing figures are quoted as being the *quantities sold*. Starting with the 1963 Freedom from Hunger issue the quantities are stated as being the number *sold, issued* or *printed*. These are defined as follows:

Sold   Actual quantities sold after accounting for undistributed stocks and unsold stocks returned to stores for destruction.

Issued   Quantities issued from Post Office Stores Department to post offices, including the Philatelic Bureau. These figures are given for the 1965 issues (Churchill to I.T.U.) and for which we do not have actual sales figures. Some may have been withdrawn and destroyed.

Printed Quantities actually supplied by the printers. These often differ from advance announcements of quantities ordered, owing to spoilage, etc.

We also quote figures for sales of Presentation Packs and these were only made available after the total quantities sold, etc., had been announced. The quantities for Packs are not additional as they have already been included in the figures for the numbers sold, issued or printed.

We have noticed slight variations in the figures given for quantities sold, etc., stated in other publications and would point out that the figures we have given are those furnished to us by the Post Office. However, the differences are insignificant. See note above No. W178.

SHEET MARKINGS. Reference should be made to the descriptions of sheet markings given in the General Notes for Section S, as most of these apply to this section and the information given there is not repeated here. In the commemorative issues the markings are most interesting as they begin with the same basic markings as for the definitives for the first monocoloured issues but as more colours were introduced other markings began to appear. They are described here in the order of their appearance.

Normal at side   At foot

Harrison   De La Rue

Cylinder Numbers

Cylinder Numbers. These are described in Section S but we show above how they occur on stamps printed in more than one colour. In the listing of cylinder number blocks for stamps printed in more than one colour we give the colour of each cylinder number in order, reading downwards. The information is sometimes helpful in connection with varieties and flaws where more than one cylinder has been used for the same colour in combination with others.

Plate Numbers. The Plate Numbers used by Bradbury, Wilkinson for the 2s.6d. Shakespeare and the 2s.6d. Westminster Abbey are as shown in our notes on the sheet markings for Section T. It should be stated that some of the sheet-fed commemorative stamps were printed by Harrisons on a Linotype and Machinery No. 4 press which uses curved plates and on these the "cylinder numbers" are, strictly speaking, plate numbers. However, as they appear just like the cylinder numbers they are referred to as such.

Colour Register Marks. These are coloured crosses of very fine lines, one for each colour superimposed, as illustrated. They appear on all sheets of stamps printed in more than one colour, starting with the 1960 Europa issue.

Photo-etched Solid

Stippled

Autotron Marks. Coloured bars which may be photo-etched solid or stippled (dotted lines). They serve as an electronic control on colour registration and were first used on the 1961 C.E.P.T. issue.

Colour Designations. These consist of colour names usually preceded by a figure and the letter "G" which stands for "Gear". They are usually trimmed off but sometimes appear on extra wide right-hand margins on double and single pane reel-fed printings. They are to indicate which side the cylinder should be fitted and aligned with the colour gear in the press. They are not always shown in the colour indicated. They began to be used on the 1961 C.E.P.T. issue, but do not appear on correctly trimmed sheets of £.s.d. stamps after the 1969 Notable Anniversaries issue.

Boxed

Partially Boxed

Harrison

De La Rue

"Traffic Lights". This term is used to denote coloured check dots which were first introduced on the 1963 N.P.Y. issue. They are intended as a means of checking sheets for missing colours before delivery to the Post Office. They may be fully boxed or partially boxed as shown but we have not distinguished between these. We quote the colours in the order of their appearance reading downwards. Sometimes they are in the same order as the cylinder numbers in which case we state this to save space. Rather larger dots were used by De La Rue.

Coloured Crosses. These are most usually found on sheet-fed printings and they serve as trimming lines and as an additional check on colour registration. They are often trimmed off. They first appeared on the 1s.3d. 1964 Botanical stamp.

(a)   (b)   (c)   D.L.R.

Perforation Guide Holes. At first the styles as shown in the General Notes for Section S were used but the types illustrated above were introduced as follows:—
(a) Double "S O N" box for the 6d. 1965 Parliament
(b) Single "S O N" box for the 4d. 1966 Landscapes
(c) Single "S N" box for the 4d. 1966 World Football Cup
The letters stand for "Selvedge", "Off-side" and "Near-side" and they appear in the reverse order on the other side of the sheet. The "S" or "S O" and part of the box are liable to be trimmed off. We also show the styles used by De La Rue for the 1969 Post Office Technology set and 1970 Commonwealth Games issue respectively.

TOTAL SHEET VALUE   £ 4. 10. 0.

Total Sheet Values. As an aid to counter clerks in stocktaking and in selling stamps by the sheet, the "TOTAL SHEET VALUE" and amount was printed in the margin. This practice was introduced with the 1969 Anniversaries issue and this was presumably found to be necessary with the introduction of stamps of unusual size and sheet make-up.

EMBOSSED HEAD. Starting with the 1968 British Paintings set the Queen's head was sometimes embossed over the gold printing. This gives rise to missing embossing varieties which are listed, although we do not list misplaced embossing. Provision is also made for an embossed dot in the traffic lights.

DESIGN INDEX

This index gives an easy reference to the inscriptions and designs of the Special Stamps 1953 to 1970. Where a complete set shares an inscription or type of design, then only the catalogue number of the first stamp is given. Paintings, inventions, etc., are indexed under the name of the artist or inventor, where this is shown on the stamp.

*PRICES FOR CYLINDER BLOCKS WITH ASTERISKS

These denote cylinder blocks containing a listed flaw.

W1
(Des. E. G. Fuller)

W2
(Des. Michael Goaman)

W3
(Des. Edmund Dulac)

W4
(Des. M. C. Farrar-Bell)

(Portrait by Dorothy Wilding Ltd (except 1s.3d.))

1953 (JUNE 3). CORONATION OF QUEEN ELIZABETH II

Celebrating the Coronation of Queen Elizabeth II.

Cat. No.	S.G. No.	Type	Wmk.	Description	Mint	Used
W1	532	**W1**	**W.22**	2½d. Carmine-red	10	25
a. Missing pearl (Cyl. 3 Dot, R. 1/4) ..			15·00			
b. Pearls retouched			8·00			
W2	533	**W2**	**W.22**	4d. Ultramarine	40	1·50
a. Daffodil leaf flaw (Cyl. 1 No dot, R. 19/1)			3·75			
W3	534	**W3**	**W.22**	1s.3d. Deep yellow-green	3·50	2·50
a. Clover leaf flaw (Cyl. 2 No dot, R. 20/1)			5·00			
W4	535	**W4**	**W.22**	1s.6d. Deep grey-blue	6·00	3·50
a. Mis-shapen emblems (Cyl. 1 Dot, R. 1/6)			10·00	*b*. Thistle flaw (Cyl. 1 Dot, R. 16/5) .. .. 12·00		

First Day Cover (W1/4) ..	..	.. 40·00

Nos. W1/4 are known used from an Army Post Office in Egypt on 2 June.

Reprints, in black, of these four stamps were included in the *Penrose Annual* for 1954. These reprints were printed in photogravure by Harrisons, on ungummed paper, but were perforated. They were inscribed on the reverse " Reproduction only—no postal or philatelic value ".

Listed Varieties

W1*a*   W1*b*

Normal   W3*a*

W2a

W4a

W4b

Cylinder Numbers (Blocks of Six)

Perforation Type A

	Cyl. No.			No dot	Dot		Cyl. No.			No dot	Dot
2½d.	1	..	..	3·00	3·00	4d.	1	..	..	7·00*	4·25
	2	..	..	1·00	1·00	1s.3d.	2	..	..	25·00*	22·00
	3	..	..	1·00	1·00	1s.6d.	1	..	..	38·00	38·00
	4	..	..	1·00	1·00						

Minor Constant Flaws

2½d. Cyl. 1 no dot
  19/2 Spur to top of A of POSTAGE

2½d. Cyl. 3 dot
  13/2 Bulge on left-hand fraction bar

2½d. Cyl. 4 no dot
  1/3 White flaw in diadem (Th. A7)
  1/4 White spur on left-hand crown (Th. B2)
  7/1 Red spot behind hair level with ear-ring (Th. D8–9)
  14/2 Red spot on face level with ear-ring (Th. D7)
  17/1 White spot on branch below left-hand crown (Th. C3)

4d. Cyl. 1 dot
  1/4 Retouched stem of daffodil (Th. F2–3)

1s.3d. Cyl. 2 dot
  2/6 Retouch behind upper part of E of E R and white flaw at top of sceptre (Th. B4)

1s.6d. Cyl. 1 no dot
  18/2 Malformed foot to R of REVENUE

1s.6d. Cyl. 1 dot
  19/1 White flaw on wreath below R of REVENUE (Th. B9)

Sheet Details

Sheet size: 120 (6 × 20). Double pane reel-fed

Sheet markings:
  Cylinder numbers: Opposite R.18/1
  Guide holes: Boxed opposite rows 14/15, at left (no dot) or right (dot)
  Marginal arrows:
    "V" shaped, hand engraved at top and bottom of sheet
    "W" shaped, photo-etched at both sides
  Marginal rule: At bottom of sheet

Imprimaturs from the National Postal Museum Archives

Nos. W1/4 imperforate, watermark Type W.22

Watermark upright (*set of* 4)

Quantities Sold

2½d. 415,034,000; 4d. 19,816,000; 1s.3d. 8,012,000; 1s.6d. 5,987,200

W5.   Scout Badge and
"Rolling Hitch"
(Des. Mary Adshead)

W6.   "Scouts coming
to Britain"
(Des. Pat Keely)

W7.   Globe within a Compass
(Des. W. H. Brown)

1957 (AUGUST 1).   WORLD SCOUT JUBILEE JAMBOREE

Commemorating the 50th Anniversary of the founding of the Boy Scout Movement.
The Jubilee Jamboree was held at Sutton Coldfield.

Cat. No.	S.G. No.	Type	Wmk.	Description	Mint	Used
W5	557	**W5**	**W.23**	2½d. Carmine-red	15	10
a. Broken rope strand				b. Neck retouch		
(Cyl. 4 Dot, R. 1/1)	..		3·50	(Cyl. 5 No dot, R. 11/5)	.. 4·50	
W6	558	**W6**	**W.23**	4d. Ultramarine	50	1·00
a. Solid pearl at right						
(Cyl. 1 No dot, R. 14/5)	..	6·00				
W7	559	**W7**	**W.23**	1s.3d. Green	4·50	4·50
a. Major retouch						
(Cyl. 1 Dot, R. 2/4)	..	.. 8·00				

> First Day Cover (W5/7) ..   ..   .. 12·00

Listed Varieties

W5a

W5b

W6a

W7a

Cylinder Numbers (Blocks of Six)

Perforation Type A

	Cyl. No.			No dot	Dot		Cyl. No.			No dot	Dot
2½d.	4	..	..	1·50	1·50	4d.	1	..	..	12·00	12·00
	5	..	..	1·50	1·50	1s.3d.	1	..	..	28·00	28·00

	Perforation Type B						Perforation Type C			
4d,	1	..	..	4·50	4·50	4d.	1	..	..	†	4·50

Minor Constant Flaws

2½d. Cyl. 4 dot
11/2 Red spot over Queen's left eyebrow, later retouched (Th. C9)
14/1 Red spot in rope between L E (Th. G5)
16/5 White spot in rope at junction with fifth line at left (Th. C1)
17/3 Red spot in large 2 just left of curve
19/2 White dot after small 2
20/4 White stop after M

2½d. Cyl. 5 dot
13/4 Red spot in top of A

1s.3d. Cyl. 1 dot
18/2 Green spot in compass point above badge (Th. E2)

Coils

Special rolls were prepared of this issue for servicing first day covers mechanically. They were produced from different cylinders and printed on continuous reels of paper. The cylinders bore 126 impressions in 21 rows of six. The cylinders were numbered J1 for the 2½d. and 4d. and J2 for the 1s.3d. The reels were cut so as to provide single rolls of 4800 stamps, numbered 1 to 6. Some very minor flaws have been noted on these coil stamps.

The rolls were put on sale at the London Chief Office but as the quantities were too large for stamp collectors, some were rewound into smaller rolls of 480 for the 2½d. and 4d. and 240 for the 1s.3d. and put on sale there on 2 September.

Sheet Details

Sheet size: 120 (6 × 20). Double pane reel-fed

Sheet markings:
  Cylinder numbers: Opposite R.18/1
  Guide holes: Opposite rows 14/15, at left (no dot) or right (dot)
  Marginal arrows:
    "V" shaped, hand engraved at top and bottom of sheet
    "W" shaped, hand engraved on both sides
  Marginal rule: At bottom of sheet

Imprimaturs from the National Postal Museum Archives

Nos. W5/7 imperforate, watermark Type W.23

Watermark upright (*set of* 3)

Quantities Sold

Sheets and coils: 2½d. 137,235,286; 4d. 9,318,477; 1s.3d. 3,820,478
Coils:

Value	Size	Printed	Sold	Size	Printed	Sold
2½d.	4800	487	23	480	100	49
4d.	4800	480	21	480	100	37
1s.3d.	4800	482	20	240	100	33

Total number of coil stamps sold or used on covers:
  2½d. 133,920; 4d. 118,560; 1s.3d. 103,920

Only 60,632 covers were serviced and 14 large rolls of each value were used for this purpose.

Withdrawn 11.9.57

W8

(Des. M. C. Farrar-Bell with added lettering)

1957 (SEPTEMBER 12).   46th INTER-PARLIAMENTARY UNION CONFERENCE

To mark the 46th Conference held at Church House, Westminster. The Union was founded in 1889.

Cat. No.	S.G. No.	Type	Wmk.	Description	Mint	Used
W8	560	**W8**	**W.23**	4d. Ultramarine	1·00	1·00
a. Broken wreath (R.2/6)		..	6·00	c. Partial double frame line		
b. Broken frame (R.12/5)		..	5·00	(R.17/3, 17/6 and 18/6)	..	4·00

First Day Cover (W8)	..	..	..	90·00

Listed Varieties

W8*a*   W8*b*   W8*c*

Cylinder Numbers (Blocks of Six)

	Cyl. No.	Perf. Type B	Perf. Type C
4d.	2	.. 7·00	7·00

Minor Constant Flaws

4d. Cyl. 2 no dot

    1/5 Blue blob in frame over last N of CONFERENCE (Th. E6)
    1/6 Outline of left-hand jewel of diadem incomplete (Th. A/B3)
    2/1 Line joining shamrock leaf to bottom frame (Th. G–H1)
    3/2 Blue scratch on right frame near bottom (Th. H6)
    8/7 Small break in frame opposite last E in CONFERENCE
    14/6 Fine scratch from ear right across neck (Th. E4)
    15/8 Blue blob in bottom right corner (Th. H6)
    18/1 Blue spot below A of POSTAGE

Sheet Details

Sheet size: 240 (12 × 20). Single pane reel-fed
Sheet markings:
    Cylinder number: Opposite R.18/1
    Guide holes: Six. Opposite rows 1 and 7/8 at both sides and also boxed opposite rows 14/15 at both sides
    Marginal arrows:
        "V" shaped, hand engraved at top and bottom of sheet
        "W" shaped, etched in photogravure at both sides
    Marginal rule: At bottom of sheet

Imprimatur from the National Postal Museum Archives

No. W8 imperforate, watermark Type W.23

Watermark upright

Quantity Sold   10,472,160

Withdrawn   13.10.57

W9. Welsh Dragon
(Des. Reynolds Stone)

W10. Flag and Games Emblem
(Des. W. H. Brown)

SPECIMEN

A

W11. Welsh Dragon
(Des. Pat Keely)

1958 (JULY 18).   SIXTH BRITISH EMPIRE AND COMMONWEALTH GAMES

The 1958 Empire and Commonwealth Games were held at Cardiff.

Cat. No.	S.G. No.	Type	Wmk.	Description	Mint	Used
W9	567	W9	W.23	3d. Deep lilac	15	10

a. Short scale (Cyl. 2 Dot, R. 1/1) .. — 2·75
b. Shoulder flaw (Cyl. 2 Dot, R. 12/2) .. .. — 4·00
c. Shoulder flaw retouched .. .. — 3·00
d. Body flaw. State II (Cyl. 2 Dot, R. 20/3) .. .. — 4·00
e. Body flaw, State III .. .. — 3·00

f. Retouched face (Cyl. 7 Dot, R. 10/6) .. .. — 3·00
g. "H" flaw (Cyl. 7 Dot, R. 11/2) .. — 7·00
h. "H" flaw retouched .. .. .. — 2·75
s. "Specimen", Type A .. .. — 15·00

W10	568	W10	W.23	6d. Reddish purple	25	45

s. "Specimen", Type A .. .. — 15·00

W11	569	W11	W.23	1s.3d. Green	2·25	2·25

s. "Specimen" Type A .. .. — 15·00

First Day Cover (W9/11) .. .. 55·00

Listed Varieties

Part of the shading is missing on the scale
near "M" of "EMPIRE".

Normal   W9a

White flaw on shading of
dragon's body above
shoulder. Later re-
touched with an irregular
pattern of dots.

W9b   W9c

W9*d*   W9*e*   W9*f*

Flaw on body above second "E" of "EMPIRE". This is a progressive flaw. Initially normal, the first stage showed the faintest outline of a flaw. State II shows the flaw solid and state III with a dark outline and pale centre.

The retouches across the Queen's cheek and below the chin are quite marked on Cyl. 7 dot, R.10/6 but there are other minor retouches in this position in stamp No. 6 in rows 2 to 1?.

W9*g*

White flaw crossing line behind dragon's left foreleg shows as a letter "H". After retouching there is a light vertical line across the flaw.

Cylinder Numbers (Blocks of Six)

Perforation Type A

	Cyl. No.		No dot	Dot		Cyl. No.		No dot	Dot
3d.	2	.. ..	1·50	1·50	6d.	6	.. ..	2·00	2·00
	7	.. ..	3·00	3·00	1s.3d.	3	.. ..	16·00	16·00

Minor Constant Flaws

3d. Cyl. 2 no dot
13/1 Dark diagonal line across last two fins of dragon's tail; later the upper line was touched out (Th.F–G9)
19/3 Dots to left of right stroke of H in BRITISH (Th. D2)

3d. Cyl. 7 no dot
8/4 White spot on M in EMPIRE; later retouched (Th. E2)

3d. Cyl. 7 dot
3/4 White flaw on fin of dragon's tail above E of COMMONWEALTH (Th. F8)
4/5 Break in left frame by top of 3 (Th. E1)
20/3 White flaw on dragon's ankle above N of COMMONWEALTH (Th. F7)

6d. Cyl. 6 no dot
18/6 Dot between O and N of COMMONWEALTH (Th. A6)

6d. Cyl. 6 dot
10/1 BRI thicker than normal and retouch under left corner of flag (Th. G3)
11/1 IRE thicker than normal
16/1 IR thicker than normal
20/3 Dent in bottom frame below Queen (Th. H10–11)

1s.3d. Cyl. 3 no dot
12/3 Retouched background above RE of EMPIRE (Th. G5)

1s.3d. Cyl. 3 dot
16–19/5 Vertical scratch of varying length in left-hand margin, petering out in rows 18/19

Sheet Details

Sheet size: 120 (6 × 20). Double pane reel-fed

Sheet markings:
  Cylinder numbers: Opposite R.18/1
  Guide holes: Boxed opposite rows 14/15, at left (no dot) or right (dot)
  Marginal arrows:
    "V" shaped, hand engraved at top and bottom of sheet
    "W" shaped, photo-etched at both sides
    In the early printings of the 6d. the arrow was omitted in the right margin on the no dot pane, and in the left margin on the dot pane. Later they were inserted by hand engraving and appear quite rough
  Marginal rule: At bottom of sheet

Imprimaturs from the National Postal Museum Archives

Nos. W9/11 imperforate, watermark Type W.23

Watermark upright (*set of* 3)

Quantities Sold 3d. 320,400,000; 6d. 28,595,880; 1s.3d. 9,870,000

CROWNS WATERMARK

The Multiple Crowns watermark, Type **W.24,** was used for all the following special issues up to the 1967 Wild Flowers issue.

W12. Postboy of 1660
(Des. Reynolds Stone)

W13. Posthorn of 1660
(Des. Faith Jacques)

1960 (JULY 7). TERCENTENARY OF ESTABLISHMENT OF "GENERAL LETTER OFFICE"

Charles II Act of 1660 establishing the G.P.O. "legally settled" the Post Office and was the first of a long series of laws for the regulation of postal matters.

The watermark is sideways on the 1s.3d.

Cat. No.	S.G. No.	Type	Description	Mint	Used
W12	619	**W12**	3d. Deep lilac	20	10
a. Broken mane (Cyl. 1 No dot,			*b.* Face scratch (Cyl. 1 Dot,		
R.17/2)		2·50	R. 17/3)	2·50	
W13	620	**W13**	1s.3d. Green	3·50	3·50
		First Day Cover (W12/13)	.. .. 40·00		

Part of the printing of the **3d.** was on chalk-surfaced paper.

Listed Varieties

Normal

W12a

W12b

Scratch extends from eye to hair

Cylinder Numbers (Blocks of Six)

	Cyl. No.		Perforation Type A	
			No dot	Dot
3d.	1	.. ..	1·75	1·75
			Perf. Type B	Perf. Type C
1s. 3d.	1	.. ..	25·00	25·00

The 1s.3d. is with sheet orientated showing head to right.

Minor Constant Flaws

3d. Cyl. 1 no dot
  1/2 White dot in bottom of large C (Th. B1)
  10/5 White notch in bottom frame below r of Letter (Th.H7)
  13/1 r of Letter weak (Th. G7)
  15/6 White patch on left foreleg of horse (Th. E5)

3d. Cyl. 1 dot
  11/6 White dot in hair near top of ear (Th. D12)
  20/5 White nick in back of boy (Th. D4)

1s.3d. Cyl. 1 no dot
  1/18 White bulge inside o of 1960 (Th. E7)
  2/20 White bulge on stem of acorn under horn (Th. L3)
  5/19 White spot in centre of leaf on right of portrait (Th. G6)
  6/5 White dot at junction of two acorns under Queen's shoulder (Th. G5)

Sheet Details

Sheet sizes:
  3d. 120 (6×20). Double pane reel-fed; 1s.3d. 120 (20×6). Single pane reel-fed
Sheet markings:
  Cylinder numbers: 3d. opposite R.18/1; 1s.3d. opposite R.4/1
  Guide holes:
    3d. opposite rows 14/15, at left (no dot) or right (dot)
    1s.3d. Six. Above and below vertical rows 1, 7/8 and boxed above and below 14/15
  Marginal arrows (hand engraved):
    3d. "V" shaped at top and bottom of sheet; "W" shaped on both sides
    1s.3d. "V" shaped on both sides: "W" shaped at top and bottom of sheet.
  Marginal rule: 3d. at bottom of sheet and 1s.3d. at right-hand side

Imprimaturs from the National Postal Museum Archives

Nos. W12/13 imperforate, watermark Type W.24

Watermark upright (3d.) or sideways (1s.3d.) (*set of 2*)

Quantities Sold   3d. 143,390,520; 1s.3d. 6,090,840

Withdrawn   31.12.60

CHALKY PAPER
All the following special issues are on chalk-surfaced paper, unless otherwise stated.

W14.   Conference Emblem
(Des. Reynolds Stone, emblem by P. Rahikainen)

Miniature Sheets
On the occasion of the EUROSTAMP—1962 London Stamp Exhibition, organised with the help of the Council of Europe, a miniature sheet, size 114 × 124 mm., was produced comprising three each of Nos. W14/15 *se-tenant* in a block of six (2 × 3) printed in grey-blue, imperforate and surrounded by a brown frame and inscriptions in black on white unwatermarked gummed paper. The stamps were printed by Harrison & Sons in photogravure and the rest of the sheet was printed by Wm. Clowes & Sons by letterpress. The sheet had no franking value.
A similar sheet exists, size 110 × 125 mm., but with the stamps printed in black and surrounded by a green frame and inscription giving details of the issue in red. The stamps were printed in photogravure and the rest of the sheet by letterpress by Harrison & Sons. The sheet had no franking value.

1960 (SEPTEMBER 19).   FIRST ANNIVERSARY OF EUROPEAN POSTAL AND TELE-COMMUNICATIONS CONFERENCE
Celebrating the first Anniversary of the Conference of European Postal and Telecommunications Administrations.

Cat. No.	S.G. No.	Type		Description		Mint	Used
W14	621	**W14**		6d. Bronze-green and purple		40	60
a. Broken diadem (R.1/2) ..		..	4·50	b. Blurred E (R.13/5)	.. ..	4·25	
W15	622	**W14**		1s.6d. Brown and blue		5·00	4·50
a Broken diadem (R.1/2)		..	12·00				
b. Major retouch (R.9/2)		..	10·00	c. Blurred E (R.13/5)	.. ..	12·00	

First Day Cover (W14/15)	..	..	28·00

Printing Screen. Nos. W14/15 were the last photogravure commemoratives from Harrisons to utilise the 200-line screen. On the 1s.6d. a 200-line screen was used for the portrait and the new 250-line version for the background.

Listed Varieties

W14/15a	W14b, W15c	W15b

Normal at top

217

Cylinder Numbers (Blocks of Four)

	Cyl. Nos. (No dot)				Perf. Type B	Perf. Type C
6d.	1 (purple)–1A (green)	..	..	..	2·50	2·50
1s.6d.	2 (blue)–1A (brown)	..	..	..	26·00	26·00

The same cylinder 1A was used for both values.

Minor Constant Flaws

6d. Cyls. 1–1A no dot
   1/4 Pale purple spots in bottom of oval and below bottom frame (Th. G9–10 and H10)
   6/2 Two short lines in scroll above T of TELECOMMUNICATIONS (Th. E2)
   9/3 Small coloured line in scroll above E of EUROPEAN (Th. B1)
   12/2 Dot in M of ADMINISTRATION
   19/1 Vertical scratch left of scroll containing EUROPEAN (Th. B–D1)
   20/5 Two scratches in scroll left of C of CONFERENCE (Th. A1–2)

1s.6d. Cyls. 2–1A no dot
   10/4 Retouch to spine of P of EUROPA
   12/2 Dot in M of ADMINISTRATION
   17/4 Dotted retouch above CO (Th. F4)
   18/5 Retouch in background above first M of TELECOMMUNICATIONS

Sheet Details

Sheet size: 120 (6 × 20). Single pane reel-fed
Sheet markings:
   Cylinder numbers: Bottom margin below R.20/5
   Guide holes: Opposite rows 1 and 7/8, at both sides and boxed opposite rows 14/15, at both sides
   Marginal arrows (hand engraved):
      "V" shaped at top and bottom and "W" shaped at both sides
   Marginal rule: At bottom of sheet
   Colour register marks: Opposite rows 2 and 19 at both sides

Imprimaturs from the National Postal Museum Archives

Nos. W14/15 imperforate, watermark Type W.24
Watermark upright (*set of 2*)

Quantities Printed   6d. 16,990,320; 1s.6d. 7,682,520

Withdrawn 31.12.60, but placed on sale again during "Stampex" exhibition in March 1961

W16. "Growth of Savings"
(Des. Michael Goaman)

W15. Thrift Plant
(Des. Peter Gauld)

W17. Thrift Plant
(Des. Michael Goaman)

1961 (AUGUST 28). POST OFFICE SAVINGS BANK CENTENARY

To mark the centenary of the establishment of the P.O. Savings Bank.
The watermark is sideways on the 2½d.

Cat. No.	S.G. No.	Type	Description	Mint	Used

A. "TIMSON" Machine

2½d. Cyls. 1E–1F no dot. Deeply shaded portrait (dull black)
3d. Cyls. 3D–3E no dot. Sharp portrait with good contrast and bright highlights

W16	623I	**W15**	2½d. Dull black and red	10	10
a. Dull black (Queen's Head) omitted £6000			*b.* Forehead retouch (R.4/19) ..	2·50	
W17	624I	**W16**	3d. Orange-brown and violet	10	10
a. Orange-brown omitted £130					
b. Perf. through right sheet margin 26·00 23·00			*ca.* Do. and orange-brown omitted		
ba. Do. and orange-brown omitted £400			*d.* Nick in " S " (R.9/3) ..	10·00	
c. Extension hole in top or bottom sheet margin .. .. .. 6·00			*e.* Nick retouched	3·00	
W18	625	**W17**	1s.6d. Red and blue	2·25	2·00
a. Phantom oval in light blue (R.19/3) .. .. 12·00					

First Day Cover (W16/18) .. .. 60·00	

B. "THRISSELL" Machine

2½d. Cyls. 1D–1B no dot or dot. Lighter portrait (grey-black)
3d. Cyls. 3C–3B no dot or dot. Dull portrait, lacking in contrast

W19	623II	**W15**	2½d. Grey-black and red	2·00	1·75
W20	624II	**W16**	3d. Orange-brown and violet	25	25
a. Orange-brown omitted £250					
b. Notch in flower (No dot, R.7/1) 2·50			*c.* Notch in leaf (No dot, R.14/4).. 2·50		

A very small quantity of all values was pre-released at the Chorley, Lancs., P.O. on 21 August, 1961.

Listed Varieties

W16b

W17d
Nick in S

W17e
Nick filled in but centre
of S is narrower

W18a

W20b

W20c

Cylinder Numbers (Blocks of Four)

A. "Timson" printings. Single pane cylinders only (no dot). Nos. W16/18

Cyl. Nos.			Perforation Types		
			B	C	F(L)
2½d. 1E (black)–1F (red)* ..	..	..	1·00	1·00	—
3d. 3D (violet)–3E (brown)	..	..	1·00	1·00	32·00
1s.6d. 2E (blue)–2C (red) ..	..	..	18·00	18·00	†

*The black number is superimposed over the red.

B. "Thrissell" printings. Double pane cylinders. Nos. W19/20

Cyl. Nos.			Perforation Type A	
			No dot	Dot
2½d. 1D (black)–1B (red)† ..	..	..	10·00	10·00
3d. 3C (violet)–3B (brown)††	..	..	8·00	2·50

†In the 2½d. dot pane the dot was omitted in error after 1B.
††In the 3d. no dot pane "3E" was wrongly inserted and the "C" was engraved over the "E".

Two blocks of four are needed to show both cylinders in the 3d. no dot "Thrissell" printing as the numbers are below R.20/2 and R.20/5 on the bottom margin.

The 2½d. is with sheet orientated showing head to right.

Minor Constant Flaws

2½d. Cyls. 1E–1F no dot
  1/13 Two white dots on right curve below last S of SAVINGS
  1/16 Two black dots right of Queen's left eye (Th. D4)
  1/17 State I. Dark red patch left of top thrift flower (Th. H3)
       State II. Later printings show whitish patch
  2/3 White horizontal line from Queen's hair to OF of OFFICE (Th. C3)
  5/3 White spot on top of right arm of V of SAVINGS

3d. Cyls. 3D–3E no dot
  8/1 Diagonal retouch across Queen's cheek from right of her left eye to nose (Th. D9–10)
  11/5 Brown spot on squirrel's neck (Th. D5)
  17/1 Retouch on Queen's chin (Th. E9)
  17/2 Retouch on neck (Th. E10)
  19/2 Retouch above necklace (Th. E–F10)
  20/1 Vertical violet line on branch in bottom right corner (Th. F–G13)

3d. Cyls. 3C–3B no dot
  1/4 Additional serif at top of K of BANK
  3/3 Notch in upper right leaf on lowest right-hand branch of tree (Th. E7)
  4/2 Retouch on neck below ear-ring (Th. E10)
  4/6 Dot in B of BANK
  7/3 Retouch above necklace (Th. E10)

Sheet Details

	Timson	Thrissell
Sheet sizes:		
2½d. **120** (20 × 6)	Single pane reel-fed	Double pane reel-fed
3d. **120** (6 × 20)	Single pane reel-fed	Double pane reel-fed
1s.6d. **120** (6 × 20)	Single pane reel-fed	
Sheet markings:		
Cylinder numbers:		
2½d.	Bottom margin below R.6/19	Bottom margin below R.6/19
3d.	Bottom margin below R.20/5	Bottom margin below R.20/2
1s.6d.	As 3d.	and R.20/5
Guide holes:		
2½d.	Above and below vertical rows 1, 7/8 and (boxed) 14/15	Below vertical rows 14/15 (no dot) or above (dot), boxed
3d.	Opposite rows 1, 7/8 and (boxed) 14/15, both sides	Opposite rows 14/15, at left (no dot) or right (dot), boxed
1s.6d.	As 3d.	
Marginal arrows (hand engraved):		
2½d.	"V" shaped on both sides; "W" shaped at top and bottom	As Timson
3d.	"V" shaped, all round	"V" shaped, at top and bottom; "W" shaped at both sides
1s.6d.	"V" shaped, at top and bottom; "W" shaped, at both sides	
Marginal rule:		
2½d.	At right-hand side	As Timson
3d.	At bottom	As Timson
1s.6d.	At bottom	

Colour register marks:

2½d.	Above and below vertical rows 2/3 and 17/18	Below vertical rows 2/3 and 17/18 (no dot) or above (dot)
3d.	Opposite rows 3/4 and 17/18 at both sides	Opposite rows 3/4 and 17/18 at left (no dot) or right (dot)
1s.6d.	Opposite rows 2/3 and 18/19 at left (no dot) or right (dot)	

Colour designations (usually trimmed off):

2½d.	None
3d.	" BROWN " opposite row 11 and " BLUE " opposite row 12, right margin, dot pane
1s.6d.	" RED " opposite row 15 and " BLUE " opposite row 16, right margin

In the case of marginal copies the differences in sheet markings, in conjunction with the different types of perforators used, provide helpful clues for identifying the printing machine used.

Autotron markings were engraved on the Thrissell cylinders during the printing run.

Imprimaturs from the National Postal Museum Archives

Nos. W16/18 imperforate, watermark Type W.24

Watermark upright (3d., 1s.6d.) or sideways (2½d.) (*set of* 3)

Quantities Sold   2½d. 24,720,000; 3d. 114,360,000; 1s.6d. 7,560,000

W18.   C.E.P.T. Emblem

W19.   Doves and Emblem

W20.   Doves and Emblem

(All values des. Michael Goaman, doves by T. Kurpeschoek)

1961 (SEPTEMBER 18).   EUROPEAN POSTAL AND TELECOMMUNICATIONS (C.E.P.T.) CONFERENCE

Representatives of nineteen countries met at Torquay on 11 September for the Second Anniversary Conference of the European Postal and Telecommunications Administrations.

These were the first stamps of Great Britain to be printed in three colours

Cat. No.	S.G. No.	Type		Description	Mint	Used
W21	626	**W18**		2d. Orange, pink and brown	10	10
a. White ear (Dot, R.11/2)		..	3·00			
W22	627	**W19**		4d. Buff, mauve and ultramarine	20	10
W23	628	**W20**		10d. Turquoise, pale green and Prussian blue	40	35
a. Pale green omitted	..	..	£3000			
b. Turquoise omitted	..	..	£1800			

First Day Cover (W21/3)	..	..	2·50

Listed Variety

W21*a*

Cylinder Numbers (Blocks of Four)

	Cyl. Nos.	Perforation Type A	
		No dot	Dot
2d.	1A (brown)—1B (orange)—1C (pink) ..	90	90
4d.	2E (ultramarine)—2B (buff)—2C (mauve)	1·50	1·50
10d.	3G (Prussian blue)—3D (green)—3A (turq.)	2·50	2·50

The panes were transposed, the dot being on the left and the no dot on the right.

Minor Constant Flaws

2d. Cyls. 1A–1B–1C no dot
   6/4 Pale spot on neck below necklace (Th. F10)
   17/4 Dot in lower right pink horn (Th. F12)
   18/1 Diagonal dark brown patch across Queen's cheek. Later retouched (Th. E10)

2d. Cyls. 1A–1B–1C dot
   6/4 Small white dot to left of P
   18/6 Hairline from right-hand frame to sheet margin (Th. E13–14)

4d. Cyls. 2E–2B–2C dot
   5/3 Flaw at top right of E
   12/6 Dark patch above diadem (Th. A8)
   15/3 Flaw down Queen's forehead and nose (Th. C–D6)
   17/6 Pale patch on cheek (Th. D7)

10d. Cyls. 3G–3D–3A no dot
   4/6 White patch above Queen's right eye (Th. C10)
   6/1 Pale patch to right of Queen's neck (Th. E12–13 F12–13)
   10/3 White patch on Queen's forehead (Th. C10). Started during the run gradually becoming more prominent
   15/5 Small white patch at top centre of Queen's forehead (Th. C10)

10d. Cyls. 3G–3D–3A dot
   4/3 Break in loop of posthorn around P (Th. C7)
   4/6 Notch in frame at top right (Th. A13)
   14/2 Dark patch to right of lower right posthorn (Th. C8)

Sheet Details

Sheet size: 120 (6 × 20). Double pane reel-fed
Sheet markings:
   Cylinder numbers: Bottom margin below R. 20/5
   Guide holes: Opposite rows 14/15, at left (dot) or right (no dot), boxed
   Marginal arrow (hand engraved):
      "V" shaped at top and bottom; "W" shaped at both sides
   Marginal rule: At bottom of sheet
   Colour register marks:
      2d. Opposite rows 2/3 and 17/18 at left (dot) or right (no dot)
      4d. Opposite rows 2/3 and 18/19 at left (dot) or right (no dot)
      10d. None
   Autotron marks (solid):
      2d. Respectively brown, pink and orange opposite rows 18/20, at left (dot) or right (no dot)
      4d. Respectively ultramarine and mauve opposite rows 18/19, at left (dot) or right (no dot)
      10d. Respectively Prussian blue, green and turquoise opposite rows 18/20, at left (dot) or right (no dot)
   Colour designations:
      2d. "BROWN" in right margin reading upwards opposite rows 14/13 (no dot)
      4d. "YELLOW", "MAUVE", "BLUE" respectively in right margin opposite rows 11/12, 12/13 and 13 (no dot)
      10d. None

Imprimaturs from the National Postal Museum Archives

   Nos. W21/23 imperforate, watermark Type W.24

   Watermark upright (*set of* 3)

Quantities Sold   2d. 47,530,920; 4d. 7,614,480; 10d. 5,427,780

W21. Hammer Beam Roof,   **W22.** Palace of Westminster
Westminster Hall

(Des. Faith Jacques)

1961 (SEPTEMBER 25). SEVENTH COMMONWEALTH PARLIAMENTARY CONFERENCE

The "Empire Parliamentary Association" was formed at the Coronation of King George V and in 1948 its name was changed to its present form.

The watermark is sideways on the 1s.3d.

Cat. No.	S.G. No.	Type	Description	Mint	Used
W24	629	**W21**	6d. Purple and gold	25	25
a. Gold omitted	..	..	.. £300		
W25	630	**W22**	1s.3d. Green and blue	2·50	2·00
a. Blue (Queen's head) omitted	.. £4000				

First Day Cover (W24/5)	..	.. 26·00

Cylinder Numbers (Blocks of Four)

Cyl. Nos. (No dot)				Perforation Types	
				Type B	Type C
6d. 1B (gold)—1D (purple)	..	..	..	2·00	2·00
1s.3d. 2A (green)—2B (blue)	..	..	..	14·00	14·00

The 1s.3d. is with sheet orientated showing head to right.

Minor Constant Flaws

6d. Cyls. 1B–1D no dot
    3/4 Dot in middle bar of second E in CONFERENCE
    5/5 Enlarged white patch in Queen's hair (Th. C7)
    6/3 Two small retouches in neck above necklace (Th. F7–8)
    10/3 Patch of retouching below crossed maces (Th. G5–6)

1s.3d. Cyls. 2A–2B no dot
    5/4 White patch on Queen's forehead (Th. D4)
    6/2 Small white vertical line on Queen's forehead (Th. C–D4)

Sheet Details

Sheet sizes: 6d. 120 (6 × 20); 1s.3d. 120 (20 × 6). Single pane reel-fed
Sheet markings:
    Cylinder numbers: Bottom margin below R. 20/5 (6d.) or 6/19 (1s.3d.)
    Guide holes:
        6d. opposite rows 1 and 7/8, at both sides and boxed opposite rows 14/15, at both sides
        1s.3d. above and below vertical rows 1 and 7/8 and boxed above and below vertical rows 14/15
    Marginal arrows (hand engraved):
        6d. "V" shaped at top and bottom and "W" shaped at both sides
        1s.3d. "V" shaped at both sides and "W" shaped at top and bottom
    Marginal rule: 6d. at bottom of sheet; 1s.3d. at right side
    Colour register marks:
        6d. Opposite both sides of rows 2/3 and 18/19
        1s.3d. Above and below vertical rows 2/3 and 18/19

Imprimaturs from the National Postal Museum Archives

Nos. W24/25 imperforate, watermark Type W.24

Watermark upright (6d.) or sideways (1s.3d.) (*set of 2*)

Quantities Sold   6d. 16,680,000; 1s.3d. 5,760,000

W23. "Units of Productivity"

W24. "National Productivity"

W25. "Unified Productivity"

(Des. David Gentleman)

The National Productivity Year issue was the first commemorative series to appear with phosphor bands and presents a number of other interesting facets:

The watermark on the 2½d. and 3d. is inverted for the reason explained in the General Notes to this section.

There were several printings on the low values which are characterised by their distinct shades and confirmed by different states of some of the flaws and varieties. It is believed that the second printing of the 2½d. comes from sheets numbered between about 439,000 and 450,000. Only the third printing was used for the phosphor stamps. There was considerable variation in the carmine-red during the printing and carmine-rose shades are quite common.

2½d. During the first printing both green cylinders were seriously damaged, hence the major repairs in the later printings.

3d. There were several printings of this value which fall into two shade groups. The violet cylinder 2A provided a number of minor flaws and was quickly replaced. It is believed that stamps from this cylinder were supplied only to Canterbury and Chelmsford.

1962 (NOVEMBER 14). NATIONAL PRODUCTIVITY YEAR

The stamps emphasised the need for greater productivity as an essential element in the continuing prosperity of Great Britain.

The watermark is inverted on the 2½d. and 3d.

Cat. No.	S.G. No.	Type		Description	Mint	Used

A. Ordinary

W26	631	**W23**		2½d.		
a. Emblem and arrows retouch (No dot, R. 3/3) (2)				(1) Myrtle-green and carmine-red	20	10
b. Ditto (3)			2·75	(2) Deep green and bright carmine-red	25	15
c. Arrow head retouch (No dot, R. 4/4) (2)			2·25	(3) Blackish olive and carmine-red	30	15
d. Ditto (3)			2·25	*k.* Smudged red centre cube (Dot R. 18/3) (2)	2·75	
e. Retouches, arrows 2 and 6 (No dot, R. 4/5) (2)			2·25	*i.* Ditto (3)	2·75	
f. Ditto (3)			2·25	*m.* Arrow head retouch (Dot, R. 19/6) (2)	3·00	
g. White nose (Dot, R. 2/6) (1)			2·25	*n.* Ditto (3)	3·00	
h. Neck retouch (Dot, R. 15/4) (1)			3·00			
i. Ditto (2)			3·00			
j. Ditto (3)			3·00			
W27	632	**W24**		3d.		
a. Lightblue(Queen'shead)omitted			£600	(1) Light blue and violet	25	10
b. Lake in Scotland (Cyls. 2A–2B Dot, R. 1/3)			7·00	(2) Light blue and deep bluish purple	30	15
c. "Kent" omitted (Cyls. 2C–2B No dot, R. 18/2)			5·00			
d. Lake in Yorkshire (Cyls. 2C–2B Dot, R. 19/1)			4·00	*f.* Ditto, removed	3·50	
e. Forehead line (Cyls. 2D–2B No dot, R. 17/6)			4·00	*g.* Ditto retouched	3·00	

Cat. No.	S.G. No.	Type	Description	Mint	Used
W28	633	**W25**	1s.3d. Carmine, light blue and	1·75	1·60
			deep green		

a. Light blue (Queen's head) omitted £3500

First Day Cover (W26/8)   .. .. 30·00

B. Phosphor

(2½d. has one band at left; others have three bands, all applied flexo.)

WP26   631p   **W23**   2½d. Blackish olive and car-
  a. Emblem and arrows retouch (No   mine-red   1·00   40
    dot, R. 3/3) ..   ..   ..   4·00
  b. Arrow head retouch (No dot,
    R. 4/4) ..   ..   3·00   *e.* Smudged red centre cube (Dot,
  c. Retouches, arrows 2 and 6 (No   R. 18/3)   ..   ..   ..   3·50
    dot, R. 4/5) ..   ..   ..   3·00   *f.* Arrow head retouch (Dot,
  d. Neck retouch (Dot, R. 15/4) ..   3·50   R. 19/6)   ..   ..   ..   4·00

WP27   632p   **W24**   3d. Light blue and violet   1·00   50
  a. Left-hand band omitted   ..   *c.* Forehead line (Cyls. 2D–2B,
  b. Narrow band at left or right   No dot, R. 17/6)   ..   ..   5·00
    (stamp with vert. margin)   ..   2·00   *d.* Forehead line removed   ..   4·00

WP28   633p   **W25**   1s.3d. Carmine, light blue and
  a. Narrow band at left or right   deep green   21·00 18·00
    (stamp with vert. margin)   ..   35·00

First Day Cover (WP26/8)   .. .. 95·00

About 60 2½d., 350 3d. and 20 1s.3d. were pre-released at a Lewisham post office, London
on 16 and 17 October, 1962.

Listed Varieties

2½d. Arrows numbered for easy identification
of varieties and flaws

W26a/b, WP26a

N and arrow head of
emblem strongly shaded
with diagonal cuts and
dashes, also arrows 4, 10
and 14

W26e/f, WP26c

In W26c/d, WP26b the arrow head alone is
retouched with diagonal lines and in W26m/n,
WP26f with irregular dots
Less marked retouches occur in the same area on
dot cyl., R. 19/2 and 19/4

W26g   W26h/j, WP26d   W26k/l, WP26e
This may not be fully constant

W27b   W27c   W27d

W27e, WP27c   W27f, WP27d   W27g

The original variety was a horizontal line from Queen's left eye to hair which was later removed, leaving a white gap and this was finally partly filled in by retouching

Cylinder Numbers (Blocks of Four)

(a) Ordinary

	Cyl. Nos.			Perforation No dot	Type A Dot
2½d.	1D (red)–1B (green) (shade 1)	..	..	1·50	1·50
	1D (red)–1B (green) (shade 2)	..	..	2·00	4·75*
	1D (red)–1B (green) (shade 3)	..	..	2·75	5·00*
3d.	2A (violet)–2B (blue)	..	..	25·00	25·00
	2C (violet)–2B (blue)	..	..	2·00	2·00
	2D (violet)–2B (blue)	..	..	2·50	2·50
1s.3d.	3C (carmine)–3B (blue)–3E (green)		..	10·00	†

		No dot Type B	No dot Type C
1s.3d.	3C (carmine)–3B (blue)–3E (green) ..	15·00	15·00

(b) Phosphor

				Perforation No dot	Type A Dot
2½d.	1D (red)–1B (green) (shade 3)	..	..	5·00	8·00*
3d.	2D (violet)–2B (blue)	..	..	5·00	5·00
1s.3d.	3C (carmine)–3B (blue)–3E (green)		..	£100	†

Minor Constant Flaws

2½d. Cyls. 1D–1B no dot
    1/2 Two small green dots right of arrow 2 (Th. B–C4) all shades, OP
    3/2 Scratch through top of bottom right cube (Th. F–E4) all shades, OP
    3/4 Minor retouches to face around mouth (Th. D–E10) shades 2/3, OP
    5/1 White scratch below Queen's nose and through mouth (Th. D–E10) all shades, OP
    17/5 Small retouch to cheek to right of mouth (Th. D10–11) all shades, OP

3d. Cyls. 2C–2B no dot
    1/4 Retouch in Scotland (Th. C3), O
    6/5 Dark patch above R of PRODUCTIVITY (Th. G6), O
    13/5 Line of retouching above blue sea of Ireland (Th. C2), O

3d. Cyls. 2C–2B dot
    7/1 Purple line across Solway Firth (Th. D3), O
    15/6 Row of dots from Queen's left eye to hair (Th. C11), O

3d. Cyls. 2D–2B no dot
    13/5 Lines of retouching above blue sea of Ireland (Th. C2), OP

3d. Cyls. 2D–2B dot
    1/3 Retouch in Yorkshire (Th. D4), OP

1s.3d. Cyls. 3C–3B–3E no dot
    3/4 White flaw at back of Queen's hair (Th. D12), OP
    6/2 Retouch on tail of large blue arrow (Th. D2), OP
    13/4 White flaw left of ear-ring (Th. E11), OP

Sheet Details

Sheet size: 120 (6 × 20)
    2½d. and 3d. Double pane reel-fed on a Timson machine
        1s.3d. Single pane reel-fed on a new Thrissell machine capable of using five colours

Sheet markings:
    Cylinder numbers: Bottom row below R. 20/5
    Guide holes:
        2½d. and 3d. Opposite rows 14/15 (boxed), at left (no dot) or right (dot)
        1s.3d. Opposite rows 1 and 7/8, at both sides and boxed opposite rows 14/15, at both sides
    Marginal arrows (photo-etched): "W" shaped at top, bottom and sides
    Marginal rule: At bottom of sheet
    Colour register marks:
        2½d. and 3d. Opposite rows 2/3 and 18/19, at left (no dot) or right (dot)
        1s.3d. Opposite rows 2/3 and 18/19, at both sides
    Autotron marks (stippled):
        2½d. and 3d. Bottom margin in various positions
        1s.3d. Respectively red, green, blue, green, red below vertical rows 4/6
    Colour designations (usually trimmed off):
        2½d. "G GREY" (not green) opposite rows 8/9 and "G RED" opposite row 13, right margin on the dot
           cylinder
        3d. "G BLUE" opposite rows 8/9 and "G MAUVE" (Cyl. 2C) opposite row 13 or "G PURPLE" (Cyl. 2D)
           opposite rows 6/7, right margin on the dot cylinder
        1s.3d. "G BLUE" opposite row 9 and "G GREEN" opposite rows 12/3, left margin
    Traffic lights (boxed):
        2½d. Green, red opposite R. 20/6 dot pane
        3d. Blue, violet opposite R. 20/6 dot pane
        1s.3d. Blue, red, green boxed opposite R. 20/6

Imprimaturs from the National Postal Museum Archives

A. Ordinary

Nos. W26/28 imperforate, watermark Type W.24

Watermark upright (*set of 3*)

B. Phosphor

Nos. WP26/28 imperforate, watermark Type W.24

Watermark upright (*set of 3*)

Quantities Sold

	Ordinary	Phosphor
2½d.	99,240,000	7,320,090
3d.	182,580,000	13,320,000
1s.3d.	8,832,000	1,320,000

Of the 2½d. ordinary it is estimated that about 62 million came from the first printing, 3 million from the second printing and 34 million from the third printing

W26.   Campaign Emblem and Family   **W27.**   Children of Three Races

(Des. Michael Goaman)

1963 (MARCH 21).   FREEDOM FROM HUNGER

The stamps were part of a world-wide co-operative effort to focus attention on the problem of hunger and malnutrition.

The watermark is inverted

Cat. No.	S.G. No.	Type	Description	Mint	Used
A. Ordinary					
W29	634	**W26**	2½d. Crimson and pink	10	10
a. Line through MPA (Cyls. 1D–1H			*b.* Broken R in FREEDOM (Cyls.		
Dot, R. 7/2) .. .. 3·50			1D–1H No dot, R. 16/2) ..	3·00	
W30	635	**W27**	1s.3d. Bistre-brown and yellow	2·00	1·75

First Day Cover (WP29/30) ..   .. 28·00

B. Phosphor (applied flexo.)

WP29	634p	**W26**	2½d. One band	1·00	1·00
a. Line through MPA (Cyls. 1D–1H			*b.* Broken R in FREEDOM (Cyls.		
Dot, R. 7/2) .. .. 5·00			1D–1H No dot, R. 16/2) ..	5·00	
WP30	635p	**W27**	1s.3d. Three bands	21·00	18·00
a. Vert. pair, one stamp with					
phosphor omitted, the other			*b.* Narrow band at left or right		
with short bands			(stamp with vert. margin.).. ..	24·00	

First Day Cover (WP29/30) ..   .. 30·00

The 2½d. value was pre-released at Chipping Norton on 20 March.

Listed Varieties

W29*a*, WP29*a*
An unsuccessful attempt was
made to touch this out

W29*b*, WP29*b*

Cylinder Numbers (Blocks of Four)

(a) Ordinary

Cyl. Nos.				Perforation Types		
				A		E
				No dot	Dot	No Dot
2½d.	1D (pink)–1G (crimson)	..	..	..	15·00	15·00	†
	1D (pink)–1H (crimson)	..	..	..	1·25	1·25	†
1s.3d.	2E (yellow)–2G (brown)	..	..	..	10·00	10·00	—
(b) Phosphor						
2½d.	1D (pink)–1H (crimson)	..	..	..	5·00	5·00	†
1s.3d.	2E (yellow)–2G (brown)	..	..	..	£100	£100	£100

Only the lower halves of sheets from the 2½d. 1D–1G cylinders were released.
In the 1s.3d. the panes are reversed, the dot pane being on the left and the no dot pane on the right.

Minor Constant Flaws
2½d. Cyls. 1D–1H no dot
  9/6 Dot in upper part of second A of CAMPAIGN, OP
  15/2 Retouch from base of portrait to M of CAMPAIGN (Th. E11 and F12–13), OP
2½d. Cyls. 1D–1H dot
  8/1 and 7/1 Hairline extends from under GN on 8/1 to CAMPAIGN on 7/1, OP
  19/1 Retouch on left cheek and jawbone (Th. D10), OP
1s.3d. Cyls. 2E–2G no dot
  1/2 Small white line in extreme right wheatsheaf (Th. C6), OP

Sheet Details
Sheet size: 120 (6 × 20). Double pane reel-fed
Sheet markings:
  Cylinder numbers: Bottom row below R. 20/5
  Guide holes:
    2½d. Opposite rows 14/15 (boxed), at left (no dot) or right (dot)
    1s.3d. Opposite rows 14/15 (boxed), at left (dot) or right (no dot)
  Marginal arrows (photo-etched): "W" shaped at top, bottom and sides
  Marginal rule: At bottom of sheet
Colour register marks:
  2½d. Opposite rows 2/3 and 18/19, at left (no dot) or right (dot)
  1s.3d. Opposite rows 2/3 and 18/19, at left (dot) or right (no dot)
Autotron marks (stippled):
  2½d. Below vertical rows 2/3, no dot pane
  1s.3d. Below vertical rows 2/3, dot pane
Colour designation:
  1s.3d. "G2" in brown opposite row 7 at right, no dot, on wide cut margins
Traffic lights (boxed):
  2½d. Red, pink opposite R. 20/6, dot pane
  1s.3d. Brown, yellow opposite R. 20/6, no dot pane

Imprimaturs from the National Postal Museum Archives

A. Ordinary
Nos. W29/30 imperforate, watermark Type W.24

Watermark upright (*set of* 2)

B. Phosphor
Nos. WP29/30 imperforate, watermark Type W.24

Watermark upright (*set of* 2)

Quantities Sold

	Ordinary	Phosphor
2½d.	97,050,000	2,784,920
1s.3d.	9,009,000	624,960

Withdrawn   1.5.64

W28.   "Paris Conference"
(Des. Reynolds Stone)

1963 (MAY 7). PARIS POSTAL CONFERENCE CENTENARY
   A postal conference was held in Paris to commemorate the centenary of the first international meeting of postal authorities held in 1863.

   The watermark is inverted

Cat. No.	S.G. No.	Type	Description	Mint	Used

A. Ordinary

W31   636   **W28**   6d. Green and mauve   50   40
   a. Green omitted ..   ..   ..   £1200   *b.* White spot in frame line (No
                           dot, R. 19/3) ..   ..   ..   3·75

> First Day Cover (W31)   ..   ..   12·00

B. Phosphor (applied flexo)

WP31   636p   **W28**   6d. Three bands   6·00   5·00
   a. Pair, with and without phosphor 40·00   *c.* Narrow band at left or right
   b. Horiz. pair; one stamp without   (stamp with vert. margin) ..   8·00
   phosphor, the other with two   *d.* White spot in frame line (No
   bands ..   ..   50·00   dot, R. 19/3) ..   ..   ..   8·50

> First Day Cover (WP31)..   ..   ..   20·00

Listed Variety

W31*b*, WP31*d*

Cylinder Numbers (Blocks of Four)

Cyl. Nos.		Perforation Type A	
		No dot	Dot
6d. 2A (mauve)–1B (green) Ordinary		3·00	3·00
6d. 2A (mauve)–1B (green) Phosphor ..		30·00	30·00

The panes were reversed, the dot being on the left and the no dot on the right.

Minor Constant Flaws

6d. Cyls. 2A–1B no dot
  1/1 Flaw in oval frame at 11 o'clock (Th. B9) and lack of definition in top right rose (Th. B13), OP
  14/6 First N of CONFERENCE appears white, OP
  19/5 Dot under R of CENTENARY, OP
  20/5 White spot on ivy stem below first E of CONFERENCE and coloured dot in right frame near top
     (Th. A13), OP

6d. Cyls. 2A–1B dot
  14/2 White spot in R of CONFERENCE, OP

Sheet Details

Sheet size: 120 (6 × 20). Double pane reel-fed
Sheet markings:
  Cylinder numbers: Below R. 20/5
  Guide holes: Opposite row 15 (boxed), at left (dot) or right (no dot)
  Marginal arrows (photo-etched): "W" shaped at top, bottom and sides
  Marginal rule: At bottom of sheet
  Colour register marks: Opposite rows 2/3 and 18/19, at left (dot) or right (no dot)
  Autotron marks (stippled): Bottom margin, dot pane
  Traffic lights (boxed): Green, mauve opposite R. 20/6, no dot pane

Imprimaturs from the National Postal Museum Archives

A. Ordinary

No. W31 imperforate, watermark Type W.24

Watermark upright

B. Phosphor

No. WP31 imperforate, watermark Type W.24

Watermark upright

Quantities Sold   Ordinary 18,536,400; phosphor 1,430,800

Withdrawn   1.6.64

W29.   Posy of Flowers
(Des. Stanley Scott)

W30.   Woodland Life
(Des. Michael Goaman)

1963 (MAY 16).   NATIONAL NATURE WEEK

The Council for Nature organised a Nature Week from 18–25 May in order to draw attention to the natural history movement and the importance of wild life conservation. The 4½d. value was the first stamp of Great Britain to be printed in five colours.

Cat. No.	S.G. No.	Type		Description	Mint	Used
A. Ordinary						
W32	637	**W29**		3d. Yellow, green, brown and	25	20
a. "Caterpillar" flaw (Dot, R. 3/2)			4·00	black		
W33	638	**W30**		4½d. Black, blue, yellow,	40	40
a. Nose retouch (Cyl. 2E, R. 14/4)			4·00	magenta and brown-red		

First Day Cover (W32/3)	.. ..	14·00

B. Phosphor						
WP32	637p	**W29**		3d. Three bands, applied photo.	50	50
a. Narrow band at left or right						
(stamp with vert. margin)		..	2·00	b. "Caterpillar" flaw (Dot, R. 3/2)	4·00	
WP33	638p	**W30**		4½d. Three bands, applied flexo.	2·50	2·50
a. Narrow band at left or right				b. Nose retouch (Cyl. 2E No dot,		
(stamp with vert. margin)		..	3·50	R. 14/4)	5·50	

First Day Cover (WP32/3)	.. ..	28·00

No. W32 is known pre-released on 15 May 1963 at Highbury, London.

Listed Varieties

W32a, WP32b
Several states exist, later retouched

W33a, WP33b

Cylinder Numbers (Blocks of Six)

(a) Ordinary

	Cyl. Nos.	Perforation Type A	
		No dot	Dot
3d.	1A (black)–3B (brown)–1C (green)–1D (yellow)	2·50	2·50

		No dot	
		Rows 12/13	Rows 18/19
4½d.	1A (brown-red)–1B (yellow)–1C (magenta)–		
	1D (blue)–2E (black)	3·75	3·75
	1A (brown-red)–1B (yellow)–1C (magenta)–		
	1D (blue)–3E (black)	4·25	5·00

(b) Phosphor

		No dot	Dot
3d.	1A (black)–3B (brown)–1C (green)–1D		
	(yellow)	4·50	4·50

		No dot	
		Rows 12/13	Rows 18/19
4½d.	1A (brown-red)–1B (yellow)–1C (magenta)–		
	1D (blue)–2E (black)	20·00	20·00
	1A (brown-red)–1B (yellow)–1C (magenta)–		
	1D–(blue)–3E (black)	22·00	24·00

In the 3d. the panes were reversed, the dot being on the left and the no dot on the right.

In the 4½d. there are two sets of cylinder numbers in the left-hand margin opposite rows 12/13 and 18/19. In position 18/19 the "1D" is in grey-blue superimposed over an additional "1C" in magenta. Also in position 12/13 the black "2" is superimposed over a black "1". The cylinder numbers are engraved more boldly in position 12/13 and are boxed, the others being without boxes.

Minor Constant Flaws

3d. Cyls 1A–3B–1C–1D no dot
2/1 Retouch to Queen's left jaw (Th. D–E11), OP
2/5 Dot between top of A and T of NATURE, OP
2/6 White line through top of 3 of value, OP
4/4 Green flaw at bottom right foot of I of NATIONAL, OP
5/4 First N of NATIONAL blurred at top left, OP
6/5 Diagonal green line crosses petals of left-hand daisy (Th. B–C3), OP
7/1 Retouch on Queen's left cheek (Th. D11), OP
9/1 Green dot near centre of N of NATURE, OP
9/2 White flaw at top of left-hand buttercup (Th. B2), OP
10/1 Patch of white to left of Queen's right eye (Th. C10), OP
10/4 Green dot at top right of 2, OP
12/6 White patch just above NA of NATIONAL, OP
13/6 Green spot above EK of WEEK, OP
14/1 White spot above 3 of value (Th. E8), OP
16/6 Dark spot to right of Queen's mouth (Th. E11–12), OP
18/3 Retouch above second A of NATIONAL, later retouched, appearing as a whitish blob (Th. F5), OP
18/5 White flaw under top left buttercup, at right (Th. C2), OP
19/3 Brown flaw to bottom right of T of NATURE, later retouched, OP
19/5 Large green blob above second A of NATIONAL, later touched out, OP
20/4 White dot between top of 3 of value and leaf (Th. E7–8), OP

3d. Cyls. 1A–3B–1C–1D dot
2/3 White dot just left of top of 3 of value, OP
6/6 Retouch under jaw extending to bottom of ear (Th. E10–11), OP
8/1 Brown dot under right leg of last A of NATIONAL, OP
8/3 Retouch by L of NATIONAL (Th. G6), OP
9/6 Brown dot under right leg of second N of NATIONAL, OP
14/1 Retouch above first E of WEEK, OP
14/4 Retouch left of 3 of value (Th. F7–8), OP
15/4 White flaw at bottom of oblique stroke in first N of NATIONAL, OP
15/5 Greyish smear over dot of value, OP
16/5 Retouch from mouth to ear (Th. D11), OP
18/4 Green dot above upper lip (Th. D10), OP
19/6 Small white retouch between 63 of 1963 and dark hairline between 3 of value and leaf (Th. F8), OP

4½d. Cyls. 1A–1B–1C–1D–2E no dot and 1A–1B–1C–1D–3E no dot
3/3 Dark spot under fawn (Th. G10), OP
7/1 Yellow patch above fawn's right ear (Th. E11), OP
14/1 Brown spot in second upper leaf from butterfly (Th. B3), OP
19/3 Retouch in background behind woodpecker (Th. E9), OP

Sheet Details

Sheet size: 120 (6 × 20). 3d. double pane reel-fed; 4½d. single pane reel-fed

Sheet markings:
  Cylinder numbers:
    3d. Below row 20/5
    4½d. Opposite rows 18/19 and boxed numbers opposite rows 12/13
  Guide holes:
    3d. Opposite rows 14/15 (boxed), at left (dot) or right (no dot)
    4½d. Opposite rows 14/15 (boxed), at both sides
  Marginal arrows (photo-etched): "W" shaped at top, bottom and sides
  Marginal rule: At bottom of sheet
  Colour register marks:
    3d. Opposite rows 2/3 and 17/19, at left (dot) or right (no dot)
    4½d. Opposite rows 3/4 and 17/18, at left (no dot) or right (dot)
  Autotron marks (stippled):
    3d. Between panes vertically, opposite rows 6/9 (seen either in right or left margin)
    4½d. Below vertical rows 1/3 and 4/6 but omitted from rows 1/3 in the first printing
  Colour designations (usually trimmed off):
    3d. "G BROWN" (rows 4/5), "G GREEN" (rows 6/7), "G YELLOW" (rows 8/9), "G ORANGE" (row 13), left margin dot pane reading downwards
    4½d. "G1 BROWN G2 YELLOW G3 RED G4 BLUE G5 BLACK" in left margin reading downwards opposite rows 5/9
  Traffic lights (boxed):
    3d. Yellow, black, green, brown opposite R. 20/6, no dot pane
    4½d. Black, blue, magenta, yellow, brown-red opposite rows 19/20 at right

Imprimaturs from the National Postal Museum Archives

A. Ordinary

Nos. W32/33 imperforate, watermark Type W.24

Watermark upright (*set of* 2)

B. Phosphor

Nos. WP32/33 imperforate, watermark Type W.24

Watermark upright (*set of* 2)

Quantities Sold

	Ordinary	Phosphor
3d.	148,560,000	8,640,000
4½d.	12,480,000	1,140,000

Withdrawn   1.6.64

W31.   Rescue at Sea   **W32.**   19th-century Lifeboat

W33.   Lifeboatmen
(Des. David Gentleman)

1963 (MAY 31). NINTH INTERNATIONAL LIFEBOAT CONFERENCE

The International Lifeboat Conferences are held every four years. In 1963 the Conference was held at Edinburgh from 3 to 5 June.

Cat No.	S.G. No.	Type		Description	Mint	Used
A. Ordinary						
W34	639	**W31**		2½d. Blue, black and red	10	10
a. Missing neckline (No dot, col. 1)			2·00	*b.* Shaded diadem (Dot, R. 20/6)	2·00	
W35	640	**W32**		4d. Red, yellow, brown, black		
a. Spot on boom (R. 6/6) ..		..	3·25	and blue	40	30
b. Spot under I (R. 13/3) ..		..	3·25			
W36	641	**W33**		1s.6d. Sepia, yellow and grey-blue	2·50	2·50

> First Day Cover (W34/6)   ..   ..   26·00

B. Phosphor (applied flexo.)

WP34	639p	**W31**		2½d. One band	40	50
a. Missing neckline (No dot, col. 1)			3·75	*c.* White flaw in hair (No dot, R. 9/6)	3·25	
b. Shaded diadem (Dot, R. 20/6)..			4·25	4d. Three bands	20	50
WP35	640p	**W32**		*b.* Spot on boom (R. 6/6)	2·75	
a. Narrow band at left or right				*c.* Spot under I (R. 13/3).. ..	2·75	
(stamp with vert. margin) ..			1·00	1s.6d. Three bands	25·00	24·00
WP36	641p	**W33**				
a. Narrow band at left or right						
(stamp with vert. margin) ..			30·00			

> First Day Cover (WP34/6)   ..   ..   38·00

In the 1s.6d. the grey-blue is lighter on the phosphor stamps, presumably in order to show the phosphor more clearly.

All values are known pre-released on 30 May.

Listed Varieties

W34*a*, WP34*a*

Occurs on all stamps in
first vertical row in
varying degrees

W34*b*, WP34*b*

Occurred during the
course of printing

WP34*c*

W35*a*, WP35*b*

W35*b*, WP35*c*

Cylinder Numbers (Blocks of Six)

(a) Ordinary

Cyl. Nos.

		Perforation Type A			
		No dot		Dot	
		Row 12	Row 19	Row 12	Row 19
2½d.	3A (red)–3B (black)–1C (blue)	1·00	1·25	1·00	1·25
4d.	1A (blue)–1B (black)–1C (red)–1D (brown)–1E (yellow)	4·25	4·25	†	†
			Row 18		
1s.6d. 3A (blue)–1B (sepia)–1C (yellow)		20·00	20·00		

(b) Phosphor

		Row 12	Row 19		
2½d.	3A (red)–3B (black)–1C (blue)	4·25	4·25	4·25	4·25
4d.	1A (blue)–1B (black)–1C (red)–1D (brown)–1E (yellow)	2·00	2·50	†	†
			Row 18		
1s.6d. 3A (blue)–1B (sepia)–1C (yellow)		£160	£160	†	†

In the 2½d. the cylinder numbers in row 12 are shown as A (red)–B (black)–1C (blue) in left margin of left pane and the same in the right margin of right pane but without dot after C.

In the 1s.6d. the 1C is shown twice opposite row 18.

Minor Constant Flaws

2½d. Cyls. 3A–3B–1C no dot
   7/5 Scratch down Queen's face from hair to chin (Th. C–D11), OP
   8/5 Scratch continues from hair to shoulder (Th. C–D11), OP
   9/1 White scratch on dress above ENC (Th. F12), OP
   11/1 Scratch from hair to ear (Th. C–D12), OP
   14/3 Black dot below lower lip (Th. D10), OP

2½d. Cyls. 3A–3B–1C dot
   3/4 Retouch left of Queen's ear (Th. C11), OP
   9/6 Retouch on Queen's forehead (Th. C10), OP
   19/6 Pale grey patch over back of shoulder, normal in State I (Th. F12–13), OP

4d. Cyls. 1A–1B–1C–1D–1E no dot
  1/6 Retouch on Queen's nose (Th. B–C10), OP
  3/5 Vertical line of retouching on Queen's face down to shoulder (Th. C–E11), OP
  4/2 Vertical black line through shoulder to just above EN (Th. E–F12), OP
  13/1 Pale blue streak across top frame line at apex of sail (Th. A5), OP
  13/2 Yellow scratch across main sail from mast to rigging (Th. D6), OP
  18/2 Black dot over Queen's left eye (Th. C10), OP
  20/2 Blue dot on Queen's neck (Th. E11), OP
  20/3 Vertical red line down first N of CONFERENCE, OP

1s.6d. Cyls. 3A–1B–1C no dot
  6/5 Length of retouching on Queen's collar (Th. E11–12), OP
  15/6 Retouch over Queen's right eye (Th. B10), OP

Sheet Details

Sheet size: 120 (6 × 20). 2½d. double pane reel-fed; others single pane reel-fed

Sheet markings:

Cylinder numbers:
  2½d. Boxed opposite R. 12/1 (no dot pane) or R. 12/6 (dot pane)
    Also opposite R. 19/1 on both panes without box
  4d. Boxed opposite R. 12/1 and without box in left margin opposite rows 17/20
  1s.6d. Boxed opposite rows 11/12, left margin and unboxed opposite R. 18/1

Guide holes:
  2½d. Opposite rows 14/15 (boxed), at left (no dot) or right (dot)
  4d. and 1s.6d. Opposite rows 14/15 (boxed), at both sides

Marginal arrows (photo-etched): " W " shaped, at top, bottom and sides

Marginal rule: At bottom of sheet

Colour register marks:
  2½d. Opposite rows 3/4 and 18/19, at left (no dot) or right (dot)
  4d. Opposite rows 2/3 and 17/18, at both sides
  1s.6d. Opposite rows 2/4 and 18/19, at both sides

Autotron marks (stippled):
  2½d. Blue, black, red below vertical rows 4/6 on dot pane
  4d. Yellow, brown, black, red, blue below vertical rows 4/6
  1s.6d. Yellow, sepia, blue below vertical rows 4/6

Colour designations (usually trimmed off):
  2½d. "G RED G BLACK G BLUE " opposite rows 6, 7 and 9 respectively reading upwards at left (no dot) or right (dot)
  4d. " G YELLOW G BROWN G BLACK G RED G BLUE " in right margin reading upwards opposite rows 14/10
  1s.6d. "G BLUE G BROWN G YELLOW " in left margin reading downwards opposite rows 6/9

Traffic lights (boxed):
  2½d. Blue, black, red opposite R. 20/6, dot pane
  4d. Yellow, brown, black, red, blue opposite R. 20/6
  1s.6d. Yellow, sepia, blue opposite R. 20/6

Imprimaturs from the National Postal Museum Archives

A. Ordinary

Nos. W34/36 imperforate, watermark Type W.24

Watermark upright (*set of* 3)

B. Phosphor

Nos. WP34/36 imperforate, watermark Type W.24

Watermark upright (*set of* 3)

Quantities Sold

	Ordinary	Phosphor
2½d.	81,405,000	4,239,000
4d.	7,475,040	840,000
1s.6d.	7,484,780	886,000

Withdrawn 1.6.64

W34.   Red Cross

W35.   Red Cross

W36.   Red Cross
(Des. H. Bartram)

1963 (AUGUST 15).   RED CROSS CENTENARY CONGRESS

The congress which opened in Geneva on 2 September marked the Centenary of the establishment of the Red Cross organisation.

Cat. No.	S.G. No.	Type	Description	Mint	Used
A. Ordinary					
W37	642	**W34**	3d. Red and deep lilac	10	10
a. Red omitted £1750					
b. Repaired cross (Cyls. 2A–2B, No. dot, R.5/6.) .. .. 4·00					
W38	643	**W35**	1s.3d. Red, blue and grey	2·75	2·50
W39	644	**W36**	1s.6d. Red, blue and bistre	2·50	2·50
a. Retouch in C of Cross (R. 14/4) 7·00					
b. Retouch over 1 of 1/6 (R. 16/4) 7·00					

> First Day Cover (W37/9)   ..   .. 28·00

B. Phosphor (applied flexo.)					
WP37	642p	**W34**	3d. Three bands	60	60
a. Red omitted £5500			c. Narrow band at left or right		
b. Two bands only..			(stamp with vert. margin) ..	1·00	
WP38	643p	**W35**	1s.3d. Three bands	32·00	30·00
a. Narrow band at left or right					
(stamp with vert. margin) .. 48·00					
WP39	644p	**W36**	1s.6d. Three bands	23·00	20·00
a. Narrow band at left or right			b. Retouch in C of Cross (R. 14/4)	30·00	
(stamp with vert. margin) .. 25·00			c. Retouch over 1 of 1/6 (R. 16/4)	30·00	

> First Day Cover (WP37/9)   ..   .. 60·00

Listed Varieties

W37b

W39a, WP39b

W39b WP39c

Cylinder Numbers (Blocks of Four)

(a) Ordinary

	Cyl. Nos.						Perforation Types		
							A	A	E
							No dot	Dot	Dot
3d.	2A (lilac)–2B (red)	..	..	..	..	..	.	90	90	3·00
	3A (lilac)–2B (red)	..	..	..	..	..	..	90	90	†
	3A (lilac)–3B (red)	..	..	..	..	..	..	1·00	1·00	†
1s.3d.	1A (grey)–3B (blue)–1C (red)	..	..	..	..	..	15·00	†	†
1s.6d.	1A (blue)–1B (red)–1C (bistre) ..	..	..	..	..	14·00	†	†

(b) Phosphor

3d.	3A (lilac)–2B (red)	..	..	..	..	..	..	4·25	4·25	†
	3A (lilac)–3B (red)	..	..	..	..	..	..	4·25	4·25	†
1s.3d.	1A (grey)–3B (blue)–1C (red) ..	..	..	..	..	£140	†	†
1s.6d.	1A (blue)–1B (red)–1C (bistre)..	..	..	..	..	£110	†	†

Minor Constant Flaws

3d. Cyl. 3A no dot in combination with red cyls. 2B or 3B no dot
  2/3 Lilac coloured spot above t of Centenary. Retouched with cyl. 3B (Th. F10-11), OP

3d. Cyl. 2B no dot in combination with lilac cyls. 2A or 3A no dot
  4/1 Red retouch in top left centre of cross (Th. D4), OP
  7/3 Pale centre to cross (with cyl. 3A only), OP

3d. Cyl. 3A dot in combination with red cyls. 2B or 3B dot
  4/3 Coloured spur on C of Congress (Th. G9), OP
  15/2 Scratch above 3D. Retouched with cyl. 3B (Th. B8–C9), OP
  17/5 Retouching in and around D of 3D (Th. D9), OP

3d. Cyl. 2B dot in combination with lilac cyls. 2A or 3A dot
  16/1 Red retouches in left arm and top left centre of cross (Th. D3–4), OP
  19/1 Red retouch in lower arm of cross (Th. E4), OP

1s.3d. Cyls. 1A–3B–1C no dot
  11/4 Diagonal scratch from Queen's nose to jaw (Th. D7), OP
  12/1 White spot to left of Queen's ear-ring (Th. D8), OP
  12/5 Dark patch to right of Queen's left eye (Th. C7), OP
  15/3 Line through words Red Cross, OP
  18/4 Large retouch on Queen's neck (Th. E7), OP

1s.6d. Cyls. 1A–1B–1C no dot
  15/3 Large retouch in right arm of cross (Th. C–D8), OP

Sheet Details

Sheet size: 120 (6 × 20). 3d. double pane reel-fed; others single pane reel-fed
Sheet markings:
  Cylinder numbers: Opposite R. 19/1, boxed
  Guide holes:
    3d. Opposite rows 14/15 (boxed), at left (no dot) or right (dot)
    1s.3d. and 1s.6d. Opposite rows 14/15 (boxed), at both sides
  Marginal arrows (photo-etched): "W" shaped, at top, bottom and sides
  Marginal rule: At bottom of sheet
  Colour register marks:
    3d. Opposite rows 2/3 and 18/19, at left (no dot) or right (dot)
    1s.3d. and 1s.6d. Opposite rows 17/19, at both sides
  Autotron marks (stippled):
    3d. Lilac, red below vertical rows 2/3 on no dot panes
    1s.3d. Grey, blue, red below vertical rows 1/3
    1s.6d. Blue, red, bistre below vertical rows 1/3 and 4/6
  Colour designations (usually trimmed off):
    3d. "G RED" in right margin opposite rows 5/6 (Cyls. 3A–3B dot)
    1s.3d. "G1 GREY G2 BLUE G3 YELLOW" in right margin reading downwards opposite rows 9/4
    1s.6d. None
  Traffic lights (boxed):
    3d. Lilac, red opposite R. 19/6
    1s.3d. Grey, blue, red opposite R. 19/6
    1s.6d. Blue, red, bistre opposite R. 19/6

Imprimaturs from the National Postal Museum Archives

A. Ordinary

Nos. W37/39 imperforate, watermark Type W.24

Watermark upright (*set of* 3)

B. Phosphor

Nos. WP37/39 imperforate, watermark Type W.24

Watermark upright (*set of* 3)

Quantities Sold

	Ordinary	Phosphor
3d.	157,277,800	10,349,280
1s.3d.	7,278,120	929,040
1s.6d.	6,995,160	1,038,840

Withdrawn 1.9.64

W37. "Commonwealth Cable"
(Des. Peter Gauld)

CANCELLED

B

1963 (DECEMBER 3). OPENING OF "COMPAC"

The Trans-Pacific Cable (COMPAC) was the first telephone cable to be laid across the Pacific Ocean. It links Canada with Australia and New Zealand by way of Hawaii and Fiji.

Cat. No.	S.G. No.	Type	Description	Mint	Used

A. Ordinary

W40   645   **W37**   1s.6d. Blue and black   2·50   2·25
    a. Black omitted £2000
    s. " Cancelled ", Type B, in red ..   18·00

First Day Cover (W40) ..   ..   .. 22·00

B. Phosphor (applied flexo.)

WP40   645p   **W37**   1s.6d. Three bands   15·00   13·50
    a. Left band omitted   ..   ..   40·00
    b. Narrow band at left or right
       (stamp with vert. margin)   ..   25·00

First Day Cover (WP40)..   ..   .. 24·00

The stamp handstamped "CANCELLED" was applied to Philatelic Bulletin No. 3 (November 1963) so that it only exists unused, no gum.

No. WP40 has a " blue " phosphor overprint but it is known with bands giving a short greenish after-glow after irradiation to ultra-violet light.   It is probable that this was due to contaminated phosphor rather than the use of " green " phosphor.

Cylinder Numbers (Blocks of Four)

	Cyl. Nos.				Perforation Type F. No dot	
					Ordinary	Phosphor
1s.6d. 1A (blue)–1B (black)	..	..	..	..	14·00	75·00

Minor Constant Flaws

1s.6d. Cyls. 1A–1B no dot
   17/6 Bulge at top of figure 1 of value (Th. F10), OP
   19/1 Extra white dot on Queen's right eye (Th. C10), OP

Sheet Details

Sheet size: 120 (6 × 20). Single pane reel-fed

Sheet markings:
   Cylinder numbers: Opposite R. 19/1, boxed
   Guide holes: at top above R. 1/2 and at bottom below R. 20/4, cutting marginal arrow
   Marginal arrows (photo-etched): " W " shaped, at top, bottom and sides
   Marginal rule: At bottom of sheet
   Colour register marks: Opposite rows 1/2 and 17/8, at both sides
   Autotron marks (stippled): Below vertical rows 2/3
   Colour designations: " G1 BLUE " (row 9), " G2 BLACK " (row 12), left margin
   Traffic lights: Black, blue (boxed), opposite R. 19/6

Imprimaturs from the National Postal Museum Archives

A. Ordinary

No. W40 imperforate, watermark Type W.24

Watermark upright

B. Phosphor

No. WP40 imperforate, watermark Type W.24

Watermark upright

Quantities Sold   Ordinary 8,015,880; phosphor 824,280

Withdrawn   1.9.64

W38.   Puck and Bottom
(*A Midsummer Night's Dream*)

W39.   Feste
(*Twelfth Night*)

W40.   Balcony Scene
(*Romeo and Juliet*)

W41.   "Eve of Agincourt"
(*Henry V*)

(All the above des. David Gentleman)

W42.   Hamlet contemplating Yorick's Skull
(*Hamlet*)

(Des. Christopher and Robin Ironside. Recess printed, Bradbury, Wilkinson)

1964 (APRIL 23). SHAKESPEARE FESTIVAL

Issued on the occasion of the 400th Anniversary of the Birth of William Shakespeare. An additional feature of this issue was the introduction of Presentation Packs by the G.P.O. The packs include one set of stamps and details of the designs, the designer and the stamp printer. They were issued for this and almost all later commemorative issues.

The 2s.6d. is perf. 11 × 12, comb.

Cat. No.	S.G. No.	Type		Description	Mint	Used
A. Ordinary						
W41	646	**W38**		3d.		
a. Black dots across Puck's head				(1) Yellow-bistre, black and		
(Dot. R. 7/6)		4·50		deep violet-blue	10	10
b. "Cancelled", Type B		£110		(2) Bistre-brown, black and		
				deep violet-blue	15	10
W42	647	**W39**		6d.		
a. Broken "H" (R. 12/3)		4·50		(1) Yellow, orange, black and		
b. Missing floorboards (R. 20/1 and				yellow-olive	20	30
20/2)		4·00		(2) Yellow, orange, black and		
c. Olive spots by Queen's mouth				olive-green	25	30
(R. 9/6)		3·00				
d. "Cancelled", Type B						
W43	648	**W40**		1s.3d.		
a. Watermark inverted				(1) Cerise, blue-green, black		
b. Large pearl (Dot, R. 13/2) ..		3·75		and sepia	15·00	
c. "Cancelled", Type B (Shade (1))				(2) Cerise, turquoise, black		
				and sepia	90	1·00
W44	649	**W41**		1s.6d.		
a. Watermark inverted				(1) Violet, turquoise, black		
b. "Cancelled", Type B				and blue	1·25	1·00
				(2) Pale violet, turquoise,		
				black and blue	2·75	2·75

Cat. No.	S.G. No.	Type	Description	Mint	Used
W45	650	**W42**	2s.6d.		

W45 ... £300
a. Watermark inverted ..
b. " Cancelled ", Type B (jet-black shade) .. ..

2s.6d.
(1) Deep slate-purple — 2·00 2·00
(2) Blackish brown — 4·00 3·50

First Day Cover (W41/5)	.. ..	11·00
Presentation Pack (W41/5)	.. ..	10·00

B. Phosphor (Three bands) (3d. applied photo.; others flexo.)

WP41   646p   **W38**
a. Narrow band at left or right (stamp with vert. margin) .. 1·00
b. Black dots across Puck's head (Dot, R. 7/6) .. .. .. 5·00

3d.
(1) Yellow-bistre, black and deep violet-blue — 20 30
(2) Bistre-brown, black and deep violet-blue — 30 25

WP42   647p   **W39**
a. Narrow band at left or right (stamp with vert margin) .. 2·00
b. Broken "H" (R. 12/3) .. .. 5·50

6d. Yellow, orange, black and yellow-olive — 60 70
c. Missing floorboards (R. 20/1 and 20/2) .. .. 4·75
d. Olive spots by Queen's mouth (R. 9/6) .. .. 3·75

WP43   648p   **W40**
a. Watermark inverted £100
b. Narrow band at left or right (stamp with vert. margin) .. 7·50

1s.3d. Cerise, turquoise, black and sepia — 5·75 5·50
c. Large pearl (Dot, R. 13/2) .. 8·00

WP44   649p   **W41**
a. Narrow band at left or right (stamp with vert. margin) .. 12·00

1s.6d. Violet, turquoise, black and blue — 9·00 5·75

First Day Cover (WP41/4)	.. ..	11·00

Shades. The listed shades of the 6d. to 2s.6d. result from different printings. The 3d. and 6d. shades are quite distinct, the blue-green shade of the 1s.3d. comes from the scarce first printing from cylinder 1B, and although the pale violet in the 1s.6d. may only be due to under-inking, it came from part of the second printing. There were three printings of the 2s.6d. which produced a number of shades, but they fall into the two groups listed. In addition a rare jet-black shade exists, possibly from proof sheets issued in error. Most examples have a " CANCELLED " overprint.

The 3d. is known with yellow-bistre missing on the top two-thirds of the figures of Puck and Bottom. This occurred on the top row only of a sheet.

Listed Varieties

W41a, WP41b

SHAKESPE

W42a, WP42b
Also grey patch on Shakespeare's right cheek. Both later retouched

W42c, WP42d

Normal   W42b, WP42c
Other less prominent states of missing floorboards also occur on R. 19/1, 19/2, 19/6 and 20/6

W43a, WP43c

Cylinder Numbers (Blocks of Four)

(a) Ordinary

		Perforation Type A	
Cyl. Nos.		No dot	Dot
3d. 1A (violet-blue)–1B (black)–1C (bistre)	..	1·00	1·00
6d. 1A (olive-green)–1B (orange)–1C (yellow)–1D (black)	..	5·50*	†

		Perforation Type A(T)	
		No dot	Dot
1s.3d. 3A (sepia)–1B (blue-green)–1C (cerise)–1D (black) ..	..	75·00	75·00
3A (sepia)–2B (turquoise)–1C (cerise)–1D (black) ..	..	4·25	4·25
1s.6d. 1A (blue)–1B (violet)–1C (black)–1D (turquoise) ..	..	7·00	7·00

(b) Phosphor

		Perforation Type A	
		No dot	Dot
3d. 1A (violet-blue)–1B (black)–1C (bistre)	..	1·50	1·50
6d. 1A (olive-green)–1B (orange)–1C (yellow)–1D (black)	..	8·00*	†

		Perforation Type A(T)	
		No dot	Dot
1s.3d. 3A (sepia)–2B (turquoise)–1C (cerise)–1D (black) ..	..	28·00	25·00
1s.6d. 1A (blue)–1B (violet)–1C (black)–1D (turquoise) ..	..	42·00	42·00

The 3d. no dot cylinders exist with a false dot after the 1B but this was later removed.
In the dot cylinders of the 1s.6d. the dots appear to the left of 1C and 1D.

Plate Numbers (Blocks of Four)

		Perforation Type A		
2s.6d. Plate1	10·00	Plate 1A	10·00

Minor Constant Flaws

3d. Cyls. 1A–1B–1C no dot
  9/5 White scratch on boards above AL (Th. 9/5), OP
  19/1 White line in floorboard division above S of FESTIVAL (Th. G8), OP
  20/1 White patch on Queen's collar, later retouched (Th. E12), OP

3d. Cyls. 1A–1B–1C dot
  2/5 White patch on floorboards above F (Th. G7), OP
  7/5 Retouches on Queen's left cheek, later partly retouched (Th. D11), OP
  11/5 Retouch below Queen's left eye (Th. C11), OP
  16/2 White spur to bottom arc of 3, OP
  20/1 Dark flaw in stage above VA, later retouched (Th. G9), OP

1s.3d. Cyls. 3A–2B–1C–1D no dot
  18/2 Outline of Shakespeare's nose cut short, later corrected (Th. C3), OP

1s.6d. Cyls. 1A–1B–1C–1D no dot
  1/6 White flaw on stage above EAR (Th. F4–G5), OP
  18/1 Black flaw at base of tent over last A of SHAKESPEARE, (Th. F5), OP
  20/2 Vertical scratches on Queen's face (Th. B–D11), OP

1s.6d. Cyls. 1A–1B–1C–1D dot
  13/3 Flaw on stage above EA (Th. G4), OP

Sheet Details

Sheet sizes:
  3d. 120 (6 × 20). Double pane reel-fed
  6d. 120 (6 × 20). Single pane reel-fed
  1s.3d., 1s.6d. 120 (6 × 20). Double panes sheet-fed
  2s.6d. 40 (4 × 10). Double pane sheet-fed

The 1s.3d. and 1s.6d. were printed by the Linotype and Machinery No. 4 machine, a
rotary sheet-fed double pane machine.

Sheet markings:
  Cylinder numbers: Opposite R. 19/1, boxed
  Plate numbers (2s.6d.): Bottom margin below vertical rows 5/6
  Guide holes:
    3d. Opposite rows 14/15 (boxed), at left (no dot) or right (dot)
    6d. Opposite row 13 (boxed), at both sides
    1s.3d. Opposite rows 15/16 (boxes only, no holes), at left (no dot) or right (dot)
    1s.6d. Opposite rows 14/15 (boxes only, no holes), at left (no dot) or right (dot)
    2s.6d. Opposite row 6 (unboxed), at left (Plate 1) or right (Plate 1A)
  False boxes appear in both margins opposite rows 14/15 in the 6d. value and these are deleted by a diagonal
  black line.
  Marginal arrows (photo-etched): "W" shaped, at top, bottom and sides (none on 2s.6d.)
  Marginal rule: At bottom of sheet (except 2s.6d.)

Colour register marks:
  3d. Opposite rows 2 and 17/18, at left (no dot) or right (dot)
  6d. Opposite rows 1/3 and 17/18, at both sides (usually trimmed off)
  Others, none

Autotron marks:
  3d In central gutter alongside rows 14/16
  6d. Below vertical rows 1/3: black (stippled), olive (solid), orange (stippled), yellow (solid)
  Others, none
Colour designations (usually trimmed):
  3d. "G BLUE" (rows 13/12), "G BLACK" (rows 9/8), "G YELLOW" (rows 5/4) reading upwards,
    right margin dot pane
  Others, none
Traffic lights (boxed): All R. 19/6
  3d. Violet-blue, black, bistre
  6d. Black, yellow, orange, olive
  1s.3d. Black, cerise, turquoise, sepia
  1s.6d. Turquoise, black, violet, blue

Imprimaturs from the National Postal Museum Archives

A. Ordinary

Nos. W41/45 imperforate, watermark Type W.24

Watermark upright (*set of* 5)

B. Phosphor

Nos. WP41/44 imperforate, watermark Type W.24

Watermark upright (*set of* 4)

Quantities Sold

	Ordinary	Phosphor		Ordinary	Phosphor
3d.	133,670,000	10,427,880	1s.6d.	6,910,120	657,120
6d.	19,238,200	1,318,560	2s.6d.	3,664,920	—
1s.3d.	7,067,200	727,800	Pack	108,541	—

Withdrawn   31.3.65 (3d. ordinary sold out earlier)

W43. Flats near Richmond Park
("Urban Development")

W44. Shipbuilding Yards, Belfast
("Industrial Activity")

W45. Beddgelert Forest Park,
Snowdonia ("Forestry")

W46. Nuclear Reactor, Dounreay
("Technological Development")

(Des. Dennis Bailey)

1964 (JULY 1). 20TH INTERNATIONAL GEOGRAPHICAL CONGRESS

The first International Geographical Congress was held in 1871; since then one has normally been held at four-yearly intervals. London was chosen in 1964 and the Congress lasted from 20 to 28 July.

Cat. No.	S.G. No.	Type	Description	Mint	Used

A. Ordinary

W46	651	**W43**	2½d. Black, olive-yellow, olive-	10	10
a. Short line under 2½d. (various)..	3·00		grey and turquoise-blue		
b. Line repaired (No dot, R. 18/5)	3·75				
c. Retouched lawn (No dot, R. 11/1					
and 11/6)	3·25				
W47	652	**W44**	4d. Orange-brown, red-brown,	25	25
a. Violet omitted	£150		rose, black and violet		
b. Red-brown omitted			*d.* Watermark inverted	£500	
c. Violet and red-brown omitted..	£150		*e.* Scarred neck (R. 20/3) ..	4·00	
W48	653	**W45**	8d. Yellow-brown, emerald,	60	50
a. Green (lawn) omitted	£3500		green and black		
b. Watermark inverted	£250				
W49	654	**W46**	1s.6d. Yellow-brown, pale pink,	3·25	3·25
a. Watermark inverted	19·00		black and brown		
b. Neck flaw (R. 8/4)	7·00				

First Day Cover (W46/9)	.. ..	18·00
Presentation Pack (W46/9)	.. ..	80·00

B. Phosphor (2½d. applied photo.; others flexo.)

WP46	651p	**W43**	2½d. One band	50	40
a. Short line under 2½d. (various)..	2·50				
b. Line repaired (No dot, R. 18/5)..	5·00				
c. Retouched lawn (No dot, R. 11/1					
and 11/6)	4·00				
WP47	652p	**W44**	4d. Three bands	75	70
a. Narrow band at left or right			*b.* Scarred neck (R. 20/3)	5·00	
(stamp with vert. margin) ..	1·50				
WP48	653p	**W45**	8d. Three bands	1·75	1·50
a. Narrow band at left or right					
(stamp with vert. margin) ..	2·50				
WP49	654p	**W46**	1s.6d. Three bands	20·00	18·00
a. Narrow band at left or right			*b.* Neck flaw (R. 8/4)	25·00	
(stamp with vert. margin) ..	23·00				

First Day Cover (WP46/9)	.. ..	27·00

A pair of No. WP47 exists with phosphor bands printed diagonally on the gum but omitted from the printed side. This was due to a paper fault which affected the corner of the sheet.

Listed Varieties

2½d
W46a, WP46a

The short lower line occurs on no dot R. 5/5, 9/5 (most marked) and 10/2 and on dot R. 3/4, 4/5 and 7/5 (short at left).
In No. W46b and WP46b the line has been repaired but there remains a short gap unfilled.

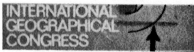

W46c, WP46c

The illustration shows the retouch on R. 11/1. On 11/6 it starts further over the line and is less extensive.

W47e, WP47b

W49b, WP49b
Later retouched

Cylinder Numbers (Blocks of Four)

(a) Ordinary

	Cyl. Nos.	Peforation Types		
		A No dot	A Dot	F No dot
2½d.	3D (black)–1C (yellow)–1B (grey)–1A (blue) ..	1·00	1·00	†
4d.	1E (orange-brown)–1D (red-brown)–1C (rose)–1B (black)–1A (violet)	†	†	2·00
8d.	1D (brown)–1C (green)–1B (emerald)–1A (black) ..	7·50	†	4·25
1s.6d.	1D (yellow-brown)–1C (pink)–1B (black)–1A(brown)	18·00	†	†

(b) Phosphor

		A No dot	A Dot	F No dot
2½d.	3D (black)–1C (yellow)–1B (grey)–1A (blue) ..	3·00	3·00	†
4d.	1E (orange-brown)–1D (red-brown)–1C (rose)–1B (black)–1A (violet)	†	†	4·25
8d.	1D (brown)–1C (green)–1B (emerald)–1A (black) ..	†	†	10·00
1s.6d.	1D (yellow-brown)–1C (pink)–1B (black)–1A (brown)	†	†	£100

Minor Constant Flaws

2½d. Cyls. 3D–1C–1B–1A no dot
- 2/4 Black line from Queen's left eye to base of back of diadem, later retouched and showing as faint white line (Th. C12–13), O
- 4/1 Blue spot on Queen's collar, later retouched (Th. E12), OP
- 12/3 Green spot at foot of hills above second N of INTERNATIONAL (Th. F5), OP
- 15/2 Blue dot left of oval and above left end of upper value bar, later retouched (Th. E10), OP
- 19/3 Green blob above 2 of 20th (Th. E1), OP
- 20/3 White dot in portrait oval above right corner of central cross of crown (Th. A12), OP
- 20/5 White flaw in hair below central cross of crown (Th. B11), OP

2½d. Cyls. 3D–1C–1B–1A dot
- 7/5 Small retouch to right of Queen's nostril (Th. C11), OP
- 9/3 Retouch by Queen's left eye, later retouched on phosphor only (Th. B–C12), OP
- 12/3 White flaw in h of 20th, OP
- 12/5 Blue dot by grey panel opposite value (Th. G10), OP
- 13/5 Blue scratch on Queen's left cheek (Th. C11), OP
- 15/2 Two diagonal white lines above central cross of crown (Th. A12), OP
- 15/4 Blue patch in hills above black arrow (Th. D8) and slight retouch to right of L of GEOGRAPHICAL, OP
- 15/5 White flaw in hair above Queen's left eye (Th. B12), OP
- 17/4 Retouch on Queen's neck above collar (Th. E12), OP

4d. Cyls. 1E–1D–1C–1B–1A no dot
  1/1 Horizontal black line joining centre of 2 to left frame line, OP
  1/2 Black spur on frame line below last S in CONGRESS, OP
  1/5 White dot in panel to right of rear cross of crown (Th. B13), OP
  1/6 Small flaw under right arm of N of CONGRESS (Th. H2), OP
  3/5 White flaw on left of crown (Th. A11), OP
  3/6 White spike projecting from back of neck (Th. D12), OP
  6/1 Several small black dots on collar (Th. E11–12), OP
  7/1 Horizontal line between Queen's lips and ear (Th. C11–12), OP
  7/2 Similar retouch but lower down (Th. D11–12), OP
  8/1 Violet dot to right of d in value (Th. G12), OP
  14/2 Horizontal grey line through NATION, OP
  16/5 Broken R in GEOGRAPHICAL, OP
  18/1 Break in vertical lines above AT of INTERNATIONAL and small black dot to left of break (Th. E3)
    OP
  20/2 Black dot above Queen's nostril (Th. D11), and break in vertical frame line to left of value, OP
  20/5 Corner break in frame line left of value (Th. H9), OP
    Numerous other minor frame breaks are known

8d. Cyls. 1D–1C–1B–1A no dot
  1/1 Extensive retouching to back of Queen's collar (Th. E12–13), OP
  4/2 Dark patch in front of Queen's neck (Th. D–E11), OP
  4/6 Nick in final A of GEOGRAPHICAL, OP
  6/6 Retouch at back of Queen's collar (Th. E13), OP
  7/6 Shading on Queen's forehead, later retouched appearing as white patch (Th. B11–12), OP
  16,4–6 Green line runs through emerald field below brown area, OP
  17/5 Horizontal white line across Queen's face (Th. C11–12), OP
  18/5 Two horizontal white lines across face and chin (Th. C–D–11–12), OP

1s.6d. Cyls. 1D–1C–1B–1A no dot
  1/1 Dark flaw in front of Queen's collar (Th. E11), OP
  2/2 White scratch across necklace (Th. D12), OP
  13/3 White dot in panel below rear cross in crown (Th. B13), OP
  20/6 Dark spot below Queen's nose (Th. C12), OP

Sheet Details

Sheet size: 120 (6 × 20). 2½d. double pane reel-fed; others single pane sheet-fed

Sheet markings:
  Cylinder numbers: Opposite rows 19/20 at left, boxed
  Guide holes:
    2½d. Opposite rows 14/15 (boxed), at left (no dot) or right (dot)
    Others: Usually trimmed off
  Marginal arrows (photo-etched): "W" shaped, at top, bottom and sides
  Marginal rule: At bottom of sheet
  Colour register marks:
    2½d. Opposite rows 2/3 and 18/19, at left (no dot) or right (dot)
    Others: Above and below vertical rows 1 and 5/6
  Autotron marks (stippled):
    2½d. Black, blue, yellow, grey opposite rows 6/8, at right (no dot) or left (dot)
    Others: Trimmed off
  Colour designations (usually trimmed):
    2½d. "G1 GREY G2 DARK GREEN G3 YELLOW G4 BLACK" reading upwards, right margin dot pane
    Others: Trimmed off
  Traffic lights (boxed): All opposite rows 19/20 at right
    2½d. Black, yellow, blue, grey
    4d. Orange-brown, red-brown, rose, black, violet
    8d. Brown, green, black, emerald
    1s.6d. Order not known

Imprimaturs from the National Postal Museum Archives

A. Ordinary

Nos. W46/49 imperforate, watermark Type W.24

Watermark upright (*set of 4*)

B. Phosphor

Nos. WP46/49 imperforate, watermark Type W.24

Watermark upright (*set of 4*)

Quantities Sold

	Ordinary	Phosphor		Ordinary	Phosphor
2½d.	109,768,120	3,377,520	1s.6d.	10,154,040	519,000
4d.	15,241,680	577,800	Pack	29,952	—
8d.	8,226,800	465,720			

Withdrawn 2.7.65 (2½d. ordinary sold out earlier)

W47. Spring Gentian

W48. Dog Rose

W49. Honeysuckle

W50. Fringed Water Lily

(Des. Sylvia and Michael Goaman)

1964 (AUGUST 5). TENTH INTERNATIONAL BOTANICAL CONGRESS

Botanical Congresses are held every five years each alternate one taking place in Europe. The King of Sweden was Hon. President of the 1964 Congress, which took place in Edinburgh.

Cat. No.	S.G. No.	Type	Description	Mint	Used
A. Ordinary					
W50	655	**W47**	3d. Violet, blue and sage-green	10	10
a. Blue omitted £3500					
b. Broken petal (Cyls. 3A–1B–1C Dot, R. 1/2) .. .. .. 4·00			*s.* " Cancelled ", Type B .. .. 12·00		
W51	656	**W48**	6d. Apple-green, rose, scarlet and green	20	20
a. Inverted watermark			*s.* " Cancelled ", Type B .. .. 12·00		
b. Rose hip flaw (No dot, R. 2/2) 4·50					
W52	657	**W49**	9d. Lemon, green, lake and rose-red	1·80	2·00
a. Green (leaves) omitted.. .. £3500					
b. Watermark inverted .. .. 32·00			*s.* " Cancelled ", Type B .. .. 12·00		
c. Line through " INTER "(R. 1/1) 6·00					
W53	658	**W50**	1s.3d. Yellow, emerald, reddish violet and grey-green	2·50	1·90
a. Yellow (flowers) omitted .. £7500					
b. Watermark inverted £225			*s.* " Cancelled ", Type B .. .. 12·00		
c. Fruit flaw (R. 14/2) .. .. 7·00					

```
First Day Cover (W50/3)       ..   .. 18·00
Presentation Pack (W50/3)     ..   .. 80·00
```

B. Phosphor (applied flexo.)

WP50	655p	**W47**	3d. Three bands	20	20
a. Right band omitted			*c.* Broken petal (Cyls. 3A–1B–1C Dot, R. 1/2) .. .. .. 5·00		
b. Narrow band at left or right (stamp with vert. margin) .. 1·00					
WP51	656p	**W48**	6d. Three bands	1·25	1·00
a. Four bands .. .. .. 10·00			*c.* Rose hip flaw (No dot, R. 2/2) .. 6·00		
b. Narrow band at left or right (stamp with vert. margin) .. 2·00					
WP52	657p	**W49**	9d. Three bands	3·75	3·00
a. Narrow band at left or right (stamp with vert. margin) .. 5·00			*b.* Line through " INTER " (R. 1/1) 7·00		
WP53	658p	**W50**	1s.3d Three bands	20·00	16·00
a. Narrow band at left or right (stamp with vert. margin) .. 22·00			*b.* Fruit flaw (R. 14/2) .. .. 25·00		

```
First Day Cover (WP50/3)   ..   .. 28·00
```

Nos. W50s/53s have the "CANCELLED" handstamp as used on No. W40 applied in black spread over two values. It was used on sample first day covers distributed by the Post Office with the notice announcing the service.

All values were accidentally released before the official date of issue at several post offices and by the Philatelic Bureau. The earliest known date is 27 July.

The, possibly unique, example of No. W53a shows the yellow printed on the gummed side due to a paper fold.

Listed Varieties

Normal   W50b, WP50c

Petal is broken where the violet overlaps the blue

W51b, WP51c

White flaw in rose hip

W52c, WP52b

W53b, WP53b

Grey-green overlaps centre of fruit

Cylinder Numbers (Blocks of Four)

(a) Ordinary

	Cyl. Nos.	Perforation Types		
		A	A	F
		No dot	Dot	No dot
3d.	2A (violet)–1B (blue)–1C (sage-green)	1·00	1·00	†
	3A (violet)–1B (blue)–1C (sage-green)	1·00	1·00	†
6d.	1D (apple-green)–1C (rose)–1B (scarlet)–1A (green)	1·50	1·50	†
9d.	2D (lemon)–2C (green)–2B (lake)–2A (rose-red) ..	†	†	10·00
1s.3d.	1D (yellow)–1C (emerald)–1B (reddish violet)–1A (grey-green)	†	†	14·00

(b) Phosphor

		A	A	F
3d.	3A (violet)–1B (blue)–1C (sage-green)	1·50	1·50	†
6d.	1D (apple-green)–1C (rose)–1B (scarlet)–1A (green)	9·00	7·00	†
9d.	2D (lemon)–2C (green)–2B (lake)–2A (rose-red) ..	†	†	22·00
1s.3d.	1D (yellow)–1C (emerald)–1B (reddish violet)–1A (grey-green)	†	†	£100

Minor Constant Flaws

3d. Cyls. 2A–1B–1C and 3A–1B–1C no dot
  1/4 White dot between 3rd and 4th fruits below portrait (Th. E12), OP
  2/4 Curved white line across right petal of left Gentian (Th. C3), OP
  6/1 Small white vertical line on same petal as above (Th. C–D3), OP

3d. Cyl. 3A no dot
  2/5 Retouch on upper lip, OP
  7/5 Blue dash on small leaf pointing left below first flower (Th. F2), OP
  10/5 White dot below first S of CONGRESS, OP
  12/5 Line of damage extends from Queen's upper lip to base of ear (Th. C10–12), OP
  12/6 Line of damage extends from Queen's right cheek across nose to ear (Th. C10–12), OP
  13/1 Clear line of white dots joins SS of CONGRESS, OP
  19/3 White flaw at edge of petal under 3 (Th. C1), OP
  20/2 Retouch from Queen's left eye to ear (Th. B11–C12), OP

3d. Cyls. 2A–1B–1C and 3A–1B–1C dot
1/4 Small patch of white on Queen's forehead (Th. B10), OP
5/6 White dot in pod above R of CONGRESS (Th. F12), OP
15/5 Green dots in leaves above OT of BOTANICAL (Th. E–F7), OP
17/1 Retouch under necklace below ear-ring (Th. D12), O but almost completely repaired on 3A phosphor
19/1 White dot on right petal of partly opened bud (Th. B8), OP
19/2 Retouch between Queen's left eyebrow and hair (Th. B11), OP

3d. Cyl. 2A dot
10/6 Coloured line across Queen's neck (Th. D11), O

3d. Cyl. 3A dot
6/4 Violet dot in Queen's forehead (Th. B10), OP
12/5 Flaw in Queen's left eye, OP
13/3 Thin white line from leaf to R of INTER (Th. G2), OP
13/6 Small white dash above O of BOTANICAL and violet spot above middle of collar (Th. D12), OP
19/6 Diagonal white line above ES of CONGRESS, and retouch from centre of cheek to ear-ring (Th. C11–12), OP
20/1 Light patch in background above 2nd N in INTERNATIONAL, OP

6d. Cyls. 1D–1C–1B–1A no dot
2/6 Green flaws in T of INTER, OP
5/4 Green spot between eyebrows (Th. B10), OP
6/4 Retouch above necklace (Th. D11) and green dot on lower petal of flower nearest to portrait (Th. C–D9), OP
10/1 White spot in hair below flowers of crown (Th. B12), OP
11/1 Retouch in Queen's collar (Th. D12), OP
17/2 Small retouch in front of Queen's ear (Th. C11), OP
18/2 Green indent in left side of seed pod (Th. F10), OP
20/1 Green spot in lowest leaf above TE of INTER (Th. F2), OP
20/4 Retouch on Queen's left cheek (Th. C11–12), OP

6d. Cyls. 1D–1C–1B–1A dot
2/6 Green flaws in T of INTER and line of yellow dots on middle leaf at left (Th. D1), OP
4/4 Three scarlet dots to right of Queen's left eye (Th. B11), OP
20/4 Retouch on Queen's left cheek (Th. C11–12), OP
20/5 Two green spots on seed pod (Th. F10), OP

9d. Cyls. 2D–2C–2B–2A no dot
4/4 ON of INTERNATIONAL joined by white line, OP
7/1 Red spot under jewel of necklace (Th. E11), OP
13/2 White dot between two left stamens of lower bloom (Th. F3), OP
14/2 Green dot above Queen's upper lip (Th. C11), OP
14/3 Red dot above Queen's right eye (Th. B10–11), OP

1s.3d. Cyls. 1D–1C–1B–1A no dot
5/1 White line through NI and above C of BOTANICAL, OP
8/3 Grey-green flaw at base of E of CONGRESS, OP
11/1 Retouch on Queen's jaw line and neck (Th. C11), OP
12/6 Horizontal dark line on left-hand bud (Th. B–C1–2), OP
13/2 Green spot on stem of largest bloom (Th. C5), OP
15/6 Pale patch in background adjoining Queen's lips (Th. C10), OP
18/3 Three dark horizontal dots above L of INTERNATIONAL (Th. G5–6), OP
19/1 Dark spot in leaf below left-hand flower (Th. D–E2), OP
20/1 Tops of IN of INTER joined, OP
20/6 White scratch through seed extending from above C of BOTANICAL to R of CONGRESS (Th. G8–12), OP

Sheet Details

Sheet size: 120 (6 × 20)
    3d., 6d. double pane reel-fed
    9d., 1s.3d. single pane sheet-fed
Sheet markings:
    Cylinder numbers: Boxed, opposite R. 20/1 3d., 19–20/1 others
    Guide holes:
        3d., 6d. Opposite rows 14/15 (boxed), at left (no dot) or right (dot)
        9d., 1s.3d. None
    Marginal arrows (photo-etched): "W" shaped, at top, bottom and sides
    Marginal rule: At bottom of sheet
    Colour register marks:
        3d., 6d. None
        9d., 1s.3d. Above and below vertical rows 1 and 6
    Autotron marks:
        3d. Solid, violet, blue, sage-green opposite rows 4/5 and 15/16 at right (no dot) or left (dot)
        6d. Stippled, green, scarlet, rose, apple-green opposite rows 4/6 at right (no dot) or left (dot) and again
            apple-green, rose, scarlet opposite rows 14/15 at right (no dot) or left (dot)
        9d., 1s.3d. None
    Coloured crosses (partly trimmed):
        1s.3d. Above and below vertical rows 1/2
        Others: None

Colour designations (usually trimmed off):
   3d. " G1 GREEN G2 BLUE G3 MAUVE " in right margin of dot panes
Traffic lights (boxed):
   3d. Violet, blue, sage-green, opposite R. 20/6
   6d. Apple-green, rose, scarlet, green opposite R. 19–20/6
   9d. Lemon, green, lake, rose-red opposite R. 19–20/6
   1s.3d. Yellow, emerald, reddish violet grey-green opposite R. 19-20/6

Imprimaturs from the National Postal Museum Archives

A. Ordinary

Nos. W50/53 imperforate, watermark Type W.24

Watermark upright (*set of* 4)

B. Phosphor

Nos. WP50/53 imperforate, watermark Type W.24

Watermark upright (*set of* 4)

Quantities Sold

	Ordinary	Phosphor		Ordinary	Phosphor
3d.	166,491,720	6,764,880	1s.3d.	15,664,600	650,920
6d.	25,361,120	996,720	Pack	16,140	—
9d.	11,896,060	498,460			

Withdrawn 2.7.65

W51.   Forth Road Bridge

W52.   Forth Road and
Railway Bridges

(Des. Andrew Restall)

1964 (SEPTEMBER 4).   OPENING OF FORTH ROAD BRIDGE

At that time the largest suspension-bridge in Europe and the fourth largest in the world.
Opened by Her Majesty The Queen.

Cat. No.	S.G. No.	Type	Description	Mint	Used
A. Ordinary					
W54	659	**W51**	3d. Black, blue and reddish violet	15	10

a. Imperforate between stamp and
top margin £350
b. Dotted "3" (Cyl. 2A Dot,
R. 15/1) .. ..   3·50

| W55 | 660 | **W52** | 6d. Black, light blue and carmine-red | 45 | 40 |

a. Light blue omitted £1500 £1500
b. Watermark inverted .. ..   2·00

First Day Cover (W54/5)	..	..	5·00
Presentation Pack (W54/5)	..	..	£180

B.   Phosphor (3d. applied photo., 6d. flexo.)

WP54	659p		3d. Three bands	50	50

a. Narrow band at left or right
(stamp with vert. margin) ..   1·50

b. Dotted "3" (Cyl. 2 A Dot,
R. 15/1) .. ..   5·00

| WP55 | 660p | **W52** | 6d. Three bands | 4·50 | 4·50 |

a. Watermark inverted .. ..   55·00
b. Narrow band at left or right
(stamp with vert. margin) ..   5·25

First Day Cover (WP54/5)	..	..	10·00

Listed Variety

W54b, WP54b

Cylinder Numbers (Blocks of Four)

(a) Ordinary

Cyl. Nos.			Perforation Type A	
			No dot	Dot
3d. 1C (blue)–1B (black)–2A (violet)	..	..	1·25	1·25
1C (blue)–1B (black)–3A (violet)	..	..	10·00	10·00
1C (blue)–1B (black)–4A (violet)	..	..	1·50	1·50
2C (blue)–1B (black)–4A (violet)	..	..	2·00	2·00
6d. 1C (blue)–2B (black)–2A (red)*	..	..	2·75	2·75

			Perforation Type A(T)	
			No dot	Dot
6d. 1C (blue)–2B (black)–2A (red)*	..	..	4·75	4·75

(b) Phosphor

		Perforation Type A	
		No dot	Dot
3d.	1C (blue)–1B (black)–2A (violet)	4·00	3·50
	1C (blue)–1B (black)–4A (violet)	20·00	20·00
		Perforation Type A(T)	
		No dot	Dot
6d.	1C (blue)–2B (black)–2A (red)*	22·00	22·00

*In the 6d. no dot pane the cylinder numbers are expressed in error thus: " 1C–2.B.–2A "

Minor Constant Flaws

3d. Cyl. 1C no dot in combination with cyls. 1B–2A or 1B–4A no dot
    4/2 Blue spot to left and above B of BRIDGE, OP
    8/1 Blue spot below B of BRIDGE, OP
    13/6 Blue spot in sky S.W. of moon (Th. B1), O

3d. Cyl. 1C dot in combination with cyls. 1B–2A, 1B–3A or 1B–4A dot
    18/6 Blue dash to left of 3d. (Th. F–G11); also blue spot to left of tanker (Th. G3), latter coincident with
    a similar violet spot on cyl. 2A

3d. Cyl. 1B no dot in combination with cyls. 1C–2A, 1C–3A, 1C–4A, or 2C–4A no dot
    1/3 Detail at rear of diadem is weak (Th. B–C10), OP
    2/3 Scratch on necklace and collar (Th. E9), OP
    4/4 Lack of detail at rear of diadem (Th. B–C10), OP
    8/4 Black flaw on Queen's neck above large jewel (Th. E9), OP
    9/2 White spot on Queen's nose (Th. D8), OP
    9/4 Black scratch on Queen's forehead (Th. C8–9), OP
    14/4 Black spot below Queen's left nostril (Th. D8), OP
    16/4 Loss of detail at back of Queen's neck and collar. Almost normal with cyl. 3A (Th. E10–F10–11),
    OP
    18/1 Black spots under G of BRIDGE (Th. A10), OP

3d. Cyl. 1B dot in combination with cyls. 1C–2A, 1C–3A, 1C–4A or 2C–4A dot
    2/2 White flaw in sea appears as extra wave (Th. B9), OP
    13/2 Weak top to O of FORTH, OP
    18/4 Small white flaw in hair above Queen's left eye (Th. B9), OP

3d. Cyls. 2A, 3A and 4A no dot (multipositive flaws)
    17/4 White patch at left side of moon (Th. B2), OP. Less pronounced on cyl. 3A
    19/4 Large retouch in sky left of bridge (Th. D1), OP. Most marked on cyl. 4A
    20/1 White tower on hill above funnel (Th. F3), OP. Retouched on cyls. 3A and 4A
    20/4 Large retouch in sky left of moon (Th. A–B1), OP. Most pronounced on cyls. 3A and 4A

3d. Cyls. 1C–1B–2A no dot
    10/6 Violet retouches below 1 and 4 of 1964 (Th. B11 and B13), OP
    18/5 White arc at top left of moon (Th. A–B2), OP

3d. Cyl. 4A no dot in combination with cyls. 1C–1B or 2C–1B no dot
    12/6 Faint acute accent over d of 3d (Th. F13), OP
    14/4 Small nick in left edge of value panel (Th. D11), OP
    16/2 Retouch in sky above funnel (Th. E–F3), OP

3d. Cyl. 4A dot in combination with cyls. 1C–1B or 2C–1B dot
    14/2 Violet coloured flaw in sky at left of pylon (Th. E2), OP

3d. Cyls. 2C–1B–4A dot
    17/3 Dark patch on skyline under bridge (Th. F5), O

6d. Cyls. 1C–2B–2A no dot
    5/1 Small nick in top of 9 of 1964, OP
    5/5 Red scratch over D of BRIDGE, OP
    7/1 Red scratch over 6 of 6d, OP
    7/3 Two small breaks in bridge below portrait (Th. G8), OP
    8/2 Black spot on Queen's collar (Th. E10), OP
    15/6 Dark red patch below 4 of 1964 (Th. B13), OP
    16/1 Black dot in front of D of ROAD, OP
    16/5 Mottled portrait, OP
    17/6 Mottled portrait, OP
    18/4 Black spot in water between left-hand towers of bridge (Th. F1), OP

6d. Cyls. 1C–2B–2A dot
    1/4 White scratch on Queen's cheek (Th. D9), OP
    15/5 Two small coloured flaws on Queen's forehead (Th. C9); also two small red spots below portrait by
    bridge (Th. G9), OP
    17/2 Diagonal red stroke by value panel (Th. D11), OP
    19/1 Queen's face is a mass of white dots (State I) OP; later appears normal (State II), O only. Other
    stamps in the sheet show a similar appearance but this is the most marked

Sheet Details

Sheet size: 120 (6 × 20). 3d. double pane reel-fed; 6d. double pane sheet-fed

Sheet markings:

Cylinder numbers: Opposite R. 19/1, boxed

Guide holes:
  3d. Opposite rows 14/15 (boxed), at left (no dot) or right (dot)
  6d. None

Marginal arrows (photo-etched): "W" shape, at top, bottom and sides

Marginal rule: At bottom of sheet

Colour register marks:
  3d. Opposite rows 2/3 and 17/18, at left (no dot) or right (dot)
  6d. Opposite rows 1/2 and 17/18, at left (no dot) or right (dot)

Autotron marks (solid):
  3d. Black, blue, violet opposite rows 4/6 and violet, blue, black opposite rows 13/15 at right (no dot) or left (dot)
  6d. None

Colour designations (usually trimmed off):
  3d. "G MAUVE G BLUE G BLACK" in right margin reading upwards opposite rows 8/4 on dot panes only
  6d. None

Traffic lights (boxed):
  3d. Violet, blue, black opposite R. 19/6
  6d. Blue, red, black opposite R. 19/6

Imprimaturs from the National Postal Museum Archives

A. Ordinary

Nos. W54/55 imperforate, watermark Type W.24

Watermark upright (*set of* 2)

B. Phosphor

Nos. WP54/55 imperforate, watermark Type W.24

Watermark upright (*set of* 2)

Quantities Sold

	Ordinary	Phosphor
3d.	108,098,480	8,020,920
6d.	12,055,960	1,240,800
Pack	11,450	—

Withdrawn 2.7.65

PHOSPHOR BANDS

From the Churchill issue onwards all phosphor bands were applied in photogravure, *unless otherwise stated.*

W53.   Sir Winston Churchill   **W54.**   Sir Winston Churchill
(Des. David Gentleman and Rosalind Dease, from photograph by Karsh)

1965 (JULY 8). CHURCHILL COMMEMORATION

Cat. No.	S.G. No.	Type	Description	Mint	Used

I. "REMBRANDT" Machine

Cyls. 1A–1B dot and no dot. Lack of shading detail on Churchill's portrait. Queen's portrait appears dull and coarse. This was a sheet-fed rotary machine.

A. Ordinary

W56	661	W53		4d. Black and olive-brown	15	10
a. Watermark inverted	..	..	1·75			
b. Vertical scratch (Dot, R. 20/3)			2·00			

B. Phosphor

WP56	661p	W53		4d. Three bands	30	30
a. Left band omitted	..	..	15·00			
b. Vertical scratch (Dot, R. 20/3)	..		3·50			

II. "TIMSON" Machine

Cyls. 5A–6B no dot. More detail on Churchill's portrait—furrow on forehead, his left eye-brow fully drawn and more shading on cheek. Queen's portrait lighter and sharper. This was a reel-fed, two-colour, 12-in. wide rotary machine. The differences in impression were due to the greater pressure applied by the cylinders.

Ordinary only

W57	661a	W53	4d. Black and pale olive-brown	25	25

III. "LINOTYPE AND MACHINERY NO. 4" Machine

Cyls. 1A–1B no dot. The "Linotype and Machinery No. 4" machine was a sheet-fed rotary press machine. Besides being used for printing the 1s.3d. stamps it was also employed to overprint the phosphor bands on both values.

A. Ordinary

W58	662	W54		1s.3d. Black and grey	45	30
a. Watermark inverted	..	..	65·00			

First Day Cover (W56 and W58)	..	2·00
Presentation Pack (W56 and W58)	..	13·00

B. Phosphor

WP58	662p	W54	1s.3d. Three bands	3·00	3·25
a. Narrow band at left or right					
(stamp with vert. margin)	..	5·00			

First Day Cover (WP56 and WP58)	..	4·50

These are known postmarked 7 July.

Two examples of the 4d. value exist with the Queen's head omitted, one due to something adhering to the cylinder and the other due to a paper fold. The stamp also exists with Churchill's head omitted, also due to a paper fold.

Listed Variety

W56b, WP56b

Cylinder Numbers (Blocks of Four)

(a) Ordinary

Cyl. Nos.		A(T) No dot	A(T) Dot	F No dot
		Perforation Types		
4d.	1A (olive-brown)–1B (black) Rembrandt	1·25	1·25	†
4d.	5A (olive-brown)–6B (black) Timson	†	†	2·00
1s.3d.	1A (black)–1B (grey) Linotype and Machinery No. 4 ..	†	†	2·75

(b) Phosphor

4d.	1A (olive-brown)–1B (black) Rembrandt	2·50	2·50	†
1s.3d.	1A (black)–1B (grey) Linotype and Machinery No. 4 ..	†	†	16·00

Minor Constant Flaws

4d. Cyls. 1A–1B no dot
  1/1 Background retouch left of Churchill's right eye (Th. D2), scratch from Churchill's ear to Queen's chin (Th. D8–11), small background retouch to right of Churchill's left ear (Th. C9), OP
  6/6 Queen's face mottled with white streaks (Th. B–D10–12), OP
  14/1 Dark patch above Queen's left eye (Th. B11), OP

4d. Cyls. 1A–1B dot
  1/6 Vertical line of white dots near hair above Churchill's right eye (Th. A–C3), OP
  4/3 Disturbance under Churchill's left eye (Th. D6), OP
  7/1 Queen's face mottled with white specks (Th. B–D10–12), OP
  7/2 Queen's face mottled with white specks (Th. B–D10–12), OP
  20/5 Brown diagonal line on bridge of Queen's nose (Th. C11), OP

The mottled face of the Queen varieties on no dot R. 6/6 and dot R. 7/1 and 7/2 are very marked and occur on ordinary and phosphor but only on some sheets. Many other stamps on this cylinder show signs of mottling

4d. Cyls. 5A–6B no dot (ordinary only)
  4/2 Retouch in background between portraits (Th. B9)
  6/4 Retouch at top of Churchill's nose (Th. D5)
  10/4 Two spots in vertical white line level with Churchill's shoulder (Th. E10)
  12/3 Small white flaw by Queen's right eye (Th. C10)
  14/5 Background retouch just above Churchill's right shoulder (Th. E–F2) and brown flaw in margin below Churchill's chin (Th. H5)
  15/5 Brown flaw left of Churchill's head (Th. A2)

1s.3d. Cyls. 1A–1B no dot
  1/4 Line of white dots in Queen's hair (Th. C12), OP
  7/1 Small white dot over Queen's left eyelid (Th. C11), OP
  15/4 White flaw at base of Queen's neck (Th. D2), OP
  19/4 Spur on top jewel of emblems in diadem (Th. A12), OP

Sheet Details

Sheet size: 120 (6 × 20)
- 4d. Rembrandt double pane sheet-fed
  Timson single pane reel-fed
- 1s.3d. L. & M. No. 4 single pane sheet-fed

Sheet markings:
  Cylinder numbers: Opposite R. 19/1, boxed
  Guide holes:
    4d. Timson above vertical row 2 (boxed) and below vertical rows 3/4 (unboxed and over arrow)
    Others: None
  Marginal arrows (photo-etched): "W" shaped, at top, bottom and sides; Rembrandt very small at bottom; others normal
  Marginal rule: At bottom of sheet
  Colour register marks:
    4d. Rembrandt, none
    4d. Timson, opposite rows 1/2 and 17/18, at both sides
    1s.3d. Above and below vertical rows 1/2 and 6
  Autotron marks (solid):
    4d. Timson: Brown, black above R. 1/2 and 1/3
    Others: None
  Colour designations: None
  Traffic lights (boxed): All R. 19/6
    4d. Black, brown; 1s.3d. Grey, black

Imprimaturs from the National Postal Museum Archives

A. Ordinary

Nos. W56, W58 imperforate, watermark Type W.24

Watermark upright (*set of* 2)

B. Phosphor

Nos. WP56, WP58 imperforate, watermark Type W.24

Watermark upright (*set of* 2)

Quantities Issued

	Ordinary	Phosphor		Ordinary	Phosphor
4d. Rembrandt	103,217,520	10,322,760	1s.3d.	7,893,480	864,960
4d. Timson	32,040,000	—	Pack	38,500	—

Withdrawn   4d. phosphor sold out Dec. 1965, remainder withdrawn 28.2.66

W55. Simon de Montfort's Seal

(Des. Stewart R. Black)

W56. Parliament Buildings
(after engraving by Hollar, 1647)

(Des. Prof. Richard Guyatt)

1965 (JULY 19). 700th ANNIVERSARY OF SIMON DE MONTFORT'S PARLIAMENT

Simon de Montfort summoned the first parliament representing many cities and shires and it met in various buildings at Westminster in January 1265.

Cat. No.	S.G. No.	Type	Description	Mint	Used
A. Ordinary					
W59	663	**W55**	6d. Olive-green	10	10
a. Imperforate between stamp and top margin £900					
W60	664	**W56**	2s.6d. Black, grey and pale drab	1·25	1·25
a. Watermark inverted .. .. 12·00					

First Day Cover (W59/60)	..	..	12·00
Presentation Pack (W59/60)	..	..	35·00

B. Phosphor

Cat. No.	S.G. No.	Type	Description	Mint	Used
WP59	663p	**W55**	6d. Three bands	40	40

First Day Cover (WP59)..	..	..	16·00

Both values were accidentally released in several post offices in the London area on 8 July, the date of issue of the Churchill stamps. Covers are also known with both values, bearing the " First Day " cancellation of the Philatelic Bureau dated 8 July.

Cylinder Numbers (Blocks of Four)

Cyl. Nos.					Perforation Type A	
					No dot	Dot
6d. 2 (olive-green). Ordinary	..	..	..	..	1·00	1·00
6d. 2 (olive-green). Phosphor	..	..	..	..	2·75	2·75

The 2s.6d. sheets had no cylinder numbers. Perforation is Type A(T)

Minor Constant Flaws

6d. Cyl. 2 no dot
  1/1 Background scratch behind right cross of diadem (Th. C11–12), OP
  5/3 Small background blemish above jewels in diadem (Th. B11), OP
  9/4 Retouch at rear of horse's belly (Th. E4), OP
  15/2 Dot below e of Anniversary, OP
  17/3 Cut in m of Parliament, OP
  17/5 Background retouch to right of diadem, (Th. C11), OP

6d. Cyl. 2 dot
  10/6 Spur to m of Parliament, OP
  14/5 White flaw on Queen's necklace (Th. E10), OP

2s.6d. No numbers
  4/1 Vertical line running through river wall and building in centre of stamp (Th. E–F9)
  4/6 Vertical line from left of steps at centre through Thames to frame line (Th. G–H7)
  6/3 Blemish between 5th and 6th windows of building in front of Westminster Hall (Th. E10)
  8/1 White scratches above V of ANNIVERSARY
  10/1 Nick in S of ANNIVERSARY

Sheet Details

Sheet sizes:
   6d. 120 (6 × 20). Double pane reel-ted
   2s.6d. 80 (8 × 10). Single pane sheet-fed

Sheet markings:
   Cylinder numbers: 6d. opposite R. 19/1, boxed; 2s.6d. none
   Guide holes:
      6d. In double photo-etched box opposite rows 14/15, at left (no dot) or right (dot). In the left margin the
      boxes are lettered "S O N", the "S" being in left box (usually trimmed off), the "O" below centre line
      and the "N" above right line. In the right margin the sequence is reversed. The letters are very small
      and denote respectively selvedge, off-side and near-side
      2s.6d. None
   Marginal arrows (photo-etched): "W" shaped, at top, bottom and sides
   Marginal rule: At bottom of sheet
   Colour register marks, Autotron marks, colour designations: None
   Traffic lights (boxed):
      6d. None
      2s.6d. Grey, drab and black opposite R. 9/8, boxed
   This shows that the stamp was printed in three colours and accounts for misplacement of the Queen's
head downwards in some badly registered sheets

Imprimaturs from the National Postal Museum Archives

A. Ordinary

Nos. W59/60 imperforate, watermark Type W.24

Watermark upright (*set of* 2)

B. Phosphor

No. WP59 imperforate, watermark Type W.24

Watermark upright

Quantities Issued

	Ordinary	Phosphor
6d.	12,973,800	1,537,920
2s.6d.	4,055,120	—
Pack	24,450	—

Withdrawn   28.2.66

W57. Bandsmen and Banner
(Des. M. C. Farrar-Bell)

W58. Three Salvationists
(Des. G. Trenaman)

1965 (AUGUST 9). SALVATION ARMY CENTENARY

A religious militant movement, the Salvation Army was founded in 1865 by William Booth who became its General in 1880.

Cat. No.	S.G. No.	Type		Description	Mint	Used
A. Ordinary						
W61	665	**W57**		3d. Indigo, grey-blue, cerise,	10	10
a. Diadem flaw (R. 16/6) ..		..	1·75	yellow and brown		
b. Retouch to " V " (R. 19/3)		..	2·50			
W62	666	**W58**		1s.6d. Red, blue, yellow and		
a. Extra pearl (R. 17/1) ..		..	3·50	brown	1·00	1·00

First Day Cover (W61/2)	..	.. 20·00

Cat. No.	S.G. No.	Type		Description	Mint	Used
B. Phosphor						
WP61	665p	**W57**		3d. One band	40	40
a. Diadem flaw (R. 16/6) ..		..	3·50			
b. Retouch to " V " (R. 19/3)		..	2·50			
WP62	666p	**W58**		1s.6d. Three bands	2·75	3·25
a. Extra pearl (R. 17/1) ..		..	5·00			

First Day Cover (WP61/2)	..	.. 22·00

Listed Varieties

W61*a*, WP61*a*   W61*b*, WP61*b*   W62*a* WP62*a*

Cylinder Numbers (Blocks of Six)

(a) Ordinary

	Cyl. Nos. (No dot)	Perforation Type A
3d.	2A (blue)–2B (indigo)–1C (brown)–1D (cerise)–1E (yellow) ..	1·00
1s.6d.	1A (red)–1B (brown)–1C (blue)–1D (yellow)	7·00

(b) Phosphor

3d	2A (blue)–2B (indigo)–1C (brown)–1D (cerise)–1E (yellow) ..	4·00
1s.6d.	1A (red)–1B (brown)–1C (blue)–1D (yellow)	20·00

Minor Constant Flaws

3d. Cyls. 2A–2B–1C–1D–1E no dot
  1/6 Pale area below D of 3D (Th. G13), OP
  2/1 Dark spot on Queen's chin (Th. D11), OP
  3/6 Vertical scratch below flag-bearer's collar (Th. D–E4), OP
  8/1 Spur at foot of T of SALVATION at bottom of stamp, OP
  11/2 Blue scratch in white vertical dividing line to left of Queen s lips (Th. D10); also blue spot to left of flag-bearer's lips (Th. D4), both OP
  15/6 Grey flaw protruding from collar under Queen's chin (Th. E11), OP
  16/1 Due to faulty registration on the multipositive, the cerise colour is positioned slightly to the right resulting in a white line at left of flag in sky, also cerise colour overlaps ear and face below ear (Th. B–C3 and C4), OP. *Note*—This variety is not an ordinary colour shift and is therefore best collected in a positional block. A similar variety, although much less marked, is found on R. 14/1, also OP
  17/4 White spot in lower part of V of SALVATION at bottom of stamp, OP

1s.6d. Cyls. 1A–1B–1C–1D no dot
  1/1 Retouch on right arm of left-hand man (Th. D1–2), OP
  1/4 White flaw on Queen's hair behind ear (Th. D12), OP
  15/6 Retouch on right leg of left-hand man (Th. G2), OP
  19/3 Diagonal scratch across Queen's forehead and nose (Th. B–C10), OP
  20/1 White flaw on Queen's neck by necklace (Th. E11), OP
  20/3 Small red flaw at back of Queen's hair (Th. D12), OP
  20/5 A wispy line of blue dots by left leg of right-hand man (Th. F7), OP

Sheet Details

Sheet size: 120 (6 × 20). Single pane reel-fed
Sheet markings:
  Cylinder numbers:
    3d. Opposite rows 18/19 at left, boxed
    1s.6d. Opposite row 19 at left, boxed
  Guide holes: Opposite rows 14/15 (boxed), at both sides
  Marginal arrows (photo-etched): "W" shaped, at top, bottom and sides
  Marginal rule: At bottom of sheet
  Colour register marks:
    Opposite rows 1/2 and 17/18, at both sides
  Autotron marks (solid):
    3d. Blue, indigo, brown, cerise, yellow below vertical rows 1/3
    1s. 6d. Red, brown, blue, yellow below vertical rows 1/3
  Colour designations:
    3d. "G1 YELLOW G2 RED G3 BROWN G4 BLUE BLACK G5 BLUE" in right margin reading upwards opposite rows 9/3 ("G1 YELLOW" is very faint on some sheets)
    1s.6d. "G1 YELLOW G2 BLUE G3 BROWN G4 RED" in right margin reading upwards opposite rows 9/3
  Traffic lights (boxed):
    3d. Blue, indigo, brown, cerise, yellow opposite rows 18/19 at right
    1s.6d. Red, brown, blue, yellow opposite rows 18/19 at right

Imprimaturs from the National Postal Museum Archives

A. Ordinary

Nos. W61/62 imperforate, watermark Type W.24

Watermark upright (*set of 2*)

B. Phosphor

Nos. WP61/62 imperforate, watermark Type W.24

Watermark upright (*set of 2*)

Quantities Issued

	Ordinary	Phosphor
3d.	54,312,000	4,261,200
1s.6d.	5,244,120	652,320

Withdrawn 28.2.66 (3d. ordinary sold out Dec. 1965)

W59.   Lister's Carbolic Spray
(Des. Peter Gauld)

W60.   Lister and Chemical Symbols
(Des. Frank Ariss)

1965 (SEPTEMBER 1).   CENTENARY OF JOSEPH LISTER'S DISCOVERY OF ANTISEPTIC SURGERY

Cat. No.	S.G. No.	Type			Description	Mint	Used

A.   Ordinary

W63	667	**W59**			4d. Indigo, brown-red and grey-black	10	10
a. Brown-red (tube) omitted			£150	75·00			
b. Indigo omitted			£1500				
c. Corner scratch (No dot, R. 17/1)			3·50				
d. Face retouch (No dot, R. 18/1)			3·50				
e. Filled " e " (Dot, R. 20/4)			3·50				
W64	668	**W60**			1s. Black, purple and new blue	1·00	1·25
a. Watermark inverted			£140				

First Day Cover (W63/4)	.. .. 9·50

B.   Phosphor

WP63	667p	**W59**			4d. Three bands	15	20
a. Brown-red (tube) omitted			£1100				
b. Narrow band at left or right (stamp with vert. margin)			1·00				
c. Two broad bands			20·00				
ca. One thin and one broad band			25·00				
d. Corner scratch (No dot, R. 17/1)			3·50				
e. Face retouch (No dot, R. 18/1)			3·50				
WP64	668p	**W60**			1s. Three bands	1·60	1·60
a. Watermark inverted			£140				
b. Narrow band at left or right (stamp with vert. margin)			2·75				
c. Two broad bands			30·00				

First Day Cover (W63/4)	.. .. 8·50

Nos. W63/4 exist postmarked 1 August 1965 at Skeabost Bridge (Skye), and can also be found cancelled 31 August elsewhere.

Nos. WP63c/ca came from a sheet showing misplaced phosphor bands; No. WP63ca were from the left-hand vertical row only.

Listed Varieties

W63c, WP63d

W63e

" e "   of   " Antiseptic "
nearly filled by white
flaw (later retouched leaving malformed " e ")

W63d, WP63e

Large grey retouch outlines
face. Similar, but more
minor flaws can be found on
Row 19/2, 20/1

Cylinder Numbers (Blocks of Four)

Cyl. Nos.			Perforation Types		
			A	A	F
			No dot	Dot	No dot
4d. 4A (black)–1B (blue)–1C (red). Ordinary	..	..	2·50	1·00	†
4A (black)–1B (blue)–1C (red). Phosphor	..	..	3·50	1·75	†
1s. 1A (black)–1B (purple)–1C (blue). Ordinary	..	..	†	†	5·00
1A (black)–1B (purple)–1C (blue). Phosphor	..	..	†	†	8·00

Minor Constant Flaws

4d. Cyls. 4A–1B–1C no dot
4/1 Line of white dots under apparatus (Th. H3–4), OP
4/4 Two dark flaws to lower right of apparatus (Th. G5–6), OP
5/6 Prominent retouch in front of Queen's dress (Th. E–F10), OP
6/6 Grey flaw hanging from rear jewel of tiara (Th. B12), OP
10/3 Grey flaw on Queen's forehead (Th. B10), OP
11/4 to 12/4 Grey line under g of Surgery extending across gutter joining frames, OP
11/6 Diagonal grey line from top left corner to apparatus (Th. A1–B2), OP
16/5 Retouch on Queen's forehead (Th. B10), OP
17/2 White flaw in loop of d of value, OP
19/6 Grey spots on Queen's forehead (Th. B10–11), OP
19/6 and 20/6 Grey line extends down right-hand margin, OP
20/3 Vertical grey line from lower left corner of stamp to gutter (Th. H1), OP
20/6 Base of 4 joined to tube by dark line (Th. B7), OP

4d. Cyls. 4A–1B–1C dot
1/4 Blue spot between p and t of antiseptic, OP
8/2 Retouch on Queen's collar (Th. E12), OP
10/2 Diagonal grey line above te of Lister and in front of Queen's collar (Th. F8–E10), OP
13/3 Retouch behind Queen's necklace (Th. D12), OP
18/1 Retouch on Queen's jaw close to ear (Th. D11), OP
19/2 White scratch above ur of Surgery, OP
20/1 Two dark spots at right of Queen's mouth (Th. D11), OP
20/6 Retouch in front of Queen's neck (Th. E10), OP

1s. Cyls. 1A–1B–1C no dot
1/5 Large black spot at rear of Queen's collar (Th. E13), OP
3/1 Retouch along Lister's right shoulder (Th. D3–C4), OP
3/2 Broken frame line behind Queen's portrait was retouched by dots (Th. C13), OP
6/1 Missing portions of jewels left of large cross on diadem heavily retouched (Th. A10), OP
8/1 White retouch on Queen's throat (Th. D11), OP
11/2 Extra pearl half way up necklace (Th. D11), OP
11/3 Small retouch on Queen's left cheek (Th. D11), OP
14/2 Retouch on Queen's collar (Th. E12), OP
15/6 Line from Queen's left eyebrow into hair (Th. B11), OP
16/4 Retouch on back of Queen's collar (Th. E13), OP
17/6 Blue spot normally found by Lister's right wrist is missing (Th. E6), OP
19/1 Dark spot under Queen's nose (Th. C10), OP
20/3 Retouch below Queen's necklace (Th. D12), OP

Sheet Details

Sheet size: 120 (6 × 20). 4d. double pane reel-fed; 1s. single pane sheet-fed
Sheet markings:
  Cylinder numbers: Opposite R. 19/1, boxed
  Guide holes: Opposite rows 14/15 (boxed), at left (no dot) or right (dot)
  Marginal arrows (photo-etched): "W" shaped, at top, bottom and sides
  Marginal rule: At bottom of sheet
  Colour register marks:
    4d. Opposite rows 2/3 and 16/17, at left (no dot)
    1s. Above and below vertical rows 1/2 and 5/6
  Autotron marks (solid):
    4d. Black, indigo, brown-red opposite rows 3/5, at right (no dot) or left (dot)
    1s. None
  Colour designations: None
  Traffic lights (boxed):
    4d. Black, indigo, brown-red opposite R. 19/6
    1s. Black, purple, blue opposite R. 20/6

Imprimaturs from the National Postal Museum Archives

A. Ordinary

Nos. W63/64 imperforate, watermark Type W.24

Watermark upright (*set of 2*)

B. Phosphor

Nos. WP63/64 imperforate, watermark Type W.24

Watermark upright (*set of 2*)

Quantities Issued

	Ordinary	Phosphor
4d.	92,167,440	10,732,800
1s.	8,368,800	1,452,360

Withdrawn 15.4.66

W61. Trinidad Carnival Dancers   **W62.** Canadian Folk-dancers

(Des. David Gentleman and Rosalind Dease)

1965 (SEPTEMBER 1).   COMMONWEALTH ARTS FESTIVAL

The Festival was aimed at promoting the cultural traditions of Commonwealth countries and was held in London and other centres between 16 September and 2 October.

Cat. No.	S.G. No.	Type	Description	Mint	Used
A. Ordinary					
W65	669	**W61**	6d. Black and orange	10	10
W66	670	**W62**	1s.6d. Black and light reddish violet	1·25	1·50

First Day Cover (W65/6) .. .. 10·00	

Cat. No.	S.G. No.	Type	Description	Mint	Used
B. Phosphor					
WP65	669p	**W61**	6d. Three bands	30	30
a. Narrow band at left or right (stamp with vert. margin) .. 1·25					
WP66	670p	**W62**	1s.6d. Three bands	2·25	2·25
a. Narrow band at left or right (stamp with vert. margin) .. 2·50					
b. Error. Two broad bands .. 15·00					
c. Error. Two bands (9·5 and 6 mm.) .. .. 25·00					

First Day Cover (WP65/6) .. .. 10·00	

Nos. W65/6 are known postmarked 1 August 1965 at Skeabost Bridge (Skye).

No. WP66c come from the right-hand side of the sheet where the narrow band occurs on the stamp instead of the first vertical row of perforations.

Cylinder Numbers (Blocks of Four)

	Cyl. Nos.					Perforation Type F(L) No dot
6d.	1A (orange)–1B (black). Ordinary					1·25
	1A (orange)–1B (black). Phosphor					2·75
1s.6d.	1A (violet)–1B (black). Ordinary					7·00
	1A (violet)–1B (black). Phosphor					11·00

Minor Constant Flaws

6d. Cyls. 1A–1B (no dot)

1/2 Damaged right arm of v of Festival, OP

1/6 Black spot at back of Queen's neck under hair (Th. C12), OP

11/2 S shaped line of white dots on Queen's neck (Th. D–E11), OP

17/1 Pale area in background by right sleeve of central figure (Th. D3–4), OP

1s.6d. Cyls. 1A–1B no dot
   2/3 White flaw under n of Commonwealth, OP
   3/4 Vertical scratch from Queen's ear to neck (Th. C–D12), OP
   5/6 Vertical line from diadem to Queen's neck (Th. B–D11), OP
   7/5 Pale area below C of Commonwealth, OP
   9/2 White triangle in Queen's hair (Th. B11), OP
  15/1 Diagonal scratch to right of C of Commonwealth (Th. G1–2), OP
  13/6 White spot between emblems and rear cross of diadem (Th. B12), OP
  20/6 Two dots to right of Queen's left eyebrow (Th. C11), OP

Sheet Details

Sheet size: 120 (6 × 20). Single pane reel-fed

Sheet markings:
  Cylinder numbers: Opposite R. 19/1, boxed
  Guide holes: Above vertical rows 3/4 and below vertical row 5, unboxed
  Marginal arrows (photo-etched): "W" shaped, at top, bottom and sides
  Marginal rule: At bottom of sheet
Colour register marks:
  6d. Opposite rows 1/2 and 18/19, at both sides and opposite rows 10/11 (orange only), at left
  1s.6d. Opposite rows 1/2, at both sides, rows 9/10 (violet only), at left and rows 18/19, at left and 17/18
    at right
Autotron marks (solid):
  6d. Orange, black above and below vertical rows 3/4
  1s.6d. Violet, black above and below vertical rows 3/4
Colour designations:
  6d. "G ORANGE G BLACK" reading upwards opposite rows 14/12, right margin
  1s.6d. "G MAUVE G BLACK" reading upwards opposite rows 15/13, right margin
Traffic lights (boxed):
  6d. Black, orange opposite R. 19/6
  1s.6d. Black, violet opposite R. 19/6

Imprimaturs from the National Postal Museum Archives

A. Ordinary

Nos. W65/66 imperforate, watermark Type W.24

Watermark upright (*set of 2*)

B. Phosphor

Nos. WP65/66 imperforate, watermark Type W.24

Watermark upright (*set of 2*)

Quantities Issued

	Ordinary	Phosphor
6d.	12,264,840	1,621,080
1s.6d.	5,003,000	788,880

Withdrawn 15.4.66

W63. Flight of Spitfires

W64. Pilot in Hurricane

W65. Wing-tips of Spitfire
and Messerschmitt "ME–109"

W66. Spitfires attacking
Heinkel "HE–111" Bomber

W67.   Spitfires attacking
Stuka Dive-bomber

W68.   Hurricanes over Wreck
of Dornier "DO–17z2" Bomber

W69.   Anti-aircraft Artillery
in Action

W70.   Air-battle over St. Paul's
Cathedral

(Des. Andrew Restall (9d.), David Gentleman and Rosalind Dease (others))

1965 (SEPTEMBER 13).   25th ANNIVERSARY OF BATTLE OF BRITAIN

The "Battle of Britain" was the first major campaign in world history to be fought entirely between opposing air forces.

The 4d. values were issued together *se-tenant* in blocks of six (3 × 2) within the sheet

Cat. No.	S.G. No.	Type			Description	Mint	Used
A. Ordinary							
W67	671	**W63**			4d. Yellow-olive and black	30	35
a. Block of 6. Nos. W67/72			5·50	5·50			
W68	672	**W64**			4d. Yellow-olive, olive-grey and black	30	35
W69	673	**W65**			4d. Red, new blue, yellow-olive, olive-grey and black	30	35
b. Damaged wing (Cyl. 3D Dot, R. 19/3)			2·50				
W70	674	**W66**			4d. Olive-grey, yellow-olive and black	30	35
W71	675	**W67**			4d. Olive-grey, yellow-olive and black	30	35
b. Stuka retouch (Cyl. 1E No dot, R. 2/2)			3·00				
W72	676	**W68**			4d. Olive-grey, yellow-olive, new blue and black	30	35
b. New blue omitted			—	£3000			
c. Damaged tailplane (Cyl. 3D Dot, R. 20/3)			2·50				
W73	677	**W69**			9d. Bluish violet, orange and slate-purple	1·25	1·25
a. Watermark inverted			25·00				
W74	678	**W70**			1s.3d. Light and deep grey, black and light and bright blue	1·25	1·25
a. Watermark inverted			18·00				

First Day Cover (W67/74)	.. ..	18·00
Presentation Pack (W67/74)	.. ..	48·00

Cat. No.	S.G. No.	Type	Description	Mint	Used

B. Phosphor

WP67	671p	**W63**	4d. Three bands	40	50
a. Block of 6. Nos. WP67/72		10·50	9·00		
b. Narrow band at left (stamp with vert. margin) ..		2·00			
WP68	672p	**W64**	4d. Three bands	40	50
WP69	673p	**W65**	4d. Three bands	40	50
b. Narrow band at right (stamp with vert. margin) ..		2·00			
c. Damaged wing (Cyl. 3D Dot, R. 19/3)		3·50			
d. Two bands					
WP70	674p	**W66**	4d. Three bands	40	50
b. Narrow band at left (stamp with vert. margin)		2·00			
WP71	675p	**W67**	4d. Three bands	40	50
b. Stuka retouch (Cyl. 1E No dot, R. 2/2)		3·50			
WP72	676p	**W68**	4d. Three bands	40	50
b. Narrow band at right (stamp with vert. margin)		2·00			
c. Damaged tailplane (Cyl. 3D Dot, R. 20/3)		3·50			
WP73	677p	**W69**	9d. Three bands	1·25	80
a. Narrow band at left or right (stamp with vert. margin) ..		2·75			
b. Two bands					
WP74	678p	**W70**	1s.3d. Three bands	1·25	80
a. Watermark inverted		3·50			
b. Narrow band at left or right (stamp with vert. margin) ..		3·00			

First Day Cover (WP67/74)   ..   .. 18·00

Listed Varieties

W69*b*, WP69*c*

W71*b*, WP71*b*
This variety only occurs in
combination with cyls. 3A–1B–
1C–3D. With cyls. 2A–1B–1C–
3D it is normal

W72*c*, WP72*c*

Cylinder Numbers (Blocks of Twelve (3 × 4) (4d.), Four (9d.), Six (1s.3d.))

(a) Ordinary

	Cyl. Nos.	Perforation Types		
		A No dot	A Dot	F No dot
4d.	2A (black)–1B (blue)–1C (red)–3D (olive-grey)–1E (yellow-olive)	11·00	11·00	†
	3A (black)–1B (blue)–1C (red)–3D (olive-grey)–1E (yellow-olive)	11·00	15·00*	†
9d.	1A (slate-purple)–1B (violet)–1C (orange)	†	†	7·50
1s.3d.	1A (black)–1B (light blue)–1C (light grey)–1D (deep grey)–1E (bright blue)	†	†	10·00

(b) Phosphor

		Cyl. Nos.			Perforation Types		
					A	A	F
					No dot	Dot	No dot
4d.	3A (black)–1B (blue)–1C (red)–3D (olive-grey)–1E (yellow-olive)				18·00	22·00*	†
9d.	1A (slate-purple)–1B (violet)–1C (orange)				†	†	7·50
1s.3d.	1A (black)–1B (light blue)–1C (light grey)–1D (deep grey)–1E (bright blue)				†	†	10·00

Minor Constant Flaws

4d. Cyls. 1B–1C–3D–1E no dot in combination with black cyls. 2A or 3A no dot
1/3 Horizontal scratch retouch under right of cross (Th. F5–7), OP
1/6 Similar retouch under centre of cross (Th. F3–6), OP
15/2 Nick in centre line of fuselage at left (Th. D1), OP
20/1 Small dark area on left wing of bomber (Th. D2), OP

4d. Cyl. 3A no dot
1/4 Nick in lower curve of B in BRITAIN, OP
7/2 Black spot in front of Queen's ear (Th. C12), OP
12/3 White scar across Queen's left cheek (Th. C12), OP
13/2 Fine vertical line on Queen's left cheek (Th. C12), OP
18/3 Extra white dot in Queen's hair behind ear-ring (Th. C13), OP

4d. Cyls. 1B–1C–3D–1E dot in combination with black cyls. 2A or 3A dot
5/3 Dark horizontal line below right arm of cross (Th. F5–6), OP
8/1 Dark spot at left end of bomber's wing (Th. C1), OP
11/2 Line of white dots on pilot's right shoulder (Th. E8–F10), OP
16/1 Dark spot at right end of bomber's wing (Th. B9), OP
16/3 Notch in bomber's tail under B of Battle (Th. A4), OP

9d. Cyls. 1A–1B–1C no dot
11/2 Line across Queen's face under eyes (Th. C10–11), OP
12/3 Retouch in sky behind hat of man with flag (Th. C1), OP
20/5 White patch below where vapour trails cross (Th. C5–6), OP

1s.3d. Cyls. 1A–1B–1C–1D–1E no dot
4/4 Scratch below 1 of 1940 (Th. H5), OP
5/3 Horizontal bright blue line above building at right (Th. F8–10), OP
5/4 Dark line between Br of Britain (Th. G–H5), OP
9/5 Retouches in sky at lower right (Th. D–E9–10), OP
14/4 Blue dot in front of Queen's ear (Th. C12), OP
20/3 Line under value is shorter at right, OP

Sheet Details

Sheet size: 120 (6 × 20)
  4d. In *se-tenant* blocks of six, double pane reel-fed
  9d. and 1s.3d. Single pane sheet-fed
Sheet markings:
  Cylinder numbers:
    4d. and 1s.3d. Opposite rows 18/19 at left, boxed
    9d. Opposite R. 19/1, boxed
  Guide holes:
    4d. In double "S O N" box opposite rows 14/15, at left (no dot) or right (dot)
    Others: None
  Marginal arrows (photo-etched): "W" shaped, at top, bottom and sides
  Marginal rule: At bottom of sheet
  Colour register marks:
    4d. None
    9d. Above and below vertical rows 1/2 and 6
    1s.3d. Above and below vertical rows 1/2 and 5/6
      There is a large violet blob of colour under vertical rows 1/2 in the 9d. value
  Autotron marks (solid):
    4d. Black. red, blue, olive-grey, yellow-olive opposite rows 3/7, at right (no dot) or left (dot)
    Others: None
  Colour designations: None
  Traffic lights (boxed):
    4d. Olive-grey, red, black, blue, yellow-olive opposite rows 18/19 at right
    9d. Violet, orange, slate-purple opposite R. 19/6
    1s.3d. Deep grey, light blue, light grey, black, bright blue opposite rows 18/19 at right

Imprimaturs from the National Postal Museum Archives

A. Ordinary

Nos. W73/74 imperforate, watermark Type W.24

Watermark upright (2 *values*)

B. Phosphor

Nos. WP73/74 imperforate, watermark Type W.24

Watermark upright (2 *values*)

Quantities Issued

	Ordinary	Phosphor
4d.	103,417,440	11,560,440
9d.	6,195,960	1,143,120
1s.3d.	6,469,440	1,239,840
Pack	28,524	—

Withdrawn   31.5.66

W71.   Post Office Tower and
Georgian Buildings

W72.   Post Office Tower and
"Nash" Terrace, Regent's Park

(Des. Clive Abbott)

1965 (OCTOBER 8).   OPENING OF POST OFFICE TOWER

The tallest building in London, the Post Office Tower is 620 feet high and helps to provide more long distance telephone circuits and more television channels. An additional feature of this issue was the inclusion of the names of both the designer and printers at the foot of the stamps and this became the practice for many later issues until 1969.

Watermark sideways on 3d.

Cat. No.	S.G. No.	Type		Description	Mint	Used
A. Ordinary						
W75	679	**W71**		3d. Olive-yellow, new blue		
a. Olive-yellow (tower) omitted..			£500	and bronze-green	10	10
b. Extra window (Dot. R. 4/18) ..			3·00			
W76	680	**W72**		1s.3d. Bronze-green, yellow-		
a. Watermark inverted ..		..	38·00	green and blue	65	75

First Day Cover (W75/6)	..	.. 6·00
Presentation Pack (W75/6)	..	.. 2·50

The one phosphor band on No. WP75 was produced by printing broad phosphor bands across alternate rows of vertical perforations. Individual examples show the band at right or left (*same prices either way*).

B.   Phosphor

Cat. No.	S.G. No.	Type			Description	Mint	Used
WP75	679p	**W71**			3d. One band at left	10	10
a. Band at right ..	..	..	..	10	10		
ab. Nos. WP75/*a* (horiz. pair)..		..		20			
ac. Broad band *se-tenant* with missing							
phosphor horiz. pair)		..	..	35·00	*b.* Extra window (Dot, R. 4/18) ..	3·50	
WP76	680p	**W72**			1s.3d. Three bands	50	50
a. Watermark inverted ..		..		35·00			
b. Left-hand band omitted			..	15·00			

First Day Cover (WP75/6)	..	.. 8·00
Presentation Pack* (WP75/6)	..	.. 2·50

*See note under "Withdrawn" at end of listing

The above are known pre-released on 4 October at Aish, South Brent (Devon).

Listed Variety

W75*b*, WP75*b*

Cylinder Numbers (Blocks of Four)

(a) Ordinary   Cyl. Nos.

			Perforation Types		
			A	A	F
			No dot	Dot	No dot
3d.	1A (blue)–1B (green)–1C (yellow)*	.. ..	1·00	1·00	†
1s.3d.	1A (yellow-green)–1B (bronze-green)–1C (blue)	.. ..	†	†	4·25

(b) Phosphor

3d.	1A (blue)–1B (green)–1C (yellow)*	.. .. ..	1·00	1·00	†
1s.3d.	1A (yellow-green)–1B (bronze-green)–1C (blue)	..	†	†	3·00

*In the 3d. dot pane the dot after "1C" is omitted in error
The 3d. is with sheet orientated showing head to left

Minor Constant Flaws

3d. Cyls. 1A–1B–1C dot
  1/20 White spot at base of tower (Th. L3), OP
  2/19 Olive-yellow spot below second ground floor window of building at base of tower at right (Th. M4), OP
  2/20 Blue spot below SO of HARRISON, OP
  5/2 White spot in O of OFFICE, OP
  5/8 Blue spot surrounded by pale area below T of TOWER, OP
  5/16 Pale spot in blue panel to left of 3d (Th. J4), OP

1s.3d. Cyls. 1A–1B–1C no dot
  1/5 Pale area around lower tip of 3 of 1/3, OP
  3/1 Small retouch below T of TOWER (Th. C–D1), OP
  4/1 Horizontal line of retouching below 1/3 (Th. D11–12), OP
  6/2 Scratch in sky above roof of left-hand terrace (Th. E2), OP
  10/3 Dark spot to left of Queen's nose (Th. C8), OP
  10/4 Retouch to background at top right of 1 of 1/3, OP
  15/4 White scratch through E and over R of TOWER, OP

Sheet Details

Sheet sizes:
  3d. **120** (20 × 6). Double pane reel-fed
  1s.3d. **120** (6 × 20). Single pane sheet-fed
Sheet markings:
  Cylinder numbers:
    3d. Above vertical row **2**, boxed
    1s.3d. Opposite R. 19/1, boxed
  Guide holes:
    3d. In double "S O N" box above vertical rows 6/7 (no dot) or below (dot)
    1s.3d. None
  Marginal arrows (photo-etched): "W" shaped, at top, bottom and sides
  Marginal rule: 3d. At left of sheet; 1s.3d. At bottom of sheet
  Colour register marks:
    3d. None
    1s.3d. Above and below vertical rows 1/2 and 5/6
  Autotron marks (solid):
    3d Yellow, green, blue below vertical rows 15/17 (no dot) or above (dot)
    1s.3d. None
  Colour designations: None
  Traffic lights (boxed):
    3d. Yellow, green. blue, reading left to right below vertical row 2
    1s.3d. Yellow-green, bronze-green, blue opposite R. 19/6

Imprimaturs from the National Postal Museum Archives

A. Ordinary

Nos. W75/76 imperforate, watermark Type W.24

Watermark upright (1s.3d.) or sideways (3d.) (*set of* 2)

B. Phosphor

Nos. WP75/76 imperforate, watermark Type W.24

Watermark upright (1s.3d.) or sideways (3d.) (*set of* 2)

Quantities Issued

	Ordinary	Phosphor
3d.	51,291,120	4,274,880
1s.3d.	5,722,320	1,107,480
Pack	25,060 (ordinary and phosphor)	

Withdrawn 30.6.66
    When the Post Office Tower was opened on 19 May 1966 these stamps were issued from automatic machines giving a block of four of the 3d. and a pair of the 1s.3d. dispensed in envelopes, and packs were also issued from a machine. These continued to be available after the stamps had been withdrawn everywhere else and early in 1968 the ordinary stamps were replaced by phosphor stamps and packs. These were withdrawn on the introduction of decimal currency.

W73.   U.N. Emblem

W74.   I.C.Y. Emblem

(Des. Jeffery Matthews)

1965 (OCTOBER 25).   20th ANNIVERSARY OF THE UNITED NATIONS

Commemorating the 20th Anniversary of the formation of the United Nations in 1945. 1965 was also designated International Co-operation Year and the symbol of the clasped hands is shown on the 1s.6d. value.

Cat. No.	S.G. No.	Type	Description	Mint	Used
A. Ordinary					
W77	681	**W73**	3d. Black, yellow-orange and		
a. Broken circle (Dot. R. 11/4) ..	2·75		light blue	15	20
b. Lake in Russia (Dot, R. 19/3) ..	2·75				
c. "Flying saucer" flaw (Dot, R. 18/3)	4·00				
d. Retouched	2·50				
W78	682	**W74**	1s.6d. Black, bright purple and		
a. Watermark inverted			light blue	1·10	90

First Day Cover (W77/8)	.. ..	11·00

Cat. No.	S.G. No.	Type	Description	Mint	Used
B. Phosphor					
WP77	681p	**W73**	3d. One centre band	25	25
a. Broken circle (Dot. R. 11/4) ..	2·75				
b. Lake in Russia (Dot, R. 19/3)	2·75				
c. "Flying saucer" flaw (Dot, R. 18/3)	4·00				
d. Retouched	2·50				
WP78	682p	**W74**	1s.6d. Three bands	2·50	2·50

First Day Cover (WP77/8)	.. ..	9·50

Listed Varieties

W77a, WP77a	W77b, WP77b	W77c, WP77c Stroke over " S " of " ANNIVERSARY " and smudge	W77d, WP77d Retouched. Smudge removed

Cylinder Numbers (Blocks of Four)

(a) Ordinary

		Perforation Types		
	Cyl. Nos.	A No dot	A Dot	F No dot
3d.	1A (black)–1B (blue)–1C (orange)*	1·25	1·25	†
1s.6d.	1A (black)–1B (blue)–1C (purple)	†	†	6·50

	Perforation Types		
	A	A	F
(b) Phosphor	No dot	Dot	No dot
3d. 1A (black)–1B (blue)–1C (orange)*	2·50	2·50	†
1s.6d. 1A (black)–1B (blue)–1C (purple)	†	†	14·00

*In the 3d. dot pane the dot is before instead of after the "1C"

Minor Constant Flaws

3d. Cyls. 1A–1B–1C no dot

  1/1 Diagonal scratch across Queen's face (Th. C11–12), OP
  1/4 Round pale grey flaw by Queen's left eye (Th. C11–12), OP
  2/2 Pale patch on Queen's neck (Th. E12), OP
  8/5 Dotted white scratch on right side of o of large 2o (Th. D8–9), OP
  9/2 Black flaw in lower loop of 3, OP
  10/4 Small break in middle of S of ANNIVERSARY, OP
  13/1 Curved white scratch in bottom right-hand corner of blue panel (Th. H9–10), OP
  14/4 Scratch on Queen's neck by necklace (Th. E12), OP
  15/6 Black spot on Queen's forehead (Th. C11), OP
  19/4 Horizontal white scratch over VERSARY, OP
  20/6 Black flaws between laurel leaves over middle of large 2 (Th. D3), OP

3d. Cyls. 1A–1B–1C dot
  20/1 White scratch through ARY U, OP

1s.6d. Cyls. 1A–1B–1C no dot
  2/1 White scratch behind Queen's neck (Th. D12–E12), OP
  5/1 Small patch of white dots to right of Queen's head (Th. B13), OP
  6/2 Pale patch to left of top of large U (Th. B1), OP
  10/1 Pale patch in background to left of Queen's mouth (Th. D10), OP
  11/2 Pink spot central below large N (Th. F7), OP
  15/1 White scratch in base of large U, (Th. E2), OP
  20/1 Vertical white scratch in background behind Queen's head (Th. C–D13), OP
  20/5 Retouch to background within upper thumb of symbol (Th. B5), OP

Sheet Details

Sheet size: 120 (6 × 20). 3d. double pane reel-fed; 1s.6d. single pane sheet-fed

Sheet markings:
  Cylinder numbers: Opposite R. 19/1, boxed
  Guide holes:
    3d. In double " S O N " box opposite rows 14/15, at left (no dot) or right (dot). An unusual feature of this
    stamp is that there is an additional single box printed in orange beneath the double box which is in
    black
    1s.6d. None
  Marginal arrows (photo-etched): "W" shaped, at top, bottom and sides
  Marginal rule: At bottom of sheet
  Colour register marks:
    3d. None
    1s.6d. Above and below vertical rows 1 and 6
  Autotron marks (solid):
    3d. Black, blue, orange opposite rows 5/6 at right (no dot) or left (dot)
    1s.6d. None
  Colour designations (usually trimmed off):
    3d. "G1 BROWN G2 BLUE G3 BLACK" in right margin reading upwards opposite rows 8/5 on dot panes
    1s.6d. None
  Traffic lights (boxed):
    3d. Black, blue, orange opposite R. 19/6
    1s.6d. Black, blue, purple opposite R. 19/6

Imprimaturs from the National Postal Museum Archives

A. Ordinary

Nos. W77/78 imperforate, watermark Type W.24

Watermark upright (*set of* 2)

B. Phosphor

Nos. WP77/78 imperforate, watermark Type W.24

Watermark upright (*set of* 2)

Quantities Issued

	Ordinary	Phosphor
3d.	50,598,720	4,488,240
1s.6d.	5,476,800	1,018,560

Withdrawn   30.6.66

W75. Telecommunications Network   **W76.** Radio Waves and Switchboard
(Des. Andrew Restall)

1965 (NOVEMBER 15). I.T.U. CENTENARY

The aims of the Union created in 1865, then known as the International Telegraph Union, were to promote, maintain and extend international co-operation in telecommunications.

Cat. No.	S.G. No.	Type		Description	Mint	Used
A. Ordinary						
W79	683	**W75**		9d. Red, ultramarine, deep slate-violet, black and pink		
a. Watermark inverted			12·00		20	20
W80	684	**W76**		1s.6d. Red, greenish blue, indigo, black and light pink		
a. Light pink omitted			£850			
b. Watermark inverted			45·00			
c. Retouched arm (R. 1/4) ..			3·75		1·40	1·10

First Day Cover (W79/80)	..	..	11·00

B. Phosphor

WP79	683p	**W75**		9d. Three bands		60	50
a. Watermark inverted			60·00				
b. Two bands			50·00				
c. Narrow band at left (stamp with vert margin)			1·75				
WP80	684p	**W76**		1s.6d. Three bands		4·50	4·50
a. Two bands			20·00				
b. Narrow band at left (stamp with vert. margin)			9·00				
c. Red pin with arm (R. 1/4) ..			12·00				
d. Retouched			12·00				

First Day Cover (WP79/80)	..	..	11·50

Originally scheduled for issue on 17 May 1965, supplies from the Philatelic Bureau were sent in error to reach a dealer on that date and another dealer received his supply on 27 May. Ordinary and phosphor sets exist on cover postmarked Stretford on 18 May 1965.

Listed Varieties

WP80a. This variety was caused by a misplacement of the phosphor bands

WP80c   W80c, W80d

On the phosphor printing the red pin has a projecting arm at right; this was later re-touched leaving faint traces of red on the pink background and it is known only in the retouched state on the ordinary printing.

274

Cylinder Numbers (Blocks of Six)

(a) Ordinary

		Cyl. Nos. (No dot)	Perforation Type F

9d. 1A (ultram.)–1B (red)–1C (violet)–1D (pink)–2E (black) .. 1·75
1s.6d. 2A (blue)–1B (indigo)–1C (pink)–1D (red)–2E (black) .. 10·00

(b) Phosphor

9d. 1A (ultram.)–1B (red)–1C (violet)– 1D (pink)–2E (black) 4·75
1s.6d. 2A (blue)–1B (indigo)–1C (pink)–1D (red)–2E (black) .. 30·00

The same black cylinder was used for both values.

Minor Constant Flaws

9d. and 1s.6d. Cyl. 2E
    2/4 Small white curl in hair behind Queen's ear (Th. C12), OP
    5/2 Small nick in diagonal stroke of first N of UNION, OP

9d. Cyls. 1A–1B–1C–1D–2E
    6/5 Small break in diagonal blue network line at right (Th. B8), OP
    9/5 Diagonal white scratch in blue background above ATIO of INTERNATIONAL (Th. E3), OP
    10/5 Damaged lower half of 1 of 1865, shows as white nick and white scratch, OP
    17/6 Small nick in right-hand stroke of first M of TELECOMMUNICATION, OP
    20/5 Wavy scratch in background over OMMUNI of TELECOMMUNICATION (Th. E7–9), OP

1s.6d. Cyls. 2A–1B–1C–1D–2E
    3/3 Retouches to background above first C of TELECOMMUNICATION, P

Sheet Details

Sheet size: 120 (6 × 20). Single pane sheet-fed
Sheet markings:
    Cylinder numbers: Opposite rows 18/19 at left, boxed
    Guide holes: None
    Marginal arrows (photo-etched): "W" shaped, at top, bottom and sides
    Marginal rule: At bottom of sheet
    Colour register marks: Above and below vertical rows 1/2 and 5/6
    Autotron marks: None
    Colour designations: None
    Traffic lights (boxed):
        9d. Ultramarine, red, violet, pink, black opposite rows 18/19 at right
        1s.6d. Blue indigo, pink, red, black opposite rows 18/19 at right

Imprimaturs from the National Postal Museum Archvies

A. Ordinary

Nos. W79/80 imperforate, watermark Type W.24

Watermark upright (*set of 2*)

B. Phosphor

Nos. WP79/80 imperforate, watermark Type W.24

Watermark upright (*set of 2*)

Quantities Issued

	Ordinary	Phosphor
9d.	5,321,880	556,080
1s.6d.	5,287,920	589,800

Withdrawn 30.6.66 (1s.6d. phosphor sold out December 1965)

W77. Robert Burns (after Skirving chalk drawing)   **W78.** Robert Burns (after Nasmyth portrait)

(Des. Gordon F. Huntly)

1966 (JANUARY 25). BURNS COMMEMORATION

Robert Burns (1759-1796), Scotland's celebrated national poet, was born in Alloway, near Ayr.

Cat. No.	S.G. No.	Type	Description	Mint	Used
A. Ordinary					
W81	685	**W77**	4d. Black, deep violet-blue and new blue	15	15
W82	686	**W78**	1s.3d. Black, slate-blue and yellow-orange	70	70

First Day Cover (W81/2)	..	..	2·50
Presentation Pack (W81/2)	..	..	34·00

B. Phosphor					
WP81	685p	**W77**	4d. Three bands	25	25
a. Narrow band at left or right (stamp with vert. margin)	..	1·00			
WP82	686p	**W78**	1s.3d. Three bands	1·00	1·00

First Day Cover (WP81/2)	..	..	3·50

These are known postmarked 24 January.

Cylinder Numbers (Blocks of Four)

(a) Ordinary

Cyl. Nos.		Perforation Types		
		A	A	F
		No dot	Dot	No dot
4d.	1A (violet–blue)–1B (black)–1C (new blue) ..	1·25	1·25	†
	1A (violet–blue)–2B (black)–1C (new blue) ..	1·25	1·25	†
	1s.3d. 2A (slate-blue)–1B (black)–1C (orange) ..	†	†	4·00

(b) Phosphor

4d.	1A (violet-blue)–1B (black)–1C (new blue) ..	2·50	2·50	†
	1s.3d. 2A (slate-blue)–1B (black)–1C (orange) ..	†	†	5·50

Minor Constant Flaws

4d. Cyls. 1A–1B–1C dot and 1A–2B–1C dot
   9/4 Small white flaw at front of diadem (Th. A10), OP
   18/1 Coloured spot above Queen's upper lip (Th. C10), OP
   19/3 White flaw on Queen's neck above centre of collar (Th. E11), OP

4d. Cyls. 1A–2B–1C dot only
   15/1 White spot at back of Burns's hair by parting (Th. A5), OP

1s.3d. Cyls. 2A–1B–1C no dot
   2/6 Pale background flaw in front of Queen's neck (Th. D9), OP
   3/6 Grey spot on Burns's nose near his right eye (Th. C5), OP
   4/6 Grey diagonal line through white line to panel at lower right (Th. E8–G9), OP
   6/5 White patch to right of Queen's left eyebrow (Th. B11), OP
   9/4 Large dark retouch in Burns's hair left of parting (Th. B4), OP
   19/1 Flaw on Burns's right cheek (Th. D4), OP
   19/5 Dark flaw on Burns's shirt touching left lapel (Th. F5), OP

Sheet Details

Sheet size: 120 (6 × 20). 4d double pane reel-fed; 1s.3d. single pane sheet-fed

Sheet marking:
  Cyiinder numbers: R. 19/1, boxed
  Guide holes:
    4d. In double "S O N" box opposite rows 14/15, at left (no dot) or right (dot)
    1s.3d. None
  Marginal arrows (photo-etched): "W" shaped, at top, bottom and sides
  Marginal rule: At bottom of sheet
  Colour register marks:
    4d. None
    1s.3d. Above and below vertical rows 1 and 6
  Coloured crosses:
    4d. None
    1s.3d. Above and below vertical row 2
  Autotron marks (solid):
    4d. Violet-blue, black, new blue opposite rows 5/6, at right (no dot) or left (dot)
    1s.3d. None
  Colour designations: None
  Traffic lights (boxed):
    4d. New blue, black, violet-blue opposite R. 19/6
    1s.3d. Orange, black, slate-blue opposite R. 19/6

Imprimaturs from the National Postal Museum Archives

A. Ordinary

Nos. W81/82 imperforate, watermark Type W.24

Watermark upright (*set of* 2)

B. Phosphor

Nos. WP81/82 imperforate, watermark Type W.24

Watermark upright (*set of* 2)

Quantities Sold

	Ordinary	Phosphor
4d.	77,905,176	8,738,520
1s.3d.	5,685,096	1,226,160
Pack	38,968	—

Withdrawn   29.7.66 but later put on sale again in error for a short time at the Philatelic Counter in London, the Philatelic Bureau in Edinburgh and at the Edinburgh Festival.

W79.   Westminster Abbey
(Des. Sheila Robinson)

W80.   Fan Vaulting, Henry VII Chapel
(Des. and eng. Bradbury, Wilkinson)

1966 (FEBRUARY 28).   900th ANNIVERSARY OF WESTMINSTER ABBEY

Westminster Abbey, officially the Collegiate Church of St. Peter, Westminster, is the nation's Coronation Church and a mausoleum for England's greatest men and women.

The 2s.6d. is recess-printed on chalk-surfaced paper by Bradbury, Wilkinson and comb perf. 11 × 12.

Cat. No.	S.G. No.	Type		Description	Mint	Used
A. Ordinary						
W83	687	**W79**		3d. Black, red-brown and new	15	10
a. Diadem flaw (No dot, R. 16/2)..			2·00	blue		
b. Retouch on Queen's cheek (Dot, R. 15/6)			2·00			
W84	688	**W80**		2s.6d. Black	85	90

First Day Cover (W83/4)	..	..	4·50
Presentation Pack (W83/4)	..	..	17·00

Cat. No.	S.G. No.	Type		Description	Mint	Used
B. Phosphor						
WP83	687p	**W79**		3d. One band	30	30
a. Diadem flaw (No dot, R. 16/2)			2·75			
b. Retouch on Queen's cheek (Dot, R. 15/6)			2·50			
c. Two bands			4·00			

First Day Cover (WP83)..	..	..	7·50

Listed Varieties

W83*a*, WP83*a*

W83*b*, WP83*b*

Cylinder and Plate Numbers (Blocks of Four)

Cyl. or Plate Nos.

					Perforation Type A	
					No dot	Dot
3d.	2A (blue)–1B (black)–1C (brown). Ordinary	..	..		1·25	1·25
3d.	2A (blue)–1B (black)–1C (brown). Phosphor	..	..		2·75	2·75
2s.6d. Plate 1. Ordinary	..	..	..	..	4·50	†
2s.6d. Plate 1A. Ordinary	..	..	..	..	6·00	†

Minor Constant Flaws

3d. Cyls. 2A–1B–1C no dot

 1/6 Vertical scratch to right of Queen's head and running through bottom frame of panel (Th. D–E12), OP
 15/1 Small white dots touching E and second A of ANNIVERSARY, OP

2s.6d. Plate 1

 2/2 Broken horizontal line in top margin over Y of ANNIVERSARY (Th. A1)
 6/1 Scratch in bottom margin below Y of ABBEY (Th. I13–14)
 10/2 Second o of 900 joined to t of th

2s.6d. Plate 1A

 5/3 Horizontal line in margin left of Y of ANNIVERSARY and vertical line in top margin at left (Th. A1 and A2)
 7/4 Scratch through Y of ANNIVERSARY

Sheet Details

Sheet sizes:
 3d. 120 (6 × 20). Double pane sheet-fed
 2s.6d. 40 (4 × 10). Double pane sheet-fed

Sheet markings:
  Cylinder numbers: 3d. R. 19/1, boxed
  Plate numbers: 2s.6d. Bottom margin below vertical rows 3/4
  Guide holes:
    3d. In double "S O N" box opposite rows 14/15, at left (no dot) or right (dot)
    2s.6d. In circle opposite row 6, at left (Pl. 1) or right (Pl. 1A)
  Marginal arrows (photo-etched): 3d. "W" shaped, at top, bottom and sides; 2s.6d. none
  Marginal rule: 3d at bottom of sheet; 2s.6d. none.
  Colour register marks: None
  Coloured cross (black): 2s.6d. opposite row 6, at right (Pl. 1) or left (Pl. 1A)
  Autotron marks (solid):
    3d. Blue, black, red-brown opposite rows 6/7, at right (no dot) or left (dot); 2s.6d. none
  Colour designations: None
  Traffic lights (boxed):
    3d. Blue, black, red-brown opposite R. 19/6

Imprimaturs from the National Postal Museum Archives

A. Ordinary

Nos. W83/84 imperforate, watermark Type W.24

Watermark upright (*set of 2*)

B. Phosphor

No. WP83 imperforate, watermark Type W.24

Watermark upright

Quantities Sold

	Ordinary	Phosphor
3d.	48,703,426	5,247,720
2s.6d.	2,819,056	—
Pack	24,272	—

Withdrawn 31.8.66 3d. (2s.6d. sold out in April 1966)

The 3d. was later put on sale again in error for a short time at the Philatelic Counter in London and at the Philatelic Bureau in Edinburgh

W81. View near Hassocks, Sussex

W82. Antrim, Northern Ireland

W83. Harlech Castle, Wales

W84. Cairngorm Mountains, Scotland

(Des. Leonard Rosoman. Queen's portrait adapted by David Gentleman from coinage)

1966 (MAY 2). LANDSCAPES

Britain's first special pictorial stamps featuring scenes in England, Northern Ireland, Wales and Scotland.
The Queen's profile design on this, and following special issues to 1967 Christmas, was taken from the coinage design by Mrs. Mary Gillick and adapted by David Gentleman.

279

Cat. No.	S.G. No.	Type	Description	Mint	Used

A. Ordinary

W85	689	**W81**		4d. Black, yellow-green and new blue	15	15

a. Dash before " ENGLAND " (No dot, R. 20/5) .. .. 2·50
b. Green flaw on tree trunk (Dot, R. 3/4) .. .. 2·50

| W86 | 690 | **W82** | 6d. Black, emerald and new blue | 15 | 15 |

a. Watermark inverted .. .. 4·50
b. " AN " for " AND " (R. 10/3).. 10·00
c. Retouched, with misaligned " D " .. .. 3·00

| W87 | 691 | **W83** | 1s.3d. Black, greenish yellow and greenish blue | 35 | 35 |

a. Broken " D " (R. 14/2) .. 3·00

| W88 | 692 | **W84** | 1s.6d. Black, orange and Prussian blue | 50 | 50 |

a. Watermark inverted .. .. 8·00

First Day Cover (W85/8) .. .. 6·00

B. Phosphor

| WP85 | 689p | **W81** | 4d. Three bands | 15 | 15 |

a. Narrow band at left or right (stamp with vert. margin) .. 1·00
b. Green flaw on tree trunk (Dot, R. 3/4) .. .. 2·75

| WP86 | 690p | **W82** | 6d. Three bands | 25 | 25 |

a. Watermark inverted .. .. 25·00
b. " AN " for " AND " (R. 10/3).. 4·00

| WP87 | 691p | **W83** | 1s.3d. Three bands | 35 | 35 |

a. Broken " D " (R. 14/2) .. 2·75

| WP88 | 692p | **W84** | 1s.6d. Three bands | 50 | 50 |

First Day Cover (WP85/8) .. .. 6·00

These are known postmarked 26 April in Winchester.

No. W85 exists with Queen's head and value omitted, due to a paper fold, with the stamp above showing value only omitted. A vertical pair of No. W86 exists with the Queen's head and value omitted from the upper stamp and partial omission on the lower stamp, both due to a paper fold.

Listed Varieties

W86b and WP86b.   40,000 sheets, including all the phosphor stamps, were printed before this was discovered and the " D " was then added to the cylinder, forming W86c.

W85a
(Later retouched)

W85b, WP85b

W87a, WP87a

Cylinder Numbers (Blocks of Four)

(a) Ordinary

	Cyl. Nos.					Perforation Type A	
						No dot	Dot
4d.	2A (blue)–1B (black)–1C (yellow-green)	..	..	..		1·25	1·25
						No dot	
						Type F	Type F(L)
6d.	1A (blue)–3B (black)–1C (green)	..	..	..	..	1·25	†
1s.3d.	2A (blue)–2B (black)–1C* (yellow)	..	..	..	..	2·50	†
1s.6d.	1A (blue)–1B (orange)–1C (black)	..	..	..	..	3·00	3·00

(b) Phosphor

		Perforation Types		
		A	A	F
		No dot	Dot	No dot
4d.	2A (blue)–1B (black)–1C (yellow-green)	1·25	1·25	†
6d.	1A (blue)–3B (black)–1C (green)	†	†	2·00
1s.3d.	2A (blue)–2B (black)–1C* (yellow)	†	†	2·50
1s.6d.	1A (blue)–1B (orange)–1C (black)	†	†	3·00

*The figure one of this cylinder is inverted

Minor Constant Flaws

4d. Cyls. 2A–1B–1C no dot
  11/2 Pale area behind Queen's collar above value (Th. E–F12–13), OP
  14/5 Dark spot in green field at top left corner (Th. A1–2), OP

4d. Cyls. 2A–1B–1C dot
  2/4 Retouching in sky between clouds (Th. A2), OP

6d. Cyls. 1A–1B–1C no dot
  2/2 Horizontal blue line across Queen's neck, later retouched on ordinary (Th. D11), OP
  5/4 Green spot between N. and I, OP
  17/2 Curved green flaw on trees opposite Queen's chin (Th. D9), OP
  18/1 Blue mark in field left of cottage (Th. F5), OP
  19/2 Green line running across Queen's head (Th. B10–12), OP
  20/6 Diagonal black flaw below second R of HARRISON, OP

1s.3d. Cyls. 2A–2B–1C no dot
  6/1 Pale diagonal white line above ES of WALES, OP
  9/2 Pale area between 1 and 3 of value (Th. F11–12), OP
  19/1 Dot before " M " of " ROSOMAN " (Th. H2), OP

1s.6d. Cyls. 1A–1B–1C no dot
  1/6 Blurred area at back of Queen's hair (Th. B–C12), OP
  4/6 Several blemishes in background between mountains which appear as italic figures 20 (Th. A4–5), OP
  8/1 Retouch above d of value (Th. F13), OP
  13/4 Retouch behind Queen's neck (Th. D12), OP
  18/3 White spot between AN of SCOTLAND and foot of A is enlarged, OP

Sheet Details

Sheet size: 120 (6×20). 4d. double pane reel-fed; others single pane sheet-fed
Sheet markings:
  Cylinder numbers: R. 19/1, boxed
  Guide holes:
    4d. In single "S O N" box opposite rows 14/15, at left (no dot) or right (dot). The centre bar of the double box has been erased
    Others: None
  Marginal arrows (photo-etched): "W" shaped, at top, bottom and sides
  Marginal rule: At bottom of sheet
  Colour register marks:
    4d. None
    Others: Above and below vertical rows 1/2 and 5/6
  Autotron marks (solid):
    4d. Blue, black, yellow-green opposite rows 5/6, at right (no dot) or left (dot); others, none
  Colour designations: None
  Traffic lights (boxed):
    4d. Blue, black, yellow-green opposite R. 19/6
    6d. Blue, black, green opposite R. 19/6
    1s.3d. Blue, black, yellow opposite R. 19/6
    1s.6d. Black, blue, orange opposite R. 19/6

Imprimaturs from the National Postal Museum Archives

A. Ordinary

Nos. W85/88 imperforate, watermark Type W.24

Watrmark upright (*set of* 4)

B. Phosphor

Nos. WP85/88 imperforate, watermark Type W.24

Watermark upright (*set of* 4)

Quantities Sold

	Ordinary	Phosphor		Ordinary	Phosphor
4d.	80,326,440	11,283,720	1s.3d.	5,286,000	1,242,720
6d.	11,531,760	2,459,280	1s.6d.	5,462,640	1,204,200

Withdrawn 1.5.67 but 6d. phosphor was sold out in January

W86. Goalmouth Mêlée
(Des. William Kempster)

W85. Players with Ball
(Des. David Gentleman)

W87. Goalkeeper saving Goal
(Des. David Caplan)

1966 (JUNE 1). WORLD FOOTBALL CUP COMPETITION

Sixteen countries took part in the final stages of the World Football Competition for the Jules Rimet Cup in England during July, 1966.

Watermark sideways on 4d.

Cat. No.	S.G. No.	Type			Description	Mint	Used
A. Ordinary							
W89	693	**W85**			4d. Red, reddish purple, bright	15	10
a. Patch on thigh (No dot, R. 3/20)				2·00	blue, flesh and black		
b. Broken shadow (No dot, R. 5/17)				2·00			
W90	694	**W86**			6d. Black, sepia, red, apple-	20	20
a. Black omitted	..		..	85·00	green and blue		
b. Apple-green omitted	..		..	£1800			
c. Red omitted	..		..	£1800			
d. Watermark inverted	..			1·25			
W91	695	**W87**			1s.3d. Black, blue, yellow, red	50	50
a. Blue omitted	..		..	£150	and light yellow-olive		
b. Watermark inverted	..		..	60·00			
c. Darned stocking (R. 19/2)			..	3·00			

First Day Cover (W89/91)	..	..	6·50
Presentation Pack (W89/91)	..	..	14·00

B. Phosphor							
WP89	693p	**W85**			4d. Two bands	15	10
a. Narrow band at left (stamp with							
vert. margin)	..	..	..	1·00			
b. Extra phosphor band at right	..						
c. One broad band	..	..	..	15·00			
d. Patch on thigh (No dot, R. 3/20)				2·50			
e. Red patch below ball (No dot,							
R. 4/16)	.	..	..	2·50			
f. Broken shadow (No dot, R. 5/17)				2·00			
WP90	694p	**W86**			6d. Three bands	20	20
a. Black omitted	..	..	..	£300			
WP91	695p	**W87**			1s.3d. Three bands	50	50
a. Watermark inverted	..	..		1·25			
b. Darned stocking (R. 19/2)		..		3·00			
c. Error. Two bands	..	..		6·00			

First Day Cover (WP89/91)	..	..	6·50

The 4d. ordinary has been seen postmarked 31 May in Hereford.

Listed Varieties

W89a, WP89d, W96a

W89b, WP89f, W96c

WP89e, W96b

W91c, WP91b

Cylinder Numbers (Blocks of Six)

(a) Ordinary

	Cyl. Nos.	Perforation Type A	
		No dot	Dot
4d.	1A (black)-1B (blue)-1C (red)-1D (purple)- 1E (flesh)*	.. 1·50	1·50

		Perforation Types	
		F	F(L)
		No dot	No dot
6d.	1A (blue)-1B (green)-1C (red)-1D (sepia)-1E (black)	.. 1·75	†
	2A (blue)-1B (green)-1C (red)-1D (sepia)-1E (black)	.. 2·50	†
1s.3d.	1A (black)-1B (yellow)-1C (yellow-olive)-1D (blue)-1E (red)	6·00*	8·00*
	1A (black)-1B (yellow)-1C (yellow-olive)-1D (blue)-2E (red)	6·00*	7·00*

(b) Phosphor

		Perforation Types		
		A	A	F
		No dot	Dot	No dot
4d.	1A (black)-1B (blue)-1C (red)-1D (purple)-1E (flesh)*	1·50	1·50	†
6d.	1A (blue)-1B (green)-1C (red)-1D (sepia)-1E (black)	†	†	1·75
1s.3d.	1A (black)-1B (yellow)-1C (yellow-olive)-1D (blue)			
	-2E (red)	†	†	6·00*

*In the 4d. **no** dot pane the flesh cylinder is expressed in error thus: "1E.".

The 4d. is with sheet orientated showing head to left.

Minor Constant Flaws

4d. Cyls. 1A–1B–1C–1D–1E no dot
3/1 Horizontal scratch through top of ball (Th. K1-2), OP
5/6 Blue patch below u of Cup, OP
6/18 Blue spots over T of LTD, OP

4d. Cyls. 1A–1B–1C–1D–1E dot
4/20 Red line joins head and left arm of player at left (Th. F3), OP
5/10 Dark spot on ball (Th. K1), OP
5/17 Grey coloured spur to top of l of World, OP

6d. Cyls. 1B–1C–1D–1E in combination with blue cyls. 1A or 2A no dot
5/4 Diagonal scratch on barrier next to grass below crowd (Th. G5-7), OP

6d. Cyl. 1A no dot
17/4 Pale area around top of 1 of 1966, OP

1s.3d. Cyls. 1A–1B–1C–1D no dot in combination with red cyls. 1E or 2E
1/3 Patch on sock of central player (Th. G2), OP
9/2 Black spur on head of right-hand player (Th. B7), OP
14/5 Break in black frame line around players opposite U of CUP, OP
18/1 Black spot to right of stroke of 1/3; also black spot below second R of HARRISON OP
20/1 Black spot below second A of CAPLAN, OP

1s.3d. Cyl. 2E no dot
1/6 Red scratch on face of central player, OP

Sheet Details

Sheet size:
  4d. 120 (20 × 6). Double pane reel-fed
  6d. and 1s.3d. 120 (6 × 20). Single pane sheet-fed
Sheet markings:
  Cylinder numbers:
    4d. Above vertical rows 2/3, boxed
    6d. and 1s.3d. Opposite rows 18/19 at left, boxed
  Guide holes:
    4d. In single photo-etched box above vertical rows 6/7 (no dot) or below (dot). On the no dot pane the box is now lettered "S N", the "S" being on the left in the box (usually trimmed off), and the "N" above the right line. On the dot pane the sequence is reversed.
    6d. and 1s.3d. None
  Marginal arrows (photo-etched): "W" shaped, at top, bottom and sides, except that early printings of the **6d.** from cylinder 1A both ordinary and phosphor were without any arrow markings in the margins. These were later inserted by hand.
    Minimum price for marginal strip showing arrow omitted: £10 Ordinary or phosphor
  Marginal rule:
    4d. At left of sheet
    6d. and 1s.3d. At bottom of sheet
  Colour register marks:
    4d. Above vertical rows 3/4 and 18/19 (no dot) or below (dot)
    6d. and 1s.3d. Above and below vertical rows 1/2 and 6
  Coloured crosses:
    4d. None
    6d. Above and below vertical row 3
    1s.3d. Above and below vertical rows 3/4
  Autotron marks (solid):
    4d. Red, purple, flesh, blue, black below vertical rows 15/18 (no dot) or above (dot)
    6d. and 1s.3d. None
  Colour designations:
    4d. "5 BLACK G4 BLUE MAROON G3 G2 RED G1 LIGHT RED" below vertical rows 11/16 on dot panes only
    6d. and 1s.3d. None
  Traffic lights (boxed):
    4d. Black, blue, red, purple, flesh reading left to right below vertical rows 2/3
    6d. Blue, green, red, sepia, black opposite rows 18/19 at right
    1s.3d. Black, yellow, yellow-olive, blue, red opposite rows 18/19 at right

Imprimaturs from the National Postal Museum Archives

A. Ordinary

Nos. W89/91 imperforate, watermark Type W.24

Watermark upright (6d., 1s.3d.) or sideways (4d.) (*set of* 3)

B. Phosphor

Nos. WP89/91 imperforate, watermark Type W.24

Watermark upright (6d., 1s.3d.) or sideways (4d.) (*set of* 3)

Quantities Sold

	Ordinary	Phosphor
4d.	129,764,160	16,397,880
6d.	17,086,680	3,357,480
1s.3d.	7,026,240	1,761,240
Pack	48,732	—

Withdrawn 31.5.67

W88. Black-headed Gull   **W89.** Blue Tit

W90. Robin   **W91.** Blackbird

(Des. J. Norris Wood)

1966 (AUGUST 8). BRITISH BIRDS

These were the first British stamps to be printed in eight colours. On the blackbird design the black was printed over the bistre.

Issued together in *se-tenant* blocks of four within the sheet

Cat. No.	S.G. No.	Type			Description	Mint	Used

A. Ordinary

W92	696	**W88**			4d. Grey, black, red, emerald-		
a. Block of 4. Nos. W92/5		..	1·00	1·00	green, bright blue,		
Missing colours:					greenish yellow and		
b. Black (value, etc.), blue and					bistre	10	15
bistre	..	..	..	£225			
c. Black (value, etc.)	..	..					
d. Greenish yellow ..	..	..	£400		*h.* Bistre	90·00	
e. Red	..	..	£400		*i.* Watermark inverted	3·00	
f. Emerald-green ..	..	..	75·00		*j.* " HARRISO " omitted (No dot,		
g. Bright blue ..	..	..	£250		R. 15/5)*..	10·00	
W93	697	**W89**			4d. Black, greenish yellow,		
Missing colours:					grey, emerald-green,		
b. Black blue and bistre ..	..	£225			bright blue and bistre	10	15
c. Black	..	..					
d. Greenish yellow ..	..	..	£400				
e. Emerald-green ..	..	..	75·00		*g.* Bistre	90·00	
f. Bright blue	..	..	£250		*i.* Watermark inverted	3·00	
W94	698	**W90**			4d. Red, greenish yellow, black,		
Missing colours:					grey, bistre, reddish		
b. Black, bistre and reddish brown	£225			brown and emerald-		
c. Black	..	..			green	10	15
d. Greenish yellow ..	..	..	£400				
e. Red	..	..	£400				
f. Emerald-green ..	..	..	75·00		*h.* Reddish brown ..	..	80·00	
g. Bistre ..	..	..	90·00		*i.* Watermark inverted	3·00	
W95	699	**W91**			4d. Black, reddish brown,		
Missing colours:					greenish yellow, grey and		
b. Black and reddish brown	..	£225		bistre	10	15
c. Black	..	..					
d. Greenish yellow	..	..	£400				
e. Reddish brown	..	..	80·00				
f. Bistre	..	..	90·00		*i.* Watermark inverted	3·00	

First Day Cover (W92/5)	..	..	6·50
Presentation Pack (W92/5)	..	..	7·00

Cat. No.	S.G. No.	Type			Description				Mint	Used

B. Phosphor

WP92	696p	**W88**			4d. Three bands				10	15
a. Block of 4. Nos. WP92/5			1·00	1·00						
Missing colours:										
b. Emerald-green ..	..	..	75·00		*d.* Bistre	..	..	90·00		
c. Bright blue ..	..	..	£500		*e.* Watermark inverted	..	..	14·00		
WP93	697p	**W89**			4d. Three bands				10	15
Missing colours:										
b. Emerald-green ..	..	..	75·00		*d.* Bistre	..	..	90·00		
c. Bright blue ..	..	..	£500		*e.* Watermark inverted	..	..	14·00		
WP94	698p	**W90**			4d. Three bands				10	15
Missing colours:										
b. Emerald-green ..	..	..	75·00		*d.* Reddish brown ..	..	..	80·00		
c. Bistre ..	..	..	90·00		*e.* Watermark inverted	..	..	14·00		
WP95	699p	**W91**			4d. Three bands				10	15
Missing colour:										
b. Reddish brown	..	.. ..	80·00							
c. Bistre ..	..	.. ..	90·00		*e.* Watermark inverted	..	..	14·00		

> First Day Cover (WP92/5) ..   ..   6·50

Prices for missing colour errors and inverted watermarks in blocks of four:

	Ordinary	Phosphor			Ordinary	Phosphor
Black, bright blue, bistre			Emerald green		£225	£225
and reddish brown ..	£4000	†	Bright blue		£500	£1000
Black	—	†	Bistre		£325	£325
Greenish yellow	£1600	†	Reddish brown		£160	£160
Red	£600	†	Watermark inverted		12·00	60·00

*"HARRISON" is omitted except for fragments of the "N" and on the stamp below (W94) the imprint is very faint, particularly "AND SO". The price is for a block containing both varieties. The damage was quickly discovered and repaired during the early stages of the printing.

These are known postmarked at various places with dates from **17** July due to supplies prematurely released by the Philatelic Bureau.

Cylinder Numbers (Blocks of Eight)

	Cyl. Nos.		Perforation Type F. No dot	
			Ordinary	Phosphor
2A (black)–1B (grey)–1C (yellow)–1D (red)–1E (green)–2F				
(blue)–2G (bistre)–1H (brown)			3·50	3·50
2A (black)–1B (grey)–1C (yellow)–1D (red)–1E (green)–2F				
(blue)–2G (bistre)–2H (brown)			.. 10·00	†

Minor Constant Flaws

4d. Cyls. 2A–1B–1C–1D–1E–2F–2G with 1H or 2H no dot
  1/2 Small brown dot under main twig (Th. B3), OP
  4/3 Small brown dot to right of Robin's tail (Th. B7), OP
  5/1 Small black dot in gull's wing (Th. D5), OP
  6/2 Red spot between blackbird's claws (Th. F6), OP
  7/1 Small black dot in gull's wing (Th. D6), OP
  7/4 Extension to main twig at right (Th. A6), OP
  9/6 Horizontal bistre line above main twig at left (Th. A–B3-4), O

Sheet Details

Sheet size: **120** (6×20). In *se-tenant* blocks of four, single pane sheet-fed
Sheet markings:
  Cylinder numbers: Opposite rows **17/19** at left, boxed
  Guide holes: None
  Marginal arrows (photo-etched): "W" shaped, at top, bottom and sides
  Marginal rule: At bottom of sheet
  Colour register marks: Above and below vertical rows 1/3 and 5/6
  Coloured crosses: Above and below vertical rows 3/4
  Autotron marks and colour designations: None
  Traffic lights (boxed): In same order as cylinder numbers opposite rows 18/19 at right

A number of sheets from the end of the printing run showed part of the design in the left-hand margin by row 20.   This was caused by incomplete masking of the multipositive; touched out before printing, but then wearing through.

Imprimaturs from the National Postal Museum Archives

A. Ordinary

Nos. W92/95 imperforate, watermark Type W.24

Watermark upright (*set of* 4)

B. Phosphor

Nos. WP92/95 imperforate, watermark Type W.24

Watermark upright (*set of* 4)

Quantities Sold

Ordinary 88,047,742; phosphor 14,613,120; Pack (ordinary) 42,888

Withdrawn 7.8.57

W92. Cup Winners
(Des. David Gentleman)

1966 (AUGUST 18). ENGLAND'S WORLD CUP FOOTBALL VICTORY

England won the World Cup Football Competition by defeating West Germany 4–2 at Wembley on 30 July 1966.

Watermark sideways

Cat. No.	S.G. No.	Type		Description	Mint	Used
Ordinary only						
W96	700	**W92**		4d. Red, reddish purple, bright		
a. Patch on thigh (No dot, R. 3/20)			2·00	blue, flesh and black	20	20
b. Red patch below ball (No dot,						
R. 4/16)			2·00			
c. Broken shadow (No dot, R. 5/17)			2·00			

First Day Cover (W96)	2·00

The above was only put on sale at post offices in England, the Channel Islands and the Isle of Man, and the Philatelic Bureau in London and also, on August 22, in Edinburgh on the occasion of the opening of the Edinburgh Festival as well as at Army post offices at home and abroad.

It was also pre-released on 17 August at an Army Camp P.O. in Great Britain.

An example of No. W89 with forged additional inscription on Edinburgh (22 August) first day cover is known.

Listed Varieties

W96*a*, W96*b* and W96*c*. See illustrations after Nos. WP89/91.

Cylinder Numbers (Blocks of Six)

	Cyl. Nos.	Perforation Type A	
		No dot	Dot
4d	1A (black)–1B (blue)–1C (red)–1D (purple)–1E (flesh)* ..	1·75	1·75

*In the no dot pane the flesh cylinder is expressed in error thus: " 1E." and on the dot pane the black cylinder is shown as ".1A."

The above is with sheet orientated showing head to left.

Minor Constant Flaws

4d. Cyls. 1A–1B–1C–1D–1E no dot
  1/15 Black dot in second N of ENGLAND
  2/9 Black spur on left player's right boot (Th. J–K5)
  3/1 Horizontal scratch through top of ball (Th. K1–2)
  5/6 Blue patch below u of Cup
  6/13 White patch on heel of left player's left boot (Th. J3)
  6/18 Blue spots over T of LTD

4d. Cyls. 1A–1B–1C–1D–1E dot
  4/11 Black dot between W and I of WINNERS
  5/10 Dark spot on ball (Th. K1)
  5/17 Grey coloured spur to top of l of World

Sheet Details

Sheet size: 120 (20 × 6). Double pane reel-fed

Sheet markings:
  Cylinder numbers: Above vertical rows 2/3, boxed
  Guide holes: In single "S N" box above vertical rows 6/7 (no dot) or below (dot)
  Marginal arrows (photo-etched): "W" shaped, at top, bottom and sides
  Marginal rule: At left of sheet
  Colour register marks: Above vertical rows 3/4 and 18/19 (no dot) or below (dot)
  Autotron marks (solid): Red, purple, flesh, blue, black below vertical rows 15/18 (no dot) or above (dot)
  Colour designations: "5 BLACK G4 BLUE MAROON G3 G2 RED G1 LIGHT RED" below vertical rows
   11/16 on dot panes only
  Traffic lights (boxed): Black, blue, red, purple, flesh reading left to right below vertical rows 2/3

Imprimatur from the National Postal Museum Archives

Ordinary paper

No. W96 imperforate, watermark Type W.24

Watermark sideways

Quantity Sold 12,452,640

Sold Out Soon after issue

W93. Jodrell Bank Radio Telescope

W94. British Motor-cars

(Des. David and A. Gillespie)

W95. SRN 6 Hovercraft

W96. Windscale Reactor

(Des. Andrew Restall)

1966 (SEPTEMBER 19).   BRITISH TECHNOLOGY

The designs represent British Technological achievements.

Cat. No.	S.G. No.	Type	Description	Mint	Used
A. Ordinary					
W97	701	**W93**	4d. Black and lemon	15	15
a. Struts flaw (No dot, R. 4/6) ..		2·00			
W98	702	**W94**	6d. Red, deep blue and orange	15	15
a. Red (Mini-cars) omitted ..		£4000			
b. Blue (Jaguar and inscr.) omitted		£2500			
			c. Broken " D " (R. 19/6) ..	2·25	
W99	703	**W95**	1s.3d. Black, orange-red, slate and light greenish blue	30	40
W100	704	**W96**	1s.6d. Black, yellow-green, bronze-green, lilac and deep blue	45	50

First Day Cover (W97/100)	..	..	3·00		
Presentation Pack (W97/100)	..	..	7·00		

289

B. Phosphor

WP97	701p	**W93**		
a. Pair, with and without phosphor			15·00	
b. Narrow band at left or right (stamp with vert. margin)			1·50	
WP98	702p	**W94**		
a. Narrow band at left or right (stamp with vert. margin)			1·50	
b. Broken " D " (R. 19/6)			2·50	
WP99	703p	**W95**		
WP100	704p	**W96**		
a. Narrow band at left or right (stamp with vert. margin)			1·50	
b. Two broad bands			20·00	

4d. Three bands	15	15
c. Struts flaw (No dot, R. 4/6)	2·00	
6d. Three bands	15	15
1s.3d. Three bands	45	50
1s.6d. Three bands	65	60

First Day Cover (WP97/100) ..   .. 3·00

Listed Varieties

W97a, WP97c
Strong retouch consisting of three strong
black strokes in the form of an arrow

W98c, WP98b

Cylinder Numbers (Blocks of Six)

(a) Ordinary

Cyl. Nos.	Perforation Type A	
	No dot	Dot
4d. 1A (lemon)–1B (black)	1·50	1·50
6d. 1A (orange)–1B (red)–1C (blue)	1·50	†
1s.3d. 1A (blue)–1B (slate)–1C (orange)–1D (black)	4·00	†
1s.6d. 1A (bronze-green)–1B (lilac)–1C (black)–1D (yellow-green)–1E (blue)	4·25	†

(b) Phosphor

4d. 1A (lemon)–1B (black)	3·00	1·50
6d. 1A (orange)–1B (red)–1C (blue)	1·50	†
1s.3d. 1A (blue)–1B (slate)–1C (orange)–1D (black)	4·25	†
1s.6d. 1A (bronze-green)–1B (lilac)–1C (black)–1D (yellow-green)–1E (blue)	5·00	†

Minor Constant Flaws

4d. Cyls. 1A–1B no dot

  1/1 Lines of retouching above Queen's head resemble a thumb-print (Th. A9–12); also small pale area in left of telescope bowl (Th. C3–4), both OP
  1/2 Retouch to background right of value (Th. B3–4), OP
  1/6 Retouch to background top left corner of stamp (Th. A1), OP
  5/4 Retouch to background in front of Queen's neck (Th. E9), OP
 10/6 Horizontal line of retouching to background behind Queen's head (Th. D12–13), OP
 19/6 Horizontal white line above ON AND SONS of imprint, OP
 20/5 Horizontal white line below portrait (Th. F10–12), OP
 20/6 As 20/5 but stronger line, OP

4d. Cyls. 1A–1B dot

  3/3 Retouch to background in front of Queen's neck (Th. E10), OP
  5/5 White scratch in right of telescope bowl (Th. B6–7), OP
  9/3 Small white patch in background below portrait (Th. F–G12), OP
  9/5 Retouch to background at left of telescope bowl (Th. E–F1), OP
 13/4 Small white patch in background bottom left of portrait (Th. F–G9), OP
 13/5 Pale patch in background to left of telescope bowl (Th. E–F2), OP
 14/6 Yellow spot in right of telescope bowl (Th. D6), OP

6d. Cyls. 1A–1B–1C no dot

  5/6 Retouch to background above Queen's head (Th. A10–11), OP
 10/3 Vertical blue line in Queen's portrait (Th. A–C10), OP
 13/3 Pale area above value (Th. A2), OP
 17/4 Spur of first S of SONS, OP

1s.3d. Cyls. 1A–1B–1C–1D no dot

  1/1 Retouch in background behind Queen's head (Th. C–D13), OP
  1/4 White spot below e of Hovercraft (Th. G7), OP
  1/6 Retouch in sea, bottom centre (Th. G7), OP
 12/6 Horizontal orange coloured line extends from sea to sheet margin (Th. G13–15), OP

1s.6d. Cyls. 1A–1B–1C–1D–1E no dot

  1/3 Retouch in sky in front of Queen's neck (Th. C–D10), OP
  1/5 Grey coloured flaw in sky top right of Queen's head (Th. A13), OP
  2/2 Lower part of left stroke of n of Advanced is broken off, OP
 16/3 Vertical blue line in gutter between design edge and perforation (Th. D–G13), OP
 16/5 Wispy whitish line runs vertically above v of Advanced (Th. F–G2), OP
 20/1 Small white flaw in large door of building (Th. F6), OP

Sheet Details

Sheet size: 120 (6 × 20). 4d. double pane reel-fed; others single pane reel-fed

Sheet markings:

Cylinder numbers:
  4d., 6d., 1s.3d. Opposite R. 19/1, boxed
  1s.6d. Opposite rows 18/19 at left, boxed

Guide holes:
  4d. In single "S N" box opposite rows 14/15, at left (no dot) or right (dot)
  Others. In single "S O N" box opposite rows 14/15, at both sides

Marginal arrows (photo-etched): "W" shaped, at top, bottom and sides

Marginal rule: None

Colour register marks:
  4d. Opposite rows 1/2 and 20, at left (no dot) or right (dot)
  6d., 1s.3d. Opposite rows 2/3 and 17/18, at both sides
  1s.6d. Opposite rows 3/4 and 17/18, at both sides

Autotron marks (solid):
  4d. Black, lemon, opposite row 5, at right (no dot) or left (dot)
  6d. Blue, red, orange below vertical rows 1/3
  1s. 3d. Black, orange, blue, slate below vertical rows 1/3.   Additional black below vertical row 3
  1s 6d. Black, lilac, bronze-green, yellow-green, blue below vertical rows 1/3 and additionally black below vertical row 1.   During printing the correct sequence, black, blue, bronze-green, lilac, yellow-green, was engraved below vertical rows 4/6

Colour designations:
  4d. "G1 YELLOW G2 BLACK" in right margin reading upwards opposite rows 8/5 on dot panes only
  6d. "G2 RED G3 BLUE" in right margin reading upwards opposite rows 7/6
  1s. 3d. "G1 GREY G2 BLUE G3 RED G4 BLACK" in right margin reading upwards opposite rows 7/4
  1s. 6d. "G1 BLUE G2 YELLOW G3 GREEN G4 MAUVE G5 BLACK" in right margin reading upwards opposite rows 9/5

Traffic lights (boxed):
  4d. Lemon, black opposite R. 19/6
  6d. Orange, red, blue opposite R. 19/6
  1s.3d. Blue, slate, orange, black opposite rows 18/19 at right
  1s.6d. Black, lilac, bronze-green, yellow-green, blue opposite rows 18/19 at right

Imprimaturs from the National Postal Museum Archives

A. Ordinary

Nos. W97/100 imperforate, watermark Type W.24

Watermark upright (*set of* 4)

B. Phosphor

Nos. WP97/100 imperforate, watermark Type W.24

Watermark upright (*set of* 4)

Quantities Sold

	Ordinary	Phosphor		Ordinary	Phosphor
4d.	79,112,278	12,737,520	1s.6d.	5,284,069	1,414,320
6d.	11,087,516	2,388,720	Pack	35,437	—
1s.3d.	5,199,900	1,431,000			

Withdrawn   18.9.67 (6d. phosphor sold out earlier)

W97.   W98.

W99.   W100.

W101.   W102.

Types **W97/102** show battle scenes and were issued together *se-tenant* in horizontal strips six within the sheet

W103.   Norman Ship   W104.   Norman Horsemen attacking
                                              Harold's Troops

(Des. David Gentleman)

(Printed in photogravure with the Queen's head die-stamped in gold 6d., 1s.3d.)

1966 (OCTOBER 14).   900th ANNIVERSARY OF BATTLE OF HASTINGS

The scenes depicted are all reproduced from the celebrated Bayeux Tapestry which records the Norman invasion of England.

Watermark sideways on 1s.3d. (normal is top of crown pointing to left when stamps are viewed from the *back*)

Cat. No.	S.G. No.	Type				Description	Mint	Used
A. Ordinary								
W101	705	**W97**				4d. Black, olive-green, bistre,		
a. Strip of 6. Nos. W101/6			..	2·00	2·00	deep blue, orange,		
Missing colours:						magenta, green, blue		
b. Olive-green	..	..	..	25·00		and grey	10	15
c. Bistre ..	..	..	..	25·00				
d. Deep blue		..	..	35·00		*h.* Blue	20·00	
e. Orange ..	..	..	..	25·00		*i.* Blue	20·00	
f. Magenta ..	..	..	..	30·00		*j.* Watermark inverted ..	5·00	
g. Green ..	..	..	..	25·00				
W102	706	**W98**				4d. Black, olive-green,		
Missing colours:						deep blue, orange,		
b. Olive-green	..	..	..	25·00		magenta, green, blue		
c. Bistre ..	..	..	..	25·00		and grey	10	15
d. Deep blue	..	..	..	35·00				
e. Orange ..	..	..	..	25·00		*h.* Blue	20·00	
f. Magenta ..	..	..	..	30·00		*i.* Grey	20·00	
g. Green ..	..	..	..	25·00		*j.* Watermark inverted ..	5·00	
W103	707	**W99**				4d. Black, olive-green, bistre,		
Missing colours:						deep blue, orange,		
b. Olive-green	..	..	..	25·00		magenta, green, blue		
c. Bistre ..	..	..	..	25·00		and grey	10	15
d. Deep blue	..	..	..	35·00				
e. Orange ..	..	..	..	25·00		*h.* Blue	20·00	
f. Magenta ..	..	..	..	30·00		*i.* Grey	20·00	
g. Green ..	..	..	..	25·00		*j.* Watermark inverted ..	5·00	
W104	708	**W100**				4d. Black, olive-green, bistre,		
Missing colours:						deep blue, magenta,		
b. Olive-green	..	..	..	25·00		green, blue and grey	10	15
c. Bistre ..	..	..	..	25·00				
d. Deep blue	..	..	..	35·00		*h.* Blue	20·00	
f. Magenta ..	..	..	..	30·00		*i.* Grey	20·00	
g. Green ..	..	..	..	25·00		*j.* Watermark inverted ..	5·00	
W105	709	**W101**				4d. Black, olive-green, bistre,		
Missing colours:						deep blue, orange,		
b. Olive-green	..	..	..	25·00		magenta, green, blue		
c. Bistre ..	..	..	..	25·00		and grey	10	15
d. Deep blue	..	..	..	35·00				
e. Orange ..	..	..	..	25·00		*h.* Blue	20·00	
f. Magenta ..	..	..	..	30·00		*i.* Grey	20·00	
g. Green ..	..	..	..	25·00		*j.* Watermark inverted ..	5·00	
W106	710	**W102**				4d. Black, olive-green, orange,		
Missing colours:						deep blue, orange,		
b. Olive-green	..	..	..	25·00		magenta, green, blue		
c. Bistre ..	..	..	..	25·00		and grey	10	15
d. Deep blue	..	..	..	35·00				
e. Orange ..	..	..	..	25·00		*h.* Blue	20·00	
f. Magenta ..	..	..	..	30·00		*i.* Grey	20·00	
g. Green ..	..	..	..	25·00		*j.* Watermark inverted ..	5·00	
W107	711	**W103**				6d. Black, olive-green, violet,		
a. Watermark inverted	..	..	35·00			blue, green and gold	10	10
b. Yellowish gold ..		..	..	1·00				
W108	712	**W104**				1s.3d. Black, lilac, bronze-		
a. Lilac omitted ..		..	..	£450		green, rosine, bistre-		
b. Watermark sideways inverted						brown and gold	20	20
(top of crown pointing to right)			30·00					
c. Club flaw (R. 7/2)		..	..	4·00				

First Day Cover (W101/8)	..	..	3·00
Presentation Pack (W101/8)	..	..	7·00

Cat. No.	S.G. No.	Type	Description	Mint	Used

B. Phosphor

WP101   705p   **W97**   4d. Three bands   10   25

   a. Strip of 6. Nos. WP101/6   ..   2·00   2·00
   Missing colours:
   b. Olive-green   ..   ..   ..   25·00   *g.* Green   ..   ..   25·00
   c. Bistre   ..   ..   30·00   *h.* Blue   ..   ..   35·00
   d. Deep blue   ..   ..   ..   35·00   *i.* Grey   ..   ..   ..   20·00
   e. Orange   ..   ..   ..   20·00   *j.* Magenta and green   ..   ..
   f. Magenta ..   ..   30·00   *k.* Watermark inverted   ..   ..   2·00

WP102   706p   **W98**   4d. Three bands   10   25

   Missing colours:
   b. Olive-green   ..   ..   ..   25·00   *g.* Green   ..   ..   25·00
   c. Bistre   ..   ..   30·00   *h.* Blue   ..   ..   35·00
   d. Deep blue   ..   ..   ..   35·00   *i.* Grey   ..   ..   ..   20·00
   e. Orange   ..   ..   ..   20·00   *j.* Magenta and green   ..   ..
   f. Magenta ..   ..   30·00   *k.* Watermark inverted   ..   ..   2·00

WP103   707p   **W99**   4d. Three bands   10   25

   Missing colours:
   b. Olive-green   ..   ..   ..   25·00   *g.* Green   ..   ..   25·00
   c. Bistre   ..   ..   30·00   *h.* Blue   ..   ..   ..   35·00
   d. Deep blue   ..   ..   ..   35·00   *i.* Grey   ..   ..   ..   20·00
   e. Orange   ..   ..   ..   20·00   *j.* Magenta and green   ..   ..
   f. Magenta ..   ..   30·00   *k.* Watermark inverted   ..   ..   2·00

WP104   708p   **W100**   4d. Three bands   10   25

   Missing colours:
   b. Olive-green   ..   ..   ..   25·00   *g.* Green   ..   ..   ..   25·00
   c. Bistre   ..   ..   ..   30·00   *h.* Blue   ..   ..   ..   35·00
   d. Deep blue   ..   ..   35·00   *i.* Grey   ..   ..   ..   20·00
   f. Magenta ..   ..   ..   30·00   *j.* Magenta and green   ..   ..
        k. Watermark inverted   ..   ..   2·00

WP105   709p   **W101**   4d. Three bands   10   25

   Missing colours:
   b. Olive-green   ..   ..   ..   25·00   *g.* Green   ..   ..   ..   25·00
   c. Bistre   ..   ..   ..   30·00   *h.* Blue   ..   ..   ..   35·00
   d. Deep blue   ..   ..   35·00   *i.* Grey   ..   ..   ..   20·00
   e. Orange   ..   ..   ..   20·00   *j.* Magenta and green   ..   ..
   f. Magenta ..   ..   30·00   *k.* Watermark inverted   ..   2·00

WP106   710p   **W102**   4d. Three bands   10   25

   Missing colours:
   b. Olive-green   ..   ..   ..   25·00   *g.* Green   ..   ..   ..   25·00
   c. Bistre   ..   ..   ..   30·00   *h.* Blue   ..   ..   ..   35·00
   d. Deep blue   ..   ..   35·00   *i.* Grey   ..   ..   ..   20·00
   e. Orange   ..   ..   ..   20·00   *j.* Magenta and green   ..   ..
   f. Magenta ..   ..   30·00   *k.* Watermark inverted   ..   ..   2·00

WP107   711p   **W103**   6d. Three bands   10   10

   a. Watermark inverted   ..   ..   45·00
   b. Yellowish gold ..   ..   ..   1·00

WP108   712p   **W104**   1s.3d. Four bands   20   20

   a. Lilac omitted £650
   b. Three bands   ..   ..   7·00
   c. Watermark sideways inverted
     (top of crown pointing to right)   11·00   *d.* Club flaw (R. 7/2)   ..   ..   4·00

> First Day Cover (WP101/8)   ..   ..   3·00

4d. *Prices for missing colour errors and inverted watermarks in strips of six:*

	Ordinary	Phosphor		Ordinary	Phosphor
Olive-green	£150	£150	Green	£150	£150
Bistre	£150	£180	Blue	£120	£225
Deep blue	£225	£225	Grey	£120	£120
Orange (on five stamps) ..	£125	£100	Magenta and green	†	—
Magenta	£180	£150	Watermark inverted	35·00	15·00

Nos. W101 and W105 with grey and blue omitted have been seen commercially used, posted from Middleton-in-Teesdale.

The 6d. and 1s.3d. were also issued with the die-stamped gold head omitted but as these can also be removed by chemical means we are not prepared to list them unless a way is found of distinguishing the genuine stamps from the fakes which will satisfy the Expert Committees. However, three examples of No. W108 in a right-hand top corner block of 10 (2 × 5) are known with the Queen's head omitted as a result of a double paper fold prior to die-stamping. The perforation is normal. Of the other seven stamps, four have the Queen's head misplaced and three are normal.

Listed Variety

W108c, WP108d

The fallen knight has what appears to be a
large black club at his right hand

Cylinder Numbers (Blocks of Twenty-Four (4d.), Six (6d.), Eight (1s.3d.))

		Cyl. Nos	Perforation Types F No dot	
			Ordinary	Phosphor
4d.	1A (black)–1B (olive-green)–1C (bistre)–1D (deep blue)– 1E (orange)–1F (magenta)–1G (green)–1H (blue)–1J (grey)		10·00	8·00
	2A (black)–1B (olive-green)–1C (bistre)–1D (deep blue)– 1E (orange)–1F (magenta)–1G (green)–1H (blue)–1J (grey)		8·00	†

			G			
			No dot	Dot	No dot	Dot
			Ordinary		Phosphor	
6d.	1A (black)–1B (olive-green)–1C (violet)–1D (blue 1E (green)		1·00	1·00	1·00	1·00

			A(T) No dot	
			Ordinary	Phosphor
1s.3d.	1A (black)–1B (lilac)–1C (bronze-green)–1D (rosine)– 1E (bistre-brown)		5·50*	5·50*

Minor Constant Flaws

4d. Cyls. 1B–1C–1D–1E–1F–1G–1H–1J no dot in combination with black cyls. 1A or 2A
3/4 Spur on second S of HASTINGS, OP
4/1 Horizontal black line to left of Queen's forehead (Th. A10–11), OP (1A only)
4/5 Black line under Queen's chin (Th. C11), OP (1A only)
9/1 Right hind leg of dark horse is paler than normal (Th. F–G8), OP
9/2 Second S of SONS pale and distorted, possibly hand drawn (OP) (1A only)
19/4 White spot on horseman's leg (Th. F7), OP
20/3 LTD heavier than normal, OP (1A only)
20/4 HARRISON AND heavier than normal, OP (1A only)

4d. Cyl. 2A no dot
10/1 H of HARRISON is indistinct, O
11/1 Hastings 1066 weaker than normal, O

6d. Cyls. 1A–1B–1C–1D–1E no dot
1/1 Blue patch on hull due to lack of black shading (Th. F9) OP
4/1 Small dot after final s of Hastings, OP
6/1 Diagonal black line through figures in small boat (Th. C3–B5), OP
8/4 diagonal spur on first t of Battle, OP

6d. Cyls. 1A–1B–1C–1D–1E dot
1/1 Partial break in main left-hand rigging of main vessel (Th. D3), OP
3/1 Extra gold enlarges Queen's throat at both sides (Th. C–D12), P
8/5 Horizontal black line in upper part of first 6 of 1966, OP
8/6 Horizontal black line through HAR of HARRISON, OP

1s.3d. Cyls. 1A–1B–1C–1D–1E no dot
6/2 Dot in g of Hastings, OP
8/1 Diagonal hairline runs from bottom of red shield of second soldier through toes of right foot to bottom of stamp (Th. E–H12), O
9/1 Line continues to right-hand arm of first soldier (Th. A12), O
10/4 Bronze-green dot upper left of 1 of 1/3 (Th. F8), OP

Sheet Details

Sheet sizes:
4d. 120 (6 × 20). In *se-tenant* strips of six, single pane sheet-fed
6d. 60 (6 × 10). Double pane reel-fed
1s.3d. 60 (6 × 10). Single pane reel-fed

Sheet markings:
  Cylinder numbers:
    4d. Opposite rows 17/19 at left, boxed
    6d. Opposite rows 8/9 at left, boxed
    1s.3d. Opposite rows 7/8 at left, boxed
  Guide holes: None
  Marginal arrows (photo-etched): " W " shaped, at top bottom and sides
  Marginal rule: None
  Colour register marks:
    4d. Above and below vertical rows 1 and 5/6
    6d. Above vertical rows 1 and 5/6 (no dot) or below them (dot)
    1s.3d. Opposite rows 1/2 and 9/10, at both sides
  Coloured crosses:
    4d. Above and below vertical rows 3/4
    6d. Above vertical rows 3/4 (no dot) or below them (dot)
    1s.3d. Opposite rows 5/6, at both sides
  Autotron marks and colour designations: None
  Traffic lights (boxed and in same order as cylinder numbers):
    4d. Opposite rows 17/19 at right
    6d. Opposite rows 8/9 at right
    1s.3d. Opposite rows 7/8 at right

Imprimaturs from the National Museum Archives

A. Ordinary

Nos. W107/108 imperforate, watermark Type W.24

Watermark upright (6d.) or sideways (1s.3d.) (2 *values only*)

B. Phosphor

No. WP107 imperforate, watermark Type W.24

Watermark upright (6d.)

Quantities Sold

	Ordinary	Phosphor
4d.	89,197,226	15,861,960
6d.	12,012,328	2,820,360
1s.3d.	5,721,426	1,646,280
Pack	51,332	—

Withdrawn   13.10.67 (6d. phosphor sold out in September)

W105. King of the Orient   **W106.** Snowman

(Des. Miss Tasveer Shemza)   (Des. James Berry)

(Printed in photogravure with the Queen's head die-stamped in gold)

1966 (DECEMBER 1).   CHRISTMAS

These designs, executed by two six-year-old children, were chosen frcm nearly 5,000 entries in a Post Office competition for Britain's first adhesive Christmas stamps.

Watermark sideways on 3d.

Cat. No.	S.G. No.	Type		Description	Mint	
A. Ordinary						
W109	713	**W105**		3d. Black, blue, green, yellow, red and gold	10	10
a. Queen's head double	..	..				
b. Green omitted ..		— £150				
c. Missing " T " (No dot, R. 6/2)..	2·00					
W110	714	**W106**		1s.6d. Blue, red, pink, black and gold	35	35
a. Pink (hat) omitted	..	..	£750			
b. Watermark inverted	..	..	9·00			

First Day Cover (W109/10)	..	..	1·50
Presentation Pack (W109/10)	..	..	7·00

The one phosphor band on No. WP109 was produced by printing broad phosphor bands across alternate vertical rows of perforations. Individual examples show the band at right or left (*same prices either way*).

B. Phosphor

WP109	713p	**W105**			3d. One band at left	10	10
a. Band at right ..	..	..	..	10	10		
ab. Nos. WP109/a (horiz. pair)	..	20					
ac. Pair, with and without phosphor	10·00			b. Missing "T" (No dot, R. 6/2) ..	2·00		
WP110	714p	**W106**			1s.6d. Two bands	35	35
a. Watermark inverted	..	..	38·00				

First Day Cover (WP109/10)	..	..	1·50

Listed Variety

W109*c*, WP109*b*

Both values were also issued with the die-stamped gold head omitted but as these can also be removed by chemical means we are not prepared to list them unless a way is found of distinguishing the genuine stamps from the fakes which will satisfy the Expert Committees. However, the gold head and embossing omitted also occurred on the last vertical row of a sheet of the 3d. ordinary due to a major displacement to the left. Examples in horizontal marginal pairs can be considered to be genuine. Another example shows two gold head omissions, due to a paper fold, with three partial gold heads on the gummed side.

No. WP109 exists with a horizontal phosphor band across the top of the stamp. This was caused by phosphor spillage under the doctor blade and occurred on the top horizontal row of a sheet.

Cylinder Numbers (Blocks of Six)

(a) Ordinary

	Cyl. Nos.		Perforation Types	
			A	A
			No dot	Dot
3d.	1A (blue)–2B (black)–1C (green)–1D (yellow)–1E (red)	..	16·00	16·00
	1A (blue)–3B (black)–1C (green)–1D (yellow)–1E (red)	..	1·00	1·00
	1A (blue)–4B (black)–1C (green)–1D (yellow)–1E (red)	..	1·00	1·00

			A	A(T)
			No dot	No dot
1s.6d.	1A (blue)–1B (black)–2C (red)–1D (pink)		4·00	4·00

(b) Phosphor

	Cyl. Nos.		Perforation Types	
			A	A
			No dot	Dot
3d.	1A (blue)–3B (black)–1C (green)–1D (yellow)–1E (red)	..	1·00	1·00
	1A (blue)–4B (black)–1C (green)–1D (yellow)–1E (red)	..	1·00	1·00

			A	A(T)
			No dot	No dot
1s.6d.	1A (blue)–1B (black)–2C (red)–1D (pink)		4·00	4·00

The above are with sheets orientated showing head to left.
In the dot panes of the 3d. the dot is missing after B in the black colour.

Minor Constant Flaws

3d. Cyls. 1A–1C–1D–1E no dot in combination with black cyls. 3B or 4B
    2/1 During the course of printing a diagonal cut developed at base of Queen's neck and later the piece of gold foil separated and dropped downwards (Th. C–D5), OP
    2/3 Blue dot in front of H of HARRISON, OP
    2/8 A of AND in imprint shorter than normal, OP
    3/4 White patch at top left corner of panel is larger than normal (Th. A1), OP
    3/8 Extra stop after T. of T. SHEMZA, OP
    7/1 Damaged top to A of AND, OP
    8/8 Red dot under first leg of H of HARRISON, OP

3d. Cyls. 1A–1C–1D–1E dot in combination with black cyls. 3B or 4B
    1/5 Two red dots in the yellow above red circle in crown (Th. F–G3), OP (3B only)
    2/1 As for no dot cyls.
    4/6 Background retouch between points of crown at right (Th. F5), OP
    4/7 First S of SONS incomplete, OP
    5/5 Red spot in white area below Queen's portrait (Th. D5), OP (3B only)
    8/1 Top of S of HARRISON incomplete, OP

1s.6d. Cyls. 1A–1B–2C–1D no dot
    3/1 White spot normally found in red scarf is filled in (Th. E4), OP
    6/7 Dark blue spot inside 6 of 1/6, OP
    8/2 Small blue projection into right-hand margin (Th. L7), OP
    9/1 Second R of BERRY is damaged, OP

Sheet Details

Sheet size: 80 (8 × 10)
    3d. double pane reel-fed, with dot pane above no dot pane
    1s.6d. single pane sheet-fed
Sheet markings:
    Cylinder numbers:
        3d. Above vertical rows 2/3, boxed
        1s.6d. Opposite R. 8/1, boxed
    Guide holes: 3d. Boxed above vertical rows 6/7; 1s.6d. none
    Marginal arrows (photo-etched): " W " shaped, at top, bottom and sides
    Marginal rule: None
    Colour register marks:
        3d. None; 1s.6d. above and below vertical rows 1/2 and 7/8
    Coloured crosses: 3d. None; 1s.6d. above and below vertical rows 4/5
    Autotron marks (solid):
        3d. Green, yellow, red, black, blue opposite rows 8/10, left margin (dot); 1s.6d. none
    Colour designations: None
    Traffic lights (boxed):
        3d. Black, blue, green, yellow, red below vertical rows 2/3
        1s.6d. Blue, red, pink, black opposite R. 8/10

Imprimaturs from the National Postal Museum Archives

A. Ordinary

Nos. W109/110 imperforate, watermark Type W.24

Watermark upright (1s.6d.) or sideways (3d.) (*set of* 2)

B. Phosphor

Nos. WP109/110 imperforate, watermark Type W.24

Watermark upright (1s.6d.) or sideways (3d.) (*set of* 2)

Quantities Sold

	Ordinary	Phosphor
3d.	153,318,160	20,774,000
1s.6d.	8,756,960	2,109,280
Pack	33,672	—

Withdrawn

The 3d. phosphor was sold out in January, the 3d ordinary and 1s.6d. phosphor were sold out in October, and the 1s.6d. ordinary was withdrawn on 30.11.67

W107. Sea Freight   **W108.** Air Freight

(Des. Clive Abbott)

1967 (FEBRUARY 20).   EUROPEAN FREE TRADE ASSOCIATION

Issued to commemorate the movement of trade between Austria, Denmark, Norway, Portugal, Sweden, Switzerland and the United Kingdom. Finland was an associate member.

Cat. No.	S.G. No.	Type	Description	Mint	Used
A. Ordinary					
WIII	715	**W107**	9d. Deep blue, red, lilac, green, brown, new blue, yellow and black	15	15

Missing colours
a. Black (Queen's head), brown, new blue and yellow £650
b. Lilac .. .. 60·00
c. Green .. .. 40·00
d. Brown .. .. 45·00
e. New blue.. .. .. 42·00
f. Yellow .. .. 42·00
g. Watermark inverted .. .. 20·00
h. Quay flaw (R. 8/3) .. .. .. 3·00

| WII2 | 716 | **W108** | 1s.6d. Violet, red, deep blue, brown, green, blue-grey, new blue, yellow and black | 30 | 30 |

Missing colours:
a. Red .. .. ..
b. Deep blue £225
c. Brown .. .. .. 45·00
d. Blue-grey .. .. .. 45·00
e. New blue .. .. .. 45·00
f. Yellow .. .. .. 45·00

g. Broken ribbon (R. 11/3) .. 3·50
h. Broken strut (R. 13/6) .. .. 3·00
j. Break in frame (R. 20/1) .. 3·00

First Day Cover (WIII/12)	..	..	1·50
Presentation Pack (WIII/12)	..	..	1·50

B. Phosphor (9d. applied flexo.; 1s.6d. applied typo.)

WPIII	715p	**W107**	9d. Three bands	15	15

Missing colours:
a. Lilac .. .. 75·00
b. Green .. .. 45·00
c. Brown .. .. 45·00
d. New blue.. .. .. 45·00
e. Yellow .. .. 75·00
f. Watermark inverted .. .. .. 10·00
g. Quay flaw (R. 8/3) .. .. .. 2·00

WPII2	716p	**W108**	1s.6d. Three bands	30	30

Missing colours:
a. Red .. ..
b. Deep blue £200
c. Brown .. .. 45·00
d. Blue-grey.. .. .. .. 45·00
e. New blue.. .. .. .. 45·00
f. Watermark inverted .. .. .. 22·00

g. Broken ribbon (R. 11/3) .. .. 3·50
h. Broken strut (R.13/6) .. .. 3·00
j. Break in frame (R. 20/1) .. .. 3·00
k. "All over" phosphor .. .. ..

First Day Cover (WPIII/12)	..	..	1·50

No. WPII2k came from the first vertical column of a sheet. It was due to a weak mixture of the phosphor ink which leaked under the phosphor doctor blade.

Listed Varieties

W111*h*, WP111*g*
Black protuberance on
quay between trucks

Normal   W112*g*, WP112*g*

W112*h*, WP112*h*
Broken strut below wing

W112*j*, WP112*j*
Break in the frame
of Portuguese flag

Cylinder Numbers (Blocks of Eight)

Cyl. Nos.

Perforation Type
F No dot

		Ordinary	Phosphor
9d.	1A (deep blue)–1B (red)–1C (lilac)–1D (green)–		
	1E (brown)–1F (new blue)–1G (yellow)–1H (black)	2·00	2·00
1s.6d.	2A (violet)–1B (red)–1C (deep blue)–1D (green)–		
	1E (brown)–1F (new blue)–1G (yellow)–2H (blue-		
	grey)–2J (black)	5·50*	5·00*

Minor Constant Flaws

9d. Cyls. 1A–1B–1C–1D–1E–1F–1G–1H no dot
  6/5 Black colour on roof of bridge is smudged (Th. D8–9), OP
  11/5 Small blue dot in base of letter E (Th. B–C2) OP
  12/5 White spot in lilac superstructure (Th. E11), OP

1s.6d. Cyls. 2A–1B–1C–1D–1E–1F–1G–2H–2J no dot
  10/1 Small violet dot in top of letter E (Th. A2), OP
  19/1 White spur in 6 of 1/6, OP

Sheet Details

Sheet size: 120 (6 × 20). Single pane sheet-fed
Sheet markings:
  Cylinder numbers:
    9d. Opposite rows 17/19 at left, boxed
    1s.6d. Opposite rows 17/20 at left, boxed
  Guide holes: None
  Marginal arrows (photo-etched): "W" shaped, at top, bottom and side.
  Marginal rule: At bottom of sheet
  Colour register marks: Above and below vertical rows 1/2 and 5/6
  Coloured crosses Above and below vertical rows 4/5
  Autotron marks and colour designations: None
  Traffic lights (boxed):
    9d. Opposite rows 17/19 at right, in same order as cylinder numbers
    1s.6d. Violet, red, deep blue, brown, green, blue-grey, new blue, yellow, black opposite rows 17/19 at
    right

Imprimaturs from the National Postal Museum Archives

A. Ordinary

Nos. W111/112 imperforate, watermark Type W.24

Watermark upright (*set of* 2)

B. Phosphor

Nos. WP111/112 imperforate, watermark Type W.24

Watermark upright (*set of* 2)

Quantities Sold

	Ordinary	Phosphor
9d.	6,553,738	5,557,104
1s.6d.	6,363,483	4,237,944
Pack	42,906	—

Withdrawn 19.2.68

W109. Hawthorn and Bramble

W110. Larger Bindweed and Viper's
Bugloss

W111. Ox-eye Daisy, Coltsfoot and
Buttercup

W112. Bluebell, Red Campion and
Wood Anemone

The above were issued together *se-tenant* in blocks of four within the sheet
(Des. Rev. W. Keble Martin)

W113. Dog Violet

W114. Primroses

(Des. Mary Grierson)

1967 (APRIL 24). BRITISH WILD FLOWERS

Cat. No.	S.G. No.	Type		Description	Mint	Used
A. Ordinary						
W113	717	**W109**		4d. Grey, lemon, myrtle-green,		
a. Block of 4. Nos. W113/16..		.. 1·25	1·25	red, agate and slate-		
b. Grey double* ..	..	.. ..		purple	15	10
c. Red omitted ..	..	.. £1500				
d. Watermark inverted		.. .. 1·50		*e.* Slate-purple omitted		
W114	718	**W110**		4d. Grey, lemon, myrtle-green,		
b. Grey double*	..	.. ..		red, agate and violet	15	10
d. Watermark inverted		.. .. 1·50				
W115	719	**W111**		4d. Grey, lemon, myrtle-green,		
b. Grey double* ..		.. ..		red and agate	15	10
d. Watermark inverted	..	.. 1·50				
W116	720	**W112**		4d. Grey, lemon, myrtle-green,		
b. Grey double* ..		.. ..		reddish purple, agate		
c. Reddish purple omitted		.. £950		and violet	15	10
d. Watermark inverted	..	.. 1·50				
W117	721	**W113**		9d. Lavender-grey, green,		
a. Watermark inverted	..	.. 75		reddish violet and		
b. Notch in leaf (R. 20/2)	..	... 4·00		orange-yellow	15	10
W118	722	**W114**		1s.9d. Lavender-grey, green,		
				greenish yellow and		
				orange	20	20

First Day Cover (W113/18) ..	..	2·50
Presentation Pack (W113/18) ..	..	2·00

Cat. No.	S.G. No.	Type	Description	Mint	Used

B. Phosphor

WP113   717p   **W109**   4d. Three bands   10   10
  a. Block of 4. Nos. WP113/16   ..   70   80
  b. Agate omitted..   ..   ..   ..   £900
  c. Slate-purple omitted £150
  d. Watermark inverted   ..   ..   1·50

WP114   718p   **W110**   4d. Three bands   10   10
  b. Agate omitted..   ..   ..   ..   £450
  c. Violet omitted..   ..   ..   £1250
  d. Watermark inverted   ..   ..   1·50

WP115   719p   **W111**   4d. Three bands   10   10
  b. Agate omitted..   ..   ..   ..   £450
  c. Watermark inverted   ..   ..   1·50

WP116   720p   **W112**   4d. Three bands   10   10
  b. Agate omitted..   ..   ..   ..   £450
  c. Violet omitted..   ..   ..   £1250
  d. Watermark inverted   ..   ..   1·50

WP117   721p   **W113**   9d. Three bands   10   10
  a. Notch in leaf (R. 20/2)   ..   ..   4·00

WP118   722p   **W114**   1s.6d. Three bands   30   20

First Day Cover (WP113/18)	2·50
Presentation Pack (WP113/18)	3·00

4d. *Prices for missing colour errors and inverted watermarks in blocks of four:*

	Ordinary	Phosphor		Ordinary	Phosphor
Red	£1500	†	Violet	†	—
Reddish purple	£1000	†	Slate purple	—	—
Agate	†	£1800	Watermark inverted ..	7·00	7·00

*The double impression of the grey printing affects the Queen's head, value and inscription.

The 1s.9d. is known postmarked 20 April in the Bristol area.

Listed Variety

W117*b*, WP117*a*

Cylinder Numbers (Blocks of Eight (4d.) or Six (others))

<table>
<tr><td></td><td colspan="2">Cyl. Nos.</td><td colspan="2">Perforation Types
F No dot</td></tr>
<tr><td></td><td></td><td></td><td>Ordinary</td><td>Phosphor</td></tr>
<tr><td>4d.</td><td>3A (grey)–1B (lemon)–2C (myrtle-green)–1D (reddish
purple)–1E (red)–1F (agate)–2G (violet)–1H (slate-purple)</td><td></td><td>2·50</td><td>2·00</td></tr>
<tr><td></td><td>3A (grey)–1B (lemon)–3C (myrtle-green)–1D (reddish
purple)–1E (red)–1F (agate)–2G (violet)–1H (slate-purple)</td><td></td><td>†</td><td>18·00</td></tr>
<tr><td></td><td></td><td></td><td colspan="2">A No dot</td></tr>
<tr><td>9d.</td><td>2A (lavender-grey)–3B (green)–3C (reddish violet)–
2D (orange-yellow) ..   ..</td><td></td><td>4·00*</td><td>4·00*</td></tr>
<tr><td>1s.9d.</td><td>2A (lavender-grey)–2B (green)–2C (greenish yellow)–
2D (orange) ..   ..</td><td></td><td>2·00</td><td>4·00</td></tr>
</table>

Minor Constant Flaws

4d. Cyls. 3A–1B–2C–1D–1E–1F–2G–1H no dot
  1/4 Green flaw in large leaf above flower (Th. A4), OP
  4/6 Yellow spot by Queen's chin (Th. C10), P
  8/6 Small spot by upper leaf of wood anemone (Th. A6), OP
  10/2 Small green spot in lower wood anemone (Th. D9), OP
  15/6 Style on left-hand flower of right-hand plant is incomplete (Th. A6), OP
  16/2 Green spot at left of bluebell leaf (Th. E1), P

9d. Cyls. 2A–3B–3C–2D no dot
  9/6 Diagonal hairline running down from small right-hand leaf (Th. F10), OP
  13/5 Green spot between left leaf and centre violet flower (Th. D3), OP
  14/1 Fine vertical yellow line at right of right-hand leaf on top left-hand stamen (Th. B–C3), OP
  20/6 Green spot in lower left-hand leaf (Th. G1), OP

1s.9d. Cyls. 2A–2B–2C–2D no dot
  1/2 Diagonal yellow hairline in the white portion from Queen's neck to top of value (Th. C–E11), OP
  1/6 Retouch between top of stroke and 9 of value (Th. F12), OP
  2/2 Retouch over 9 of value (Th. F13), OP
  10/1 M of MARY is weak, OP
  15/1 Line of green dots between two right-hand primroses (Th. E9), OP
  19/4 Dotted green line projecting left from top left-hand leaf (Th. C–D1), OP
  19/5 Horizontal green hairline on central primrose (Th. D4), OP
  19/6 N of HARRISON is weak, OP
  20/1 Break in outline of petals in topmost primrose (Th. B7), OP

Sheet Details

Sheet size: 120 (6 × 20)
  4d. In *se-tenant* blocks of four, single pane sheet-fed
  9d. and 1s.9d. Single pane reel-fed
Sheet markings:
  Cylinder numbers:
    4d. Opposite rows 17/19 at left, boxed
    9d., 1s.9d. Opposite rows 18/19 at left, boxed
  Guide holes:
    4d. None
    9d., 1s.9d. Opposite row 15 (boxed), at both sides
  Marginal arrows (photo-etched): "W" shaped at top, bottom and sides
  Marginal rule: At bottom of sheet
  Colour register marks:
    4d. Above and below vertical rows 1/2 and 5/6
    9d., 1s.9d. Opposite rows 1/2 and 20, at both sides
  Coloured crosses:
    4d. Above and below vertical rows 3/4
    9d., 1s.9d. None
  Autotron marks (solid):
    4d. None
    9d. Lavender-grey, green, reddish violet, green over orange, below vertical rows 1/3
    1s 9d. Lavender-grey, orange, green, greenish yellow, below vertical rows 1/3
  Colour designations:
    4d. None
    9d. "G1 GREEN G2 MAUVE G3 ORANGE G4 GREY" in right margin reading upwards opposite
      rows 9/3
    1s.9d. "G1 YELLOW G2 GREEN G3 ORANGE G4 GREY" in right margin reading upwards opposite
      rows 13/7
  Traffic lights (boxed and in same order as cylinder numbers):
    4d. Opposite rows 17/19 at right
    9d., 1s.9d. Opposite rows 18/19 at right

Imprimaturs from the National Postal Museum Archives

A. Ordinary

Nos. W117/118 imperforate, watermark Type W.24

Watermark upright (2 *values only*)

B. Phosphor

Nos. WP117/118 imperforate, watermark Type W.24

Watermark upright (2 *values only*)

Quantities Sold

	Ordinary	Phosphor
4d.	78,331,778	37,133,952
9d.	5,873,042	5,701,608
1s.9d.	3,259,521	4,929,648
Pack (including ordinary and phosphor)	53,446	

Withdrawn 23.4.68

PHOSPHOR BANDS. All the following commemorative issues were normally issued with phosphor bands only; however, most also exist with phosphor omitted in error.

W115. "Master Lambton"
(Sir Thomas Lawrence)

W116. "Mares and Foals in a
Landscape" (George Stubbs)

W117. "Children Coming Out of
School" (L. S. Lowry)

(Des. Stuart Rose)

1967 (JULY 10).   BRITISH PAINTINGS

This is the first issue of British Paintings for which Harrisons made photographs from the originals.

No watermark.   Two phosphor bands, applied by flexography

Cat. No.	S.G. No.	Type		Description	Mint	Used
W119	748	**W115**		4d. Rose-red, lemon, brown,		
a. Gold omitted (value and Queen's				black, new blue and gold	10	10
head)			£180			
b. New blue omitted		.. ..	£2500	c. Phosphor omitted	5·00	
W120	749	**W116**		9d. Venetian red, ochre, grey-		
a. Black omitted (Queen's head and				black, new blue, greenish		
value)			£400	yellow and black	20	20
b. Greenish yellow omitted		..	£1200			
c. Phosphor omitted		..	£450	d. One broad band	15·00	
W121	750	**W117**		1s.6d. Greenish yellow, grey,		
a. Gold omitted (Queen's head)..			£750	rose, new blue, grey-		
b. New blue omitted		.. ..	£140	black and gold	35	25
c. Grey omitted ..		.. ..	85·00			
d. Phosphor omitted		.. ..	£300	f. Extra window (No dot, R. 9/1)..	3·00	
e. One broad band		.. ..	6·00			

First Day Cover (W119/21)	..	..	1·50
Presentation Pack (W119/21)	..	..	5·50

The 9d. also exists with Queen's head only omitted, and also with value at right of Queen's head but they are due to a major colour shift.

All values were put on sale in error on 30 June at the Lincoln head post office.

Listed Variety

W121*f*

Cylinder Numbers (Blocks of Four (4d.) or Six (others))

	Cyl. Nos.	Perforation Type A(T)	
		No dot	Dot
4d.	3A (gold)–1B (lemon)–1C (rose-red)–1D (new blue)–1E (brown)–1F (black)	90	90
	3A (gold)–1B (lemon)–2C (rose-red)–1D (new blue)–1E (brown)–1F (black)	90	90
	4A (gold)–1B (lemon)–1C (rose-red)–1D (new blue)–1E (brown)–1F (black)	90	90
	4A (gold)–1B (lemon)–2C (rose-red)–1D (new blue)–1E (brown)–1F (black)	90	90
	5A (gold)–1B (lemon)–2C (rose-red)–1D (new blue)–1E (brown)–1F (black)	90	90
9d.	2A (black)–1B (greenish yellow)–1C (Venetian red)–1D (ochre)–1E (new blue)–3F (grey-black)	1·75	1·75
1s.6d.	2A (grey-black)–1B (greenish yellow)–1C (rose)–1D (new blue)–1E (grey)–1F (gold)	3·50	3·50

The 4d. is with sheet orientated showing head to right. In the 4A dot pane the dot is omitted for the gold cylinder and it appears before the C in the rose-red cylinder.

In the 9d. the greenish yellow 1B is very faint in the dot pane and is sometimes almost invisible. Also in the dot pane the dot appears before the 2A.

In the 1s.6d. dot pane the dot appears before the 1F.

Minor Constant Flaws

4d. Cyls. 1B–2C–1D–1E–1F in combination with gold cyls. 3A, 4A or 5A no dot
2/1 Two small dots on boy's left leg (Th. K6, L6)
3/1 Gold dot on boy's right collar (Th. F5)
5/4 Dark spot on right leg of boy's breeches (Th. I4)

4d. Cyls 1B–2C–1D–1E–1F in combination with gold cyls. 3A, 4A or 5A dot
1/11 Red spot in left gutter, sometimes lost in perforations (Th. JO)
2/11 Small red spot on boy's right collar (Th. E5)
3/4 Small spot in the "V" of boy's collar (Th. F5)
5/3 Dark spot on inside of boy's left elbow (Th. F7)

9d. Cyls. 2A–1B–1C–1D–1E–3F no dot
3/1 Break in first S of STUBBS
4/3 Dark spot in foliage of lower centre branch (Th. C5)
7/1 Dark spot between right-hand foal's forelegs (Th. G7) and another in the grass just below (Th. H7)

9d. Cyls. 2A–1B–1C–1D–1E–3F dot
2/5 Slight nick in upright stroke of d of value
9/3 Small retouch in sky above white horse (Th. D10)
10/1 Break in first R of HARRISON
11/1 Dark dot below horse's hind hoof in bottom left corner (Th. H1)

1s.6d. Cyls. 2A–1B–1C–1D–1E–1F no dot
1/1 Circular patch in building below 1 of value (Th. C2)
1/5 Small dot by leg of foreground figure left of centre (Th. I6)
9/4 Small spot above roof of small house in side street (Th. E9)

1s.6d. Cyls. 2A–1B–1C–1D–1E–1F dot
1/1 Break in Y of LOWRY
1/4 Lack of colour on second red door from right (Th. F–G11)
12/1 Line of small dots in top gutter

Sheet Details

Sheet size: 4d. 60 (12 × 5), others (5 × 12). All double pane sheet-fed

Sheet markings:

  Cylinder numbers:
    4d. Opposite R. 4/1, boxed
    Others. Opposite rows 10/11 at left, boxed

  Guide holes: None

  Marginal arrows (photo-etched): "W" shaped, at top and bottom (4d.) or at both sides (others)

  Marginal rule: At bottom of sheet

  Colour register marks, coloured crosses, autotron marks and colour designations: None

  Traffic lights (boxed and in same order as cylinder numbers):
    4d. Opposite R. 4/12
    Others. Opposite rows 10/11 at right

Imprimaturs from the National Postal Museum Archives

Nos. W119/121 imperforate

No watermark (*set of* 3)

Quantities Sold

4d. 102,443,229; 9d. 9,568,991; 1s.6d. 9,660,509; Pack 46,017

Withdrawn

9.7.68 (4d. sold out October 1967, 9d. sold out January 1968)

W118. *Gipsy Moth IV*
(Des. Michael and Sylvia Goaman)

1967 (JULY 24). SIR FRANCIS CHICHESTER'S WORLD VOYAGE

Sir Francis Chichester voyaged single-handed from England to Australia and back in *Gipsy Moth IV* and was knighted by the Queen on his return.

No watermark. Three phosphor bands, applied by flexography

Cat. No.	S.G. No.	Type		Description	Mint	Used
W122	751	**W118**		1s.9d. Black, brown-red, light		
a. Broken ribbon (R. 19/3)		..	2·50	emerald and blue	25	25

First Day Cover (W122) ..	..	..	1·00

Listed Variety

Normal   W122*a*

Cylinder Numbers (Blocks of Six)

Cyl. Nos.

Perforation Type A
No dot

1s.9d. 2A (black)–1B (emerald)–1C (blue)–1D (brown-red)   ..   ..   2·00

Minor Constant Flaws

1s.9d. Cyls. 2A–1B–1C–1D no dot
1/6 Dark flaw in Queen's hair below ribbon (Th. B12–13)
2/1 Grey flaw at top of main sail (Th. A7) and flaw in rear sail (Th. C8–9)
6/5 Diagonal line running across main sail (Th. D6–7)
13/1 Line of small blue dots in rear sail (Th. D–E8)
14/4 White flaw in figure 1 of value (Th. G12)
16/2 Break in rigging near main-mast (Th. D5)
17/6 Line of blue dots on hull below main sail (Th. E4–5)
18/5 Scratch through rear sail to grey clouds (Th. E8–D11)
18/6 Same scratch extends to foresail (Th. C1–B5)
19/1 Small spur protrudes from top right of rear sail (Th. B–C9)
20/1 Curved dotted blue line between rear sail and Queen's portrait (Th. C9)
20/2 Diagonal blue line in top gutter (Th. 9–13 in gutter)
20/3 Vertical white line at bottom left of main sail (Th. D–E5)
20/4 Blue flaw at top of main sail (Th. A7)
20/6 Dot between ON of HARRISON

Sheet Details

Sheet size: 120 (6 × 20). Single pane reel-fed

Sheet markings:
Cylinder numbers: Opposite rows 18/19 at left, boxed
Guide holes: Boxed, opposite row 14, at both sides. Boxes without holes also appear opposite row 15, at both sides
Marginal arrows (photo-etched): "W" shaped, at top, bottom and sides
Marginal rule: At bottom of sheet
Colour register marks: Opposite rows 1/2 and 20, at both sides
Autotron marks (solid):
Black, blue, emerald, brown-red, below vertical rows 1/3
Coloured crosses and colour designations: None
Traffic lights (boxed): Blue, brown-red, black, emerald, opposite rows 18/19 at right

Imprimatur from the National Postal Museum Archives

No. W122 imperforate

No watermark (*single*)

Quantity Sold   10,060,867

Withdrawn   23.7.68

W119. Radar Screen   **W120.** Penicillin Mould
(Des. Clive Abbott)

W121. "VC–10" Jet Engines   **W122.** Television Equipment
(Des. Negus and Sharland team)

1967 (SEPTEMBER 19). BRITISH DISCOVERY AND INVENTION

Watermark Multiple Crowns, sideways on 1s.9d. This was the last commemorative issue to bear a watermark.

Three phosphor bands (4d.) or two phosphor bands (others)

Cat. No.	S.G. No.	Type		Description	Mint	Used
W123	752	**W119**		4d. Greenish yellow, black and vermilion	10	10
a. Phosphor omitted			1·25			
b. Major scale break (R. 10/2)			2·75			
W124	753	**W120**		1s. Blue-green, light greenish blue, slate-purple and bluish violet	10	10
a. Phosphor omitted			7·00			
b. Watermark inverted			10·00			
W125	754	**W121**		1s.6d. Black, grey, royal blue, ochre and turquoise-blue	25	15
a. **Phosphor omitted**			£500			
b. **Watermark inverted**			30·00			
c. **Cowling flaw (R. 1/2)**			3·25			
W126	755	**W122**		1s.9d. Black, grey-blue, pale olive-grey, violet and orange	30	20
a. **Grey-blue omitted**						
b. **Phosphor omitted**			£500			

First Day Cover (W123/6)	.. ..	1·00
Presentation Pack (W123/6)	.. ..	2·00

All values are known on a special cover prepared by the Edinburgh G.P.O. Philatelic Bureau but postmarked 8 August 1967.

Listed Varieties

W123*b*

W125*c*

Cylinder Numbers (Blocks of Six)

<table>
<tr><td></td><td>Cyl. Nos. (No dot)</td><td colspan="2">Perforation Types</td></tr>
<tr><td></td><td></td><td>A</td><td>F</td></tr>
<tr><td>4d.</td><td>1A (vermilion)–1B (yellow)–1C (black) ..   ..   ..</td><td>1·00</td><td>†</td></tr>
<tr><td>1s.</td><td>1A (violet)–1B (green)–1C (blue)–1D (slate-purple) ..</td><td>†</td><td>1·00</td></tr>
<tr><td>1s.6d.</td><td>1A (black)–1B (ochre)–1C (blue)–1D (grey)–1E (turquoise-blue) ..   ..</td><td>†</td><td>2·00</td></tr>
<tr><td>1s.9d.</td><td>1A (black)–1B (violet)–1C (olive-grey)–1D (grey-blue)–1E (orange) ..   ..</td><td>†</td><td>3·75</td></tr>
</table>

The 1s.9d. is with sheet orientated showing head to right.

Minor Constant Flaws

4d. Cyls. 1A–1B–1C
2/2 Break in outer ring of radar screen at top centre (Th. A6)
8/5 Break in scale division of radar screen just to left of centre bottom mark (Th. G5)
14/5 Break in scale division of radar screen in centre left mark (Th. D3)

1s. Cyls. 1A–1B–1C–1D
19/3 Retouch to background at right of value (Th. F12–13)
19/6 Violet coloured flaw in bottom right of white outer ring (Th. G6)

1s.6d. Cyls. 1A–1B–1C–1D–1E
12/3 Small break in outer frame-line to right of 1/6 (Th. G13)
13/2 Pale area in background above first e of engine (Th. F8)
19/5 White scratch to background—extends to next stamp (Th. G3–10)
19/6 White scratch to background—extending from previous stamp (Th. G4–10)
20/3 The small grey coloured projection of the tailplane at right of the engines is malformed (Th. C8)

1s.9d. Cyls. 1A–1B–1C–1D–1E
1/18 Two of the holes of the disc at left are joined (Th. E1)
5/1 One of the slits in grey-blue disc below portrait is joined to hub by white flaw (Th. E5)

Sheet Details

Sheet sizes:
4d. 120 (6 × 20). Single pane reel-fed
1s. and 1s.6d. 120 (6 × 20). Single pane sheet-fed
1s.9d. 120 (20 × 6). Single pane sheet-fed

Sheet markings:
Cylinder numbers:
4d. and 1s. Opposite R. 19/1, boxed
1s.6d. Opposite rows 18/19 at left, boxed
1s.9d. Opposite rows 5/6 at left, boxed
Guide holes:
4d. Opposite rows 14/15 (boxed), at both sides; others, none
Marginal arrows (photo-etched): "W" shaped, at top, bottom and sides
Marginal rule: At bottom of sheet
Colour register marks:
4d. Opposite rows 3/4 and 17/18, at both sides
1s. and 1s.6d. Above and below vertical rows 1 and 6
1s.9d. Opposite rows 1 and 6 bottom margin, at both sides
Coloured crosses:
4d. None
1s. and 1s.6d. Above and below vertical rows 2/3
1s.9d. Opposite rows 4/5, at both sides
Autotron marks (solid):
4d. Black, yellow, vermilion below vertical rows 1/3. An additional semi-solid mark in red appears below vertical row 1; others, none
Colour designations: None
Traffic lights (boxed):
4d. and 1s. In same order as cylinder numbers opposite R. 19/6
1s.6d. In reverse order to cylinder numbers opposite rows 18/19 at right
1s.9d. Violet, black, olive-grey, grey-blue, orange opposite rows 5/6 at right

Imprimaturs from the National Postal Museum Archives

Nos. W123/126 imperforate, watermark Type W.24

Watermark upright (4d., 1s., 1s.6d.) or sideways (1s.9d.) (*set of* 4)

Quantities Sold

4d. 104,165,625; 1s. 10,718,389; 1s.6d. 10,380,413; 1s.9d. 7,469,585; Pack 59,117

Withdrawn 18.9.68

NO WATERMARK. All commemorative stamps from here onwards were printed on paper without watermark.

W123. "The Adoration of the Shepherds" (School of Seville)

W124. "Madonna and Child" (Murillo)

W125. "The Adoration of the Shepherds" (Louis Le Nain)

(Des. Stuart Rose)

1967. CHRISTMAS

The 4d. was issued on 18 October and the others were put on sale on 27 November. One phosphor band (3d.) or two phosphor bands (others), applied by flexography

Cat. No.	S.G. No.	Type	Description	Mint	Used
W127	756	**W123**	3d. Olive-yellow, rose, blue, black and gold	10	10
a. Gold omitted (value and Queen's head) .... 60·00					
b. Rose omitted					
c. Imperforate between stamp and left margin £500			*d.* Phosphor omitted	50	
			e. Printed on the gummed side ..	£300	
W128	757	**W124**	4d. Bright purple, greenish yellow, new blue, black and gold	10	10
a. Gold omitted (value and Queen's head) .. .. .. 60·00					
b. Greenish yellow (Child, robe and Madonna's face) omitted ..					
c. Phosphor omitted £100			*e.* One broad band	30·00	
d. Right-hand band omitted ..			*f.* Brown flaw (Dot, R. 2/3) ..	2·75	
W129	758	**W125**	1s.6d. Bright purple, bistre, lemon, black, orange-red, ultramarine, gold	35	35
a. Gold omitted (value and Queen's head) £200					
b. Ultramarine omitted £300					
c. Phosphor omitted .. .. .. 10·00					
d. One broad band .. .. .. 30·00					

First Day Cover (W128)	.. ..	25
First Day Cover (W127 and W129)	..	75

There is a wide variation on shades of the 3d. and 4d. but they are not listed as there are a number of intermediate shades. In the 4d. value, stamps emanating from one machine show a darker background and give the appearance of the greenish yellow being omitted, but this is not so. These should not be confused with the true missing greenish yellow, No. W128*b.*

The 3d. and 4d. are known with value omitted resulting from colour shifts.

Listed Variety

No. W128*f*. This marked variety on the 4d. consists of a large brown area in the lower right corner (Th. J–K 8–9) which can be clearly seen by the naked eye but which would not show up in an enlarged illustration. It occurs on cylinders 2B–2C–2D–2E dot in conjunction with gold cylinders 2A or 3A.

Cylinder Numbers (Blocks of Six)

	Cyl. Nos.	Perforation Types A	
		No dot	Dot
3d.	1A (gold)–1B (olive-yellow)–1C (rose)–1D (blue)–1E (black)..	90	†
	2A (gold)–1B (olive-yellow)–1C (rose)–1D (blue)–1E (black)..	90	†
4d.	2A (gold)–1B (bright purple)–1C (new blue)–1D (greenish yellow)–1E (grey-black)..	90	90
	2A (gold)–2B (bright purple)–2C (new blue)–2D (greenish yellow)–2E (grey-black)..	2·00	2·00
	3A (gold)–2B (bright purple)–2C (new blue)–2D (greenish yellow)–2E (grey-black)	90	90
	6A (gold)–3B (bright purple)–3C (new blue)–3D (greenish yellow)–3E (grey-black)..	3·25	†
	8A (gold)–3B (bright purple)–3C (new blue)–3D (greenish yellow)–3E (grey-black)..	3·25	†
		A(T) No dot	
1s.6d.	2A (gold)–1B (ultramarine)–1C (bright purple)–1D (orange-red)–1E (lemon)–1F (bistre)–2G (black)	3·75	

The 3d. and 4d. are with the sheet orientated showing the head to right.

The gold of the Queen's portrait and the value is normally further to the left on the 6A and 8A cylinders.

Minor Constant Flaws

3d. Cyls. 1B–1C–1D–1E in conjunction with gold cyls. 1A or 2A no dot
   1/7 Black horizontal line across triangle of red above Mary's head (Th. E2–3)

3d. Cyls. 1A–1B–1C–1D–1E no dot
   1/11 Break in upright wall of building shows against sky (Th. D6)

3d. Cyls. 2A–1B–1C–1D–1E no dot
   3/10 Small black spot in Joseph's cloak (Th. D5)
   4/9 Background retouch in left pillar (Th. D2)

4d. Cyls. 2B–2C–2D–2E in conjunction with gold cyls. 2A or 3A no dot
   1/5 Prominent pale area in background at bottom right (Th. K–L 8–9)

4d. Cyls. 3A–2B–2C–2D–2E no dot
   2/12 A cut at top of diagonal of 4 of value
   7/5 Dark spot in Mother's right hand (Th. E5)

4d. Cyls. 2B–2C–2D–2E in conjunction with gold cyls. 2A or 3A dot
   4/5 Line of pale dots over 4 of value (Th. J1)

4d. Cyls. 3A–2B–2C–2D–2E dot
   2/12 Black dot over first R of HARRISON
   3/6 Black dot on Child's forehead (Th. C6)
   4/9 Spot on lower left margin of stamp (Th. K1)
   7/2 Small spot just beyond little finger of Madonna's right hand (Th. E6)
   7/12 Two small red dots over H of HARRISON

1s.6d. Cyls. 2A–1B–1C–1D–1E–1F–2G no dot
   1/2 Background disturbance above ll of shilling
   3/6 Curved green flaw left of cow's tail (Th. E1)
   4/9 Background disturbance below n of One

Sheet Details

Sheet sizes:
   3d. 120 (12 × 10). Single pane sheet-fed
   4d. 120 (12 × 10). Double pane reel-fed for gold cyls. 2A and 3A and single pane reel-fed for gold cyls. 6A and 8A
   1s.6d. 60 (10 × 6). Single pane sheet-fed
Sheet markings:
   Cylinder Numbers:
      3d. Opposite R. 9/1, boxed
      4d. Below vertical row 11, boxed
      1s.6d. Opposite rows 4/5 at right, boxed
   Guide holes:
      3d. and 1s.6d. None
      4d. Above and below vertical row 8

Marginal arrows (photo etched): "W" shaped, at top, bottom and sides
Marginal rule: None
Colour register marks:
   3d. Above and below vertical rows 1/2 and 11/12
   4d. Above and below vertical rows 1/3 (dot) and 8/10 (no dot)
   1s.6d. Opposite rows 1/2 and 6, at both sides
Coloured crosses:
   3d. Above and below vertical rows 3/4
   4d. None
   1s.6d. Next to cylinder numbers at left and traffic lights at right
Autotron marks (solid):
   3d. and 1s.6d. None
   4d. Greenish yellow, bright purple, new blue, grey-black, gold opposite rows 6/8, right margin (dot) with
     the 3A-2B-2C-2D-2E cylinders but the order of the colours is reversed with the 2A-1B-1C-1D-1E
     cylinders
Colour designations:
   3d. and 1s.6d. None
   4d. "G1 YELLOW" above vertical row 12 on the dot pane and "G2 GREY G3 GREEN G4 RED
     G5 GOLD" above vertical rows 1/4 on the no dot pane, the whole inscription being upside down.
     The "G3 GREEN" is printed in blue
Traffic lights (boxed):
   3d. In the same order as the cylinder numbers opposite R. 9/12
   4d. Greenish yellow, bright purple, gold, new blue, grey-black above vertical rows 10/11
   1s.6d. Lemon, bright purple, orange-red, ultramarine, black, bistre, gold opposite rows 4/5 at right
In the case of the 4d. value all the above information relates to the stamps printed from
gold cylinders 2A and 3A in double panes. We have not been able to examine full sheets
from the single pane cylinders 6A and 8A on which some of the markings may well be
different. However, we have seen part of the top which showed the following differences:
colour register marks above row 1/1 and 1/12 and colour designations inverted but reading
"G1 YELLOW G2 RED G3 GREEN (printed in blue) G4 GREY G5 GOLD" above vertical
rows 1/6, with the yellow above row 6 and the gold above row 1. There was no perforation
guide hole.

Imprimaturs from the National Postal Museum Archives

Nos. W127/129 imperforate

No watermark (set of 3)

Quantities Sold   3d. 270,349,845; 4d. 287,827,440; 1s.6d. 17,913,209

Withdrawn   3d. Sold out July 1968; 4d. 17.10.68; 1s.6d. 26.11.68

1967 (NOVEMBER 27). GIFT PACK 1967
WGP1 Comprising Nos. WP111/18 and W119/29   2·50

Quantity Sold   105,577

PVA GUM. All commemorative issues from here onwards printed by Harrisons are on paper with PVA gum. For further particulars about this gum see notes at the beginning of Section UA on the Machin definitive issues.

W126.   Tarr Steps, Exmoor
(Des. Jeffery Matthews)

W127.   Aberfeldy Bridge
(Des. Andrew Restall)

W128.   Menai Bridge
(Des. Leonard Rosoman)

W129.   M4 Viaduct
(Des. Jeffery Matthews)

1968 (APRIL 29).   BRITISH BRIDGES

Two phosphor bands, applied by flexography (4d., 1s.9d.) or photogravure (others)

Cat. No.	S.G. No.	Type			Description	Mint	Used
W130	763	**W126**			4d. Black, bluish violet,		
a. Printed on the gummed side ..			25·00		turquoise-blue and gold	10	10
b. Phosphor omitted ..	..	..	1·25				
c. "O" retouch (R. 20/6) ..		..	1·90				
d. No curve to slab (R. 10/6)		..	4·00				
W131	764	**W127**			9d. Red-brown, myrtle-green,		
a. Gold (Queen's head) omitted ..			£100		ultramarine, olive-brown,		
b. Ultramarine omitted	..	..	—	£3000	black and gold	10	10
c. Phosphor omitted ..		..	13·00				
d. Phosphor bands diagonal		..	25·00				
e. One broad band	..	..	15·00				
f. "HARRISON" redrawn (R. 18/3) ..	..	..	3·50				
g. "RESTALL" redrawn (R. 18/4)			3·50				
W132	765	**W128**			1s.6d. Olive-brown, red-orange,		
a. Gold (Queen's head) omitted ..			£100		bright green, turquoise-		
b. Red-orange omitted	..	..	£150		green and gold	20	15
c. Phosphor omitted	..	..	40·00				
d. Broken corner stones (R. 15/1)			5·00				
W133	766	**W129**			1s.9d. Olive-brown, greenish		
a. Gold (Queen's head) and phosphor omitted	..	..	£300		yellow, dull green, deep ultramarine and gold	25	30
b. Gold (Queen's head) omitted ..			£150				
c. Phosphor omitted ..	..	..	7·00				
d. One broad band	..	..					

First Day Cover (W130/3)	..	..	1·10
Presentation Pack (W130/3)	..	..	2·00

No. W131*b* is only known on first day covers posted from Canterbury, Kent or the Philatelic Bureau, Edinburgh.

Listed Varieties

W130c

W130d
No curve at left to central slab

W132d

Normal

W131f   W131g
Inscriptions redrawn by hand

Cylinder Numbers (Blocks of Eight)

	Cyl. Nos.	Perforation Type F No dot
4d.	3A (black)–1B (turquoise-blue)–2C (bluish violet)–2D (gold).. ..	1·10
9d.	1A (black)–1B (red-brown)–1C (ultramarine)–1D (olive-brown)– 1E (myrtle-green)–1F (gold)	1·75
1s.6d.	2A (olive-brown)–1B (red-orange)–1C (bright green)–2D (turquoise-green)–3E (gold)	2·25
1s.9d.	2A (olive-brown)–1B (gold)–1C (dull green)–1D (deep ultramarine)– 1E (greenish yellow)	2·75

Minor Constant Flaws

4d. Cyls. 3A–1B–2C–2D no dot
  4/1 Diagonal dotted line across top of bridge near far end (Th. C10)
  9/1 Lack of screening dots in left of pale green patch left of Tarr (Th G4–5)
  11/1 Similar variety but more pronounced (Th. G4–5)
  12/2 Broken tip to horizontal bar of T of Tarr
  14/2 Scratch across lower stones near far end of bridge (Th. D10–C12)
  17/2 Weakness behind and below hi of Prehistoric (Th. G11)
  19/4 Damaged H in HARRISON

9d. Cyls. 1A–1B–1C–1D–1E–1F no dot
  9/4 Break in olive-brown line at left of ultramarine area under main arch (Th. F6)
  20/4 Small dark spot under r of Bridge

1s.6d. Cyls. 2A–1B–1C–2D–3E no dot
  5/5 Two diagonal lines in sky at right (Th. B–C13)
  5/6 Diagonal line in sky extending to base of Queen's neck (extension of one of the lines in 5/5) (Th. C1)
  6/1 Small curved flaw in front of H of HARRISON
  6/2 White flaw in first arch beyond the far tower (Th. E12)
  14/5 Small white flaw at top right of near tower (Th. B8)
  19/1 Green spot on near tower above right-hand arch (Th. D7-8)

1s.9d. Cyls. 2A–1B–1C–1D–1E no dot
  2/5 Retouch in centre lane (Th. C–D8)
  10/4 Disturbance at right of pale green area below Queen (Th. D3–4)
  14/5 Vertical line appears as radio mast above building on skyline (Th. A6)
  15/1 Retouch between buildings at bend in motorway (Th. C10)
  17/4 Break at foot of s in value

Sheet Details

Sheet size: 120 (6 × 20). Single pane sheet-fed

Sheet markings:
    Cylinder numbers: Opposite rows 17/18 at left, boxed
    Guide holes: None
    Marginal arrows (photo-etched): " W " shaped, at top, bottom and sides
    Marginal rule: At bottom of sheet
    Colour register marks:
        4d. and 1s.9d. Above and below vertical rows 1/2 and 6
        9d. and 1s.6d. Above and below vertical rows 1 and 5/6
    Coloured crosses:
        4d. and 1s.6d. Above and below vertical row 3
        9d. Above and below vertical rows 3/4
        1s.9d. Above and below vertical rows 2/3
    Autotron marks and colour designations: None
    Traffic lights (boxed):
        4d. Gold, bluish violet, turquoise-blue, black above vertical row 5
        9d. Black, red-brown, ultramarine, myrtle-green, gold, olive-brown above vertical rows 4/5
        1s.6d. Gold, turquoise-green, bright green, red-orange, olive-brown above vertical row 5
        1s.9d. Gold, dull green, olive-brown, deep ultramarine, greenish yellow above vertical row 5

Imprimaturs from the National Postal Museum Archives

Nos. W130/133 imperforate

No watermark (*set of* 4)

Quantities Sold

4d. 97,458,120; 9d. 8,773,080; 1s.6d. 9,451,400; 1s.9d. 5,924,800; Pack 69,646

Withdrawn   28.4.69

W130. "T U C" and
Trade Unionists

W131. Mrs. Emmeline
Pankhurst (statue)

W132. Sopwith "Camel" and
"Lightning" Fighters

W133. Captain Cook's
Endeavour and Signature

(Des. David Gentleman (4d.), Clive Abbott (others))

1968 (MAY 29). BRITISH ANNIVERSARIES

Four famous anniversaries, with the events described on the stamps.

Two phosphor bands, applied by flexography (1s., 1s.9d.) or photogravure (others)

Cat. No.	S.G. No.	Type	Description	Mint	Used
W134	767	**W130**	4d. Emerald, olive, blue and black	10	10
a. Phosphor omitted*		10·00			
b. Retouch on large " C " (No dot, R. 3/2)		2·75			
W135	768	**W131**	9d. Reddish violet, grey and black	10	10
a. Phosphor omitted		5·50			
b. One broad band		25·00			
W136	769	**W132**	1s. Olive-brown, blue, red, slate-blue and black	20	20
a. Phosphor omitted		8·00			
W137	770	**W133**	1s.9d. Ochre, brownish ochre and blackish brown	25	25
a. Phosphor omitted†		£140			
b. Broken bulwarks (R. 8/2)		4·00			

First Day Cover (W134/7)	.. ..	3·25
Presentation Pack (W134/7)	.. ..	3·00

*The phosphor bands are normally faint and difficult to see and care is needed in identifying the phosphor omitted on the 4d. value.

†The 1s.9d. is known with phosphor removed by chemical means.   These can be detected, but care is needed in identifying genuine examples.

This issue is known postmarked at Netheravon, Salisbury, Wiltshire on 28 May.

Listed Varieties

W134*b*

W137*b*

Cylinder Numbers (Blocks of Eight (4d., 1s.), Four (9d.), Six (1s.9d.))

Cyl. Nos.	Perforation Types	
	A	A
	No dot	Dot
4d. 1A (black)–1B (blue)–1C (olive)–1D (emerald)	1·50	1·50
	F No dot	
9d. 1A (black)–1B (reddish violet)–1C (grey)	1·00	
1s. 1A (black)–1B (olive-brown)–1C (blue)–1D (slate-blue)–1E (red)	2·50	
1s.9d. 2A (blackish brown)–1B (brownish ochre)–1C (ochre).. ..	2·50	

Minor Constant Flaws

4d. Cyls. 1A–1B–1C–1D no dot
1/1 Small retouch in right cross bar of large T
2/2 Stop between Union and Congress
4/1 Retouch at top of large C (not as prominent as No. W134*b*)
10/6 Small retouch at top left of large U
11/3 Small flaw in 6 of 1968
11/6 Vertical green line from right cross bar of large T (Th. B–E3)

4d. Cyls. 1A–1B–1C–1D dot
2/6 Small spot right of 4 of value
4/5 Green spots by d of Trades (Th. F–G1)
5/5 Dotted line across back of Queen's hair (Th. B–C12)
19/1 Retouch on cheek of face shown in large T (Th. D1–2)
20/5 Two tiny dots above g of Congress

9d. Cyls. 1A–1B–1C no dot
9/4 Spur at top right of Queen's head (Th. A13)
14/6 Dark flaw on collar (Th. D10/11) and small flaw on left sleeve (Th. F11)

1s. Cyls. 1A–1B–1C–1D–1E no dot
3/1 Dot over O of ROYAL
4/4 Extension of wing joining it to last T of ABBOTT

1s.9d. Cyls. 2A–1B–1C no dot
10/3 Small flaws in background above Y of DISCOVERY level with value (Th. F10–11)
11/2 Small cut in Y of VOYAGE
13/2 Flaw in lower part of S of DISCOVERY
16/2 Sliced F in FIRST
20/5 Tail of 9 of 1968 slightly shortened

Sheet Details

Sheet size: 120 (6 × 20). 4d. double pane reel-fed; others single pane sheet-fed
Sheet markings:

Cylinder numbers:
  4d. and 1s. Opposite rows 17/18 at left, boxed
  9d. Opposite R. 19/1, boxed
  1s.9d. Opposite R. 18/1, boxed

Guide holes:
  4d. In double "S O N" box opposite rows 14/15, at left (no dot) or right (dot)
  Others: None

Marginal arrows (photo-etched): "W" shaped, at top, bottom and sides

Marginal rule: 4d. None; others at bottom of sheet

Colour register marks:
  4d. Opposite rows 2/4 and 18/20 at left (no dot) or right (dot)
  Others: Above and below vertical rows 1 and 6

Coloured crosses:
  4d. None
  9d. and 1s.9d. Above and below vertical row 3
  1s. Above and below vertical rows 2/3

Autotron marks (solid):
  4d. Black, blue, olive, emerald opposite rows 4/6, at right (no dot) or left (dot); others, none

Colour designations: None

Traffic lights (boxed):
  4d. In same order as cylinder numbers opposite rows 1/2, at right
  9d. Black, grey, reddish violet above vertical row 5
  1s. Olive-brown, blue, slate-blue, red, black above vertical row 5
  1s.9d. Brownish ochre, blackish brown, ochre above vertical row 5

Imprimaturs from the National Postal Museum Archives

Nos. W134/137 imperforate

No watermark (*set of* 4)

Quantities Sold

4d. 97,757,920; 9d. 9,135,240; 1s. 9,872,160; 1s.9d. 6,217,440; Pack 67,639

Withdrawn 28.5.69

W134. "Queen Elizabeth I"
(Unknown Artist)

W135. "Pinkie"
(Sir Thomas Lawrence)

W136. "Ruins of St. Mary
Le Port" (John Piper)

W137. "The Hay Wain"
(John Constable)

(Des. Stuart Rose)

(Printed in photogravure with the Queen's head embossed in gold)

1968 (AUGUST 12).   BRITISH PAINTINGS

This is the second issue of British Paintings for which Harrisons made photographs from the originals.

Two phosphor bands applied by photogravure (1s.9d.) or flexography (others).

Cat. No.	S.G. No.	Type	Description	Mint	Used
W138	771	**W134**	4d. Black, vermilion, greenish yellow, grey and gold	10	10
a. Gold omitted (value and Queen's head) £100					
b. Gold (value and Queen's head) and phosphor omitted £180			d. Phosphor omitted .. .. 1·00		
c. Vermilion omitted* £200			e. Embossing omitted .. .. 80·00		
			f. Blister on hand (No dot, R. 2/8) 2·00		
W139	772	**W135**	1s. Mauve, new blue, greenish yellow, black, magenta and gold	15	15
a. Gold omitted (value and Queen's head) £180					
b. Gold (value and Queen's head), embossing and phosphor omitted £200					
c. Embossing omitted			d. Phosphor omitted .. .. 6·00		
W140	773	**W136**	1s.6d. Slate, orange, black, mauve, greenish yellow, ultramarine, and gold	20	20
a. Gold omitted (value and Queen's head) £100					
b. Phosphor omitted .. .. 6·00					
c. Embossing omitted					
W141	774	**W137**	1s.9d. Greenish yellow, black, new blue, red and gold	25	25
a. Gold (value and Queen's head), embossing and phosphor omitted £450					
b. Red omitted					
c. Phosphor omitted .. .. .. 17·00					
d. Embossing omitted					

First Day Cover (W138/41) ..	..	1·00
Presentation Pack (W138/41)	..	1·40
Pack also exists with a Japanese insert card.		
Presentation Pack (German) (W138/41)		6·00

*No. W138c shows the face and hands white, and there is more yellow and olive in the costume.

The 4d. also exists with the value only omitted resulting from a colour shift.

This issue is known pre-released on a first day cover postmarked 10 August from Vauxhall Bridge P.O., S.W.1.

Listed Variety

KNOWN c.157

W138f

Cylinder Numbers (Blocks of Six)

	Cyl. Nos.	Perforation Type A(T)	
		No dot	Dot
4d.	2A (gold)–1B (embossing)–3C (black)–2D (grey)–3E (vermilion)–2F (greenish yellow)	1·00	1·00
1s.	2A (gold)–1B (embossing)–2C (black)–2D (new blue)–2E (mauve)–2F (magenta)–2G (greenish yellow) ..	1·50	1·50
	2A (gold)–2B (embossing)–2C (black)–2D (new blue)–2E (mauve)–2F (magenta)–2G (greenish yellow)	1·50	1·50
1s.6d.	1A (gold)–1B (embossing)–1C (black)–1D (ultramarine)–1E (slate)–1F (mauve)–1G (orange)–1H (greenish yellow)	1·75	1·75
1s.9d.	2A (gold)–1B (embossing)–1C (black)–1D (new blue)–1E (red)–1F (greenish yellow)	2·25	2·25

The 4d., 1s and 1s.6d. are with sheet orientated showing head to right.

In each value the 1B cylinder number appears in colourless embossing; it is difficult to see but can often be discerned with the aid of a magnifying glass.

Minor Constant Flaws

4d. Cyls. 2A–1B–3C–2D–3E–2F no dot
6/8 Thick A in HARRISON

4d. Cyls. 2A–1B–3C–2D–3E–2F dot
4/2 Black flaw on dress above Queen's right hand (Th. J4–5)

1s. Cyls. 2A–1B–2C–2D–2E–2F–2G no dot
2/4 Diagonal black line across Pinkie's shoulder (Th. D4)
5/1 Black spur to A of HARRISON
6/1 Thin diagonal black line across dress (Th. H3–5)

1s.6d. Cyls. 1A–1B–1C–1D–1E–1F–1G–1H no dot
6/1 Dark coloured spot in top right corner of dark blue area (Th. A8–9)

1s.6d. Cyls. 1A–1B–1C–1D–1E–1F–1G–1H dot
1/8 ? shaped black flaw in doorway (Th. J5)
6/6 Extra patch at upper left corner of yellow wall (Th. E8)

1s.9d. Cyls. 2A–1B–1C–1D–1E–1F no dot
9/2 Blue spot after HARRISON
10/1 Green instead of brown bush in bottom left-hand corner

Sheet Details

Sheet size: 1s.9d. 60 (6 × 10), others 60 (10 × 6). All double pane sheet-fed

Sheet markings:
  Cylinder numbers:
    4d. Opposite row 5, left margin, boxed
    1s. and 1s.6d. Opposite rows 4/5, left margin, boxed
    1s.9d. Opposite rows 8/9, left margin, boxed

Guide holes: None
Marginal arrows (photo-etched): "W" shaped, at top, bottom and sides
Marginal rule: None
Colour register marks:
    4d., 1s. and 1s.6d. Above vertical rows 1/2 and 9/10 (no dot) or below (dot)
    1s.9d. Opposite rows 1/2 and 9/10, left margin (no dot) or right margin (dot
Coloured crosses:
    4d. and 1s. Above vertical rows 6/7 (no dot) or below (dot)
    1s.6d. Above vertical rows 7/8 (no dot) or below (dot)
    1s.9d. Opposite rows 7/8, left margin (no dot) or right margin (dot)
Autotron marks, colour designations: None
Traffic lights (boxed):
    4d., 1s. and 1s.6d. In same order as cylinder numbers, except that on the 1s.6d. the gold and embossing "lights" are transposed, reading left to right above vertical rows 8/9
    1s.9d. In same order as cylinder numbers, except that the gold and embossing "lights" are transposed, reading left to right above vertical row 5

Imprimaturs from the National Postal Museum Archives

Nos. W138/141 imperforate

No watermark (*set of* 4)

Quantities Sold

4d.	185,034,000	English Pack	93,829
1s.	17,953,440	German Pack	7,880
1s.6d.	8,878,440		
1s.9d.	5,739,000		

Withdrawn 11.8.69

1968 (SEPTEMBER 16). GIFT PACK 1968

WGP2 Comprising Nos. W130/41   6·00
   a. German text   ..   ..   ..   24·00

Quantities Sold   Ordinary 41,308; German 1,650

1968 (SEPTEMBER 16). COLLECTORS PACK 1968

WCP1 Comprising Nos. W123/41   6·00

Quantity Sold   26,284

W139. Girl with
Doll's House

W138. Boy and Girl with
Rocking Horse
(Des. Rosalind Dease)

W140. Boy with
Train Set

(Printed in photogravure with the Queen's head embossed in gold)

1968 (NOVEMBER 25). CHRISTMAS

The joy of giving is emphasised on this Christmas issue; all three designs show children playing with their Christmas toys.

One centre phosphor band (4d.) or two phosphor bands (others), applied by flexography

Cat. No.	S.G. No.	Type			Description	Mint	Used
W142	775	**W138**			4d. Black, orange, vermilion,		
a. Gold omitted	..	..	..	£1500	ultramarine, bistre and		
b. Vermilion omitted*	..	..	£140		gold	10	10
c. Ultramarine and		phosphor					
omitted	..	..	..	£150			
d. Embossing omitted	..	..	5·00		*f.* Retouched dapples (Cyl. 1A,		
e. Phosphor omitted	..	..	1·25		R. 12/4)	2·40	
W143	776	**W139**			9d. Yellow-olive, black, brown,		
a. Yellow omitted ..	..	..	50·00		yellow, magenta, orange,		
b. Embossing and		phosphor			turquoise-green and gold	15	15
omitted ..	..	..	7·50		*f.* Phosphor omitted	8·00	
c. Embossing omitted	..	..	5·00				
W144	777	**W140**			1s.6d. Ultramarine, yellow-		
a. Embossing omitted	..	..			orange, bright purple,		
b. Phosphor omitted	..	..	13·00		blue-green, black and		
					gold	25	25

First Day Cover (W142/4)	..	..	1·00
Presentation Pack (W142/4)	..	..	2·00
Presentation Pack (German) (W142/4)			5·00

*The effect of the missing vermilion is shown on the rocking horse, saddle and faces which appear orange instead of red.

No. W142 is known pre-released on 24 November at Edinburgh.

A single used example of No. W142 has been seen with the bistre omitted from the mane of the rocking horse and the girl's hair. No. W142*a* also exists with a single complete omission and three partial gold heads on the gummed side due to a paper fold.

Two machines were used for printing the 4d. value:
Stamps from cylinders 1A–1B–2C–1D–1E in combination with 1F, 2F or 3F (gold) were printed entirely on the Rembrandt sheet-fed machine. They invariably have the Queen's head level with the top of the boy's head and the sheets are perforated through the left side margin (perforation type F).

Stamps from cylinders 2A–2B–3C–2D–2E in combination with 1F, 2F, 3F or 4F (gold) were printed on the reel-fed Thrissell machine in five colours (its maximum colour capacity) and subsequently sheet-fed on the Rembrandt machine for the gold Queen's head and the embossing. The position of the Queen's head is generally lower than on the stamps printed at one operation but it varies in different parts of the sheet and is not, therefore, a sure indication for identifying single stamps. Another small difference is that the boy's grey pullover is noticeably "moth-eaten" in the Thrissell printings and is normal on the Rembrandt. The Thrissell printings are perforated through the top margin (perforation type A).

Marginal copies can usually be identified by the characteristics of the perforation (if any) in the sheet margin. Ideally, cylinder blocks of six are required to show examples of the two printing machines used.

Listed Variety

Grey dapples on the horse nearest to the boy and extending to the boy's belt and trousers, are heavily retouched

Normal   W142*f*

Cylinder Numbers (Blocks of Six)

	Cyl. Nos. (No dot)	Perforation Types	
		A	F

A. "Rembrandt" only printings

		A	F
4d.	1A (black)–1B (orange)–2C (vermilion)–1D (ultramarine)– 1E (bistre)–1F (gold)..	†	1·00
	1A (black)–1B (orange)–2C (vermilion)–1D (ultramarine)– 1E (bistre)–2F (gold)	†	1·00
	1A (black)–1B (orange)–2C (vermilion)–1D (ultramarine)– 1E (bistre)–3F (gold)..	†	1·50
9d.	1A (black)–1B (brown)–1C (yellow)–2D (magenta)– 1E (orange)–1F (turquoise-green)–1G (yellow-olive)– 1H (gold)	†	1·50
1s.6d.	1A (black)–1B (ultramarine)–1C (yellow-orange)– 1D (bright purple)–1E (blue-green)–1F (gold)	†	2·00

B. "Thrissell" and "Rembrandt" printings

		A	F
4d.	2A (black)–2B (orange)–3C (vermilion)–2D (ultramarine)– 2E (bistre)–1F (gold)..	1·00	†
	2A (black)–2B (orange)–3C (vermilion)–2D (ultramarine)– 2E (bistre)–2F (gold)..	1·50	†
	2A (black)–2B (orange)–3C (vermilion)–2D (ultramarine)– 2E (bistre)–3F (gold)	2·00	†
	2A (black)–2B (orange)–3C (vermilion)–2D (ultramarine)– 2E (bistre)–4F (gold)..	2·00	†

The 9d. and 1s.6d. are with sheet orientated showing head to right.
The 1s.6d. has cyl. nos. 1B–1E unboxed.

Minor Constant Flaws

4d. Cyls. 1A–1B–2C–1D–1E in combination with gold cyls. 1F, 2F, 3F, or 4F
   3/6 Small black flaw in m of Christmas
   12/5 Small nick on right edge of upright stroke of 4 of value
4d. Cyls. 2A–2B–3C–2D–2E in combination with gold cyls. 1F, 2F, 3F or 4F
   16/4 Small black flaw above horse's left foreleg by boy's waist (Th. D9)
   20/4 Break in outline at top centre of near rocker (Th. F4–5)
9d. Cyls. 1A–1B–1C–2D–1E–1F–1G–1H
   4/3 Small black flaw between a and s of Christmas
   6/18 Break in middle of final s of Christmas
1s.6d. Cyls. 1A–1B–1C–1D–1E–1F
   2/18 Pale patch on boy's left shoulder (Th. F4)
   3/8 Thick horizontal spur on left of lower central purple slotted plate (Th. D–E4)
   5/2 Black flaws in background lower right of Queen's head (Th. C–D7)
   5/3 Two black dots between 1 and stroke of 1/6
   6/20 Purple coloured flaws in background below boy's foot (Th. J7)

Sheet Details

	Rembrandt	Thrissell/Rembrandt
Sheet sizes:		
4d. 120 (6 × 20)	Single pane sheet-fed	Single pane reel-fed for five colours, and then single pane sheet fed for the gold and embossing
9d. and 1s.6d. 120 (20 × 6)	Single pane sheet-fed	
Sheet markings:		
Cylinder numbers:		
4d.	Opposite rows 18/19, left margin, boxed	Opposite rows 18/19, left margin, boxed
9d. and 1s.6d.	Opposite rows 4/5, left margin, boxed	
Guide holes:		
4d.	None	Opposite rows 14/15 (boxed), at both sides
9d. and 1s.6d.	None	
Marginal arrows (photo-etched):		
4d.	"W" shaped, at top, bottom and sides	"W" shaped, at top, bottom and sides
9d. and 1s.6d.	As 4d.	
Marginal rule:	None	None
Colour register marks:		
4d.	Above and below vertical rows 1/2 and 6	Opposite rows 2/3 and 19/20 at both sides
9d. and 1s.6d.	Opposite rows 1/2 and 5/6 at both sides	
Coloured crosses:		
4d.	Above and below vertical row 3	Gold only below vertical row 3
9d. and 1s.6d.	Opposite rows 3/4 at both sides	
Autotron marks (solid):		
4d.	None	Black, bistre, ultramarine, vermilion, orange below vertical rows 4/6
9d. and 1s.6d.	None	
Colour designations:	None	None
Traffic lights (boxed):		
4d.	Orange, vermilion, ultramarine, bistre, black, gold, embossing opposite rows 18/19, right margin; also above vertical row 5 reading left to right	Orange, vermilion, ultramarine, bistre, black, gold, embossing opposite rows 18/19, right margin; also gold and embossing (unboxed) above vertical row 5 reading left to right
9d.	Gold, olive, green, orange, magenta, yellow, brown, black opposite rows 4/5, right margin; also embossing, gold, olive, green, orange, magenta, yellow, brown, black above vertical rows 17/19 reading left to right	
1s.6d.	Embossing, gold, green, purple, orange, ultramarine, black opposite rows 4/5, at right; also gold, green, purple, orange, ultramarine, black, above vertical rows 18/19 reading left to right	

Although the Traffic Light box in the right margin on the 9d. and the upper margin on the 1s.6d. were designed to accommodate an embossing " light " the space was not in fact used.

Imprimaturs from the National Postal Museum Archives

Nos. W142/144 imperforate

No watermark (*set of* 3)

Quantities Sold
4d. 326,078,360, 9d. 17,102,520, 1s.6d. 21,344,760, English Pack 72,474, German Pack 7,298

Withdrawn 24.11.69

W141.   R.M.S. *Queen Elizabeth 2*

W142.   Elizabethan Galleon

W145.   S.S. *Great Britain*

W143.   East Indiaman

W146.   R.M.S. *Mauretania*

W144.   *Cutty Sark*

(Des. David Gentleman)

1969 (JANUARY 15). BRITISH SHIPS

Issued as a tribute to British shipbuilders and seamen, these stamps depict five famous ships of the past and the *Queen Elizabeth 2*, which sailed on her maiden voyage to New York on 2 May 1969.

The 9d. values were issued together *se-tenant* in strips of three throughout the sheet and the 1s. values were issued together *se-tenant* in pairs throughout the sheet.

Two phosphor bands at right (1s.), one horizontal phosphor band (5d.) or two phosphor bands (9d.), applied by flexography

Cat. No.	S.G. No.	Type		Description	Mint	Used
W145	778	**W141**		5d. Black, grey, red and turquoise	10	10
a. Black omitted (Queen's head, value, hull and inscr.)			£600			
b. Grey omitted (decks, etc.)			90·00			
c. Red omitted			50·00			
d. Red and phosphor omitted			80·00			
e. Phosphor omitted			1·50			
W146	779	**W142**		9d. Red, blue, ochre, brown, black and grey	10	15
a. Strip of 3. Nos. W146/48		1·00	1·00			
b. Red, blue and phosphor omitted		£900				
c. Blue omitted		£1000				
d. Phosphor omitted		10·00				
				da. Phosphor omitted. (*strip of three*)	35·00	
W147	780	**W143**		9d. Ochre, brown, black and grey	10	15
b. Phosphor omitted		10·00				
W148	781	**W144**		9d. Ochre, brown, black and grey	10	15
b. Phosphor omitted		10·00				
W149	782	**W145**		1s. Brown, black, grey, green and greenish yellow	25	25
a. Pair, Nos. W149/50		90	85			
b. Greenish yellow omitted		£2000				
c. Phosphor omitted		25·00				
				ca. Phosphor omitted. (*pair*)	60·00	
W150	783	**W146**		1s. Red, black, brown, carmine and grey	25	25
a. Carmine (hull overlay) omitted	£7500					
b. Phosphor omitted		25·00				

First Day Cover (W145/50)	3·25
Presentation Pack* (W145/50)	3·00
Pack also exists with a Dutch or Japanese insert card.	
Presentation Pack (German) (W145/50)	22·00

*In addition to the generally issued Presentation Pack (inscribed "RMS Queen Elizabeth 2 ... she sailed on her maiden voyage to New York on 17 January 1969") a further pack (inscribed "RMS Queen Elizabeth 2 ... she sails on her maiden voyage early in 1969") was issued for sale exclusively on board the Q.E.2 during her maiden voyage which had been postponed. (*Price* £8).

9d. *Prices for missing colour errors in strips of three:*

Red, blue and phosphor	£950
Blue	£1100

1s. *Price for missing colour error in pair:*

Greenish yellow	—

First Day covers are known postmarked 14 January, Buckley, Flintshire. The year date shown as 1968 instead of 1969 exists postmarked at Brighton, Sussex.

Cylinder Numbers (Blocks of Six (5d. and 1s.) or Twelve (9d.))

Cyl. Nos. (No dot)	Perforation Types	
	A(T)	F
5d. 1A (black)–1B (grey)–1C (red)–1D (turquoise)	1·00	†
9d. 1A (black)–2B (brown)–1C (ochre)–1D (grey)–1E (red)–1F (blue)	†	3·00
1s. 2A (black)–1B (grey)–1C (green)–1D (red)–1E (carmine)–1F (brown)–1G (yellow)	2·25	†

Minor Constant Flaws

5d. Cyls. 1A–1B–1C–1D
2/5 Disturbance in sea over liz of Elizabeth
3/2 Blue flaw on superstructure halfway between funnel and stern (Th. E6) (later removed)
4/5 Weak patch in hull directly below funnel (Th. F9)

9d. Cyls. 1A–2B–1C–1D–1E–1F
16/2 Rope between second and third masts is broken (Th. D5)

1s. Cyls. 2A–1B–1C–1D–1E–1F–1G
1/6 Small brown flaw lower right of stern mast (Th. D6)
2/8 Curved black flaw just above third funnel (Th. C10)
4/2 Weak patch in hull directly below fore mast (Th. E17)
10/1 Wispy black flaw in front of Queen's chin (Th. B–C17)

Sheet Details

Sheet sizes:
All single pane sheet-fed
5d. 72 (8 × 9).
9d. 120 (6 × 20). In *se-tenant* strips of three
1s. 80 (8 × 10). In *se-tenant* pairs

Sheet markings:
Cylinder numbers:
5d. Opposite rows 7/8, left margin, boxed
9d. Opposite rows 17/18, left margin, boxed
1s. Below vertical row 7, boxed
Guide holes: None
Marginal arrows (photo-etched); " W " shaped, at top and bottom (5d.); " W " shaped, at top, bottom and sides (others)
Marginal rule: None
Colour register marks:
5d. Opposite rows 1/2 and 8/9 at both sides
9d. Above and below vertical rows 1 and 6
1s. Opposite rows 1/2 and 10 at both sides
Coloured crosses:
5d. Opposite rows 5/6 at both sides
9d. Above and below vertical rows 3/4
1s. Opposite rows 5/7 at both sides
Autotron marks, colour designations: None
Traffic lights (boxed):
5d. In same order as cylinder numbers opposite rows 7/8, right margin; also above vertical row 7 reading left to right
9d. In same order as cylinder numbers opposite rows 18/19, right margin; also above vertical rows 5/6 but in reverse order to cylinder numbers reading left to right
1s. In reverse order to cylinder numbers opposite rows 8/9, right margin; also above vertical row 8 in reverse order to cylinder numbers reading left to right

Imprimaturs from the National Postal Museum Archives

Nos. W145/150 imperforate

No watermark (*set of* 6)

Quantities Sold

5d. 67,584,528, 9d. 14,351,160, 1s. 10,784,480, English Pack 116,526, German Pack 4,416

Withdrawn 14.1.70

W147. "Concorde" in Flight
(Des. Michael and Sylvia Goaman)

W148. Plan and Elevation Views

W149. "Concorde's" Nose and Tail

(Des. David Gentleman)

1969 (MARCH 3). FIRST FLIGHT OF "CONCORDE"

Issued to commemorate the first flight of the "Concorde" supersonic airliner developed and produced jointly by Britain and France.

Two phosphor bands

Cat. No.	S.G. No.	Type		Description	Mint	Used
W151	784	**W147**	4d.	Yellow-orange, violet, greenish blue, blue-green and pale green	10	10
a. Violet omitted (value, etc.) ..		£200				
b. Yellow-orange and phosphor omitted		£100				
c. Yellow-orange omitted		90·00				
d. Phosphor omitted		75	e. "Oil slick" flaw (R. 13/2) ..		2·50	
e. Left-hand band omitted ..		40·00	f. Broken line on fuselage (R. 5/1)		4·00	
W152	785	**W148**	9d. Ultramarine, emerald, red and grey-blue		20	20
a. Phosphor omitted		£100				
W153	786	**W149**	1s.6d. Deep blue, silver-grey and light blue		30	30
a. Silver-grey omitted*		£275				
b. Phosphor omitted		7·00				

First Day Cover (W151/3)	1·25
Presentation Pack (W151/3)	2·50
Pack also exists with a Japanese insert card	
Presentation Pack (German) (W151/3)	18·00

*No. W153a affects the Queen's head which appears in the light blue colour.

Listed Varieties

W151*e*
Dark flaw in Atlantic Ocean
appears as an oil slick

W151*f*

Cylinder Numbers (Blocks of Six)

Cyl. Nos. (No dot)   Perforation Type F

4d.	1A (violet)–1B (orange)–1C (greenish blue)–1D (pale green)–	
	1E (blue-green)	1·00
9d.	2A (grey-blue)–1B (red)–1C (emerald)–1D (ultramarine) ..	1·75
1s.6d.	1A (deep blue)–1B (silver-grey)–3C (light blue)	4·00

Minor Constant Flaws

4d. Cyls. 1A–1B–1C–1D–1E
  1/2 Disturbance in background below tail (Th. F–G11)
  2/2 Disturbance in background below tail (Th. F–G12)
9d. Cyls. 2A–1B–1C–1D
  11/2 Flaw on Queen's hair below ribbons (Th. B13)
1s.6d. Cyls. 1A–1B–3C
  18/2 Small white patch below tip of Concorde's nose (Th. F13)

Sheet Details

Sheet size: 120 (6 × 20). Single pane sheet-fed
Sheet markings:
  Cylinder numbers:
    4d. Opposite rows 1/2 and 18/19, at both sides, boxed
    9d. Opposite rows 2/3 and 18/19, at both sides, boxed
    1s. 6d. Opposite rows 2 and 19, at both sides, boxed
  Guide holes: None
  Marginal arrows (photo-etched): "W" shaped, at top, bottom and sides
  Marginal rule: At bottom of sheet
  Colour register marks:
    4d. Above and below vertical rows 1/2 and 6
    9d. Above and below vertical rows 1 and 5/6
    1s.6d. Above and below vertical rows 1/2 and 6
  Coloured crosses: Above and below vertical rows 2/3
  Autotron marks, colour designations: None
  Traffic lights (boxed):
    4d. Blue-green, orange, violet, greenish blue, pale green reading left to right above vertical row 5
    9d. Ultramarine, emerald, red, grey-blue reading left to right above vertical row 5
    1s.6d. Deep blue, light blue, silver-grey reading left to right above vertical row 5

Imprimaturs from the National Postal Museum Archives

Nos. W151/153 imperforate

No watermark (*set of* 3)

Quantities Sold

4d.	91,551,720	English Pack	100,608
9d.	9,488,520	German Pack	2,827
1s.6d.	9,874,560		

Withdrawn 2.3.70

W150. Page from *Daily Mail*
and Vickers "Vimy" Aircraft
(Des. Philip Sharland)

W151. Europa and CEPT
Emblems
(Des. Michael and Sylvia Goaman)

W152. ILO Emblem
(Des. Philip Sharland)

W153. Flags of NATO Countries
(Des. Philip Sharland)

W154. Vickers "Vimy" Aircraft and
Globe showing Flight
(Des. Michael and Sylvia Goaman)

1969 (APRIL 2). NOTABLE ANNIVERSARIES

Five famous anniversaries, with the events described on the stamps.
Two phosphor bands, applied by photogravure (5d.) or flexography (others)

Cat. No.	S.G. No.	Type	Description	Mint	Used
W154	791	**W150**	5d. Black, pale sage-green,		
a. Phosphor omitted			chestnut and new blue	10	10
b. Missing windshield (R. 3/4)	3·00				
W155	792	**W151**	9d. Pale turquoise, deep blue,		
a. Phosphor omitted	16·00		light emerald-green and		
			black	20	20
W156	793	**W152**	1s. Bright purple, deep blue		
a. Phosphor omitted	5·00		and lilac	20	20
W157	794	**W153**	1s.6d. Red, royal blue, yellow-		
a. Black omitted	60·00		green, black, lemon and		
b. Yellow-green omitted	48·00		new blue	20	20
c. Yellow-green and phosphor omitted	55·00				
d. Phosphor omitted	7·00		e. Shadow variety (R. 18/6)	3·00	
W158	795	**W154**	1s.9d. Yellow-olive, greenish		
a. Uncoated paper*	£200		yellow and pale		
b. Phosphor omitted	4·00		turquoise-green	25	25

First Day Cover (W154/8)		1·50
Presentation Pack (W154/8)		2·50
Pack also exists with a Japanese insert card		
Presentation Pack (German) (W154/8)		40·00

*Uncoated paper–see General Notes for Section UA also below Nos. W159/64.
No. W154 is known postmarked 1 April.

Listed Varieties

Normal   W154*b*

W157*e*
Deficient shading in shadow
by fold

Cylinder Numbers (Blocks of Six (5d., 1s., 1s.9d.) or Eight (9d., 1s.6d.))

	Cyl. Nos. (No dot)		Perforation Types	
			A	F
5d.	1A (blue)–1B (chestnut)–1C (sage-green)–1D (black)	..	1·00	†
9d.	1A (blue)–1B (green)–1C (black)–1D (turquoise) ..	..	†	2·25
1s.	1A (blue)–1B (purple)–1C (lilac) ..	.. .. ..	†	1·75
1s.6d.	1A (new blue)–1B (lemon)–1C (red)–1D (royal blue)–			
	1E (black)–1F (green)		†	2·25
1s.9d.	2A (yellow-olive)–2B (green)–1C (yellow) ..	.. ..	†	2·50

Minor Constant Flaws

5d. Cyls. 1A–1B–1C–1D
 3/4 Black horizontal line extending through the engine and fuselage (Th. E9–12)
 4/6 Vertical black scratch top left of photograph of Alcock (Th. A–B3)
 15/3 Retouch to base of engine (Th. E10)
 15/5 White flaw on Brown's cap (Th. B6). Later retouched

9d. Cyls. 1A–1B–1C–1D
 14/1 Retouch to background below O of EUROPA (Th. F–G4)
 15/3 Weak patch in background to left of CEPT symbol (Th. E11)
 19/3 Retouch to background below EU of EUROPA (Th. F2)
 20/2 Weak patch in background above O of EUROPA (Th. B–C4)

1s. Cyls. 1A–1B–1C
 19/1 Dark patch in upper jaw of spanner (Th. F1)

1s.9d. Cyls. 2A–2B–1C
 17/4 Horizontal scratch through value (Th. A1–3)
 20/6 Pale patch in East Asia on globe (Th. B12)

Sheet Details

Sheet size: 120 (6 × 20). 5d. single pane reel-fed; others single pane sheet-fed

Sheet markings:

Cylinder numbers:
 5d. Opposite rows 18/19, left margin, boxed
 9d. Opposite rows 17/18, left margin, boxed
 1s. Opposite row 18, left margin, boxed
 1s.6d. Opposite rows 17/18, left margin, boxed
 1s.9d. Opposite row 18, left margin, boxed

Guide holes:
 5d. Opposite rows 14/15 (boxed), at both sides
 Others: None

Marginal arrows (photo-etched): "W" shaped, at top, bottom and sides

Marginal rule: None

Colour register marks:
 5d. Opposite rows 1/2 and 19/20 at both sides
 Others: Above and below vertical rows 1 and 6

Coloured crosses:
 5d. None
 9d., 1s. and 1s.9d. Above and below vertical row 3
 1s.6d. Above and below vertical rows 3/4

Autotron marks (solid):
 5d. Black, sage-green, blue, chestnut below vertical rows 1/3
 Others: None

Colour designations:
 5d. "G1 BROWN G2 BLUE G3 (blank) G4 BLACK " in right margin reading upwards opposite rows 14/9
 Others: None

331

Sheet values: Opposite rows 4/7 and 14/17 reading upwards in left margin and downwards in right margin
Traffic lights (boxed):
5d. Black, sage-green, blue, chestnut opposite rows 18/19, right margin; also in same order opposite rows 1/2, left margin
9d. Black, green, blue, turquoise opposite rows 17/18, right margin; also in reverse order reading left to right above vertical row 5
1s. In same order as cylinder numbers opposite row 18, right margin; also in reverse order reading left to right above vertical row 5
1s.6d. In same order as cylinder numbers opposite rows 17/18, right margin; also in reverse order reading left to right above vertical row 5
1s.9d. In same order as cylinder numbers opposite row 18, right margin; also in reverse order reading left to right above vertical row 5

Imprimaturs from the National Postal Museum Archives

Nos. W154/158 imperforate

No watermark (*set of* 5)

Quantities Sold

5d.	82,285,680	English Pack	90,282
9d.	9,823,200	German Pack	4,539
1s.	10,302,360		
1s.6d.	10,512,480		
1s.9d.	6,155,760		

Withdrawn 1.4.70

W155. Durham Cathedral

W156. York Minster

W157. St. Giles', Edinburgh

W158. Canterbury Cathedral

W159. St. Paul's Cathedral

W160. Liverpool Metropolitan
Cathedral

(Des. Peter Gauld)

1969 (MAY 28). BRITISH ARCHITECTURE (CATHEDRALS)

The designs show six famous British Cathedrals dating from medieval times to the present day, the Liverpool Metropolitan Cathedral being completed in 1967.

The 5d. values were issued together *se-tenant* in blocks of four throughout the sheet

Two phosphor bands, applied by flexography (5d.) or photogravure (others)

Cat. No.	S.G. No.	Type			Description	Mint	Used
W159	796	**W155**			5d. Grey-black, orange, pale	10	10
a. Block of 4. Nos. W159/62			85	1·00	bluish violet and black		
ac. Uncoated paper* (block of four)							
b. Pale bluish violet omitted			£1750				
c. Uncoated paper*							
W160	797	**W156**			5d. Grey-black, pale bluish		
b. Pale bluish violet omitted			£1750		violet, new blue and	10	10
c. Uncoated paper*					black		
W161	798	**W157**			5d. Grey-black, purple, green	10	10
b. Green omitted*			40·00		and black		
c. Uncoated paper*							
W162	799	**W158**			5d. Grey-black, green, new blue	10	10
c. Uncoated paper*					and black		
W163	800	**W159**			9d. Grey-black, ochre, pale	15	15
a. Black omitted (value)			£100		drab, violet and black		
b. Phosphor omitted			40·00				
W164	801	**W160**			1s.6d. Grey-black, pale tur-		
a. Black omitted (value)			£1850		quoise-blue, pale red-		
b. Black (value) double					dish violet, pale yellow-	15	15
c. Phosphor omitted			18·00		olive and black		
ca. Phosphor omitted and one							
stamp with diagonal phosphor							
band (pair)			27·00				

333

First Day Cover (W159/64)	2·00
Presentation Pack (W159/64)	3·00
Pack also exists with a Dutch or Japanese insert card.	
Presentation Pack (German) (W159/64)	22·00

*Uncoated paper. This does not respond to the chalky paper test, and may be further distinguished from the normal chalk-surfaced paper by the fibres which clearly show on the surface, resulting in the printing impression being rougher, and by the screening dots which are not so evident.

5d. *Prices for missing colour errors in blocks of four:*

Pale bluish violet	£3500
Green	45·00

*The missing green on the roof top is known on R. 2/5, R. 8/5 and R. 10/5 but all from different sheets and it only occurred in part of the printing, being " probably caused by a batter on the impression cylinder ". Examples are known with the green partly omitted.

Cylinder Numbers (Blocks of Eight (5d.) or Six (9d., 1s.6d.))

	Cyls. Nos.	Perforation Types		
		A	A	F
		No dot	Dot	No dot
5d.	1A (black)–1B (purple)–1C (blue)–1D (orange)–			
	2E (green)–2F (grey-black)–1G (violet)* ..	1·75	1·75	†
	1A (black)–1B (purple)–2C (blue)–1D (orange)–			
	2E (green)–2F (grey-black)–1G (violet)* ..	1·75	1·75	†
9d.	1A (black)–1B (grey-black)–2C (violet)–			
	1D (drab)–1E (ochre)**	†	†	1·50
1s.6d.	1A (black)–1B (violet)–1C (turquoise-blue)–			
	1D (yellow-olive)–1E (grey-black)	†	†	1·50

* In the 5d. dot panes the violet cylinder is expressed in error thus: " 1.G " and the black cylinder " 1.A ".
**In the 9d. the violet " 2C " often appears battered, the " 2 " sometimes being hardly discernible.

Minor Constant Flaws

5d. Cyls. 1A–1B–1D–2E–2F no dot in combination with blue cyls. 1C or 2C no dot
   12/4 Thin diagonal green line joins portrait to inset design (Th. C–E2)
5d. Cyls. 1A–1B–1D–2E–2F dot in combination with blue cyls. 1C or 2C dot
   1–4/3 Green coloured scratch extends from bottom of third stamp in row 1 to top of third stamp in row 4.
     Most noticeable in the sky of R. 3/3
   4/1 Damaged first S of ST. GILES'
   10/3 Grey-black coloured spur at right of angel (Th. F13)
9d. Cyls. 1A–1B–2C–1D–1E
   8/5 Dark spot in window on first floor just to right of centre of St. Paul's (Th. F7)
   9/1 Dot left of ground floor window next to entrance columns (Th. G3)
1s.6d. Cyls. 1A–1B–1C–1D–1E
   1/1 Retouch on Queen's head (Th. A11)
   15/1 Spur at left of third spike of central tower (Th. A5); also dot before C of CATHEDRAL

Sheet Details

Sheet sizes:
   5d. 72 (6 × 12). In *se-tenant* blocks of four, double pane reel-fed, with dot pane above no dot pane
   9d. and 1s.6d. 120 (6 × 20). Single pane sheet-fed

Sheet markings:
   Cylinder numbers:
     5d. Opposite rows 10/11, left margin, boxed
     9d. and 1s.6d. Opposite rows 18/19, left margin, boxed
   Guide holes:
     5d. Opposite rows 6/7 (boxed), at both sides
     Others: None
   Marginal arrows (photo-etched): " W " shaped, at top, bottom and sides
   Marginal rule: None
   Colour register marks:
     5d. Opposite rows 10/12, left margin, although usually trimmed off
     9d. and 1s.6d. Above and below vertical rows 1 and 6
   Coloured crosses:
     5d. None
     9d. and 1s.6d. Above and below vertical rows 3/4

Autotron marks:
   5d. Normally trimmed off
   9d. and 1s.6d. None

Colour designations: None

Sheet values:
   5d. Opposite rows 2/5 and 8/11 reading upwards in left margin and downwards in right margin
   9d. and 1s.6d. Opposite rows 5/6 and 15/16 reading upwards in left margin and downwards in right margin

Traffic lights (boxed):
   5d. In same order as cylinder numbers opposite rows 10/11, right margin; also in same order reading
     left to right above vertical rows 4/5
   9d. In reverse order to cylinder numbers opposite rows 18/19, right margin; also above vertical row 5
     but in same order as cylinder numbers reading left to right
   1s.6d. Black, yellow-olive, turquoise-blue, violet, grey-black opposite rows 18/19, right margin; also
     grey-black, yellow-olive, turquoise-blue, violet and black reading left to right above vertical row 5

Imprimaturs from the National Postal Museum Archives

Nos. W163/164 imperforate

No watermark (2 *values only*)

Quantities Sold

5d.	65,344,176	English Pack	119,828
9d.	11,065,920	German Pack	7,200
1s.6d.	11,414,280		

Withdrawn   27.5.70

W161. The King's Gate,   **W162.** The Eagle Tower,   **W163.** Queen Eleanor's Gate,
Caernarvon Castle   Caernarvon Castle   Caernarvon Castle

W164.   Celtic Cross,   **W165.** H.R.H. The Prince of Wales
Margam Abbey   (after photograph by G. Argent)

(Des. David Gentleman)

1969 (JULY 1).   INVESTITURE OF H.R.H. THE PRINCE OF WALES

The ceremony of Investiture dates back to 1284 when King Edward I presented his son to the people of Caernarvon as the first Prince of Wales.

The 5d. values were issued together *se-tenant* in strips of three throughout the sheet

Two phosphor bands, applied by flexography, the phosphor being printed between two groups of colour units.

Cat. No.	S.G. No.	Type			Description	Mint	Used
W165	802	**W161**			5d. Deep olive-grey, light olive-		
a. Strip of 3. Nos. W165/7	..	..	70	'5	grey, deep grey, light grey,		
b. Black omitted (value and inscr.)		£150			red, pale turquoise-green,		
c. Red omitted* ..	..	..	£250		black and silver	10	10
d. Deep grey omitted**	..	..	90·00				
e. Pale turquoise-green omitted	..	£250					
f. Phosphor omitted	..	..	3·00		*fa.* Phosphor omitted (strip of three)	10·00	
W166	803	**W162**			5d. Deep olive-grey, light olive-		
b. Black omitted (value and inscr.)		£150			grey, deep grey, light grey,		
c. Red omitted* ..	..	..	£250		red, pale turquoise-green,		
d. Deep grey omitted**	..	..	90·00		black and silver	10	10
e. Pale turquoise-green omitted	..	£250					
f. Phosphor omitted	..	..	3·00		*g.* Grey line flaw (R. 6/2)	.. ..	2·50
W167	804	**W163**			5d. Deep olive-grey, light olive-		
b. Black omitted (value and inscr.)		£150			grey, deep grey, light grey,		
c. Red omitted* ..	..	..	£250		red, pale turquoise-green,		
d. Deep grey omitted**	..	..	90·00		black and silver	10	10
e. Pale turquoise-green omitted	..	£250					
f. Phosphor omitted	..	..	3·00				
W168	805	**W164**			9d. Deep grey, light grey, black		
a. Phosphor omitted	..	..	..	20·00	and gold	20	10
b. One broad band	..	..	30·00				
W169	806	**W165**			1s. Blackish yellow-olive and		
a. Phosphor omitted	..	..	..	11·00	gold	20	10
b. One broad band	..	..	30·00				
c. Diagonal broad band	..	..	40·00				

First Day Cover (W165/9)	.. ..	1·40
Presentation Pack† (W165/9)	.. ..	1·40
Pack also exists with a Dutch or Japanese insert card	
Presentation Pack (German) (W165/9)	16·00

5d. *Prices for missing colour errors in strips of three.*

Black	..	..	..	..	..	..	..	..	..	..	..	£450
Red	..	..	..	..	..	..	..	..	..	..	..	£750
Deep grey	..	..	..	..	..	..	..	..	..	..	..	£275
Pale turquoise-green	..	..	..	..	..	..	..	..				

*The 5d. is also known with the red misplaced downwards and where this occurs the red printing does not take very well on the silver background and in some cases is so faint that it could be mistaken for a missing red. However, the red can be seen under a magnifying glass and caution should therefore be exercised when purchasing examples of W165/7*c*.

**The deep grey affects the dark portions of the windows and doorways.

†In addition to the generally issued Presentation Pack a further pack in different colours and with all texts printed in both English and Welsh was made available exclusively through Education Authorities for free distribution to all schoolchildren in Wales and Monmouthshire. (*Price £*4.)

First Day Covers are known postmarked in error "1 JUL 1968" at London N.W.1.

Listed Variety

Grey line just below turrets

W166*g*

Cylinder Numbers (Blocks of Nine (5d.) or Four (9d., 1s.))

	Perforation Types		
Cyl. Nos.	A No dot	A Dot	F No dot
5d. 1A (black)-1B (red)-1C (silver)-1D (green)- 1E (deep olive-grey)-1F (light olive-grey)- 1G (deep grey)-1H (light grey)	†	†	1·50

	A No dot	A Dot	A(T) No dot	A(T) Dot
9d. 1A (black)-1B (gold)-1C (deep grey)-1D (light grey)	1·50	1·50	†	†
1s. 1A (gold)-2B (blackish yellow-olive)	1·50	1·50	—	—

The above are with sheets orientated showing head to right.

Minor Constant Flaws

9d. Cyls. 1A–1B–1C–1D dot
  5/9 yw of Tywysog are joined together

1s. 1A–2B no dot
  1/10 Retouch to right of Prince's lower lip (Th. J–K6)
  3/4 Small retouch below Prince's left eye (Th. G6)

  1A–2B dot
  3/9 Dark patch below Prince's left eye (Th. G6)

Sheet Details

Sheet sizes:
  5d. 72 (12 × 6). In *se-tenant* strips of three, single pane sheet-fed
  9d. and 1s. 60 (10 × 6). Double pane sheet-fed, with no dot pane above dot pane

Sheet markings:
  Cylinder numbers:
    5d. Opposite rows 4/5, left margin, boxed
    9d. and 1s. Opposite row 6, left margin, boxed

  Guide holes: None

  Marginal arrows (photo-etched):
    5d. None
    9d. and 1s. "W" shaped, at top, bottom and sides

  Marginal rule: None

  Colour register marks:
    5d. Opposite rows 1 and 6, at both sides
    9d. Above (no dot) or below (dot) vertical rows 1/2 and 10
    1s. Above (no dot) or below (dot) vertical rows 1/2 and 9/10

  Coloured crosses:
    5d. Opposite rows 3/4, at both sides
    9d. and 1s. Above (no dot) or below (dot) vertical row 4

  Autotron marks, colour designations: None

  Sheet values:
    5d. Above and below vertical rows 2/5 and 8/11 reading left to right in top margin and right to left
      (upside-down) in bottom margin
    9d. and 1s. Opposite rows 1/3 and 4/6 reading upwards in left margin and downwards in right margin

  Traffic lights (boxed):
    5d. In same order as cylinder numbers opposite rows 4/5, right margin; also in same order reading left
      to right above vertical rows 10/11
    9d. In same order as cylinder numbers opposite row 6, right margin; also in same order reading left to
      right above vertical row 9
    1s. In reverse order to cylinder numbers opposite row 6, right margin; also in reverse order reading left
      to right above vertical row 9

Imprimaturs from the National Postal Museum Archives

Nos. W168/169 imperforate

No watermark (2 *values only*)

Quantities Sold

5d.	99,467,496	English Pack	256,709
9d.	13,384,380	German Pack	9,360
1s.	12,972,720	Welsh Schoolchildren's Pack	146,958

Withdrawn 30.6.70

W166. Mahatma Gandhi
(Des. Biman Mullick)

1969 (AUGUST 13). GANDHI CENTENARY YEAR

This stamp marking the Gandhi Centenary Year was also the first United Kingdom postage stamp to commemorate an overseas leader and the first to be designed by an overseas artist.

Two phosphor bands, applied by flexography

Cat. No.	S.G. No.	Type	Description	Mint	Used
W170	807	**W166**	1s.6d. Black, green, red-orange		
a. Printed on the gummed side ..	£300		and grey	30	30
b. Phosphor omitted	3·00				
c. Tooth Flaw (R. 20/3)	3·00				

First Day Cover (W170)	50	

The above is known pre-released on 12 August at Penyfai (Bridgend), Glamorgan and also postmarked Paisley, Renfrewshire 13 July, the latter being due to the use of an incorrect date-stamp on a first day cover.

Listed Variety

White patch in Gandhi's mouth appears as tooth. Later retouched to near normal

W170c

Cylinder Numbers (Blocks of Six)

Cyl. Nos. (No dot)   Perforation Type F

1s.6d. 2A (black)–1B (grey)–2C (green)–1D (orange) ..   ..   .. 4·00

Minor Constant Flaws

1s.6d. Cyls. 2A–1B–2C–1D
  1/6 Second white spot in Gandhi's right eye (Th. D6). Later retouched; also small nick in left arm of Y of Year
  3/4 Dark patch on arm of spectacles (Th. C4)
  3/5 Retouch on Gandhi's nose (Th. E6)
  5/3 Dark spot in front of Gandhi's right ear (Th. D3)
  8/2 Dark spot on Gandhi's temple (Th. C4). Later retouched
  12/4 White patch on Gandhi's right lapel (Th. G2)
  16/1 Retouched G of Gandhi

Sheet Details

Sheet size: 120 (6 × 20). Single pane sheet-fed
Sheet markings:
  Cylinder numbers: Opposite rows 18/19, left margin, boxed
  Guide holes: None
  Marginal arrows (photo-etched): "W" shaped, at top, bottom and sides
  Marginal rule: None
  Colour register marks: Above and below vertical rows 1 and 6
  Coloured crosses: Above and below vertical row 3
  Autotron marks and colour designations: None
  Sheet values: Opposite rows 4/7 and 14/17 reading upwards in left margin and downwards in right margin
  Traffic lights (boxed): Black, grey, green, orange opposite rows 19/20, right margin; also in reverse order reading left to right above vertical row 5

338

Imprimatur from the National Postal Museum Archives

No. W170 imperforate

No watermark (*single*)

Quantity Sold   10,804,920

Withdrawn   12.8.70

1969 (SEPTEMBER 15). COLLECTORS PACK

WCP2 Comprising Nos. W142/70   20·00

   This pack also exists with a German or Japanese insert card.

Quantity Sold   63,890

W167.   National Giro
"G" Symbol

W168.   Telecommunications—
International Subscriber Dialling

W169.   Telecommunications—
Pulse Code Modulation

W170.   Postal Mechanisation—
Automatic Sorting

(Des. David Gentleman)
(Lithography by De La Rue)

1969 (OCTOBER 1). POST OFFICE TECHNOLOGY COMMEMORATION

   Issued on the day the Post Office became a public corporation, these stamps depict some of its technological achievements. This issue in itself was a technical departure for the Post Office being the first British stamps to be printed by lithography.

   Comb perforation 13½ × 14. Two phosphor bands applied by typography

Cat. No.	S.G. No.	Type			Description	Mint	Used
W171	808	**W167**			5d. New blue, greenish blue,		
a. Phosphor omitted		..	..	4·00	pale lavender and black	10	10
b. One broad band		..	..	12·00			
W172	809	**W168**			9d. Emerald, violet-blue and		
a. One broad band		..	..	12·00	black	15	15
W173	810	**W169**			1s. Emerald, lavender and		
a. Phosphor omitted		..	..	£300	black	15	15
b. One broad band		..	..	12·00			
W174	811	**W170**			1s.6d. Bright purple, light		
a. One broad band		..	..	15·00	turquoise-blue, grey-blue		
					and black	40	40

First Day Cover (W171/4)	..	..	1·00
Presentation Pack (W171/4)	..	..	2·25
Pack also exists with a Dutch, German or Japanese insert card.			

No. W171*a* can be found with or without a " dry " impression of the typography plate.
The 1s. is known postmarked at Gloucester on 29 September and the 1s.6d. at Gutcher
Yell (Shetland Isles) on 26 September.

For advance publicity the Post Office produced sample sets of stamps sealed in a sheet of
perspex (size 4 × 6 in.) together with details of the designs, and names of the stamp designer
and printer.

Plate Numbers (Blocks of Four)

	Pl. Nos. (all Dot)					Perforation Type F (L)
5d.	2A (new blue)–2B (greenish blue)–2C (lavender)–2D (black) ..		..			90
	2A (new blue)–3B (greenish blue)–2C (lavender)–2D (black)				..	90
	2A (new blue)–3B (greenish blue)–2C (lavender)–3D (black) ..			..		90
	3A (new blue)–4B (greenish blue)–3C (lavender)–4D (black) ..				..	1·25
9d.	2A (emerald)–2B (violet-blue)–2C (black)	..	..	..		1·25
1s.	1A (emerald)–1B (lavender)–1C (black) ..	..	..	..	..	2·00
	1A (emerald)–1B–(lavender)–2C (black)	..	..	..	..	1·25
	1A (emerald)–1B (lavender)–3C (black) ..	..	..	..	..	1·25
1s.6d.	1A (purple)–1B (light turquoise-blue)–1C (grey-blue)–1D (black) ..					2·50

Although all the plate numbers are followed by a dot they were in fact only printed in
single panes.

Minor Constant Flaws

Numerous minor flaws caused by specks of dust settling on the printing plate and
preventing the ink from reaching the area appear as white inkless rings and are known as
litho "ring" flaws. Minor flecks of colour are similarly caused. As such flaws only affect
part of a printing and cannot be regarded as constant we have decided not to record them.

Sheet Details

Sheet size: 120 (10 × 12). Single pane sheet-fed

Sheet markings:

Plate numbers: Opposite rows 1/2, left margin, unboxed

Guide holes: Above and below vertical row 6 in crossed box. Reserve guide-hole boxes appear above and
below vertical row 4 but these were not used

Marginal arrows (solid): " W " shaped, at top, bottom and sides

Marginal rule: None

Colour register marks:
5d., 9d. and 1s. Below vertical rows 1 and 10 and opposite rows 1 and 12, at both sides
1s.6d. Above and below vertical rows 1 and 10 and opposite rows 1 and 12, at both sides

Coloured crosses, autotron marks, colour designations: None

Sheet values: Above and below vertical rows 2/4 and 7/9 reading left to right in top margin and right to
left (upside-down) in bottom margin

Traffic lights (unboxed):
5d. Opposite rows 8/10, right margin
9d. and 1s. Opposite rows 9/10, right margin
1s.6d. Opposite rows 9/11, right margin

Imprimaturs from the National Postal Museum Archives

Nos. W171/174 imperforate

No watermark (*set of* 4)

Quantities Sold   5d. 72,405,720; 9d. 8,472,000; 1s. 10,296,120; 1s.6d. 10,757,040; Pack
104,230

Withdrawn   30.9.70

W171. Herald Angel

W172. The Three Shepherds

W173. The Three Kings

(Des. Fritz Wegner)

(Printed in photogravure with the Queen's head (and stars 4d., 5d. and scroll-work 1s.6d. embossed in gold)

1969 (NOVEMBER 26). CHRISTMAS

Traditional religious themes are featured on these stamps by Austrian-born designer Fritz Wegner.

One 7 to 8 mm. centre phosphor band (4d.) or two phosphor bands (others), applied by photogravure (W175b) or flexography (others)

Cat. No.	S.G. No.	Type		Description	Mint	Used
W175	812	**W171**		4d. Vermilion, new blue,		
a. Gold (Queen's head etc.)				orange, bright purple,		
omitted		£2000		light green, bluish		
b. Centre band 3½ mm.		25	15	violet, blackish brown		
				and gold	10	10
W176	813	**W172**		5d. Magenta, light blue, royal		
a. Light blue (sheep, etc.) omitted		60·00		blue, olive-brown, **green,**		
b. Red omitted*		£500		**greenish yellow, red** and		
c. Gold (Queen's head etc.) omitted		£400		gold	10	10
d. Green omitted		£200				
e. Olive-brown, red and gold omit-				*f.* Embossing omitted	20·00	
ted..				*g.* Phosphor omitted	1·00	
W177	814	**W173**		1s.6d. Greenish yellow, bright		
a. Gold omitted		80·00		purple, bluish violet,		
b. Deep slate omitted ..		£250		deep slate, orange, green,		
c. Greenish yellow omitted ..		£130		new blue and gold	30	30
d. Bluish violet omitted ..		£300				
e. New blue omitted		50·00				
f. Embossing omitted		8·00		*h.* Phosphor omitted	5·00	
g. Embossing and phosphor				*i.* Broken arch (R.1/6)	2·00	
omitted		8·00				

First Day Cover (W175/7)	.. ..	1·00
Presentation Pack (W175/7)	.. ..	2·25
Pack also exists with a Dutch, German or Japanese insert card.		

*The effect of the missing red is shown on the hat, leggings and purse which appear as dull orange.

Used examples of No. W176 exist with either the olive-brown or greenish yellow omitted.

The 4d. is known postmarked at Dudley, Worcs. on 25 November.

No. W175 has one centre band 8 mm. wide but this was of no practical use in the automatic facing machines and after about three-quarters of the stamps had been printed the remainder were printed with a 3½ mm. band (No. W175b). The wide band is sometimes difficult to see. Stamps have also been seen with very wide " phantom " band measuring about 20 mm. which only reacts very faintly under the lamp and with a clear 3½ mm. band over it.

No. W176e was caused by a paper fold.

Listed Variety

Break in the arch above the crown of King at right

W177*i*

Cylinder Numbers (Blocks of Six (4d.) or Eight (5d., 1s.6d.))
Cyl. Nos.

Perforation Types
A

		7–8 mm. band		3½ mm. band	
		No dot	Dot	No dot	Dot
4d.	1A (brown)–1B (vermilion)–2C (orange)–1D (purple)–1E (new blue)–1F (green)–1G (violet)–1H (gold)	1·00	1·00	†	†
	1A (brown)–1B (vermilion)–2C (orange)–1D (purple)–1E (new blue)–2F (green)–1G (violet)–1H (gold)	2·00	2·00	2·00	2·00
		F No dot		F (L) No dot	
5d.	1A (royal blue)–1B (yellow)–1C (magenta)–1D (green)–2E (brown)–1F (light blue)–1G (red)–1H (gold)	1·25		10·00	
1s.6d.	3A (slate)–1C (gold)–1D (blue)–1E (yellow)–1F (green)–1G (violet)–1H (purple)–1J (orange)	4·00		†	

On the 4d. cylinder numbers 1A and 1H often appear as "1A1" and "1H1" on the dot and no dot panes respectively; the 1B and 1E have what appear to be small letters "IN" in place of dot, whilst the 2C is an alteration from "1C", all on the dot panes.

Minor Constant Flaws
4d. Cyls. 1A–1B–2C–1D–1E–2F–1G–1H dot
    5/3 White flaw in hem of angel's gown (later corrected) (Th. E1)
    11/1 A break in the pattern of the pillar on the right (Th. E13)
    11/4 White flaw in the pattern of the arch over the Queen's head (Th. A11)

Sheet Details
Sheet sizes:
    4d. 72 (6×12). Double pane reel-fed (one pane above the other) for four colours and phosphor, and then single pane sheet-fed for remaining four colours and embossing
    5d. and 1s.6d. 120 (6×20). Single pane sheet-fed
Sheet markings:
    Cylinder numbers:
        4d. Opposite rows 10/12, left margin, boxed
        5d. and 1s.6d. Opposite rows 17/19, left margin, boxed
    Guide holes:
        4d. Opposite rows 6/7 (boxed), at both sides
        5d. and 1s.6d. None
    Marginal arrows (photo-etched): "W" shaped, at top, bottom and sides
    Marginal rule: None
    Colour register marks:
        4d. None
        5d. and 1s.6d. Above and below vertical rows 1/2 and 5/6
    Coloured crosses:
        4d. Usually trimmed off
        5d. and 1s.6d. Above and below vertical rows 3/4
    Autotron marks, colour designations: None
Sheet values:
    4d. Opposite rows 3/4 and 9/10 reading upwards in left margin and downwards in right margin
    5d. Opposite rows 4/7 and 14/17 reading upwards in left margin and downwards in right margin
    1s.6d. Opposite rows 5/6 and 15/16 reading upwards in left margin and downwards in right margin
Traffic lights (boxed):
    4d. Vermilion, orange, purple, new blue, green, brown, violet, gold and embossing opposite rows 9/11, right margin; also in same order reading left to right above vertical rows 4/5
    5d. Embossing and then as cylinder numbers but in reverse order opposite rows 17/19, right margin; also in same order as cylinder numbers followed by embossing above vertical rows 4/5
    1s.6d. Embossing, gold, blue, yellow, slate, green, violet, purple and orange opposite rows 17/19, right margin; also in reverse order reading left to right above vertical rows 4/5

Imprimaturs from the National Postal Museum Archives
Nos. W175/177 imperforate

No watermark (*set of* 3)

Quantities Sold   4d. 271,244,808; 5d. 139,845,600; 1s.6d. 19,136,520; Pack 121,454

Withdrawn   25.11.70

W174.   Fife Harling   **W175.**   Cotswold Limestone

(Des. David Gentleman)

W176.   Welsh Stucco   **W177.**   Ulster Thatch

(Des. Sheila Robinson)

1970 (FEBRUARY 11). BRITISH RURAL ARCHITECTURE

The designs feature typical cottage architecture in Scotland, England, Wales and Northern Ireland respectively.

Two phosphor bands

Cat. No.	S.G. No.	Type	Description	Mint	Used
W178	815	**W174**	5d. Grey, grey-black, black, lemon, greenish blue, orange-brown, ultramarine and green	10	10
a. Lemon omitted		50·00			
b. Lemon omitted from chimney at left (R. 12/2)		2·25			
c. Grey (Queen's head and cottage shading) omitted		£4000			
d. Phosphor omitted		1·50			
e. Nick in hair (R. 15/6)		2·50			
W179	816	**W175**	9d. Orange-brown, olive-yellow, bright green, black, grey-black and grey	20	20
a. Phosphor omitted		6·00			
W180	817	**W176**	1s. Deep blue, reddish lilac, drab and new blue	20	20
a. New blue omitted		45·00			
b. Phosphor omitted		12·00			
c. One broad band					
W181	818	**W177**	1s.6d. Greenish yellow, black, turquoise-blue and lilac	35	35
a. Turquoise-blue omitted ..		£3500			
b. Phosphor omitted		2·25			
c. Broken panes in middle window (No dot, R. 3/2)		3·00			

First Day Cover (W178/81)	..	..	1·25
Presentation Pack (W178/81)	..	..	3·00
Pack also exists with a Dutch, German or Japanese insert card			

Used examples of No. W178 have been seen with the grey-black or greenish blue colours omitted.

First Day covers are known postmarked 11 January (Doncaster) or 1969 (Farnham).

Listed Varieties

No. 178*b*. The lemon is omitted from the chimney at left once in every sheet (later added to cylinder and appearing normal).

W178*e*   W181*c*

Cylinder Numbers (Blocks of Eight (5d.), Six (9d.), Four (1s., 1s.6d.))

	Cyl. Nos.	Perforation Types		
		F No dot	A (T) No dot	A (T) Dot
5d.	1A (black)–1B (grey-black)–1C (brown)–1D (ultramarine)–1E (greenish blue)–1F (green)–1G (grey)–1H (lemon)	1·25	†	†
9d.	1A (grey-black)–1B (yellow)–1C (brown)–1D (black)–1E (green)–1F (grey)	1·75	†	†
1s.	1A (deep blue)–2B (lilac)–1C (new blue)–1D (drab)..	†	1·50	1·50
1s.6d.	1A (black)–1B (yellow)–1C (turquoise-blue)–1D (lilac)	†	4·00	4·00

Minor Constant Flaws

5d. Cyls. 1A–1B–1C–1D–1E–1F–1G–1H no dot
    4/2 Right leg of h of harling is broken
    9/6 Pale patch on wall above left-hand first-floor window of building at right (Th. D8)
    20/6 Pale patch on wall by top of upright at the bottom of the banisters and similar patch with grey spot in it just above (Th. F1); coloured spur to centre chimney (Th. A7); and orange-brown flaw below F of Fife (Th. A2)

9d. Cyls. 1A–1B–1C–1D–1E–1F no dot
    19/1 Dark flaw on gate at left (Th. G2)

1s.6d. Cyls. 1A–1B–1C–1D no dot
    2/3 Pale flaw on left stroke of U of ULSTER and two yellow dots in front of Queen's neck

1s.6d. Cyls. 1A–1B–1C–1D dot
    5/5 White flaw to right of sixth brick from bottom (Th. G7)

Sheet Details

Sheet sizes:
    5d. and 9d. 120 (6 × 20). Single pane sheet-fed.
    1s. and 1s.6d. 60 (6 × 10). Double pane sheet-fed (etched sideways on the cylinder)

Sheet markings:
    Cylinder numbers:
        5d. Opposite rows 17/19, left margin, boxed
        9d. Opposite rows 18/19, left margin, boxed
        1s. and 1s.6d. Opposite rows 9/10, left margin, boxed

    Guide holes: None

    Marginal arrows (photo-etched): " W " shaped, at top, bottom and sides

    Marginal rule: None

    Colour register marks:
        5d. and 9d. Above and below vertical rows 1/2 and 6
        1s. Opposite rows 1/2 and 6, at left (no dot) or right (dot)
        1s.6d. Opposite rows 1 and 6, at left (no dot) or right (dot)

    Coloured crosses:
        5d. and 9d. Above and below vertical rows 3/4
        1s. Opposite row 7, at left (no dot) or right (dot)
        1s.6d. Opposite rows 6/7, at left (no dot) or right (dot)

    Autotron marks, colour designations: None

    Sheet values:
        5d. and 9d. Opposite rows 4/7 and 14/17 reading upwards in left margin and downwards in right margin
        1s. Opposite row 2/4 and 7/9 reading upwards in left margin and downwards in right margin
        1s.6d. As 1s. but reading downwards in left margin and upwards in right margin

Traffic lights (boxed):
 5d. In same order as cylinder numbers opposite rows 18/19, right margin; also in reverse order reading left to right above vertical rows 4/6
 9d. In reverse order to cylinder numbers opposite rows 18/19; also in same order as cylinder numbers above vertical row 5
 1s. In same order as cylinder numbers opposite rows 6/7, right margin; also in same order reading left to right above vertical row 5
 1s.6d. In same order as cylinder numbers opposite rows 7/8 at both sides; also in reverse order above vertical row 5

Imprimaturs from the National Postal Museum Archives

Nos. W178/181 imperforate

No watermark (*set of* 4)

Quantities Sold   5d. 81,581,880;   9d.   11,723,160;   1s.   10,258,320;   1s.6d.   8,969,280; Pack 116,983

Withdrawn   10.2.71

SALES QUANTITIES. The figures quoted for quantities actually sold of the 1970 issues are according to the best estimates available from the Post Office, as exact records of unsold returns could not be made in the circumstances following the postal strike, and the change to decimal issues. In particular the estimates for the Philympia and Christmas issues cannot be guaranteed.

W178.   Signing the Declaration of Arbroath

W179.   Florence Nightingale attending Patients

(Des. Fritz Wegner)

W180.   Signing the International Co-operative Alliance
(Des. Marjorie Saynor)

W181.   Pilgrims and *Mayflower*

(Des. Fritz Wegner)

W182. Sir William Herschel, Francis Baily, Sir John Herschel and Telescope
(Des. Marjorie Saynor)
(Printed in photogravure with the Queen's head embossed in gold)

1970 (APRIL 1). GENERAL ANNIVERSARIES

Five famous anniversaries, with the events described on the stamps.

An additional feature of this issue was the introduction of cylinder numbers for the cylinders printing the phosphor bands. They are not easy to see but are printed below the ordinary cylinder numbers.

Two phosphor bands

Cat. No.	S.G. No.	Type		Description	Mint	Used
W182	819	**W178**		5d. Black, yellow-olive, blue,		
a. Gold (Queen's head) omitted ..		£400		emerald, greenish yellow,		
b. Emerald omitted		50·00		rose-red, gold and		
c. Phosphor omitted		£300		orange-red	10	10
d. White flaw in desk (R. 2/6) ..		2·25				
e. White spot in hem (R. 5/5) ..		2·25				
f. Missing portions of desk and foot						
(R. 20/4)		3·00				
W183	820	**W179**		9d. Ochre, deep blue, carmine,		
a. Ochre omitted		£150		black, blue-green, yellow-		
b. Embossing omitted		10·00		olive, gold and blue	15	15
c. Phosphor omitted		2·25				
W184	821	**W180**		1s. Green, greenish yellow,		
a. Gold (Queen's head) omitted ..		50·00		brown, black, cerise,		
b. Green and embossing omitted		75·00		gold and light blue	25	15
c. Green omitted		75·00				
d. Brown and phosphor omitted ..		£110				
e. Brown omitted		£100				
f. Embossing and phosphor				*g.* Embossing omitted	10·00	
omitted		20·00		*h.* Phosphor omitted	4·00	
W185	822	**W181**		1s.6d. Greenish yellow, car-		
a. Gold (Queen's head) omitted ..		75·00		mine, deep yellow-olive,		
b. Emerald omitted		40·00		emerald, black, blue,		
c. Embossing omitted		5·00		gold and sage-green	30	30
d. Phosphor omitted		2·50				
e. Flag flaw (R. 20/5)		3·50				
W186	823	**W182**		1s.9d. Black, slate, lemon,		
a. Phosphor omitted		2·50		gold and bright purple	30	30
b. One broad band		7·00				

> First Day Cover (W182/6) .. .. 1·25
> Presentation Pack (W182/6) .. .. 3·00
>   Pack also exists with a Dutch,
> German or Japanese insert card

The 5d. is known with the gold partly omitted, possibly due to under-inking. Of a complete sheet seen the cylinder number did not show, the traffic lights appeared smaller and the back of the Queen's head on every stamp was rounded with no ribbons.

We have seen an example of the 1s.9d. on cover with the lemon colour omitted and two or three other covers have been reported. This error may only exist in used condition.

Nos. W182/6 were pre-released at Dorking on 25 March.

Listed Varieties

W182*d*	W182*e*	W182*f*
	Amount of white varies with the registration of colours	Large part of base of desk and front of shoe missing

All the above are multipositive flaws which appear on no dot and dot panes

Portion of blue in bottom right-hand corner of Union Jack is missing

W185e

Cylinder Numbers (Blocks of Eight (5d., 9d., 1s., 1s.6d.) or Six (1s.9d.))

	Cyl. Nos.	A (T) No dot	Dot	Perforation Types F No dot	F (L) No dot
5d.	1A (black)–1B (gold)–1C (blue)–1D (emerald)–1E (olive)–1F (rose-red)–1G (yellow)–1H (orange-red)–P1 (phosphor)	1·25	1·25	†	†
9d.	2A (blue)–1B (ochre)–1C (deep blue)–1D (green)–1E (gold)–2F (black)–1G (olive)–1H (carmine)–P2 (phosphor)	†		1·75	†
1s.	1A (black)–1B (blue)–1C (yellow)–1D (brown)–1E (gold)–2F (cerise)–1G (green)–P2 (phosphor) ..	†		2·25	16·00
1s.6d.	1A (black)–1B (sage-green)–1C (yellow)–1D (carmine)–1E (gold)–2F (blue)–1G (deep yellow-olive)–1H (emerald)–P2 (phosphor)	†		4·00	†
1s.9d.	1A (black)–1E (gold)–1B (slate)–1C (lemon)–2D (bright purple)–P2 (phosphor)	†		4·00	†

The phosphor cylinder numbers appear below the ordinary cylinder numbers opposite R. 20/1. In the 5d. the " P1 " is indented into the phosphor band but in the other values the " P2 " is to the left of the phosphor band.

In the 5d. the "1" of " 1C " and the bar below it are sometimes missing.

The 9d. is known without phosphor cylinder number.

In the 1s.9d. the cylinder numbers are always out of sequence.

Minor Constant Flaws

5d. Cyls. 1A–1B–1C–1D–1E–1F–1G–1H–P1 no dot
  2/1 Weak patches in background below r and t of Declaration
  6/1 Vertical scratch in background, through and below th of Arbroath (Th. A10 to C11)
  7/1 As 6/1

9d. Cyls. 2A–1B–1C–1D–1E–2F–1G–1H–P2 no dot
  8/6 Pale area surrounds final e of Florence
  19/4 Dark patch in background below second g of Nightingale

1s. Cyls. 1A–1B–1C–1D–1E–2F–1G–P2 no dot
  3/4 Missing top to t in Co-operative
  8/3 Dark flaw by top of first l of Alliance

1s.6d. Cyls. 1A–1B–1C–1D–1E–2F–1G–1H–P2 no dot
  8/3 Letters flo of Mayflower have hazy appearance

1s.9d. Cyls. 1A–1E–1B–1C–2D–P2 no dot
  2/3 Pale patch in background above on of Astronomical
  2/6 Small break in t of Astronomical
  19/1 Dark patch on left leg of figure at right (Th. F6)
  19/5 Bright purple coloured flaw on left sleeve of man at left due to lack of screening dots on black cylinder (Th. D3)
  20/4 Black dot on e of Society

Sheet Details

Sheet sizes: 120 (6 × 20). 5d. double pane reel-fed with no dot pane above dot pane; others single pane sheet-fed
Sheet markings:
  Cylinder numbers:
  1s.9d. Opposite rows 18/19, left margin, boxed. Others: Opposite rows 17/19, left margin, boxed.
  Guide holes: 5d. Opposite rows 6/7 (boxed), at both sides. Others: None
  Marginal arrows (photo-etched): " W " shaped, at top, bottom and sides
  Marginal rule: None

347

Colour register marks:
    5d. Opposite rows 9/12 at right (no dot) or left (dot). Others: Above and below vertical rows 1 and 6
Coloured crosses: 5d. None. Others: Above and below vertical rows 3/4
Autotron marks (solid):
    5d. Gold, black, blue, emerald, olive, rose-red, yellow, orange-red above left margin and above vertical
    rows 1/4. Others: None
Colour designations: None
Sheet values:
    1s. Opposite rows 5/6 and 15/16 reading upwards in left margin and downwards in right margin
    Others: Opposite rows 4/7 and 14/17 reading upwards in left margin and downwards in right margin
Traffic lights (boxed):
    5d. Embossing, gold, black, blue, emerald, olive, rose-red, yellow and orange-red opposite rows 16/18,
    right margin; also in same order reading left to right above vertical rows 4/5
    9d. Blue, ochre, deep blue, green, gold, embossing, black, olive and carmine opposite rows 17/19, right
    margin; also in reverse order reading left to right above vertical rows 4/5
    1s. Green, black, cerise, gold, embossing, brown, yellow and blue opposite rows 18/19, right margin; also
    blue, yellow, embossing, gold, brown, cerise, black and green reading left to right above vertical rows
    4/5
    1s.6d. Sage-green, yellow, carmine, blue, gold, embossing, deep yellow-olive, black and emerald opposite
    rows 17/19, right margin; also in reverse order reading left to right above vertical rows 4/5
    1s.9d. Black, gold, embossing, slate, lemon and bright purple opposite rows 18/19, right margin; also
    embossing, gold, black, slate, lemon and bright purple reading left to right above vertical row 5

Imprimaturs from the National Postal Museum Archives

Nos. W182/186 imperforate

No watermark (*set of* 5)

Quantities Sold   5d. 71,259,000;   9d. 10,590,120;   1s. 10,287,840;   1s.6d. 11,388,960;
                   1s.9d. 6,120,600; Pack 120,564

Withdrawn   31.3.71

W183. "Mr. Pickwick and Sam Weller" (*Pickwick Papers*)

W184. "Mr. and Mrs. Micawber" (*David Copperfield*)

W185. "David Copperfield and Betsy Trotwood" (*David Copperfield*)

W186. "Oliver asking for more" (*Oliver Twist*)

W187. "Grasmere" (from engraving by J. Farington, R.A.)

(Des. Rosalind Dease. 5d. based on etchings by "Phiz" and George Cruickshank)
(Printed in photogravure with the Queen's head embossed in gold)

1970 (JUNE 3). LITERARY ANNIVERSARIES

The four 5d. stamps, commemorating the death centenary of Charles Dickens, feature popular characters from his novels. The 1s.6d. stamp commemorates the birth bicentenary of Lakeland poet William Wordsworth.

The 5d. values were issued together *se-tenant* in blocks of four throughout the sheet

Two phosphor bands

Cat. No.	S.G. No.	Type			Description	Mint	Used
W187	824	**W183**			5d. Black, orange, silver, gold and magenta	10	10
a. Block of 4. Nos. W187/90..		..	90	90			
ab. Imperf. (*block of four*)		.. ..	£600				
ac. One broad band (*block of four*) ..			30·00				
W188	825	**W184**			5d. Black, magenta, silver, gold and orange	10	10
W189	826	**W185**			5d. Black, light greenish blue, silver, gold and yellow-bistre	10	10
b. Yellow-bistre (value) omitted ..			£1200				
W190	827	**W186**			5d. Black, yellow-bistre, silver, gold and light greenish blue	10	10
b. Yellow-bistre (background) omitted			£3000				
c. Light greenish blue (value) omitted*			£300				
W191	828	**W187**			1s.6d. Light yellow-olive, black, silver, gold and bright blue	20	20
a. Gold (Queen's head) omitted ..			£225				
b. Silver ("Grasmere") omitted ..			60·00				
c. Embossing and phosphor omitted			20·00				
d. Embossing omitted			5·00		*f.* Retouch in slope (R. 1/18) ..	3·00	
e. Phosphor omitted			4·00		*g.* Extra road (R. 6/8) ·· ..	3·00	

> First Day Cover (W187/91)   ..   ..   2·00
> Presentation Pack (W187/91)   ..   ..   3·00
>   Pack also exists with a Dutch,
>   German or Japanese insert card

*No. W190c (unlike No. W189b) results from a partial missing colour. Although it is completely missing on No. W190, it is only partially omitted on No. W189.

5d. *Prices for missing colour errors in blocks of four:*
        Yellow-bistre £3000
        Light greenish blue £350

Listed Varieties

| W191f | Normal | W191g |
Retouch consists of diagonal black lines over triangular green patch N.E. of Grasmere   /   Green line gives the impression of an extra road leading up the foothill

Cylinder Numbers (Blocks of Eight (5d.) or Four (1s.6d.))

		Cyl. Nos.		Perforation Types		
				A		F
				No dot	Dot	No dot
5d.	1A (orange)–1B (magenta)–3C (bistre)–1D (blue)–1E (black)–1F (silver)–1G (gold)–P4 (phosphor)			1·50	1·50	†
1s.6d.	1A (blue)–1B (gold)–1C (silver)–1D (black)–1E (olive)–P3 (phosphor) ..			†		1·75

The above are with sheets orientated showing head to right.
In the 5d. the 1F is printed over a figure " 2 " in both panes.

Minor Constant Flaws

5d. Cyls. 1A–1B–3C–1D–1E–1F–1G dot
5/17 Extra "button" on Sam's coat under armpit (Th. B6)
5/19 Dot by 7 of 1870 level with centre of 8

Sheet Details

Sheet size: 120 (20 × 6)
    5d. In *se-tenant* blocks of four, double pane reel-fed with no dot pane above dot pane
    1s.6d. Single pane sheet-fed
Sheet markings:
    Cylinder numbers:
        5d. above vertical rows 1/3, boxed
        1s.6d. Opposite row 5, left margin, boxed
    Guide holes:
        5d. In single box above and below vertical rows 14/15
        1s.6d. None
    Marginal arrows (photo-etched): " W " shaped, at top, bottom and sides
    Marginal rule: None
    Colour register marks:
        5d. None
        1s.6d. Opposite rows 1 and 6 at both sides
    Coloured crosses:
        5d. None
        1s.6d. Opposite rows 3/4 at both sides

Autotron marks (solid):
  5d. Opposite rows 1/4 at right on no dot pane only
  1s.6d. None
Sheet values: Above and below vertical rows 4/7 and 14/17
Traffic lights (boxed):
  5d. Embossing, gold, silver. blue, bistre, magenta, orange and black opposite rows 5/6, right margin; also in reverse order below vertical rows 3/4
  1s.6d. Embossing, gold, silver, blue, black and olive opposite row 5, right margin; also in same order above vertical rows 18/19

Imprimaturs from the National Postal Museum Archives

Nos. W187/191 imperforate

No watermark (*set of 5*)

Quantities Sold   5d. 83,472,440; 1s.6d. 10,913,360; Pack 113,770

Withdrawn   3.6.71

W188. Runners

W189. Swimmers

W190. Cyclists

(Des. Andrew Restall)

(Lithography by De La Rue)

1970 (JULY 15). BRITISH COMMONWEALTH GAMES

These were issued on the eve of the Ninth British Commonwealth Games which were held in Edinburgh. Like the Post Office Technology issue these were printed in lithography by De La Rue.

Comb perforation 13½ × 14. Two phosphor bands applied by typography

Cat. No.	S.G. No.	Type		Description	Mint	Used
W192	832	**W188**		5d. Pink, emerald, greenish yellow and deep yellow-green		
a. Greenish yellow omitted			£3500			
b. Phosphor omitted			£200		10	10
c. One diagonal broad band at right			55·00			
W193	833	**W189**		1s.6d. Light greenish blue, lilac, bistre-brown and Prussian blue		
a. Phosphor omitted			60·00		50	50
W194	834	**W190**		1s.9d. Yellow-orange, lilac, salmon and deep red-brown	50	50

First Day Cover (W192/4)		..	1·25
Presentation Pack (W192/4)		..	2·50
Pack also exists with a Dutch, German or Japanese insert card			

Plate Numbers (Blocks of Four)

		Pl. Nos.		Perforation Type F (L) No dot Dot

					No dot	Dot
5d.	1A (yellow)–1B (emerald)–1C (pink)–1D (green)	..	..	..	90	90
	2A (yellow)–1B (emerald)–1C (pink)–1D (green)	..	..	..	90	90
1s.6d.	1A (bistre-brown)–1B (greenish blue)–1C (lilac)–1D (indigo)		..		3·00	3·00
	2A (bistre-brown)–2B (greenish blue)–2C (lilac)–2D (indigo)		..		3·00	3·00
1s.9d.	1A (salmon)–1B (lilac)–1C (yellow-orange)–1D (red-brown)		..		3·00	3·00
	1A (salmon)–2B (lilac)–1C (yellow-orange)–1D (red-brown)		..		3·00	3·00

Minor Constant Flaws

The notes relating to minor flaws in lithographed stamps under the 1969 Post Office Technology issue also apply here.

Sheet Details

Sheet size: **120** (10 × 12). Double pane sheet-fed with no dot pane at top and dot pane below

Sheet markings:

Plate numbers: Opposite rows 1/2, left margin, unboxed

Guide holes: Above and below vertical row 4 in crossed box on no dot pane and below vertical row 4 in crossed box on dot pane; the reserve box in top margin was not used. In addition reserve guide-hole boxes appear above and below vertical row 6 in both panes but these were not used

Marginal arrows (solid): "W" shaped, at top, bottom and sides

Marginal rule: None

Colour register marks: Below vertical rows 1 and 12 and in right-hand margin opposite rows 1 and 12 in both panes; in addition, they occur in the left-hand margin opposite row 12 in the no dot pane

Coloured crosses, autotron marks, colour designations: **None**

Sheet values: Above and below vertical rows 2/4 and 7/9 reading left to right in top margin and right to left (upside down) in bottom margin

Traffic lights (unboxed): Opposite rows 9/10, right margin in same order as plate numbers

Imprimaturs from the National Postal Museum Archives

Nos. W192/194 imperforate

No watermark (*set of* 3)

Quantities Sold   5d. 75,255,440; 1s.6d. 10,909,760; 1s.9d. 6,303,800; Pack 114,209

Withdrawn   15.7.71

1970 (SEPTEMBER 14). COLLECTORS PACK 1970

WCP3 Comprises Nos. W171/94   24·00

This pack also exists with a German or Japanese insert card.

Quantity Sold   54,768

Withdrawn   13.9.71

W191. 1d. Black (1840)	**W192.** 1s. Green (1847)	**W193.** 4d. Carmine (1855)
	(Des. David Gentleman)	

1970 (SEPTEMBER 18). "PHILYMPIA 70" STAMP EXHIBITION

Issued for the opening of the International Philatelic Exhibition held at the Olympia Exhibition Hall, London. The 5d. depicts the first adhesive postage stamp ever issued, the famous Penny Black. This is shown with the check letters "P" and "L" for "Philympia" and "London". The 9d. and 1s.6d. show the first Great Britain stamps using the embossed and surface-printed processes respectively.

Two phosphor bands

Cat. No.	S.G. No.	Type		Description	Mint	Used
W195	835	**W191**		5d. Grey-black, brownish bistre,		
a. Phosphor omitted*			2·75	black and dull purple	10	10
b. One broad phosphor band			20·00			
c. White blob (No dot, R. 5/6)			3·50	*d.* Weak entry (Dot, R. 1/2) ..	3·00	
W196	836	**W192**		9d. Light drab, bluish green,		
a. Phosphor omitted			9·00	stone, black and dull		
				purple	35	35
W197	837	**W193**		1s.6d. Carmine, light drab,		
a. Phosphor omitted			3·00	black and dull purple	40	40
b. Missing dot over " i " (R. 6/12)			3·50			

First Day Cover (W195/7)	.. ..	1·25
Presentation Pack (W195/7)	.. ..	2·50
Pack also exists with a German or Japanese insert card		

The 5d. is known postmarked at Boughton, King's Lynn on 17 September.

*The phosphor is sometimes difficult to see on the 5d. due to "dry" prints so care is needed in identifying true missing phosphors.

Listed Varieties

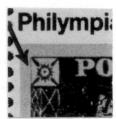

W195c	W195d
Large white blob between " OS " of " POSTAGE " (later retouched)	Weak entry of frameline in top left corner

In No. W197b the dot is missing over the " i " of " printed "

Cylinder Numbers (Blocks of Four)

	Cyl. Nos.	Perforation Types		
		A	A	A (T)
		No dot	Dot	No dot
5d.	1A (black)–1B (dull purple)–1C (brownish bistre)–1D (grey-black)–P6 (phosphor)	90	90	†
9d.	1A (black)–1B (stone)–2C (bluish green)–1D (dull purple)–1E (light drab)–P10 (phosphor)	†		2·50
1s.6d.	1A (black)–1B (light drab)–1C (dull purple)–1D (carmine)–P5 (phosphor)	†		2·75

The above are with sheets orientated showing head to right.

Minor Constant Flaw
1s.6d. Cyls. 1A–1B–1C–1D–P5 no dot
1/1 Frame flaw below N of PENCE

Sheet Details
Sheet size: 120 (12 × 10). 5d. double pane reel-fed with no dot pane above dot pane; others single pane sheet-fed

Sheet markings:
Cylinder numbers: Opposite row 9, left margin, boxed but the phosphor number is opposite row 10, left margin

Guide holes: 5d. Above and below vertical row 6 (boxed). Others: None

Marginal arrows (photo-etched): " W " shaped, at top, bottom and sides

Marginal rule: None

Colour register marks:
5d. None. Others: Above and below vertical rows 1 and 10/11

Coloured crosses: 5d. None. Others: Above and below vertical rows 3/4

Autotron marks and colour designations: None

Sheet values: Opposite rows 2/4 and 7/9 at both sides, reading up at left and down at right

Traffic lights (boxed):
5d. Dull purple, black, brownish bistre, grey-black opposite row 10 right margin; also in same order reading from left to right above vertical rows 11/12
9d. Bluish green, stone, dull purple, black, light drab opposite row 10 right margin; also in same order reading from left to right above vertical rows 11/12
1s. 6d. Light drab, dull purple; carmine, black opposite 9/10 right margin; also in reverse order reading from left to right above vertical row 12

Imprimaturs from the National Postal Museum Archives
Nos. W195/197 imperforate
No watermark (*set of* 3)

Quantities Sold   5d. 72,211,000; 9d. 16,330,000; 1s.6d. 15,203,836

Withdrawn   18.9.71

W194. Shepherds and
Apparition of the Angel

W195. Mary, Joseph and
Christ in the Manger

W196. The Wise Men
bearing Gifts

(Des. Sally Stiff)

(Printed in photogravure with the Queen's head in gold and then embossed)

1970 (NOVEMBER 25). CHRISTMAS

The designs depict traditional Nativity scenes taken from the De Lisle Psalter in the Arundel Collection at the British Museum.

The 4d. stamps were printed by the Wood machine which has a capacity for ten cylinders. Eight were used for the colours and the others for simultaneous application of the embossing and phosphor bands.

One central 4 mm. phosphor band (4d.) or two phosphor bands (others)

Cat. No.	S.G. No.	Type			Description	Mint	Used
W198	838	**W194**			4d Brown-red, blue, turquoise-		
a. Embossing omitted	..	..	40·00		green, pale chestnut,		
b. Phosphor omitted	..	..	55·00		brown, grey-black, gold		
c. Two bands	..	..			and vermilion	10	10
d. Imperf. between stamp and left							
margin	..	..	..	£110			
e. Thinned frame (No dot, R. 4/6)	..	2·25					
W199	839	**W195**			5d. Emerald, gold, blue, brown-		
a. Gold (Queens head) omitted	..	†	£2500		red, ochre, grey-black and		
b. Emerald omitted	..	..	60·00		violet	10	10
c. Imperforate (pair)	..	..	£250				
d. Embossing omitted	..	..	12·00				
e. Phosphor omitted	..	..	2·25				
W200	840	**W196**			1s.6d. Gold, grey-black, pale		
a. Salmon omitted	..	..	80·00		turquoise-green, salmon,		
b. Ochre omitted	..	..	50·00		ultramarine, ochre, red		
c. Embossing and phosphor omitted					and yellow-green	35	35
d. Embossing omitted	..	..	30·00				
e. Phosphor omitted	..	..	3·50				
f. One broad band	..	..					

First Day Cover (W199/200)	.. ..	1·00
Presentation Pack (W199/200)	.. ..	2·50
Pack also exists with a German or		
Japanese insert card		

A red slip-in wallet bearing the Royal Arms and inscribed "Christmas 1970" was issued with the "Scandinavia 71" special pack produced for sale during a visit to six cities in Denmark, Sweden and Norway by a mobile display unit between 15 April and 20 May 1971. Due to the moratorium on commemoratives at the time of the introduction of decimal issues, these 1970 £.s.d. Christmas stamps were the only recent commemoratives on sale at Special counters etc. which could be offered for sale in Scandinavia alongside the decimal definitives.

Listed Variety

Gold frame at right by shepherd's arm is thinned and has been strengthened by two parallel chestnut lines

W198*e*

Cylinder Numbers (4d. Blocks of Ten; Others Blocks of Six)

	Cyl. Nos.	Perforation Type A	
		No dot	Dot
4d.	1A (vermilion)–1B (grey-black)–1C (brown)–1D (brown-red)–1E (turquoise-green)–1F (blue)–1G (pale chestnut)–1J (gold)–P9 (phosphor)	1·50	1·50
5d.	1A (violet)–1B (brown-red)–1C (blue)–1D (ochre)–3E (grey-black)–1F (emerald)–1G (gold)–P7 (phosphor)	1·00	†
1s.6d.	1A (yellow-green)–1B (grey-black)–1D (red)–1E (salmon)–1F (pale turquoise-green)–1G (gold)–1J (ochre)–1C (ultramarine)–P7 (phosphor)	2·75	†

The above are with sheets orientated showing head to right.
On some sheets of the 4d. the J is completely omitted.

Minor Constant Flaws

4d. Cyls. 1A–1B–1C–1D–1E–1F–1G–1J–P9 no dot
    5/5 Dotted line across central shepherd's temple and through hair (Th. G6–7)
5d. Cyls. 1A–1B–1C–1D–3E–1F–1G–P7 no dot
    8/8 Diagonal line over Mary's left hand (Th. J3)
1s.6d. Cyls. 1A–1B–1D–1E–1F–1G–1J–1C–P7 no dot
    1/12 Horizontal scratch across cloaks of Three Wise Men (Th. K2–6)

The Thirkell Position Finder readings are taken with the finder over the perforations.

Sheet Details

Sheet size: 120 (12 × 10).   4d. double pane reel-fed with no dot pane above dot pane; others single pane sheet-fed

Sheet markings:
Cylinder numbers:
    4d. Bottom margin, unboxed, reading down below vertical rows 5/2
    5d. Opposite rows 8/9, left margin, boxed but the phosphor number is opposite row 10, left margin
    1s.6d. Opposite rows 8/10, left margin, boxed. The 1C was added at the bottom opposite row 10
Guide holes: 4d. Above and below vertical row 6 (boxed). Others: None
Marginal arrows (photo-etched): "W" shaped, at top, bottom and sides
Marginal rule: None
Colour register marks:
    4d. Above and below vertical rows 2/5. Others: Above and below vertical rows 1/2 and 12
Autotron marks and colour designations: None
Coloured crosses: 4d. None. Others: Above and below vertical rows 3/4
Sheet values: Opposite rows 2/4 at both sides and rows 7/8 at left and 7/9 at right, reading up at left and down at right
Traffic lights (boxed):
    4d. Vermilion, grey-black, brown, brown-red, turquoise-green, blue, pale chestnut, gold, embossing*
    opposite rows 9/10 right margin; also in same order reading from left to right above vertical rows 11/12
    5d. Violet, brown-red, blue, ochre, grey-black, emerald, gold, embossing opposite rows 9/10 r⁻ ht margin;
    also in same order reading from left to right above vertical rows 10/11
    1s.6d. Yellow-green, grey-black, ultramarine; red, salmon, pale turquoise-green, gold, ochre, embossing;
    also in same order reading from left to right above vertical rows 9/11

*The embossing is usually very faint on the 4d. traffic lights.

Imprimaturs from the National Postal Museum Archives

Nos. W198/200 imperforate

No watermark (*set of* 3)

Quantities Sold   4d. 360,016,216; 5d. 181,161,720; 1s.6d. 22,598,520

Withdrawn 25.11.71

SECTION XA
Regional £.s.d. Issues
1958–70. Photogravure

General Notes

INTRODUCTION. On 18 August 1958 the first Great Britain Regional issues were put on sale for use in Northern Ireland, Scotland and Wales and Monmouthshire and in the islands of Guernsey, Jersey and the Isle of Man. The ordinary postage stamps of Great Britain in the same values are not on sale at post offices in these regions except at the Philatelic Counters in Belfast, Cardiff, Edinburgh and Glasgow, apart from Monmouthshire where the Welsh Regionals and Great Britain postage stamps were on sale concurrently.

Although specifically issued for regional use, these issues were initially valid for use throughout Great Britain. However, they ceased to be valid in Guernsey and Jersey from 1 October 1969 when these islands each established their own independent postal administrations and introduced their own stamps. Guernsey and Jersey Regionals were withdrawn locally on 30 September 1969 but remained on sale at British Philatelic Counters until 30 September 1970.

Following the practice set by Great Britain, these issues do not bear the names of the regions, these being indicated by various devices and symbols which relate to them. The three island issues are inscribed "Postage" only and have no usage as revenue stamps as they have their own Parliaments.

The portrait used is by Dorothy Wilding, Ltd.

PRINTERS. All the Regional issues were printed in photogravure by Harrison & Sons on continuous reels of paper "on the web". The 3d., 4d. and 5d. values of Northern Ireland, Scotland and Wales and Monmouthshire were printed in double pane width, i.e. 480 stamps consisting of two panes (no dot and dot) each of 240 stamps arranged in twenty rows of twelve stamps, the panes being guillotined before issue. All the island issues and the 6d., 9d., 1s.3d., and 1s.6d. values from the other regions were made from single cylinders printing sheets of 240 stamps (i.e. no dot panes only).

PAPER AND WATERMARK. As with the Wilding definitives, for the first few years the Regional issues were printed on a creamy paper but starting in February 1962 a whiter paper was gradually introduced as new printings were made. See the General Notes for Section S for further information. Exceptionally, a chalk-surfaced paper was used for a printing of the Isle of Man 3d. in 1963.

Crowns
W.24

Only the Crowns watermark, type **W.24**, was used for the Regional issues. From 1967 new printings of a number of values were on the chalk-surfaced paper without watermark, as used for the Machin definitives.

GUM. Gum arabic was used from 1958 to 1968 after which PVA gum was introduced.

The distinction between gum arabic and PVA gum is explained in the General Notes to Section U. It is worth noting that gum arabic was used on the creamy, white and unwatermarked chalk-surfaced papers but that PVA gum exists only on the last of these.

PERFORATION. Harrisons used the same 15 × 14 comb perforation as for the Wilding definitives. A number of different perforators were used and these are described and illustrated in Appendix G. The cylinder numbers are listed and priced according to the type of perforator used.

PHOSPHOR BANDS. See the General Notes for Section S for a detailed description of these. In the Regional issues it is sufficient to state that these were applied as follows:

"Blue" 8 mm. bands: 1963–64
"Violet" 8 mm. bands: 1965–66
"Violet" 9·5 mm. bands: 1967–70
The one centre band stamps in the "violet" period were always 4 mm. bands.

Phosphor omitted. A number of values have appeared with the phosphor bands omitted in error and these are listed separately. All values are believed to have the bands applied in photogravure.

DATES OF ISSUE. Conflicting dates of issue have been announced for some of the issues, partly explained by their being released on different dates by the Philatelic Bureau in Edinburgh or the Philatelic Counter in London and in the regions. We give the earliest date, since once released the stamps could have been used anywhere in the U.K.

FIRST DAY COVERS. Prices for these are only quoted where there was a specific service provided by the Post Office. These are listed at the end of each region.

PRESENTATION PACKS. The pack containing stamps from the six regions is listed after Wales and Monmouthshire. The other packs are listed at the end of each region.

SHEET MARKINGS. Reference should be made to the descriptions of sheet markings given in the General Notes for Sections S and U, as most of them apply to this Section and the information given there is not repeated here. Additional information is given here.

Cylinder Numbers. In the Regional issues these appear in the left-hand margin opposite Row 18 No. 1 in the style as illustrated in Section S.

Phosphor Cylinder Numbers. The notes in the General Notes for Section U £.s.d. Low Values also apply here but they are only found on the Scottish 5d. and Welsh 5d.

Marginal Arrows. In the Regional issues these are "W" shaped (photo-etched) at top, bottom and sides, except for the Jersey and Isle of Man 3d. and the Northern Ireland, Scotland and Wales and Monmouthshire 3d., 6d. and 1s.3d. which are all "V" shaped (hand engraved) at top and bottom of the sheet and "W" shaped (photo-etched) at both sides (only cyl. 4 Scotland 1s.3d.).

"CANCELLED" OVERPRINT. No. XW5 comes overprinted "CANCELLED" as part of the test programme carried out by the Forensic Department of the Post Office.

WITHDRAWAL DATES. All £.s.d. Regional issues, not previously withdrawn, were taken off sale at the Post Office Philatelic Counters on 25 November 1971 and were invalidated as from 1 March 1972.

---

*PRICES FOR CYLINDER BLOCKS WITH ASTERISKS
These denote cylinder blocks containing a listed variety and the price includes the variety.

A. Guernsey

XG1   XG2

(Des. E. A. Piprell)

2½d., Type XG1 (1964)

Cat. No.	S.G. No.	Shades	Mint	Used
1964 (JUNE 8). WATERMARK CROWNS				
XG1	6	(1) Pale rose-red (Cyl. 1)	1·00	1·00
		(2) Rose-red (Cyl. 3)	35	40

Cylinder Numbers (Blocks of Six)

Single pane cylinders.   Perforation Type F (L)

Cyl. Nos.					No dot
1	..	..	..	..	8·00
3	..	..	..	..	2·75

Minor Constant Flaws

Cyl. 1   1/4   Small retouch over TA
         1/5   White patch over left part of diadem to left of central cross (Th. A3)
      17/12   Background disturbance in top loop of left-hand ribboning (Th. B1)
      19/2   White patch below left leg of R
Cyl. 3   17/5   Dark spot under topmost tip of ribboning at right (Th. B6)
      17/12 and 19/2. As on cyl. 1 (multipositive flaws)

Sheet Markings

Guide holes: Through marginal arrow above vertical rows 6/7 and below vertical row 10
Others: As given in General Notes

Quantity Sold   3,485,760 including 10,100 on First Day Covers

Withdrawn   31.8.66

3d., Type XG2 (1958–62)

1958 (AUGUST 18). WATERMARK CROWNS
A. Cream Paper

XG2	—	Deep lilac	1·00 30

B. White Paper (5 July 1962)

XG3	7	Deep lilac	35 30

Cylinder Numbers (Blocks of Six)

Cream Paper (No. XG2)				Whiter Paper (No. XG3)			
Cyl. No.	(No dot)	Perf. Types		Cyl. No.	(No dot)	Perf. Types	
		B C				B C F (L)	
4		8·00 8·00		4		3·00 3·00 3·00	
				5		† † 2·75	

Minor Constant Flaws

Cyl. 5   4/1 Background scratch above right-hand petal (Th. C–D2)
           7/10 Dark spot in left-hand margin (opposite Th. C1)
           9/10 Pale scratch in background from petal at far right down to Queen's chin (Th. D–E3)
           11/11 Diagonal background scratch from base of lily's stem to base of Queen's neck (Th. F3–E4)
           13/1 Flaw in background above centre stamen of lily (Th. C2)
           18/6 Smudge in background near Queen's mouth (Th. D3)

Sheet Markings

Guide holes: Perf. Type F (L), as for No. XG1 except that there are also boxes opposite rows 14/15 at left and right. Perf. Types B and C, not known.
Others: As given in General Notes.

Quantity Sold   25,812,360

Sold Out   6.3.68

Cat No.	S.G. No.		Shades		Mint	Used

1967 (MAY 24). ONE CENTRE PHOSPHOR BAND REACTING VIOLET. WATERMARK CROWNS

				Mint	Used
XG4	7p		(1) Deep lilac	20	20
			(2) Deep reddish lilac	45	25

Cylinder Numbers (Blocks of Six)

Single pane cylinder.   Perforation Type F (L)

Cyl. No.				No dot
5	..	..	..	..	1·75

Minor Constant Flaws

As for flaws on Cyl. 5 of No. XG3

Sheet Markings

Guide holes: As for Perf. Type F (L) on No. XG3
Others: As given in General Notes

Sold Out   11.68

4d., Type XG2 (1966-69)

1966 (FEBRUARY 7). WATERMARK CROWNS

			Mint	Used
XG5	8	Ultramarine	25	30
a.	Stem flaw (R. 12/8)	..	3·00	

Listed Variety

Coloured line across
top of stem

XG5*a*, XG6*a*, XG7*b*, XG8*c*

Cylinder Numbers (Blocks of Six)

Single pane cylinder.   Perforation Type F (L)

Cyl. No.				No dot
1	..	..	..	..	2·50

Minor Constant Flaws

Cyl. 1   1/1 Small spot above centre stamen of lily (Th. C2)
          9/5 White dot between two stamens on left-hand side (Th. D2)
          13/4 White spot on right-hand petal (Th. D3)
          20/12 Pale flaw in background to right of central diadem (Th. A5)
These are generally more marked on later issues from this cylinder.

Sheet Markings

Guide holes: Through marginal arrow above vertical rows 6/7 and below vertical row 10
Others: As given in General Notes

Quantity Sold   4,415,040 including 12,350 on First Day Covers

Sold Out   6.3.68

Cat. No.	S.G. No.	Shades	Mint	Used

1967 (OCTOBER 24). TWO 9·5 mm. PHOSPHOR BANDS REACTING VIOLET. WATERMARK CROWNS

XG6	8p	Ultramarine	20	20
a. Stem flaw (R. 12/8) .. 3·00				

For illustration of No. XG6*a*, see No. XG5*a*.

Cylinder Numbers (Blocks of Six)

Single pane cylinder. Perforation Type F (L)

	Cyl. No.			No dot
	1			1·75

Minor Constant Flaws

Cyl. 1   5/10 Circular background retouch below Queen's chin (Th. E4)
          16/12 Break in centre stamen (Th. C–D2)
          17/10 Break in second stamen from left (Th. C2)
Others: As on No. XG5

Sheet Markings

As for No. XG5

Sold Out   10.68

1968 (APRIL 16*). NO WATERMARK. CHALKY PAPER. PVA GUM. TWO 9·5 mm PHOSPHOR BANDS REACTING VIOLET

XG7	9	Pale ultramarine	10	25
a. Phosphor omitted .. .. 40·00				
b. Stem flaw (R. 12/8) .. .. 3·25				

*This was not issued in Guernsey until 22 April.
For illustration of No. XG7*b*, see No. XG5*a*.

Cylinder Numbers (Blocks of Six)

Single pane cylinder. Perforation Type F (L)

	Cyl. No.			No dot
	1			1·25

Minor Constant Flaws

Cyl. 1   2/8 Weak patch in background at upper left (Th. A1)
          19/6 Small retouch between A and G
Others: As on Nos. XG5 and XG6

Sheet Markings

As for No. XG5

Sold Out   3.69

Cat. No.	S.G. No.		Shades		Mint	Used

1968 (SEPTEMBER 4). CHANGE OF COLOUR. NO WATERMARK. CHALKY PAPER. PVA GUM. ONE CENTRE PHOSPHOR BAND REACTING VIOLET

XG8	10		Olive-sepia		15	20

     a.   Phosphor omitted   ..   ..   40·00
     b.   Phosphor horizontal ..   ..   90·00
     c.   Stem flaw (R.12/8)   ..   ..   4·00
     d.   Retouched " 4 " (R. 16/10)   ..   3·50

Listed Varieties

For illustration of No. XG8*c*, see No. XG5*a*.

Spot over " 4 " has been retouched
Corrected on No. XG9

XG8*d*

Cylinder Numbers (Blocks of Six)

Single pane cylinder.   Perforation Type F (L)

Cyl. No.					No dot
1	..	..	..	..	1·50

Minor Constant Flaws

As for No. XG7 except that flaw on R.5/10 does not show

Sheet Markings

As for No. XG5

Withdrawn   30.9.70

1969 (FEBRUARY 26). FURTHER CHANGE OF COLOUR. NO WATERMARK. CHALKY PAPER. PVA GUM. ONE CENTRE PHOSPHOR BAND REACTING VIOLET

XG9	11		Bright vermilion		15	30

     a.   Stem flaw retouched (R.12/8)   3·50

Listed Variety

The stem flaw has been retouched but still shows as a smudge to right of stem

XG9*a*

Cylinder Numbers (Blocks of Six)

Single pane cylinder.   Perforation Type F (L)

Cyl. No.					No dot
1	..	..	..	..	1·50

Minor Constant Flaws

As for No. XG8

Sheet Markings

As for No. XG5

Withdrawn   30.9.70

5d., Type XG2 (1968)

Cat. No.   S.G. No.   Shades   Mint Used
**1968 (SEPTEMBER 4). NO WATERMARK. CHALKY PAPER. PVA GUM. TWO
9·5 mm. PHOSPHOR BANDS REACTING VIOLET**

XG10   12   Royal blue   15   30
  a. Stamen flaw (R.12/1)   ..   3·50
  b. Retouched   ..   ..   ..   4·50

Listed Varieties

    XG10*a*   X10*b*
Still visible after retouch on late printing

Cylinder Numbers (Blocks of Six)
Single pane cylinder.   Perforation Type F (L)
             Cyl. No.   No dot
              1   ..   ..   1·50

Minor Constant Flaw
  Cyl. 1   12/6 Small white flaw to left of Queen's mouth (Th. D3)

Sheet Markings
  As for No. XG5

Withdrawn   30.9.70

First Day Covers

XGFC1   (8.6.64)   10,100 posted   2½d.   15·00
XGFC2   (7.2.66)   12,350 posted   4d. Ultramarine   7·00
XGFC3   (4.9.68)   52,449 posted   4d. Olive-sepia, 5d.   1·00

INVALIDATION. The regional issues for Guernsey were invalidated for use in Guernsey and Jersey on 30 September 1969 but remained valid for use in the rest of the United Kingdom. Those still current remained on sale at philatelic sales counters until 30 September 1970.

B. Jersey

XJ1
(Des. Edmund Blampied)

XJ2
(Des. William M. Gardner)

2½d., Type XJ1 (1964)

Cat. No.	S.G. No.		Shades	Mint	Used

1964 (JUNE 8). WATERMARK CROWNS

XJ1	9		Carmine-red	35	50
a.	Imperf. three sides (pair) ..	£1500			
b.	Thin " POSTAGE " (R.18/1)	6·00			

Listed Variety

Letters of " POSTAGE " are thinner, resulting in more white showing in the " O " and " G "

Normal   XJ1b

Cylinder Numbers (Blocks of Six)

Single pane cylinder.   Perforation Type F (L)

Cyl. No.	No dot
1	7·50*

Minor Constant Flaws

Cyl. 1   11/1 Two tiny dots on Queen's nose
18/2 Spot to right of mace level with O of POSTAGE

Sheet Markings

Guide holes: Through marginal arrow above vertical rows 6/7 and below vertical row 10
Others: As given in General Notes

Quantity Sold   4,770,000 including 12,800 on First Day Covers

Withdrawn   31.8.66

3d., Type XJ2 (1958–67)

1958 (AUGUST 18). WATERMARK CROWNS

A. Cream Paper

XJ2	—		Deep lilac	1·00	30
a.	Joined tomato (Cyl. 1, R.19/9)	6·00			
b.	" Halberd " flaw (Cyl. 1, R.20/3)	6·00			

B. Whiter Paper (23 September 1962)

XJ3	10		Deep lilac	35	30
a.	Scratched collar (Cyl. 2 R. 9/8)	3·00			

Listed Varieties

XJ2a	XJ2b	XJ3a, XJ4a

Both these varieties were later retouched to normal

Cylinder Numbers (Blocks of Six)

Cream Paper (No. XJ2)			Whiter Paper (No. XJ3)		
Cyl. No. (No dot)	Perf. Types B C		Cyl. No. (No dot)	Perf. Types B C F (L)	
1	8·00	8·00	1	2·75 2·75 2·75	
			2	† † 14·00	

Minor Constant Flaws

Cyl. 1   20/4 Short white line extends below left of D
Cyl. 2   3/7 Weak background below left-hand berry of middle pair on right-hand plant (Th. E5)
       14/12 Dot in left-hand margin (Opposite Th. D1)
       16/1 Dot on top left leaf of right-hand plant (Th. C5–6)
       16/12 Dot in top margin (Above Th. A4)
       20/3 Dot in top margin (Above Th. A4)

Sheet Markings

Guide holes: Perf. Types F (L), through marginal arrow above vertical rows 6/7 and below vertical row 10. Other perfs. not known. Cyl. 2 also has boxes opposite rows 14/15 at left and right.
Others: As given in General Notes and also a trimming line above and below vertical rows 8/9.

Quantity Sold   35,169,720

Sold Out   10.67

Cat. No.	S.G. No.		Shades	Mint	Used

1967 (JUNE 9). ONE CENTRE PHOSPHOR BAND REACTING VIOLET. WATERMARK CROWNS

XJ4	10p		(1) Deep lilac	20	20
a.	Scratched collar (Cyl. 2, R. 9/8) 2·75		(2) Dull reddish lilac	30	30

For illustration of No. XJ4a, see No. XJ3a.

Cylinder Numbers (Blocks of Six)

Single pane cylinder.   Perforation Type F (L)

Deep Lilac (No. XJ4(1))		Dull reddish lilac (No. XJ4(2))	
Cyl. No.	No Dot	Cyl. No.	No dot
2	1·90	2	3·00

Minor Constant Flaws

As for flaws on Cyl. 2 of No. XJ3

Sheet Markings

Guide holes: Through marginal arrow above vertical rows 6/7 and below vertical row 10 with boxes opposite rows 14/15 at left and right.
Others: As given in General Notes and also a trimming line above and below vertical rows 8/9.

Sold Out   10.68

4d., Type XJ2 (1966–69)

Cat. No.	S.G. No.	Shades	Mint	Used
1966 (FEBRUARY 7). WATERMARK CROWNS				
XJ5	11	Ultramarine	25	30
a. Leaf flaw (R. 3/6)	.. .. 3·25			
b. Neck flaw (R. 18/9)	.. .. 3·00			

Listed Varieties

Arrow-like flaw over top leaf at left. Later retouched and only exists retouched on phosphor issues

XJ5*a*

XJ5*b*, XJ6*a*, XJ7*b*, XJ8*a*

Cylinder Numbers (Blocks of Six)

Single pane cylinder. Perforation Type F (L)

Cyl. No.	No dot
1	2·50

Minor Constant Flaws

Cyl. 1   3/4 Diagonal scratch under Queen's chin (Th. E2–3)
      3/11 Spot in top margin (close to perf. hole) (Above Th. A4)
      9/10 Slight dent in left-hand frame line (Opposite Th. D–E1)
      11/10 White flaw in background behind Queen's hair (Th. C5)
      15/1 Dark patch in background to left of top leaf on left-hand side of sceptre (Th. D1). This varies in intensity and is particularly strong on No. XJ7.
      15/12 Two small white flaws in front of Queen's collar (Th. F2–3)
      18/8 Break in top frame line (Above Th. A5)
      20/8 Diagonal scratch to right of Queen's left eye (Th. C3–4)

Sheet Markings

Guide holes: Through marginal arrow above vertical rows 6/7 and below vertical row 10.
Others: As given in General Notes.

Quantity Sold   6,623,040 including 14,487 on First Day Covers

Sold Out   11.67

1967 (SEPTEMBER 5). TWO 9·5 mm. PHOSPHOR BANDS REACTING VIOLET. WATERMARK CROWNS

XJ6	11p	Ultramarine	20	25
a. Neck flaw (R.18/9)	.. .. 3·00			

For illustration of No. XJ6*a*, see No. XJ5*b*.

Cylinder Numbers (Blocks of Six)

Single pane cylinder. Perforation Type F (L)

Cyl. No.	No dot
1	1·75

Minor Constant Flaws

As for No. XJ5

Sheet Markings

As for No. XJ5

Sold Out   10.68

Cat. No.	S.G. No.		Shades	Mint	Used

1968 (SEPTEMBER 4). CHANGE OF COLOUR. NO WATERMARK. CHALKY PAPER. PVA GUM. ONE CENTRE PHOSPHOR BAND REACTING VIOLET

XJ7   12   Olive-sepia   20   25
  a. Phosphor omitted £750
  b. Neck flaw (R. 18/9)   ..   3·00
     For illustration of No. XJ7*b*, see No. XJ5*b.*

Cylinder Numbers (Blocks of Six)

Single pane cylinder.   Perforation Type F (L)

               Cyl. No.   No dot
               1   ..   ..   1·90

Minor Constant Flaws
   As for No. XJ5

Sheet Markings
   As for No. XJ5

Withdrawn   30.9.70

1969 (FEBRUARY 26). FURTHER CHANGE OF COLOUR. NO WATERMARK. CHALKY PAPER. PVA GUM. ONE CENTRE PHOSPHOR BAND REACTING VIOLET

XJ8   13   Bright vermilion   20   30
  a. Neck flaw (R. 18/9) ..   ..   3·25
     For illustration of No. XJ8*a*, see No. XJ5*b.*

Cylinder Numbers (Blocks of Six)

Single pane cylinder.   Perforation Type F (L)

               Cyl. No.   No dot
               1   ..   ..   1·90

Minor Constant Flaws
   As for No. XJ5

Sheet Markings
   As for No. XJ5

Withdrawn   30.9.70

5d., Type XJ2 (1968)

1968 (SEPTEMBER 4). NO WATERMARK. CHALKY PAPER. PVA GUM. TWO 9·5 mm. PHOSPHOR BANDS REACTING VIOLET

XJ9   14   Royal blue   20   40
  a.   Leaf dot (R. 16/6)   ..   ..   3·25
  b.   Shield flaw (R. 19/12)   ..   2·75

Listed Varieties

          XJ9*a*   XJ9*b*
White dot above lowest leaf   Leaf joined to shield

Cylinder Numbers (Blocks of Six)

Single pane cylinder.   Perforation Type F (L)

Cyl. No.					No dot
1	..	..	..	..	1·90

Minor Constant Flaws

Cyl. 1   5/1   Dot in top margin (Above Th. A2)
          6/5   White scratch from back of Queen's collar to back of neck (Th. E–F4)
          9/11   Flaw in background above middle right-hand jewel of sceptre (Th. A2)
          10/4   White scratch extending from Queen's chin to top of P
          11/1   Tiny break in left-hand frame line (Th. C1)
          14/12   Small white flaw on Queen's collar (Th. F3–4)
          17/12   Dotted line extending from right of top leaf below flower at right of sceptre across Queen's face and plant at right (Th. E2–6)

Sheet Markings

As for No. XJ5

Withdrawn   30.9.70

First Day Covers

XJFC1	(8.6.64)	12,800 posted	2½d.		15·00
XJFC2	(7.2.66)	14,487 posted	4d. Ultramarine		7·00
XJFC3	(4.9.68)	57,500 posted	4d. Olive-sepia, 5d.		1·25

INVALIDATION. The regional issues for Jersey were invalidated for use in Jersey or Guernsey on 30 September 1969 but remained valid for use in the rest of the United Kingdom. Those still current remained on sale at philatelic sales counters until 30 September 1970.

C. Isle of Man

XM1   XM2

(Des. J. H. Nicholson)

2½d., Type XM1 (1964)

Cat. No.	S.G. No.	Shades	Mint	Used
1964 (JUNE 8). WATERMARK CROWNS				
XM1	1	Carmine-red	45	80

Cylinder Numbers (Blocks of Six)
Single pane cylinder.   Perforation Type F (L)

Cyl. No.					No dot
1	..	..	..	..	4·00

Minor Constant Flaw
   Cyl. 1 11/1 Red dot to right of lower cross of crown (Th. C5)

Sheet Markings:
   Guide holes: Through marginal arrow above vertical rows 6/7 and below vertical row 10
   Others: As given in General Notes

Quantity Sold   4,298,160 including 9,237 on First Day Covers
Withdrawn   31.8.66

3d., Type XM2 (1958–68)

1958 (AUGUST 18). WATERMARK CROWNS
A. Cream Paper

XM2	—	Deep lilac	1·00	25

B. Chalky Paper (17 May 1963)

XM3	2a	Deep lilac	16·00	11·00

C. Whiter Paper (1963)

XM4	2	Deep lilac	20	10

   No. XM3 was released in London sometime after 17 May 1963.
   The paper used for No. XM3 was the residue of the heavy chalk-surfaced paper remaining from the 1961 Post Office Savings Bank Centenary issue.

Cylinder Numbers (Blocks of Six)

Cream Paper (No. XM2)		Perf. Types		Chalky Paper (No. XM3)		Perf. Type
Cyl. No.	(No dot)	B	C	Cyl. No.	(No dot)	J
1	.. ..	8·00	8·00	1	.. .. ..	£110

Whiter Paper (No. XM4)			
Cyl. No.	(No dot)		Perf. Type F(L)
1	.. ..		1·75

Minor Constant Flaw
   Cyl. 1 19/6 Fine curved line to right of second link from bottom at left (Th. G1)

Sheet Markings

Guide holes:
  Perf. Types B and C, opposite rows 1 and 7/8 at both sides and also boxed opposite rows 14/15 at both sides
  Perf. Types F (L) and J, through marginal arrow above vertical rows 6/7 and below vertical row 10.
  Boxes only opposite rows 14/15
  Others: As given in General Notes

Imprimatur from the National Postal Museum Archives

Cream paper. Imperforate, watermark Type W.24

Watermark upright

Quantity Sold   35,959,420 up to 31.3.68 and including 1,080,000 on chalky paper (No. XM3)

Sold Out   12.68

Cat. No.	S.G. No.	Shades	Mint	Used

1968 (JUNE 27). ONE CENTRE PHOSPHOR BAND REACTING VIOLET. WATERMARK CROWNS

XM5	2p	Deep lilac	20	30

This issue is known postmarked at Douglas, Isle of Man, on 19 June 1968.

Cylinder Numbers (Blocks of Six)

Single pane cylinder.   Perforation Type F (L)

	Cyl. No.				No dot
	1	..	..	..	1·75

Minor Constant Flaws

As for Nos. XM2/4

Sheet Markings

Guide holes: As for perf. Type F (L) of No. XM4
Others: As given in General Notes

Sold Out   4.69

4d., Type XM2 (1966–69)

1966 (FEBRUARY 7). WATERMARK CROWNS

XM6	3	Ultramarine	1·50	1·10

Cylinder Numbers (Blocks of Six)

Single pane cylinder.   Perforation Type F (L)

	Cyl. No.				No dot
	1	..	..	..	12·00

Minor Constant Flaws

Cyl. 1   7/12 Fine line from top of diadem to inner frame at right (Th. B3-5)
      8/7 Coloured dot left of inner frame line at right (Th. C5-6)
      17/1 Coloured scratches below Queen's left eye (Th. D3-4)
      19/1 Coloured scratch behind Queen's neck (Th. F5)

Sheet Markings

Guide holes: Through marginal arrow above vertical rows 6/7 and below vertical row 10
Others: As given in General Notes

Quantity Sold   4,353,840 including 7,553 on First Day Covers

Sold Out   11.67

Cat. No.	S.G. No.		Shades	Mint	Used

1967 (JULY 5). TWO 9·5 mm. PHOSPHOR BANDS REACTING VIOLET. WATERMARK CROWNS

XM7	3p		Ultramarine	20	15

Cylinder Numbers (Blocks of Six)

Single pane cylinder.   Perforation Type F (L)

Cyl. No.				No dot
1	..	..	..	..	1·75

Minor Constant Flaws

As for No. XM6

Sheet Markings

As for No. XM6

Sold Out   12.68

1968 (JUNE 24). NO WATERMARK. CHALKY PAPER. PVA GUM. TWO 9·5 mm. PHOSPHOR BANDS REACTING VIOLET

XM8	4		Blue	20	25

Cylinder Numbers (Blocks of Six)

Single pane cylinder.   Perforation Type F (L)

Cyl. No.				No dot
1	..	..	..	..	1·75

Minor Constant Flaws

Cyl. 1   6/7 Flaw behind lower cross of diadem (Th. D5)

    14/2 White background spot just above Queen's right eye (Th. C–D2)
    Others as for No. XM6

Sheet Markings

As for No. XM6

Sold Out   16.7.69

1968 (SEPTEMBER 4). CHANGE OF COLOUR. NO WATERMARK. CHALKY PAPER. PVA GUM. ONE CENTRE PHOSPHOR BAND REACTING VIOLET

XM9	5		Olive-sepia	20	30
a. Phosphor omitted	..	..	20·00		

Cylinder Numbers (Blocks of Six)

Single pane cylinder.   Perforation Type F (L)

Cyl. No.				No dot
1	..	..	..	..	1·75

Minor Constant Flaws

As for No. XM8

Sheet Markings

As for No. XM6

1969 (FEBRUARY 26). FURTHER CHANGE OF COLOUR. NO WATERMARK. CHALKY PAPER. PVA GUM. ONE CENTRE PHOSPHOR BAND REACTING VIOLET

XM10	6		Bright vermilion	45	60

Cylinder Numbers (Blocks of Six)

Single pane cylinder.   Perforation Type F (L)

Cyl. No.				No dot
1	..	..	..	..	4·00

Minor Constant Flaws

As for No. XM8

Sheet Markings

As for No. XM6

5d., Type XM2 (1968)

Cat. No.	S.G. No.	Shades	Mint	Used

1968 (SEPTEMBER 4). NO WATERMARK. CHALKY PAPER. PVA GUM. TWO 9·5 mm. PHOSPHOR BANDS REACTING VIOLET

XM11	7	Royal blue	45	60

  a. Phosphor omitted £150
  b. Single broad band   ..   ..   35·00
  c. Frame flaw (top right) (R. 20/1)   3·25
  d. Frame flaw (bottom left)
      (R. 20/12)   ..   ..   ..   3·00

Listed Varieties

      XM11*c*   XM11*d*

Cylinder Numbers (Blocks of Six)

Single pane cylinder.   Perforation Type F (L)

Cyl. No.				No dot
1	..	..	..	.. 8·00*

Sheet Markings
  As for No. XM6

First Day Covers

XMFC1	(8.6.64)	9,237 posted	2½d.	20·00
XMFC2	(7.2.66)	7,553 posted	4d. Ultramarine	7·00
XMFC3	(4.9.68)	42,910 posted	4d. Olive-sepia, 5d.	1·75

D.   Northern Ireland

XN1
(Des. W. Hollywood)

XN2
(Des. L. Pilton)

XN3
(Des. T. Collins)

3d., Type XN1 (1958–67)

Cat. No.	S.G No.	Shades	Mint	Used

1958 (AUGUST 18). WATERMARK CROWNS

A. Cream Paper

XN1	—	Deep lilac	1·00	15

B. Whiter Paper (21 May 1962)

XN2	NI1	Deep lilac	20	10

Cylinder Numbers (Blocks of Six)

Cream Paper (No. XN1)

Perforation Type A

Cyl. No.					No dot	Dot
3	..	..	..	..	8·00	8·00

Whiter Paper (No. XN2)

Perforation Type A

Cyl. No.					No dot	Dot
3	..	..	..	..	1·75	1·75

Perforation Type F (L)*

3**	..	..	..	..

** This is probably No. XN3 with the phosphor omitted.

Minor Constant Flaw

Cyl. 3   4/9 White flaw on edge of lowest flax flower (Th. G2)

Sheet Markings

Guide holes: Boxed opposite rows 14/15, at left (no dot) or right (dot)
Others: As given in General Notes

Imprimatur from the National Postal Museum Archives

Cream paper. Imperforate, watermark Type W.24

Watermark upright

Quantity Sold   375,417,400

Sold Out   10.67

1967 (JUNE 9). ONE CENTRE PHOSPHOR BAND REACTING VIOLET. WATERMARK CROWNS

XN3	NI1p	Deep lilac	20	15

Cylinder Numbers (Blocks of Six)

Perforation Type A

Cyl. No.					No dot	Dot
3	..	..	..	..	1·75	1·75

Perforation Type F (L)*

Cyl. No					No dot	Dot
3	..	..	..	..	1·75	1·75

Minor Constant Flaws

As for flaw on Nos. XN1/2

Sheet Markings

Guide holes: Boxed opposite rows 14/15, at left (no dot) or right (dot) but in the case of perforation Type F (L)* the boxes remain on both panes but the holes are unboxed above and boxed below the eighth vertical row in the no dot pane only
Others: As given in General Notes

4d., Type XN1 (1966-69)

Cat. No.	S.G. No.	Shades	Mint	Used

1966 (FEBRUARY 7). WATERMARK CROWNS

| XN4 | NI2 | Ultramarine | 20 | 15 |

   a. Dot on leaf (No dot, R. 3/12) .. 2·75
   b. Flower flaw (No dot, R. 7/7)   3·00
   c. Dot under " S " of " POST-
      AGE " (Dot R. 2/4) .. .. 3·50

Listed Varieties

XN4*a*, XN5*a*, XN6*a*,	XN4*b*	XN4*c*
XN7*a*, XN8*b*		

White dot on leaf of plant. Retouched on No. XN9

White spot on top flower. The above only exists on No. XN4. It was retouched and shows as a dark patch on Nos. XN5*b*, XN6*b*, XN7*b*, XN8*c* and XN9*b*

White dot under " S " of " POSTAGE ". Retouched on No. XN5

Cylinder Numbers (Blocks of Six)

Perforation Type A

Cyl. No.					No dot	Dot
1	..	..	..	..	1·75	1·75

Minor Constant Flaws

Cyl. 1 16/5 Small white spot to right of second leaf down on upright flax plant (Th. B6)
Cyl. 1. 2/1 Small coloured projection above upper frame line (Th. A2)
       3/12 Small white dot below lower right leaf of flax plant (Th. G4)
       10/6 Coloured flaw in lower left of badge (Th. E1)
       12/1 Pale patch below P of POSTAGE (Th. F1)

Sheet Markings

Guide holes: In double "SON" box opposite rows 14/15, at left (no dot) or right (dot)
Cylinder number: Opposite R.18/1. In addition, early printings of both no dot and dot panes bore a trace of cylinder numbers reading "1A" and "1A." with two sides of a box opposite R.19/1. These had been inserted in error. Attempts to remove them were only partially successful, so that they exist in varying degrees of faintness.
Others: As given in General Notes

Quantity Sold 61,449,360

Sold Out 11.68

1967 (OCTOBER 2). TWO 9·5 mm. PHOSPHOR BANDS REACTING VIOLET. WATERMARK CROWNS

| XN5 | NI2p | Ultramarine | 20 | 15 |

   a. Dot on leaf (No dot, R. 3/12) 3·00
   b. Flower flaw retouch (No dot,
      R. 7/7) .. .. 3·00

For illustration of No. XN5*a* and for description of No. XN5*b*, see Nos. XN4*a/b*.

Cylinder Numbers (Blocks of Six)

Perforation Type F (L)*

Cyl. No.					No dot	Dot
1	..	..	..	..	1·75	1·75

Minor Constant Flaws

Cyl. 1   16/5 Small white spot to right of second leaf down on upright flax plant (Th. B6)
Cyl. 1.   2/1   Small coloured projection above upper frame line (Th. A2)
          2/4   Dark patch below S of POSTAGE where former white dot, No. XN4*a*, existed (Th. F2)
          3/12 Small white dot below lower right leaf of flax plant (Th. G4)
          10/6 Coloured flaw in lower left of badge (Th. E1)
          12/1 Pale patch below P of POSTAGE (Th. F1)

Sheet Markings

Guide holes: Unboxed above and boxed below the eighth vertical row in the no dot pane only. The double "SON" boxes opposite rows 14/15 remain
Others: As given in General Notes

Sold Out 1.70

Cat. No.	S.G. No.		Shades	Mint	Used

1968 (JUNE 27). NO WATERMARK. CHALKY PAPER. TWO 9·5 mm. PHOSPHOR BANDS REACTING VIOLET

A. Gum Arabic

XN6	NI7		Ultramarine	20	15
a. Dot on leaf (No dot, R. 3/12)		3·00			
b. Flower flaw retouch (No dot, R. 7/7) ..	..	3·00			

B. PVA Gum* (23 October 1968)

XN7	NI7Ev		Ultramarine	9·00	
a. Dot on leaf (No dot, R. 3/12)		17·00			
b. Flower flaw retouch (No dot, R. 7/7) ..	..	17·00			

For illustration of Nos. XN6*a* and XN7*a* and for description of Nos. XN6*b* and XN7*b*, see Nos. XN4*a/b* respectively.

* No. XN7 was never issued in Northern Ireland.   After No. XN6 (gum arabic) had been withdrawn from Northern Ireland but whilst still on sale at the philatelic counters elsewhere, about fifty sheets with PVA gum were sold over the London Philatelic counter on 23 October 1968, and some were also on sale at the British Philatelic Exhibition Post Office.

Cylinder Numbers (Blocks of Six)

Gum Arabic (No. XN6)			PVA Gum (No. XN7)		
Perforation Type A			Perforation Type A		
Cyl. No.	No dot	Dot	Cyl. No.	No dot	Dot
1	1·75	1·75	1	70·00	†

Minor Constant Flaws

Cyl. 1   16/5 Small white spot to right of second leaf down on upright flax plant (Th. B6)
Cyl. 1.   2/1   Small coloured projection above upper frame line (Th. A2)
          2/4   Dark patch below S of POSTAGE where former white dot, No. XN4*a*, existed (Th. F2)
          3/12 Small white dot below lower right leaf of flax plant (Th. G4)
          6/12 Small coloured flaws on leaf above NU of REVENUE
          10/6 Coloured flaw in lower left of badge (Th. E1)
          12/1 Pale patch below P of POSTAGE (Th. F1)

Sheet Markings

Guide holes: In double "SON" box opposite rows 14/15, at left (no dot) or right (dot). In addition a single hand-engraved box appears below the eighth vertical row in the no dot pane only (latter only used in conjunction with perforation Type F (L)*).
Others: As given in General Notes

Sold Out No. XN6, 4.70

Withdrawn No. XN7 on the same day as released

1968 (SEPTEMBER 4). CHANGE OF COLOUR. NO WATERMARK. CHALKY PAPER. PVA GUM. ONE CENTRE PHOSPHOR BAND REACTING VIOLET

XN8	NI8			Olive-sepia	20	15
a. Phosphor omitted	..	..	£200	*c.* Flower flaw retouch (No dot,		
b. Dot on leaf (No dot, R. 3/12)		3·00		R. 7/7)	3·00	

For illustration of No. XN8*b* and for description of No. XN8*c*, see Nos. XN4*a/b* respectively.

Cylinder Numbers (Blocks of Six)

Perforation Type A

Cyl. No.				No dot	Dot
1	..	..	..	.. 1·75	1·75

Minor Constant Flaws

As for Nos. XN6/7.

Sheet Markings

Guide holes: As for Nos. XN6/7.
Cylinder number: Opposite R.18/1. In addition both no dot and dot panes bear traces of cylinder numbers reading "1A" and "1A." with two sides of a box opposite R. 19/1. These exist in varying degrees of faintness
Others: As given in General Notes

Cat. No.	S.G. No.		Shades	Mint	Used

1969 (FEBRUARY 26). FURTHER CHANGE OF COLOUR. NO WATERMARK. CHALKY PAPER. PVA GUM. ONE CENTRE PHOSPHOR BAND REACTING VIOLET

XN9	NI9	Bright vermilion	20	20
a.	Phosphor omitted	4·50		
b.	Flower flaw retouch (No dot, R. 7/7)	2·50		

For description of No. XN9b, see No. XN4b.

Cylinder Numbers (Blocks of Six)

Perforation Type A

Cyl. No.				No dot	Dot
1	..	..	..	.. 1·75	1·75

Minor Constant Flaws

Cyl. 1. 2/4 Dark patch below S of POSTAGE where former white dot, No. XN4a, existed (Th. F2)
6/12 Small coloured flaws on leaf above NU of REVENUE
10/6 Coloured flaw in lower left of badge (Th. E1)
12/1 Pale patch below P of POSTAGE (Th. F1)

Sheet Markings

Guide holes: As for Nos. XN6/7.
Cylinder number: Opposite R. 18/1. In addition both no dot and dot panes bear traces of cylinder numbers reading "1A" and "1A". with two sides of a box opposite R. 19/1. These exist in varying degrees of faintness
Others: As given in General Notes

5d., Type XN1 (1968)

1968 (SEPTEMBER 4). NO WATERMARK. CHALKY PAPER. PVA GUM. TWO 9·5 mm. PHOSPHOR BANDS REACTING VIOLET

XN10	NI10	Royal blue	20	20
a.	Phosphor omitted	25·00		
b.	"Extra leaf" (No dot, R. 13/2)	3·25		

Listed Variety

White flaw near junction of flax plant stalks appears as an extra leaf

XN10b

Cylinder Numbers (Blocks of Six)
Perforation Type A

Cyl. No.					No dot	Dot
1	..	..	..	..	1·75	1·75

Sheet Markings
Guide holes: In double "SON" box opposite rows 14/15, at left (no dot) or right (dot). In addition a single " traffic light " type box appears above and below the eighth vertical row in the no dot pane only. (These would only be used in conjunction with perforation Type F (L.)*).
Others: As given in General Notes

6d., Type XN2 (1958–62)

Cat. No.	S.G. No.	Shades	Mint	Used

1958 (SEPTEMBER 29). WATERMARK CROWNS

A. Cream Paper

XN11	—	Deep claret	1·50	30

B. Whiter Paper (4 June 1962)

XN12	NI3	Deep claret	20	20

Cylinder Numbers (Blocks of Six)

Cream Paper (No. XN11)					Whiter Paper (No. XN12)				
Cyl. No.	(No dot)			Perf. Types	Cyl. No.	(No dot)			Perf. Types
				B C					B C F (L)
1	..	..	..	15·00 15·00	1	..	..	..	2·50 2·50 2·25

Minor Constant Flaws
Cyl. 1
1/12 Flaw in background to right of diadem (Th. A4)
2/11 White coloured spur on lowest leaf of left flax plant (Th. F1)
3/9 Dot in diamond to right of 6D (Th. F4); also similar dot in diamond to right of Queen's collar (Th. E–F5)
3/10 " Ring " on little finger of hand at left (Th. F2)
3/12 Dark spot in centre of central cross of diadem (Th. B3)
4/2 Coloured line in background to right of 6D (Th. G4)
10/2 White bulge half way down stalk at left (Th. D1)
12/2 Coloured spot in background to right of Queen's hair (Th. D5)

Sheet Markings
Guide holes:
Perf. Types B and C, unboxed opposite rows 1 and 7/8 at both sides and also boxed opposite rows 14/15 at both sides
Perf. Type F (L), through marginal arrow above vertical rows 6/7 and below vertical row 10. Boxes only opposite rows 14/15 at both sides
Others: As given in General Notes

Imprimatur from the National Postal Museum Archives
Cream paper. Imperforate, watermark Type W.24
Watermark upright

Quantity Sold 28,531,180 up to 31.3.68

Sold Out 11.68

9d., Type XN2 (1967)

1967 (MARCH 1). WATERMARK CROWNS. TWO 9·5 mm. PHOSPHOR BANDS REACTING VIOLET

XN13	NI4	Bronze-green	30	50

Cylinder Numbers (Blocks of Six)
Single pane cylinder. Perforation Type F (L)

Cyl. No.				No dot
1	..	..	..	3·00

Sheet Markings

Guide holes: Through marginal arrow above vertical rows 6/7 and below vertical row 10
Others: As given in General Notes

Imprimatur from the National Postal Museum Archives

Imperforate, watermark Type W.24

Watermark upright

1s.3d., Type XN3 (1958–62)

Cat. No.	S.G. No.	Shades	Mint	Used
1958 (SEPTEMBER 29). WATERMARK CROWNS				
A. Cream Paper				
XN14	—	Green	3·50	75
B. Whiter Paper (9 November 1962)				
XN15	NI5	Green	30	50

Cylinder Numbers (Blocks of Six)

Cream Paper (No. XN14)				Whiter Paper (No. XN15)				
Cyl. No.	(No dot)	Perf. Types		Cyl. No.	(No dot)	Perf. Types		
		B	C			B	C	F (L)
1	.. ..	28·00	28·00	1	.. .. ..	3·00	3·00	2·50

Minor Constant Flaws

Cyl. 1   1/1 White dot in upper loop of S of POSTAGE; also small area of retouching above emblems in diadem (Th. A4)

3/7 White spur to O of POSTAGE (Th. E1)

Sheet Markings

Guide holes:
Perf. Types B and C, not known
Perf. Type F (L), through marginal arrow above vertical rows 6/7 and below vertical row 10. Boxes only opposite rows 14/15 at both sides
Others: As given in General Notes

Imprimatur from the National Postal Museum Archives

Cream paper. Imperforate, watermark Type W.24

Watermark upright

Quantity Sold   14,060,520 up to 31.3.68

1s.6d., Type XN3 (1967–69)

1967 (MARCH 1). WATERMARK CROWNS. TWO 9·5 mm. PHOSPHOR BANDS REACTING VIOLET				
XN16	NI6	Grey-blue	30	50
a. Phosphor omitted	.. .. £200			

Cylinder Numbers (Blocks of Six)

Single pane cylinder.   Perforation Type F (L)

Cyl. No.				No dot
1	.. .. ..	..		2·50

Minor Constant Flaws

Cyl. 1   4/12 Small area of retouching behind Queen's head.   Consists of several small dark coloured dots (Th. E5)

14/1 Dark coloured spot on Queen's cheek (Th. D4)

15/12 A multitude of tiny coloured spots over the Queen's face, neck and collar, and in the background behind her neck

17/8 Coloured spot to right of Queen's left eye (Th. D3–4)

Sheet Markings

Guide holes: Through marginal arrow above vertical rows 6/7 and below vertical row 10
Others: As given in General Notes

Imprimatur from the National Postal Museum Archives

Imperforate, watermark Type W.24

Watermark upright

Cat. No.	S.G. No.		Shades		Mint	Used

1969 (MAY 20).   NO WATERMARK.   CHALKY PAPER.   PVA GUM.   TWO 9·5 mm. PHOSPHOR BANDS REACTING VIOLET

XN17	NI11		Grey-blue		2·00	3·00
a. Phosphor omitted ..	..	..				

It is believed that only three examples exist of No. XN17a.

Cylinder Numbers (Blocks of Six)

Single pane cylinder.   Perforation Type F (L)

	Cyl. No.				No dot
	1	..	..	..	..	17·00

Minor Constant Flaws

Cyl. 1   4/12 Small area of retouching behind Queen's head.   Consists of several small dark coloured dots (Th. E5)

11/12 Small dark coloured flaw on Queen's neck, just above necklace (Th. E4)

14/1 Small dark coloured flaw on Queen's cheek (Th. D4)

15/12 A multitude of tiny dark coloured spots over the Queen's face, neck and collar, and in the background behind her neck

17/8 Area of retouching to right of Queen's left eye (Th. D3–4)

Sheet Markings

As for No. XN16

Imprimatur from the National Postal Museum Archives

Chalky paper, imperforate

No watermark

Presentation Pack

XNPP1 (9.12.70)		Seven stamps	3·00

Comprises Nos. XN3, 8/10, 13, and 15/16

Quantity Sold 28,944

Withdrawn 25.11.71

First Day Covers

XNFC1	(1.3.67)	9d., 1s. 6d.	1·50
XNFC2	(4.9.68)	4d., 5d.	50

E. Scotland

XS1
(Des. Gordon F. Huntly)

XS2
(Des. J. B. Fleming)

XS3
(Des. A. B. Imrie)

3d., Type XS1 (1958–68)

Cat. No.	S.G. No.	Shades	Mint	Used

1958 (AUGUST 18). WATERMARK CROWNS

A. Cream Paper

XS1 —   Deep lilac   50   20
- *a.* Spot on " U " of " REVENUE "
  (Cyl. 3 No dot, R. 19/8) ..   3·50
- *b.* Dot in " d " of " 3d " (Cyl. 3 Dot,
  R. 20/12) .. ..   2·75

B. Whiter Paper (9 July 1962)

XS2   S1   Deep lilac   20   15
- *a.* Spot after last " E " of " REVE-
  NUE " (Cyl. 5 No dot, R. 20/2)   2·75

Listed Varieties

XS1a

XS1b
Later retouched

**XS2a, XS3a, XS4b,
XS5b, XS7b XS8b**

Cylinder Numbers (Blocks of Six)

Cream Paper (No. XS1)   Whiter Paper (No. XS2)

Perforation Type A   Perforation Type A

Cyl. No.				No dot	Dot	Cyl. No.				No dot	Dot
3	..	..	.. ..	5·00	5·00	4	..	..	.. ..	1·75	1·75
4	..	..	.. ..	5·00	5·00	5	..	..	.. ..	1·75	3·50*

Perforation Type H

4	..	..	.. ..	5·00**	—

**Same price as perforation type A with extension holes in left margin.

Sheet Markings

Guide holes: Boxed opposite rows 14/15, at left (no dot) or right (dot)
Others: As given in General Notes

Imprimatur from the National Postal Museum Archives

Cream paper. Imperforate, watermark Type W.24

Watermark upright

Quantity Sold 1,487,481,480

Sold Out 18.3.68

1962. Miniature Sheet. On the occasion of SCOTEX the 1962 Scottish Stamp Exhibition, a miniature sheet, size 105 × 60 mm., was produced comprising Types **XS1/3** printed *se-tenant* in black, imperforate and surrounded by a decorative frame and inscription in blue on white chalk-surfaced gummed paper watermarked " HARRISON AND SONS LTD " sideways. The sheet was printed by Harrison & Sons with the use of actual stamp positives. It had no franking value. 15,000 printed.

Cat. No.	S.G. No.	Shades	Mint	Used

1963 (JANUARY 29). PHOSPHOR BANDS REACTING BLUE. WATERMARK CROWNS

A. Two 8 mm. Bands

XS3	S1p	Deep lilac	12·00	1·00

  a. Spot after last " E " of " REVE-
    NUE " (Cyl. 5 Dot, R. 20/2) .. 18·00

B. One Side Band* (30 April 1965)

XS4	—	Deep lilac (band at left)	3·00	50

  a Band at right .. .. .. 3·00   50
  ab. Nos. XS4/*a* (horiz. pair) .. 6·00
  b. Spot after last " E " of " REVE-
    NUE " (Cyl. 5 Dot, R. 20/2) .. 6·00

*The one side band stamps were produced by an 8 mm. band applied down alternate vertical rows of the sheets over the perforations so that alternate stamps have the band at left (No. XS4) or right (No. XS4*a*). In theory the width of the band on a single stamp should be 4 mm. but this will vary if the bands have not been perfectly positioned.
For illustration of Nos. XS3*a* and XS4*b*, see No. XS2*a*.

Cylinder Numbers (Blocks of Six)

Two Bands (No. XS3)   One Side Band (No. XS4)

Perforation Type A   Perforation Type A

Cyl. No.				No dot	Dot		Cyl. No.				No dot	Dot
4	..	..	..	90·00	90·00		5	..	..	..	21·00	25·00*
5	..	..	..	90·00	95·00*							

Sheet Markings

As for Nos. XS1/2

Imprimatur from the National Postal Museum Archives

Imperforate, watermark Type W.24. Two 8 mm. bands
Watermark upright

Sold Out No. XS3, 1968

1965 (DECEMBER 16). PHOSPHOR BANDS REACTING VIOLET. WATERMARK CROWNS

A. One Side Band*

XS5	S1pa	Deep lilac (band at left)	20	25

  a. Band at right 20   25
  ab. Nos. XS5/*a* (horiz. pair) .. 50
  b. Spot after last " E " of " REVE-
    NUE " (Cyl. 5 Dot, R. 20/2) .. 3·00

B. One 4 mm. Centre Band (9 November 1967)

XS6	S1pb	Deep lilac	20	15

*The note *re* one side band stamps after No. XS4*b* also applies here.
For illustration of No. XS5*b*, see No. XS2*a*.

Cylinder Numbers (Blocks of Six)

One Side Band (No. XS5)   One Centre Band (No. XS6)

Perforation Type A   Perforation Type A

Cyl. No.				No dot	Dot		Cyl. No.				No dot	Dot
5	..	..	..	1·75	5·00*		4	..	..	..	1·75	1·75

Sheet Markings

As for Nos. XS1/2

Sold Out   No. XS5, 15.7.68; No. XS6, 11.68

Cat. No.	S.G. No.	Shades	Mint	Used

1968 (MAY 16). NO WATERMARK. CHALKY PAPER. ONE CENTRE PHOSPHOR BAND REACTING VIOLET

A. Gum Arabic

XS7   S7   Deep lilac   10   15
   a. Phosphor omitted .. ..   5·50
   b. Spot after last "E" of "REVE-
      NUE" (Cyl. 5 Dot, R. 20/2) ..   2·50

B. PVA Gum (11 July 1968)

XS8   S7Ev   Deep lilac   10
   a. Phosphor omitted .. ..   2·50
   b. Spot after last "E" of "REVE-
      NUE" (Cyl. 5 Dot, R. 20/2) ..   2·00

For illustration of Nos. XS7*b* and XS8*b*, see No. XS2*a*.

Cylinder Numbers (Blocks of Six)

Gum Arabic (No. XS7)			PVA Gum (No. XS8)		
Perforation Type F (L)*			Perforation Type F (L)*		
Cyl. No.	No dot	Dot	Cyl. No.	No dot	Dot
5	1·25	3·00*	5	1·25	3·00*

Minor Constant Flaws

Cyl. 5   8/6 Retouching on Queen's forehead, nose and around lips (Th. B–D3)
        13/3 Pale patch on Queen's collar (Th. E–F4)
        15/3 Small dark flaw surrounded by white area on right side of thistle (Th. G6)
        17/7 Area of retouching on Queen's neck (Th. E4–5)
        18/1 Horizontal coloured line through G of POSTAGE

Sheet Markings

Guide holes: Unboxed above and boxed below the eighth vertical row in the no dot pane only. The boxes opposite rows 14/15 remain.
Others: As given in General Notes

4d., Type XS1 (1966–69)

1966 (FEBRUARY 7). WATERMARK CROWNS

XS9   S2   Ultramarine   20   10
   a. Dot before second "E" of
      "REVENUE" (Dot, R. 10/9)   2·75
   b. Spot on "T" (Dot, R. 4/4) ..   3·00

Listed Varieties

XS9*a*, XS10*a*
Later retouched
on No. XS10

XS9*b*, XS10*b*

Cylinder Numbers (Blocks of Six)
Perforation Type A

Cyl. No.					No dot	Dot
2	..	..	..	..	1·75	1·75

Minor Constant Flaws

Cyl. 2   7/11   White spot to left of crown at right (Th. F5)
      8/6   Small blue flaw on top left-hand leaf of thistle (Th. F5)
      20/5   Small dark flaw in background to right of d of 4d (Th. F4–5)
Cyl. 2.   8/12   Blue spot below Queen's left eye (Th. C3)
      11/7   Small blue spot on Queen's forehead (Th. B2)
      12/8   Small dark flaw in background to left of EV of REVENUE (Th. B5); also retouching on
         Queen's temple and cheek (Th. C3–4)
      20/3   Small coloured flaw above Queen's left eye (Th. B3); also small blue spot on top left-hand
         leaf of thistle (Th. F5)

Sheet Markings
Guide holes: In double "SON" box opposite rows 14/15, at left (no dot) or right (dot)
Others: As given in General Notes

Sold Out   7.70.

Cat. No.	S.G. No.	Shades	Mint	Used

1966 (FEBRUARY 7). TWO 8 mm. PHOSPHOR BANDS REACTING VIOLET. WATERMARK CROWNS

XS10	S2p	Ultramarine	20	20

a. Dot before second "E" of
   "REVENUE" (Dot, R. 10/9)   2·50
b. Spot on "T" (Dot, R. 4/4) ..   2·50
For illustrations of Nos. XS10a/b, see Nos. XS9a/b.

Cylinder Numbers (Blocks of Six)
Perforation Type A

Cyl. No.					No dot	Dot
2	..	..	..	..	1·75	1·75

Minor Constant Flaws
Cyl. 2   As for flaws on No. XS9 except that flaw on R. 20/5 was later retouched
Cyl. 2.   As for flaws on No. XS9

Sheet Markings
As for No. XS9

Sold Out   7.70.

1967 (NOVEMBER 28). NO WATERMARK. CHALKY PAPER. TWO 9·5 mm. PHOSPHOR BANDS REACTING VIOLET

A. Gum Arabic

XS11	S8	Ultramarine	10	15

a. Phosphor omitted   ..   ..   7·00

B. PVA Gum (25 July 1968)

XS12	S8Ev	Ultramarine	10	

Cylinder Numbers (Blocks of Six)

Gum Arabic (No. XS11)		PVA Gum (no. XS12)	
Perforation Type F (L)*		Perforation Type A	

Cyl. No.					No dot	Dot		Cyl. No.					No dot	Dot
2	..	..	..	..	1·25	1·25		2	..	..	..	..	1·25	1·25

Minor Constant Flaws

Cyl. 2   1/7 Retouch on Queen's forehead (Th. B3). PVA only
          3/7 Retouch on Queen's collar (Th. E4–5). PVA only
          5/10 White patches on Queen's nose and forehead
          8/6 Small blue flaw on top left-hand leaf of thistle (Th. F5)
          10/11 Retouch to right of Queen's mouth (Th. D3). PVA only
          12/12 White spot at rear tip of diadem (Th. C5)
          14/10 Retouch on Queen's forehead (Th. B3)   Less pronounced on PVA
          15/4 Retouch on Queen's cheek (Th. C–D3)
          19/7 White spot on Queen's cheek (Th. C3). Retouched on PVA where it shows as three dark
               spots
          20/5 Small dark flaw in background to right of d of 4d (Th. F4–5). Less pronounced on PVA
               but can be confirmed by additional retouches on Queen's nose and forehead (Th. C2 and B3)
          20/6 Small blue flaw on Queen's cheek (Th. C3). On PVA there is an additional white flaw on
               Queen's right cheek (Th. C2)

Cyl. 2.   1/5 Coloured spot above Queen's left eye (Th. B3).
          2/6 Retouch on Queen's collar (Th. E4)
          6/11 White spot on Queen's cheek (Th. C–D3). Retouched on PVA where it shows as a dark
               spot
          8/12 White spot below Queen's left eye where former blue spot appeared (Th. C3). Further
               retouched on PVA
          11/7 Small blue spot on Queen's forehead (Th. B2)
          12/8 Small dark flaw in background to left of EV of REVENUE (Th. B5); also retouching on
               Queen's temple and cheek, the latter much more pronounced on PVA (Th. C3–4)
          15/1 Small retouch on Queen's temple (Th. C3–4). PVA only
          15/2 Small retouch on Queen's forehead (Th. B2). PVA only
          18/4 Weak patches on Queen's chin (Th. D2–3).
          18/6 Blue spot on Queen's collar (Th. E4). Retouched on PVA but a scratch now appears
               across Queen's neck and collar (Th. E4)
          19/3 White spot on Queen's left cheek (Th. D3). Shows larger on PVA
          20/3 Small coloured flaw above Queen's left eye (Th. B3); also small blue spot on top left-hand
               leaf of thistle (Th. F5)
          20/4 Coloured spots around Queen's eyes and nose (Th. C2–3)

Sheet Markings

Guide holes:
    Perf. Type A, in double "SON" box opposite rows 14/15, at left (no dot) or right (dot). In addition
    a single hand-engraved box appears above and below the eighth vertical row in the no dot pane only
    (latter only used in conjunction with perforation Type F (L)*).
    Perf. Type F (L)*, boxed above and below the eighth vertical row in the no dot pane only. The usual
    "SON" boxes opposite rows 14/15 remain
Others: As given in General Notes

Cat. No.	S.G. No.		Shades		Mint	Used

1968 (SEPTEMBER 4). CHANGE OF COLOUR. NO WATERMARK. CHALKY PAPER. PVA GUM. ONE CENTRE PHOSPHOR BAND REACTING VIOLET

XS13	S9		Olive-sepia		10	10
a. Phosphor omitted	..	..	1·75			

Cylinder Numbers (Blocks of Six)

Perforation Type A

	Cyl. No.			No dot	Dot
	2	..	..	..	..	1·25	1·25

Minor Constant Flaws

Cyl. 2 12/12 White spot at rear tip of diadem (Th. C5)
Cyl. 2.   1/5 Coloured spot above Queen's left eye (Th. B3)
          2/6 Retouch on Queen's collar (Th. E4)
          6/11 Retouch on Queen's cheek (Th. C–D3)
          8/12 Retouch below Queen's left eye (Th. C3)
          11/7 Coloured spot on Queen's forehead (Th. B2)
          12/8 Small dark flaw in background to left of EV of REVENUE (Th. B5); also retouching on
               Queen's temple and cheek (Th. C3–4)
          15/1 Small retouch on Queen's temple (Th. C3–4)
          15/2 Small retouch on Queen's forehead (Th. B2)
          18/4 Weak patches on Queen's chin (Th. D2–4)
          18/6 Retouch on Queen's collar and also scratch across her neck and collar (Th. E4)
          19/3 Large white spot on Queen's left cheek (Th. D3)
          20/3 Small coloured flaw above Queen's left eye (Th. B3); also small coloured spot on top left-hand leaf of thistle (Th. F5)
          20/4 Coloured spots around Queen's eyes and nose (Th. C2–3)

Sheet Markings

Guide holes: As for Perf. Type A under Nos. XS11/12
Others: As given in General Notes

Cat. No.	S.G. No.		Shades	Mint	Used

1969 (FEBRUARY 26). FURTHER CHANGE OF COLOUR. NO WATERMARK. CHALKY PAPER. PVA GUM. ONE CENTRE PHOSPHOR BAND REACTING VIOLET

XS14	S10		Bright vermilion	10	10
a.	Phosphor omitted	..	1·75		

Cylinder Numbers (Blocks of Six)

Perforation Type A

Cyl. No.					No dot	Dot
2	..	..	..	..	1·25	1·25

Perforation Type A

Cyl. No.					No dot	Dot
4	..	..	..	..	1·25	1·25

Minor Constant Flaws

Cyl. 2
- 1/7 Retouch on Queen's forehead (Th. B3)
- 3/7 Retouch on Queen's collar (Th. E4–5)
- 5/10 Retouching on Queen's nose and forehead where former white patches appeared
- 8/11 Retouch by Queen's ear (Th. C–D4)
- 12/12 White spot at rear tip of diadem (Th. C5)
- 10/11 Retouch to right of Queen's mouth (Th. D3)
- 14/10 Heavy retouching on Queen's forehead (Th. B3)
- 15/4 Retouch on Queen's cheek (Th. C–D3)
- 19/7 Retouch on Queen's cheek where former white spot appeared (Th. C3)
- 20/5 Retouches on Queen's nose and forehead (Th. C2 and B3). Small dark flaw in background to right of d of 4d now hardly shows (Th. F4–5)
- **20/6** Retouches on both of the Queen's cheeks where former flaws appeared (Th. C2–3)

Cyl. 2.
- 1/5 Coloured spot above Queen's left eye (Th. B3)
- 2/6 Retouch on Queen's collar (Th. E4)
- 6/11 Heavy area of retouching on Queen's cheek (Th. C–D3)
- 8/12 Retouch below Queen's left eye (Th. C3)
- 10/5 Extensive area of retouching on Queen's temple and cheek (Th. B3 and C3–4)
- 11/7 Area of retouching on Queen's forehead where former coloured spot appeared (Th. B2)
- 12/8 Small dark flaw in background to left of EV of REVENUE (Th. B5) is now less noticeable but retouches on Queen's temple and cheek remain (Th. C3–4)
- 15/1 Small retouch on Queen's temple (Th. C3–4)
- 15/2 Small retouch on Queen's forehead (Th. B2)
- 18/4 Weak patches on Queen's chin (Th. D2–4)
- 18/6 Retouch on Queen's collar and also scratch across her neck and collar (Th. E4)
- 20/3 Small coloured flaw above Queen's left eye (Th. B3); also small coloured spot on top left-hand leaf of thistle (Th. F5)
- 20/4 Coloured spots around Queen's eyes and nose (Th. C2–3)

Sheet Markings

Guide holes: As for Perf. Type A under Nos. XS11/12
Others: As given in General Notes

5d., Type XS1 (1968)

1968 (SEPTEMBER 4). NO WATERMARK. CHALKY PAPER. PVA GUM. TWO 9·5 mm. PHOSPHOR BANDS REACTING VIOLET

XS15	S11		Royal blue	20	10
a. Phosphor omitted	..	..	42·00		
b. Shoulder retouch (Cyl. 2., R. 16/6)	3·00				

Listed Variety

XS15*b*

Large retouch on Queen's shoulder

Cylinder Numbers (Blocks of Six)

Perforation Type A

Cyl. No.				No dot	Dot
2	..	..	..	1·75	1·75
3	..	..	..	5·50	5·50

Sheet Markings

Phosphor cylinder number: "Ph 1" found on cyl. 3 dot, right margin
Guide holes: In double "S O N" box opposite rows 14/15, at left (no dot) or right (dot)
Others: As given in General Notes

6d., Type XS2 (1958–66)

Cat. No.	S.G. No.	Shades	Mint	Used
1958 (SEPTEMBER 29). WATERMARK CROWNS				

A. Cream Paper

XS16	—	Reddish purple	1·50	50
a.	Broken " V " of " REVENUE "			
	(Cyl. 1, R.11/12)	8·00		
b.	Curled leaf (Cyl. 1, R. 7/7) ..	6·50		

B. Whiter Paper (28 May 1962)

XS17	S3	Deep reddish purple	20	15
a.	Broken " V " of " REVENUE "			
	(Cyl. 1, R. 11/12)	4·00		
b.	Curled leaf (Cyl. 1, R. 7/7) ..	3·00		
c.	Cut leaf (Cyl. 4, R. 2/10) ..	3·00		

Listed Varieties

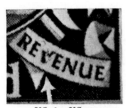

XS16a, XS17a

This is a multipositive flaw.
It was later retouched on
Cyl. 1. On Cyls. 2 and 4 it
is only known retouched and
it shows as a much thicker
" V " than normal

XS16b, XS17b
Later retouched

XS17c, XS18a

Leaf half-way down at
right has V-shaped cut in
solid colour

Cylinder Numbers (Blocks of Six)

	Cream Paper (No. XS16)				Whiter Paper (No. XS17)			
			Perf. Types				Perf. Types	
Cyl. No.	(No dot)		B	C	Cyl. No.	(No dot)	B	C	F(L)
1	.. ..		12·00	12·00	1	.. .. ..	†	†	2·50
					2	.. .. ..	1·75	1·75	†
					4	.. .. ..	†	†	1·75

Minor Constant Flaws

Cyl. 1   5/8 Small white flaw by left thistle just outside oval frame (Th. B2)
Cyl. 2 11/12 V of REVENUE retouched.   It is thicker than normal and has a fuzzy appearance
Cyl. 4 11/12 As for Cyl. 2

Sheet Markings

Guide holes:
Perf. Types B and C, unboxed opposite rows 1 and 7/8 at both sides and also boxed opposite rows 14/1
at both sides
Perf. Type F (L), through marginal arrow above vertical rows 6/7 and below vertical row 10.   Boxes
only opposite rows 14/15 at both sides
Marginal rule:
Cyl. 1: Instead of the usual "stamp width" rule below each stamp in the bottom row the rules on this
cylinder are shorter (approx. 17 mm.) and are arranged alternately with a 1 mm. wide rectangular
rule, the latter being perforated through.   The rules below vertical rows 9/12 are damaged
Cyls 2 and 4: As given in General Notes
Others: As given in General Notes

Imprimatur from the National Postal Museum Archives

Cream paper. Imperforate, watermark Type W.24

Watermark upright

Cat. No.	S.G. No.	Shades	Mint	Used

1963 (JANUARY 29). TWO 8 mm. PHOSPHOR BANDS REACTING BLUE. WATERMARK CROWNS

XS18	—	Deep reddish purple	1·50	50
a. Cut leaf (Cyl. 4, R. 2/10) .. 6·00				

Cylinder Numbers (Blocks of Six)

Single pane cylinder.   Perforation Type F (L)

	Cyl. No.	No dot
	4	12·00

Minor Constant Flaws

Cyl. 4 11/12 V of REVENUE retouched.   It is thicker than normal and has a fuzzy appearance

Sheet Markings

Guide holes: Through marginal arrow above vertical rows 6/7 and below vertical row 10.   Boxes only opposite rows 14/15 at both sides
Others: As given in General Notes

Imprimatur from the National Postal Museum Archives

Imperforate, watermark Type W.24

Watermark upright

1966 (FEBRUARY 2). TWO 8 mm. PHOSPHOR BANDS REACTING VIOLET. WATERMARK CROWNS

XS19	S3p	Deep reddish purple	20	25

Cylinder Numbers (Blocks of Six)

Single pane cylinder.   Perforation Type F (L)

	Cyl. No.	No dot
	4	1·75

Sheet Markings

As for No. XS18

Quantity Sold   26,758,320 (including No. XS18) up to 31.3.68

Sold Out   10.68

9d., Type XS2 (1967-70)

1967 (MARCH 1). WATERMARK CROWNS. TWO 9·5 mm. PHOSPHOR BANDS REACTING VIOLET

XS20	S4	Bronze-green	30	30

Cylinder Numbers (Blocks of Six)

Single pane cylinder.   Perforation Type F (L)

	Cyl. No.	No dot
	1	2·50

Sheet Markings

Guide holes: Through marginal arrow above vertical rows 6/7 and below vertical row 10
Others: As given in General Notes

Imprimatur from the National Postal Museum Archives

Imperforate, watermark Type W.24

Watermark upright

Cat. No.	S.G. No.	Shades	Mint	Used

1970 (SEPTEMBER 28). NO WATERMARK. CHALKY PAPER. PVA GUM. TWO 9·5 mm. PHOSPHOR BANDS REACTING VIOLET

XS21	S12	Bronze-green	5·00	5·50
a. Phosphor omitted	.. .. £140			

Cylinder Numbers (Blocks of Six)

Single pane cylinder. Perforation Type F (L)

Cyl. No.	No dot
1	32·00

Sheet Markings

As for No. XS20

Imprimatur from the National Postal Museum Archives

Chalky paper, imperforate

No watermark

1s.3d., Type XS3 (1958–65)

1958 (SEPTEMBER 29). WATERMARK CROWNS

A. Cream Paper

XS22	—	Green	2·50	60
a. Broken oblique in value (Cyl. 4, R. 15/2)	6·00			
b. Broken hinge (Cyl. 4, R. 19/2)	6·00			

B. Whiter Paper (31 July 1962)

XS23	S5	Green	30	30
a. Broken oblique in value (Cyl. 4, R. 15/2)	2·75			
b. Broken hinge (Cyl. 4, R. 19/2)	2·75			

Listed Varieties

XS22*a*, XS23*a*, XS24*a*, XS25*a*

XS22*b*, XS23*b*, XS24*b*, XS25*b*

Lowest "hinge" of the flag is incomplete. A multipositive flaw, (Cyls. 4 and 8, R. 19/2)

Cylinder Numbers (Blocks of Six)

Cream Paper (No. XS22)				Whiter Paper (No. XS23)			
Cyl. No.	(No dot)	Perf. Types		Cyl. No.	(No dot)	Perf. Types	
		B	C			B	C	F (L)
4		24·00*	24·00*	4		5·00*	5·00*	4·50*

Minor Constant Flaws

Cyl. 4   3/7 Green spot on shoulder of right-hand unicorn (Th. D6)
    11/12 Small break in inner frame line at right of value tablet (Th. G4)
    15/2 Hind leg of lion on standard is severed (Th. B1)

Sheet Markings

Guide holes:
    Perf. Types B and C, unboxed opposite rows 1 and 7/8 at both sides and also boxed opposite rows 14/15 at both sides
    Perf. Type F (L), through marginal arrow above vertical rows 6/7 and below vertical row 10. Boxes only opposite rows 14/15 at both sides
Marginal arrows:
    "V" shaped, hand engraved at top and bottom; "W" shaped, photo-etched at both sides. Early printings have the arrows omitted from the top and bottom of the sheet. *Price for marginal strip of 7 stamps* £40.
Others: As given in General Notes

Imprimatur from the National Postal Museum Archives

Cream paper. Imperforate, watermark Type W.24

Watermark upright

Cat. No.	S.G. No.	Shades	Mint	Used

1963 (JANUARY 29). TWO 8 mm. PHOSPHOR BANDS REACTING BLUE. WATERMARK CROWNS

XS24	—	Green	2·50	60

  a. Broken oblique in value
    (Cyl. 4, R. 15/2) .. .. .. 7·50
  b. Broken hinge (Cyl. 4, R. 19/2) .. 10·00

For illustration of Nos. XS24*a/b*, see Nos. XS22*a/b*.

Cylinder Numbers (Blocks of Six)

Single pane cylinder. Perforation Type F (L)

Cyl. No.		No dot
4	.. ..	26·00*

Minor Constant Flaws

As for Nos. XS22/3

Sheet Markings

Guide holes: Through marginal arrow above vertical rows 6/7 and below vertical row 10. Boxes only opposite rows 14/15 at both sides
Others: As given in General Notes

Imprimatur from the National Postal Museum Archives

Imperforate, watermark Type W.24

Watermark upright

1965 (NOVEMBER 26). TWO 8 mm. PHOSPHOR BANDS REACTING VIOLET. WATERMARK CROWNS

XS25	S5p	Deep Green	30	30

  a. Broken oblique in value
    (Cyl. 4, R. 15/2) .. .. 3·50
  b. Broken hinge (Cyls. 4, 8,
    R. 19/2).. .. .. .. 3·50

For illustration of Nos. XS25*a/b*, see Nos. XS22*a/b*.

Cylinder Numbers (Blocks of Six)

Single pane cylinders. Perforation Type F (L)

Cyl. No.		No dot		Cyl. No.		No dot
4	.. ..	5·50*		8	.. ..	9·00*

Minor Constant Flaws

Cyl. 4 As for Nos. XS22/3

Sheet Markings

As for No. XS24

1s.6d., Type XS3 (1967–68)

1967 (MARCH 1). WATERMARK CROWNS. TWO 9·5 mm. PHOSPHOR BANDS REACTING VIOLET

XS26	S6	Grey-blue	35	30

Cylinder Numbers (Blocks of Six)

Single pane cylinder. Perforation Type F (L)

Cyl. No.		No dot
1	.. ..	2·75

Minor Constant Flaw

Cyl. 1   1/11 Coloured spot in background to right of Queen's neck, below her hair (Th. E4)

Sheet Markings

Guide holes: Through marginal arrow above vertical rows 6/7 and below vertical row 10
Others: As given in General Notes

Imprimatur from the National Postal Museum Archives

Imperforate, watermark Type W.24

Watermark upright

Cat. No.	S.G. No.	Shades	Mint	Used

1968 (DECEMBER 12). NO WATERMARK. CHALKY PAPER. PVA GUM. TWO 9·5 mm. PHOSPHOR BANDS REACTING VIOLET

XS27	S13	Grey-blue	1·40	1·00
a.	Phosphor omitted £110			

Cylinder Numbers (Blocks of Six)

Single pane cylinder.   Perforation Type F (L)

Cyl. No.	No dot
1	10·00

Minor Constant Flaw

As for No. XS26

Sheet Markings

As for No. XS26

Imprimatur from the National Postal Museum Archives

Chalky paper, imperforate

No watermark

Presentation Pack

XSPP1 (9.12.70)	Eight stamps	13·00

Comprises Nos. XS8, 13/15, 17, 21, 25 and 27.

Quantity Sold   31,476

Withdrawn   25.11.71

First Day Covers

XSFC1	(1.3.67)	9d., 1s. 6d.	1·50
XSFC2	(4.9.68)	4d., 5d.	50

F. Wales and Monmouthshire

XW1

XW2

(Des. Reynolds Stone)

XW3

3d., Type XW1 (1958–67)

Cat. No.	S.G. No.	Shades	Mint	Used

1958 (AUGUST 18). WATERMARK CROWNS

A. Cream Paper

XW1 — Deep lilac 50 25

   a. Bulge on oval value tablet
     (Cyl. 1 No dot, R. 6/3) .. .. 3·00
   b. Wing-tail flaw (Cyl. 2 No dot,
     R. 16/1) .. .. 3·00

B. Whiter Paper (30 April 1962)

XW2   W1   Deep lilac 20 10

   a. Wing-tail flaw (Cyl. 2, No dot,
     R. 16/1) .. .. 2·40

Listed Varieties

XW1a
Later retouched

XW1b, XW2a
White flaw joins spine
of dragon's wing to its tail

Cylinder Numbers (Blocks of Six)

Cream Paper (No. XW1)

Perforation Type A

Cyl. No.				No dot	Dot
1	..	..	..	18·00	18·00
2	..	..	..	5·50	5·50

Whiter Paper (No. XW2)

Perforation Type A

Cyl. No.				No dot	Dot
2	..	..	..	1·75	1·75
3	..	..	..	1·75	1·75

Minor Constant Flaws

Multipositive flaws

No dot 1/12 Small coloured flaw on dragon's neck (Th. F–G3)
     17/10 Known in three states:
         Cyl. 1 Two pale coloured dots on back of Queen's neck just below hair (Th. D4)
         Cyl. 2 Cylinder retouched to almost normal
         Cyl. 3 Cylinder retouched but still leaving one coloured dot on back of neck
Cyl. 1   15/7 White flaw in middle of central cross of diadem (Th. A3)
Cyl. 2   6/11 White spot on end of top horizontal bar of first E of REVENUE

Sheet Markings

Guide holes: Boxed opposite rows 14/15, at left (no dot) or right (dot)
Others: As given in General Notes

Imprimatur from the National Postal Museum Archives

Cream paper. Imperforate, watermark Type W.24

Watermark upright

Quantity Sold 902,289,240

Sold Out 12.67

Cat. No.	S.G. No.	Shades	Mint	Used

1967 (MAY 16). ONE CENTRE PHOSPHOR BAND REACTING VIOLET. WATERMARK CROWNS

XW3	W1p		Deep lilac	20	15

Cylinder Numbers (Blocks of Six)

Perforation Type A

Cyl. No.				No dot	Dot
3	..	..	..	.. 1·75	1·75

Minor Constant Flaws

Multipositive flaws

No dot 1/12 Small coloured flaw on dragon's neck (Th. F-G3)
17/10 Pale coloured dot on back of Queen's neck just below hair (Th. D4)

Cyl. 3 1/7 Coloured spot on oval frame line opposite R of REVENUE (Th. A5)
1/8 Small coloured flaw just inside oval frame opposite G of POSTAGE (Th. E2)
7/11 Small coloured flaw on Queen's collar (Th. E5)
10/11 Small dot on leaf to right of final E of REVENUE (Th. E6)
11/10 Small dot on leaf to left of second E of REVENUE (Th. C6)

Cyl. 3. 1/6 Small retouch to right of Queen's mouth (Th. D3)
1/8 Retouch on Queen's cheek (Th. C-D4)
3/5 Small dot on leaf above E of POSTAGE (Th. E1)
3/9 Coloured flaw on Queen's neck just above collar (Th. E4)
4/9 Coloured diagonal flaw in front of Queen's neck (Th. E3)
5/9 Coloured spot inside lower loop of 3 of right-hand 3D
8/1 Two white flaws on dragon's front left foot (Th. G-H2)
10/2 Coloured spot on Queen's collar (Th. E4)
11/6 Small retouch on back of Queen's collar (Th. E4-5)
18/10 Retouch to background within oval to right of O of POSTAGE (Th. A-B2)
18/11 Small dot on leaf to right of T of POSTAGE (Th. C1-2)
20/6 Pale patch on Queen's shoulder (Th. E4)

Sheet Markings

As for Nos. XW1/2

Sold Out 1.68

1967 (DECEMBER 6). NO WATERMARK. CHALKY PAPER. ONE CENTRE PHOSPHOR BAND REACTING VIOLET

XW4	W7			Deep lilac	20	10
a. Phosphor omitted	..	..	40·00			

Cylinder Numbers (Blocks of Six)

Perforation Type F (L)*

Cyl. No.				No dot	Dot
3	..	..	..	.. 1·75	1·75

Minor Constant Flaws

As for multipositive and cylinder flaws on No. XW3 with the addition of the following cylinder flaws:

Cyl. 3 5/9 Retouch on Queen's cheek (Th. D3-4)
Cyl. 3. 5/8 Retouch on Queen's chin (Th. D3)
14/1 Retouch on Queen's cheek (Th. D4)
20/5 Retouch on Queen's chin (Th. D3-4) and several dark spots on her forehead, cheek and neck

Sheet Markings

Guide holes: Unboxed above and boxed below the eighth vertical row in the no dot pane only. The boxes opposite rows 14/15 remain
Others: As given in General Notes

4d., Type XW1 (1966-69)

1966 (FEBRUARY 7). WATERMARK CROWNS

XW5	W2		Ultramarine	20	15

Cylinder Numbers (Blocks of Six)

Perforation Type A

Cyl. No.				No dot	Dot
1	..	..	..	.. 1·75	1·75

Sheet Markings

Guide holes: In double "S O N" box opposite rows 14/15, at left (no dot) or right (dot)
Others: As given in General Notes

Quantity Sold   148,137,600

Sold Out   7.2.68

Cat No.	S.G. No.	Shades	Mint	Used

1967 (OCTOBER). TWO 9·5 mm. PHOSPHOR BANDS REACTING VIOLET. WATERMARK CROWNS

XW6	W2p	Ultramarine	20	15

Cylinder Numbers (Blocks of Six)

Perforation Type F (L)*

Cyl. No.				No dot	Dot
1	..	..	..	.. 1·75	1·75

Sheet Markings

Guide holes: Unboxed above and boxed below the eighth vertical row in the no dot pane only. The double "S O N" boxes opposite rows 14/15 remain
Others: As given in General Notes

Sold Out   4.70

1968 (JUNE 21). NO WATERMARK. CHALKY PAPER. PVA GUM. TWO 9·5 mm. PHOSPHOR BANDS REACTING VIOLET

XW7	W8	Ultramarine	20	10

a. White spot before " E " of
" POSTAGE " (No dot, R.
17/12) .. .. 2·50
b. White spot after " E " of
" POSTAGE " (No dot, R.
18/10) .. .. 2·50

c. Bump on dragon's head (No dot,
R. 19/2) .. .. .. 2·50
d White spot above dragon's hind
leg (No dot, R. 20/1) .. .. 2·75

Listed Varieties

XW7a, XW8a
Later retouched on No. XW8

XW7b, XW8b
Later retouched on No. XW8

XW7c, XW8c,
XW9b

XW7d, XW8c
Retouched on No. XW9

Cylinder Numbers (Blocks of Six)

Perforation Type A

Cyl. No.				No dot	Dot
2	..	..	..	.. 3·75*	1·75

394

Minor Constant Flaws

Cyl. 2   6/9 Small dot on leaf to left of second E of REVENUE (Th. C6)
          12/6 Coloured flaw on Queen's left eye-brow (Th. C4)
          13/2 Small dot on leaf above U of REVENUE (Th. D6)
          18/5 Coloured spots over Queen's face and background
          20/12 Coloured flaw over D of left-hand 4D

Cyl. 2.   1/6 Small dot on leaf above U of REVENUE (Th. D6)
          3/12 Small dot on leaf to left of N of REVENUE (Th. D6)
          4/3 Small dot on leaf to right of T of POSTAGE (Th. C1–2)
          4/6 White spot in background of oval frame opposite R of REVENUE (Th. A4)
          4/9 White spot on right-hand frame line by first E of REVENUE (Th. B6–7)
          7/2 Small dot on leaf to right of E of POSTAGE (Th. E2)
          7/11 Small coloured flaw in background of oval frame opposite VE of REVENUE (Th. C5)
          8/6 Small white flaw to right of dragon's left hind foot (Th. H5)
          11/7 Coloured spot in left-hand margin opposite P of POSTAGE (opposite Th. A1)
          12/2 Retouch on Queen's chin (Th. D3)
          12/6 White flaw over Queen's upper lip (Th. D3)
          16/10 Small coloured flaw on Queen's shoulder just above collar (Th. E4)

Sheet Markings

Guide holes: In double "S O N" box opposite rows 14/15, at left (no dot) or right (dot)
Others: As given in General Notes

Sold Out 4.70

Cat. No.	S.G. No.	Shades	Mint	Used

1968 (SEPTEMBER 4). CHANGE OF COLOUR. NO WATERMARK. CHALKY PAPER. PVA GUM. ONE CENTRE PHOSPHOR BAND REACTING VIOLET

XW8	W9	Olive-sepia	20	10

a. White spot before " E " of "POSTAGE" (No dot, R. 17/12) .. .. 2·50
b. White spot after " E " of "POSTAGE" (No dot, R. 18/10) .. .. 2·50

c. Bump on dragon's head (No dot, R. 19/2) .. .. 2·50
d. White spot above dragon's hind leg (No dot, R. 20/1) .. .. 2·75

For illustrations of Nos. XW8a/d, see Nos. XW7a/d.
Note. Varieties XW8a/b were later retouched.

Cylinder Numbers (Blocks of Six)

Perforation Type A

	Cyl. No.				No dot	Dot
	2	..	..	..	4·00*	1·75

Minor Constant Flaws

As for No. XW7

Sheet Markings

As for No. XW7

1969 (FEBRUARY 26). FURTHER CHANGE OF COLOUR. NO WATERMARK. CHALKY PAPER. PVA GUM. ONE CENTRE PHOSPHOR BAND REACTING VIOLET

XW9	W10	Bright vermilion	20	20

a. Phosphor omitted .. .. 1·75
b. Bump on dragon's head (No dot, R. 19/2) .. .. 2·50

Cylinder Numbers (Blocks of Six)

Perforation Type A

	Cyl No.				No dot	Dot
	2	..	..	..	4·00*	1·75

Minor Constant Flaws

Cyl. 2 As for flaws on No. XW7 except that flaw on R. 13/2 has been retouched
Cyl. 2. As for flaws on No. XW7 except that the following were retouched, R. 7/2, 8/6 and 12/6

Sheet Markings

As for No. XW7

5d., Type XW1 (1968)

Cat. No.	S.G. No.	Shades	Mint	Used

1968 (SEPTEMBER 4). NO WATERMARK. CHALKY PAPER. PVA GUM. TWO 9·5 mm. PHOSPHOR BANDS REACTING VIOLET

XW10	W11	Royal blue	20	10
a. Phosphor omitted	.. .. 2·25			

Cylinder Numbers (Blocks of Six)

Perforation Type A

	Cyl. No.				No dot	Dot
	2	..	..	.. ..	1·75	1·75

Minor Constant Flaws

Cyl. 2   2/3 Coloured spot in background of oval frame just above central cross of diadem (Th. A3)
16/5 Coloured flaws in background of oval frame to left of Queen's nose (Th. C–D2)
20/4 White flaw on bottom frame line below dragon's left hind foot (Th. H4)

Sheet Markings

Phosphor cylinder number: " Ph 1 " found on cyl. 2 dot, right margin
Guide holes: In double "SON" box opposite rows 14/15, at left (no dot) or right (dot). In addition a single
" traffic light " type box appears above and below the eighth vertical row in the no dot pane only. (These
would only be used in conjunction with perforation Type F (L)*).
Others: As given in General Notes

6d., Type XW2 (1958–62)

1958 (SEPTEMBER 29). WATERMARK CROWNS

A. Cream Paper

XW11	—	Deep claret	1·00	50

B. Whiter Paper (18 July 1962)

XW12	W3	Reddish purple	40	20

Cylinder Numbers (Blocks of Six)

Cream Paper (No. XW11)			Perf. Types			Whiter Paper (No. XW12)			Perf. Types		
Cyl. No.	(No dot)		B	C		Cyl. No.	(No dot)		B	C	F(L)
2	.. .. ..		8·00	8·00		3	.. .. ..		5·00	5·00	4·00

Minor Constant Flaw

Cyl. 3   16/4 Coloured spot on dragon's tail (Th. F5)

Sheet Markings

Guide Holes:
Perf. Types B and C, unboxed opposite rows 1 and 7/8 at both sides and also boxed opposite rows 14/15
at both sides
Perf. Type F (L), through marginal arrow above vertical rows 6/7 and below vertical row 10. Boxes only
opposite rows 14/15 at both sides
Marginal rule: Cyl. 2, 2½ mm. wide; Cyl. 3, 2 mm. wide
Others: As given in General Notes

Imprimatur from the National Postal Museum Archives

Cream paper. Imperforate, watermark Type W.24

Watermark upright

Quantity Sold   66,754,200

Sold Out   3.68

9d., Type XW2 (1967)

Cat. No.	S.G. No.	Shades	Mint	Used

1967 (MARCH 1). WATERMARK CROWNS. TWO 9·5 mm. PHOSPHOR BANDS REACTING VIOLET

XW13	W4	Bronze-green	30	35
a. Phosphor omitted	.. .. £300			

Cylinder Numbers (Blocks of Six)

Single pane cylinder. Perforation Type F (L)

Cyl. No.				No dot
1	..	..	..	.. 3·00

Sheet Markings

Guide holes: Through marginal arrow above vertical rows 6/7 and below vertical row 10
Others: As given in General Notes

Imprimatur from the National Postal Museum Archives

Imperforate, watermark Type W.24

Watermark upright

1s.3d., Type XW3 (1958-64)

1958 (SEPTEMBER 29). WATERMARK CROWNS

A. Cream Paper

XW14	—	Green	3·50	1·25

B. Whiter Paper (11 May 1964)

XW15	W5	(1) Myrtle-green	3·00	60
		(2) Deep dull green	30	30
		(3) Deep myrtle-green	1·00	40

Cylinder Numbers (Blocks of Six)

	Cream Paper (No. XW14)			Whiter Paper (No. XW15)		
Cyl. No.	(No dot)	Perf. Types B C	Cyl. No.	(No dot)	Perf. Type F (L)
2	.. .. ..	28·00 28·00	2	.. ..	5·00
			3	.. ..	3·00

Sheet Markings

Guide holes:
Perf. Types B and C, unboxed opposite rows 1 and 7/8 at both sides and also boxed opposite rows 14/15 at both sides
Perf. Type F (L), through marginal arrow above vertical rows 6/7 and below vertical row 10. Boxes only opposite rows 14/15 at both sides
Others: As given in General Notes

Imprimatur from the National Postal Museum Archives

Cream paper. Imperforate, watermark Type W.24

Watermark upright

Sold Out 7.70.

1s.6d., Type XW3 (1967–69)

1967 (MARCH 1). WATERMARK CROWNS. TWO 9·5 mm. PHOSPHOR BANDS REACTING VIOLET

XW16	W6	Grey-blue	35	30
a. Phosphor omitted	.. .. 40·00			

Cylinder Numbers (Blocks of Six)

Single pane cylinder. Perforation Type F (L)

Cyl. No.				No dot
1	..	..	..	.. 3·50

Minor Constant Flaws

Cyl. 1   3/11 Small dot in top of left fork of V of REVENUE
          6/7 Coloured flaw in base of second E of REVENUE
          10/1 Small dot on upper right-hand leaf of leak (Th. F6)
          10/3 Small coloured flaw on Queen's neck (Th. D4)
          15/9 Retouch on Queen's shoulder just above collar (Th. E4)

Sheet Markings

Guide holes: Through marginal arrow above vertical rows 6/7 and below vertical row 10
Others: As given in General Notes

Imprimatur from the National Postal Museum Archives

Imperforate, watermark Type W.24

Watermark upright

Cat. No.	S.G. No.	Shades	Mint	Used
1969 (AUGUST 1). NO WATERMARK. CHALKY PAPER. PVA GUM. TWO 9·5 mm. PHOSPHOR BANDS REACTING VIOLET				
XW17	W12	Grey-blue	3·00	3·00

Cylinder Numbers (Blocks of Six)

Single pane cylinder. Perforation Type F (L)

	Cyl. No.				No dot
	1	..	..	..	20·00

Minor Constant Flaws

As for No. XW16

Sheet Markings

Guide holes: Through marginal arrow above vertical rows 6/7 and boxed below vertical row 10
Others: As given in General Notes

Imprimatur from the National Postal Museum Archives

Chalky paper, imperforate

No watermark

Presentation Pack

XWPP1 (9.12.70)   Six stamps   2·50
Comprises Nos. XW4, 8/10, 13 and 16.

Quantity Sold 32,964

Withdrawn 25.11.71

First Day Covers

XWFC1 (1.3.67)   9d., 1s. 6d.   1·50
XWFC2 (4.9.68)   4d., 5d.   50

Presentation Pack (Six Regions)

XPP1 (issued 1960)   Twelve values   90·00

The issued pack contained one each of the ordinary 3d., 6d. and 1s.3d. stamps from Northern Ireland, Scotland and Wales and Monmouthshire and one each of the ordinary 3d. stamps from Guernsey, Jersey and the Isle of Man together with 6-page printed leaflet describing the stamps.

Two forms of the pack exist:

(a) Inscribed " 7s.3d." for sale in the U.K. and
(b) Inscribed " $1.20 " for sale in the U.S.A.

SECTION ZA

Postage Due Stamps

1954–1969 (Typographed) and 1968–1971 (Photogravure)

General Notes

INTRODUCTION. These stamps generally fulfil two functions: the lower values, inscribed "POSTAGE DUE", are affixed to understamped and unstamped correspondence by the Post Office, to indicate to the postman and to the addressee the amount which is to be collected on delivery (usually twice the excess). The higher values, inscribed "TO PAY", are affixed to mail from abroad for the collection of customs charges. The same basic stamp design was in continual use from 1914 until 1971.

PRINTERS. All the Postage Due stamps were typographed by Harrison & Sons with the exception of the 4d. and 8d. values of 1969 and 1968 respectively which were printed in photogravure.

They were printed on sheet-fed machines in single panes of 240 each arranged in twelve rows of twenty stamps and this applies to both printing processes.

PAPER. As with the Wilding definitives, for about the first ten years the Postage Due stamps were printed on a creamy paper but starting in 1964 a whiter paper was gradually introduced as new printings were made. See the General Notes for Section S for further information. Exceptionally, the 2s.6d. to £1 values were always printed on a yellow paper which did not change its appearance.

From 1968 unwatermarked chalk-surfaced paper, as used for the Machin definitives, was introduced for a number of values.

WATERMARKS. These were used as follows:

W.22 Tudor Crown   Nos. Z1/6 (1954–55)
W.23 St. Edward's Crown   Nos. Z7/16 (1955–57)
W.24 Crowns   Nos. Z17/37 (1959–64)
No watermark   No. Z38 onwards (1968–69)

See the General Notes for Section S for illustrations of these.

The watermarks are *always* sideways and *when seen from the front of the stamp* the normal watermark has the top of the Crowns pointing to left. In cases where the sheets were fed into the press the wrong way round (sideways inverted), the watermark appears as sideways with the Crowns pointing to right *when seen from the front of the stamp.*

GUM. This was used as follows:

Gum Arabic   Nos. Z1/39 (1954–68)
PVA Gum   No. Z40 onwards (1968–69)

The distinction between gum arabic and PVA gum is explained in the General Notes relating to Section UA.

PERFORATION. All values are comb perforated 14 × 15. The perforation types used are given following each issue, and are described and illustrated in Appendix G. In the photogravure-printed values the cylinder numbers are listed and priced according to the type of perforator used. The typographed issues do not have cylinder or plate numbers.

DATE OF ISSUE. The dates given are those on which the stamps were first issued by the Supplies Dept. to postmasters except in the case of dates for changes to chalky paper or to PVA gum when we have usually quoted dates of release by the Philatelic Bureaux.

SHEET MARKINGS. Compared with other stamps the Postage Due stamps show very few markings.

Cylinder Numbers. These only occur on the photogravure-printed stamps, opposite Row 11 No. 1 (4d.) or opposite Row 10 No. 1 (8d.). They are similar in style to the illustration in Section S.

Marginal Arrows. These are "W" shaped at top and bottom of the sheet only. They appear solid (typographed issues) or photo-etched (photogravure issues) as illustrated in Section S.

Marginal Rule. This occurs on all four sheet margins in the typographed issues only. It is similar in style to the "Narrow Rule" illustration in Section S. In the 1½d., 6d., 5s., 10s. and £1 values an additional 1 mm. square appears at each corner of the sheet thus giving a neater appearance.

"Morse Code" marking	Cross

Other Markings. On the typographed issues "Morse Code" markings as illustrated appear opposite rows 6/7 at both sides of the sheet. These are possibly allied to the way in which the printing plate is fixed to the press.

In photogravure issues the "Morse Code" markings are replaced by a cross as illustrated. These are often trimmed off.

WATERMARK. The normal sideways watermark *when seen from the front of the stamp* has the top of the Crowns pointing to left.

Z1. "POSTAGE DUE"	**Z2.** "TO PAY"

Cat. No.	S.G. No.	Date		Description	Mint	Used

1954–55. TYPE Z1 AND Z2 (2s.6d.). TYPOGRAPHED. WATERMARK TUDOR CROWN, TYPE W.22, SIDEWAYS

Cat. No.	S.G. No.	Date		Description	Mint	Used
Z1	D40	8.6.55		½d. Bright Orange	4·00	2·50
a. Wmk. Crown to right		.. ..	10·00 6·00			
Z2	D41	28.7.55		2d. Agate	2·00	2·00
a. Wmk. Crown to right		.. ..				
Z3	D42	4.5.55		3d. Violet	42·00	25·00
Z4	D43	14.7.55		4d. Blue	15·00	16·00
a. Imperf. (pair)		.. .. .. £225				
Z5	D44	19.5.55		5d. Yellow-brown	20·00	6·50
Z6	D45	–.11.54		2s.6d. Purple/*yellow*	£120	3·00
a. Wmk. Crown to right		.. ..				

Perforation Type

Type A, all values

Imprimaturs from the National Postal Museum Archives

Imperforate, watermark Type W.22 (sideways)

½d., 2d., 3d., 4d., 5d.

Perf. 14 × 15, watermark Type W.22 (sideways)

2s.6d.

1955–57. TYPE Z1 AND Z2 (2s.6d., 5s.). TYPOGRAPHED, WATERMARK ST. EDWARD'S CROWN, TYPE W.23, SIDEWAYS

Cat. No.	S.G. No.	Date	Description	Mint	Used
Z 7	D46	16.7.56	½d. Orange	1·50	2·25
a. Wmk. Crown to right		10·00			
Z 8	D47	7.6.56	1d. Violet-blue	4·00	1·25
Z 9	D48	13.2.56	1½d. Green	3·75	3·75
a. Wmk. Crown to right ..		12·00			
b. Stop after " THREE " (Row 1)		9·00			
Z10	D49	22.5.56	2d. Agate	35·00	3·00
Z11	D50	5.3.56	3d. Violet	4·50	1·25
a. Wmk. Crown to right		25·00			
Z12	D51	24.4.56	4d. Blue	18·00	3·00
a. Wmk. Crown to right		30·00			
Z13	D52	23.3.56	5d. Brown-ochre	27·00	2·00
Z14	D53	22.11.55	1s. Ochre	65·00	1·25
a. Wmk. Crown to right ..					
Z15	D54	28.6.57	2s.6d. Purple/*yellow*	£160	7·50
a. Wmk. Crown to right					
Z16	D55	25.11.55	5s. Scarlet/*yellow*	90·00	19·00
a. Wmk. Crown to right					

The 2d. (No. Z10) is known bisected (June 1956) and also the 4d. (Poplar, London, April 1959).

Listed Variety

Stop after " THREE ". Occurs on most stamps in row 1

Z9b Z19a

Perforation Types

Type A, all values, except that in the case of the 5s. the left-hand sheet margin is perforated through, possibly due to the use of a wider comb-head

Imprimaturs from the National Postal Museum Archives

Imperforate, watermark Type W.23 (sideways)

½d., 1d., 1½d., 2d., 3d., 4d., 5d., 1s., 2s.6d., 5s.

Cat. No.	S.G. No.	Date	Description	Mint	Used

1959–70. TYPE Z1 AND Z2 (2s.6d. to £1). TYPOGRAPHED. WATERMARK CROWNS, TYPE W.24, SIDEWAYS

A. Cream Paper

Cat. No.	S.G. No.	Date	Description	Mint	Used
Z17	—	18.10.61	½d. Orange	50	80
Z18	—	9.5.60	1d. Violet-blue	50	20
Z19	D58	5.10.60	1½d. Green	90	2·00
a. Stop after "THREE" (Row 1)		5·00			
Z20	—	14.9.59	2d. Agate	2·75	1·00
Z21	—	24.3.59	3d. Violet	75	25
Z22	—	17.12.59	4d. Blue	75	30
Z23	—	6.11.61	5d. Yellow-brown	90	70
a. Wmk. Crown to right .. .. 28·00					
Z24	—	29.3.62	6d. Purple	1·00	1·25
Z25	—	11.4.60	1s. Ochre	3·00	50
Z26	D65	11.5.61	2s.6d. Purple/*yellow*	4·00	45
a. Wmk. Crown to right .. .. 7·50					
Z27	D66	8.5.61	5s. Scarlet/*yellow*	7·50	80
a. Wmk. Crown to right .. .. 12·00					
Z28	D67	2.9.63	10s. Blue/*yellow*	9·00	4·00
a. Wmk. Crown to right (4.70) .. 30·00					
Z29	D68	2.9.63	£1 Black/*yellow*	40·00	7·50

Whilst the 2s.6d. and 5s. already existed with watermark Crown to right further printings were issued in 1970, as also of the 10s., on highly fluorescent paper and with watermark Crown to right. These can only be distinguished by the use of a u.v. lamp and so are not listed separately.

B. Whiter Paper

Cat. No.	S.G. No.	Date	Description	Mint	Used
Z30	D56	22.9.64	½d. Orange	10	45
a. Wmk. Crown to right .. .. 1·50					
Z31	D57	1.3.65	1d. Violet-blue	10	15
a. Wmk. Crown to right .. .. 5·00					
Z32	D59	1.3.65	2d. Agate	1·25	30
a. Wmk. Crown to right .. .. 15·00					
Z33	D60	1.6.64	3d. Violet	40	15
a. Wmk. Crown to right .. .. 3·50					
Z34	D61	3.3.64	4d. Blue	40	20
a. Wmk. Crown to right .. .. 10·00					
Z35	D62	9.6.64	5d. Yellow-brown	45	45
a. Wmk. Crown to right .. .. 5·00					
Z36	D63	30.1.64	6d. Purple	60	30
a. Wmk. Crown to right .. .. 12·00					
Z37	D64	28.8.64	1s. Ochre	1·40	25
a. Wmk. Crown to right .. .. 5·00					

The 1d. is known bisected (Newbury, Dec. 1962).

For illustration of No. Z19*a*, see No. Z9*b*.

Perforation Types

Type A, all values; 2s.6d. also Type A (T)

Imprimaturs from the National Postal Museum Archives

Imperforate, watermark Type W.24 (sideways)

Cream paper

½d., 1d., 1½d., 2d., 3d., 4d., 5d., 6d., 1s., 2s.6d., 5s., 10s., £1

Sold Out 1s. 11.68; 2d. 1.69; 4d. 11.69; 3d. 9.71; 6d. 10.71

Withdrawn. The 1½d. was withdrawn from sale to the public on 26.4.65. It had ceased to be issued on 31.1.65 but post offices continued to use existing stocks until exhausted

Cat. No.	S.G. No.	Date	Description	Mint	Used

1968-69. TYPE Z1. TYPOGRAPHED. NO WATERMARK. CHALKY PAPER

A. Gum Arabic

Z38	D69	11.4.68	2d. Agate	40	40
Z39	D71	25.4.68	4d. Blue	25	40

B. PVA Gum

Z40	D69Ev	26.11.68	2d. Agate	1·25	
Z41	D70	5.9.68	3d. Violet	25	40
Z42	D71Ev	—	4d. Blue		
Z43	D72	3.1.69	5d. Orange-brown	4·50	5·25
Z44	D73	5.9.68	6d. Purple	80	60
Z45	D74	19.11.68	1s. Ochre	80	1·00

A copy of No. Z42 has been confirmed using infra-red attenuated total reflection spectroscopy

Perforation Types

4d., 6d. Type A; other values Type A (T), except that in the case of the 2d. the right-hand sheet margin is perforated through and in the 4d. the left-hand sheet margin is perforated through, both possibly due to the use of a wider comb-head

1968-69. TYPE Z1. SMALLER FORMAT, 21½ × 17½ mm. PHOTOGRAVURE. NO WATERMARK. CHALKY PAPER. PVA GUM

Z46	D75	12.6.69	4d. Blue	5·00	5·00
Z47	D76	3.10.68	8d. Red	1·25	75

Cylinder Numbers (Block of Four (4d.) or Six (8d.))

Perforation Type A (T)

	Cyl. No.			No dot
4d.	1	..	..	24·00
8d.	1	..	..	8·50

Imprimaturs from the National Postal Museum Archives

Chalky paper, imperforate. No watermark

2d., 3d., 4d., 5d., 6d., 8d., 1s.

Perforators

General Notes

INTRODUCTION. Basically, two kinds of perforating machines were used for British stamps listed in this catalogue, 1952-70: sheet-fed and reel-fed. The sheet-fed machines generally employ a two-row comb and the reel-fed machines a three-row comb. Both kinds are full width, i.e. they are able to perforate two panes side by side.

Types A to H and J are the different *sheet perforation types* recorded in this catalogue, produced either by the sheet-fed or the reel-fed machines but they should not be regarded as representing the use of ten different machines, rather they are ten different sheet perforation types produced by various perforating machines.

Types E, E($\frac{1}{2}$v) (from sheets), I, I($\frac{1}{2}$v), AP and P relate to booklet panes.

GUIDE HOLES. Perforation guide holes can be an indication of the type of perforator used and these are recorded, where known, following the sheet perforation characteristics for each type. For reasons unknown these may not always appear in the sheet margins.

ORDER. This Appendix is divided into four sections:

1. Low Value Definitive Stamps (including Regionals and Postage Due Stamps)
2. High Value Definitive Stamps
3. Special Issues
4. Booklet Panes

ILLUSTRATIONS. The illustrations are all from definitive stamps but they are equally representative of the High Value and Special issues where the same types occur.

TABLE OF PERFORATION TYPES. The useful tabulated list of Perforation Types at the end of this Appendix is primarily designed to be used for Special issues, although, the first part may also be used in conjunction with the Low and High Value definitive stamps for Types A, A (T), B, C, E (no dot panes only).

1. Low Value Definitive Stamps

This section deals with the small size Wilding and Machin definitives, the Regionals and the Postage Due Stamps.

Type A. Horizontal two-row comb. Sheet-fed.

No dot and dot panes—
Top margin	Perforated through
Bottom margin	Imperforate
Left margin	A single extension hole
Right margin	A single extension hole
Guide holes	Opposite rows 14/15, at left (no dot panes) or right (dot panes)

In this machine an appropriate number of sheets (usually six to eight) are impaled through the guide holes and they go forward together under the comb. The imperf. margin (at the bottom) indicates the point of entry.

Type A (T). Horizontal two-row comb. Sheet-fed.

Single pane printing—
Top margin	Imperforate
Bottom margin	Perforated through
Left margin	A single extension hole
Right margin	A single extension hole
Guide holes	None

This is simply a top (T) instead of a bottom feed ot Type A. In the definitive stamps it only occurs in the Postage Due Stamps. Cylinder blocks are identical in appearance with Type C.

Types B and C. Horizontal three-row comb. Reel-fed.

Type B. No dot panes—
Top margin	Perforated through
Bottom margin	Perforated through
Left margin	Imperforate
Right margin	A single extension hole
Guide holes	Usually opposite rows 1, 7/8 and 14/15 at both sides of pane

Type C. No dot and dot panes—
Top margin	Perforated through
Bottom margin	Perforated through
Left margin	A single extension hole
Right margin	Imperforate
Guide holes	As Type B, above

Type B is the left and Type C the right halves of the same reel-fed perforator. The outer ends of the comb are without extension pins, there being only single extension pins in the interpane margin. In this machine the continuous web of paper advances under the comb in a single thickness and without interruption, hence both top and bottom margins are perforated through.

It often happened that two narrow reels were perforated together by placing them side by side on the machine so that single pane printings (i.e. no dot panes only) occur perforated with Type B and also Type C. It is only when double pane printings are perforated on this machine that no dot panes will always be Type B and dot panes will always be Type C, except that in the Special issues, the 4d. Scout Jamboree stamp from Cyl. 1 dot is known with perforation Type B and Type C.

Type E. Horizontal two-row comb. Sheet-fed.

No dot panes—
Top margin	Perforated through
Bottom margin	Imperforate
Left margin	A single extension hole on alternate rows only
Right margin	A single extension hole
Guide hole	Opposite rows 14/15, at left

Dot panes—
Top margin	Perforated through
Bottom margin	Imperforate
Left margin	A single extension hole
Right margin	A single extension hole on alternate rows only
Guide hole	Opposite rows 14/15, at right

This is a simple variation of Type A (*q.v.*) that may result from the removal of a perforating pin or a repair to a comb-head. Therefore, no dot cylinder blocks are as Type A but left margin has the single extension hole missing on alternate rows.

Cylinder blocks from the dot pane would be indistinguishable from Type A, hence only no dot cylinder blocks are recorded with Type E.

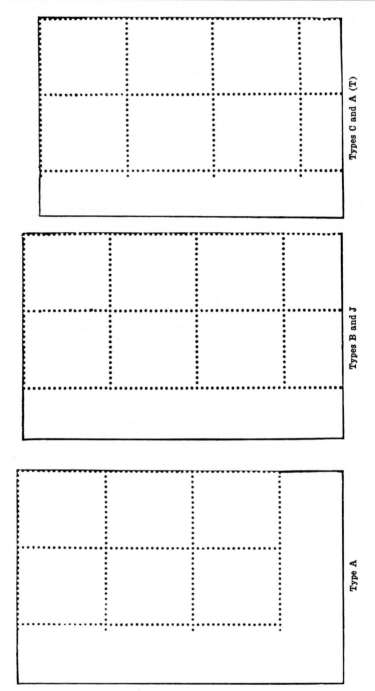

Types C and A (T)

Types B and J

Type A

Type F (L)* (dot panes) and
Type F (no dot panes)

Types F (L) and F (L)*
(no dot panes)

Type F (L). Vertical two-row comb. Sheet-fed.

No dot panes—

Top margin	A single extension hole
Bottom margin	A single extension hole
Left margin	Imperforate
Right margin	Perforated through
Guide holes	Through marginal arrow above vertical rows 6/7 and below vertical row 10

This type perforates from the left (L) through to the right side of the sheet. In this catalogue the use of this type has been restricted to single pane printings (i.e. no dot panes only).

Type F (L)*. Vertical two-row comb. Sheet-fed.

No dot panes—

Top margin	A single extension hole
Bottom margin	A single extension hole
Left margin	Imperforate
Right margin	Perforated through
Guide holes	Above and below eighth vertical row

Type F (L)* Contd.

Dot panes—

Top margin	A single extension hole
Bottom margin	A single extension hole
Left margin	Perforated through
Right margin	Perforated through
Guide holes	None (occur on no dot panes *only*)

This is the same perforator as used for Type F (L) and it is given in this catalogue when double pane printings (i.e. no dot and dot panes) have been perforated together prior to their being guillotined into single sheets. This gives no dot cylinder blocks exactly as Type F (L) but because the vertical comb has perforated horizontally from left to right across *both* panes the interpane margin is also perforated and, therefore, the dot cylinder blocks are perforated through the left margin.

Type H. Horizontal two-row comb. Sheet-fed.

No dot panes—

Top margin	Perforated through
Bottom margin	Imperforate
Left margin	A single extension hole
Right margin	Perforated through
Guide hole	Opposite rows 14/15, at left

Dot panes—

Top margin	Perforated through
Bottom margin	Imperforate
Left margin	Perforated through
Right margin	A single extension hole
Guide hole	Opposite rows 14/15, at right

This is a further variation of Type A (*q.v.*) differing by the fact that the interpane margin is perforated through instead of there being single extension holes at the end of every row at right on the no dot pane and at the end of every row at left on the dot pane. Therefore, dot cylinder blocks are as Type A but left margin is perforated through. Cylinder blocks from the no dot pane would be indistinguishable from Type A, hence only dot cylinder blocks are recorded with Type H.

Type J. Vertical two-row comb. Sheet-fed.

Single pane printing—

Top margin	A single extension hole
Bottom margin	Perforated through
Left margin	Imperforate
Right margin	Perforated through
Guide holes	Through marginal arrow above vertical rows 6/7 and below vertical row 10

This is similar to Type F (L) (*q.v.*), except that the bottom sheet margin is perforated through instead of there being only a single extension hole at the end of every row. Cylinder blocks are identical in appearance with Type B.

2. High Value Definitive Stamps

This section deals with the Wilding and Machin High Value stamps.

Wilding High Values

Perforation Type A, as described at the beginning of this Appendix, was used exclusively for these stamps. Waterlow and De La Rue both used a single-row comb and Bradbury, Wilkinson a two-row comb.

The guide holes appear opposite row 6, at left on left-hand panes and at right on right-hand panes.

For diagram showing printer's guide marks see the General Notes for Section T.

Machin £.s.d. High Values

The printer's sheet was perforated with Type A prior to being guillotined into four panes, so that the characteristics of each individual Post Office pane are different and this has, therefore, been described as perforation Type A*. The description of Type A, given at the beginning of this Appendix, applies equally to Type A*, except that Bradbury, Wilkinson used a single-row comb.

For diagram showing the printer's sheet, the method of perforation and the position of plate numbers and guide holes see the General Notes for Section UC.

3. Special Issues

Type A. In the special issues this type is exactly as described at the beginning of this Appendix except that with single pane printings (i.e. no dot panes only) the guide holes are opposite rows 14/15, at both sides of the sheet.

Type A (T). In the special issues this type is exactly as described at the beginning of this Appendix and it applies equally to both no dot and dot panes. Guide holes very rarely appear in the sheet margins but where they do this is given under "Sheet Details" in Section W.

Types B and C. In the special issues these types are exactly as described in the first part of this Appendix.

Type E. Horizontal two-row comb. Sheet-fed.
Right-hand panes—

Top margin	Perforated through
Bottom margin	Imperforate
Left margin	A single extension hole on alternate rows only
Right margin	A single extension hole
Guide hole	Opposite rows 14/15, at right

This is a variation of Type A that may result from the removal of a perforating pin or a repair to a comb-head. Therefore, cylinder blocks are as Type A but left margin has the single extension hole missing on alternate rows.
This type is only known on the 1s.3d. Freedom from Hunger and the 3d. Red Cross on the right-hand panes only (i.e. no dot* pane of 1s.3d. F.F.H. and dot pane of 3d. Red Cross). The left-hand panes in both cases are believed to be Type A but it is possible that the right margin has single extension holes on alternate rows to match the left margin of the right-hand pane.
*The panes of the 1s.3d. Freedom from Hunger issue are transposed, i.e. the dot pane is on the left and the no dot pane is on the right.

Types F and F (L). Vertical single-row comb. Sheet-fed.
Single pane printings.
Type F. Right feed—

Top margin	A single extension hole
Bottom margin	A single extension hole
Left margin	Perforated through
Right margin	Imperforate

Type F (L). Left feed—

Top margin	A single extension hole
Bottom margin	A single extension hole
Left margin	Imperforate
Right margin	Perforated through

Type F perforates from the right through to the left side of the sheet and Type F (L) perforates from the left through to the right side of the sheet. Both types are used for single pane printings (i.e. no dot panes only). Guide holes very rarely appear in the sheet margins but where they do this is given under "Sheet Details" in Section W.

Type G. Vertical single-row comb. Sheet-fed.
No dot and dot panes—

Top margin	Perforated through
Bottom margin	Perforated through
Left margin	Perforated through
Right margin	Imperforate
Guide holes	None

This was a special perforator used exclusively for the 6d. Battle of Hastings issue. The cylinder block is perforated through in both the bottom and left margins.

TABLE OF SPECIAL ISSUE PERFORATION TYPES

The table below combines a list of the different *sheet perforation types* recorded in Section W, together with the characteristics of the four sheet margins. Following the basic perforation type the characteristics given relate to the sheet viewed with the stamps the right way up.

The identification of a particular perforation type from a cylinder block (or any corner block) can easily be established by referring to this table in conjunction with the recorded types under "Cylinder Numbers" in Section W.

Whilst this table is mainly designed to be used for the special stamps, the first part may also be used in conjunction with the Low and High Value definitive stamps for Types A, A (T), B, C, E (no dot panes only) and F (L).

I. HORIZONTAL FORMAT STAMPS

Perforation Type	Top margin	Bottom margin	Left margin	Right margin
Type A (*bottom feed*)	Perforated through	Imperforate	Single extension hole	Single extension hole
Type A (T) (*top feed*)	Imperforate	Perforated through	Single extension hole	Single extension hole
Type B	Perforated through	Perforated through	Imperforate	Single extension hole
Type C	Perforated through	Perforated through	Single extension hole	Imperforate
Type E	Perforated through	Imperforate	Single extension hole alternate rows only	Single extension hole
Type F (*right feed*)	Single extension hole	Single extension hole	Perforated through	Imperforate
Type F (L) (*left feed*)	Single extension hole	Single extension hole	Imperforate	Perforated through
Type G	Perforated through	Perforated through	Perforated through	Imperforate

II. VERTICAL FORMAT STAMPS*

Perforation Type	Top margin	Bottom margin	Left margin	Right margin
Type A (*head to right*)	Single extension hole	Single extension hole	Perforated through	Imperforate
Type A (*head to left*)	Single extension hole	Single extension hole	Imperforate	Perforated through
Type A (T) (*head to right*)	Single extension hole	Single extension hole	Imperforate	Perforated through
Type A (T) (*head to left*)	Single extension hole	Single extension hole	Perforated through	Imperforate
Type B (*head to right*)	Single extension hole	Imperforate	Perforated through	Perforated through
Type C (*head to right*)	Imperforate	Single extension hole	Perforated through	Perforated through
Type F (*head to right*)	Imperforate	Perforated through	Single extension hole	Single extension hole

*The position of the head on vertical format stamps is determined by viewing the sheet with the marginal rule (normally on a short side) at the bottom. In most instances the head (or top of the stamp) is to the right; the head to the left occuring on the 3d. Post Office Tower, 4d. World Football Cup, 4d. World Cup Victory and the 3d. and 1s.6d. 1966 Christmas issue, although the latter does not in fact bear marginal rules but it should be regarded as being " head to left ".

From the 1966 Christmas issue onwards many sheets did not bear marginal rules. Where this is the case with vertical format designs the correct orientation of the sheets to determine the perforation type is given below the "Cylinder Numbers" in the listings.

Exceptionally, the 1967 British Paintings 4d. and the British Discovery and Inventions 1s.9d. show the marginal rule on a *long* side and this should be orientated to the left-hand side to show perforation Types A (T) (head to right) and F (head to right) respectively.

4. Booklet Panes

(a) Panes of Four

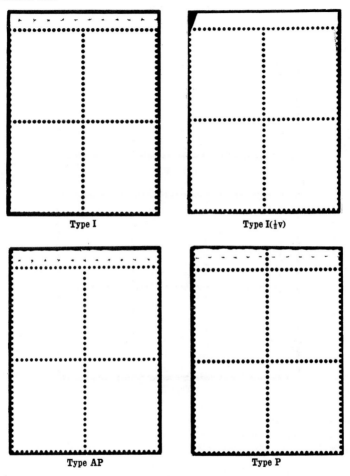

Type I   Type I($\frac{1}{2}$v)

Type AP   Type P

Type I. Margin imperforate
Type I($\frac{1}{2}$v) Ditto but with slanting cut at left or right (left illustrated)
Type AP. Margin perforated through but alternate rows imperforate
Type P. Margin fully perforated through

In order to facilitate access to the bottom selvedge, which has to be torn off by hand, a slanting scissor cut is made in the trimmed margin. This pane is termed "I($\frac{1}{2}$v)". The vertical perforations below the cut should have been torn, and not guillotined, apart.

Panes of four from the Wilding series on Crowns watermark paper exist as Type AP, but with only two extension holes at each side of the binding margin. It is believed that this was caused by a perforator with a pin missing from the bottom line of the comb.

(b) Panes of Six

Type I

Type P

Type I. Margin imperforate

Type P. Margin fully perforated through

All panes of six are perforated Type I except for UB3 which also exists Type P and UB4 which only exists Type P.

Both the 20-row and the 21-row cylinders perforated with Type I come with pairs of extension holes in the margin between the no dot and dot panes. The 20-row cylinders were perforated with a three-line comb, so that panes can be found with traces of the inter-pane extension hole at the top, in the middle or at the bottom of the binding margin. After the change to 21-row cylinders a four-row comb was used, and on these panes the extension hole can be found at the top or at the bottom of the margin. We do not distinguish these sub-types of perforation.

On 21-row cylinders the perforated web is cut at every 20th row to make sheets of 480 (two panes of 240 (12 × 20)). Consequently on successive sheets the cylinder number appears one row lower so that a pane can have it adjoining the top or bottom row. In the listing of cylinder blocks for stamps from the 4s.6d., 5s., 6s. and 10s. booklets the letter " T " after the cylinder number indicates that it is a pane with the cylinder number adjoining the top row.

(c) Panes of Fifteen

These come from the £1 " Stamps for Cooks " booklet and are all perforated Type I.

(d) Panes of Two

Type E(½v)

Type E. Extension hole in the margin in each row

Type E(½v). Ditto but with slanting cut

Type I. Margin imperforate

Type I(½v). Ditto but with slanting cut

    The panes of two stamps were made up from vertical rows 1 and 2 from sheets. The horizontal sheet margin was removed leaving a narrow vertical binding margin which was either imperforate or showed an extension hole at the top and bottom of the binding margin. In addition, both types exist with the slanting scissor cut already described under section (a) of these notes. Panes with this form of separation should show torn and not guillotined perforations below the cut. The stamps were separated towards the slanting cut ensuring that the binding margin would remain intact.

APPENDIX HA
Post Office Booklets of Stamps

General Notes

BOOKLET SHEET ARRANGEMENT. Booklets are made up from specially printed sheets which are differently arranged from normal Post Office sheets in order to facilitate economic manufacture. The arrangement of the sheet varies according to the size and format of the booklet pane required. For example, in the case of booklet panes of six, the printer's sheet of 480 stamps, consisting of two panes (no dot and dot) each of 240 stamps arranged in twenty rows of twelve stamps, has additional gutters provided between the 6th and 7th vertical rows in both panes, and the stamps in the 4th, 5th and 6th, and 10th, 11th and 12th vertical rows in both panes are inverted in relation to the others (i.e. *tête-bêche*). Two horizontal rows of the sheet (producing eight booklets) would be arranged thus:

The sheets of stamps, interleaving sheets and covers are stitched vertically, once at the two outer edges of the double pane and twice in each of the gutters as shown by the vertical rules in the diagram. Finally, the booklets are guillotined both horizontally and vertically as indicated by the arrows.

INVERTED WATERMARKS. From the diagram it is easy to see how 50% of Wilding booklets have stamps with inverted watermarks.

WATERMARK POSITIONS. Although 50% of booklet panes have the watermark inverted, in describing the contents of the booklets reference is made to the catalogue numbers of the basic stamps with normal watermark throughout the list. This is to avoid continual reference to the catalogue numbers of the inverted watermarks, etc.

WHITER PAPER. During the changeover period cream and whiter paper stamps could occur in the same booklet and we make no attempt to distinguish these.

TETE-BECHE ERRORS. These occur in booklets due to faulty manufacture, usually the result of a corner of the sheet being folded over.

ERRORS OF MAKE-UP. Such errors exist but we do not list them as it is not difficult to break up booklets and remake them to agree with known errors.

BOOKLET COVERS. All covers are printed in black except where otherwise stated.

BOOKLET CYLINDER NUMBERS. These occur in the left-hand margin of both panes (i.e no dot and dot) as normal Post Office sheets. They are illustrated in Section S except that they always have prefix letters, e.g. E4, F5, G3, but the letters are liable to be partly or completely trimmed off.
   Booklet panes of six printed from 20-row cylinders always have the cylinder number adjoining the bottom row of stamps but in the case of 21-row cylinders, the perforated web is cut at every 20th row to make sheets of 480. Consequently, on successive sheets the cylinder number appears one row lower and thus a pane can have it adjoining the top or bottom row.
   Booklet panes of four and fifteen usually have the cylinders trimmed off completely.

DATES. The month and year dates are those found printed on the booklets, either on the outer back cover or on the white leaves. No dates are given on the 1s. booklets, the 2s. booklets Nos. N1/3, the 5s. "Philympia" booklet No. HP34 and the £1 booklet No. ZP1. The dates of issue of every booklet in a new cover design or composition are given in brackets where known.

QUANTITIES. The quantities given are of the numbers manufactured, but some of the figures are shared by two or more booklets and this is indicated in the listing.

PATTERN BOOKS. These were dummy books, including the postal rates panel dated December 1952, with "SPACE AVAILABLE FOR COMMERCIAL ADVERTISING" printed on the reverse of the front cover, reverse of second end leaf and on both sides of the back cover. The panes of stamps were represented by perforated and gummed labels. In the 2s.6d. booklet the third pane had the three labels in the upper row inscribed "1d." and "SPACE AVAILABLE FOR COMMERCIAL ADVERTISING" printed across the lower row.

These pattern books were produced prior to the re-introduction of commercial advertising and were distributed to potential advertising contractors.

The contractor was responsible for selling the advertising space and for the provision of copy to the printer. The printed material, both commercial and official matter, was then submitted to the Post Office in galley form for approval. These proofs were then used to prepare paste-up examples of each book, so that the make-up could be checked.

ADVERTISERS' VOUCHER COPIES. With the introduction of commercial advertising in 1953 the Post Office began to supply voucher copies of the various booklets to the firms whose advertisements appeared in them.

In 1953 the 2s.6d. September, October, and November editions, together with the 5s. September, were supplied as voucher copies with the stamps torn out. Subsequent editions of the 2s., 2s.6d., 3s.9d., 4s.6d., 5s., 6s., 10s. and £1 (sewn, and without black binding) booklets were made up as voucher copies without the stamp panes.

Of particular interest are the 2s.6d. booklets containing the *se-tenant* pane of three 1d. stamps and three labels. Between January 1954 and January 1955 voucher copies of these booklets come with these *se-tenant* labels shown, but not the stamps. In the January 1954 edition the labels were printed on ungummed paper, imperforate, but on subsequent occasions they come perforated on gummed paper with the Harrison "house" watermark.

CATALOGUE NUMBERS. In order to avoid confusion we have used the same booklet numbers as in the *Concise Catalogue*. Many of these booklets bear the same prefix letters as other stamps listed in the *Great Britain* Specialised Catalogues so that when quoting numbers in this Appendix it should be made clear that booklets are being referred to.

Varieties shown thus "(*a*)" are those listed in the *Great Britain* Specialised Catalogues only.

ILLUSTRATIONS. The illustrations of the covers are ¾ size except where otherwise stated.

BOOKLET PRICES. Prices in this Appendix are for booklets containing panes with "average" perforations (i.e. full perforations on two edges of the pane only). Booklets containing panes with complete perforations are worth more.

NON-PICTORIAL TYPES OF BOOKLET COVERS

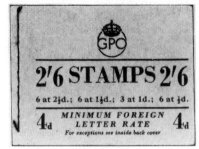

Type A
Circular GPO Cypher

Type B
Oval Type GPO Cypher

Type C
Oval Type GPO Cypher 15mm wide

Type D
Larger Oval GPO Cypher 17mm wide

Section A. Wilding Issues

1s. BOOKLETS FOR USE IN SLOT MACHINES

Booklet Series "D"

Contents: $4 \times 1\frac{1}{2}$d., 4×1d., $4 \times \frac{1}{2}$d. in panes of two

I. WHITE UNPRINTED COVER. Not interleaved. For use in experimental machines
Watermark Tudor Crown (Nos. S1, S13, S25)

E1 No date (issued 2.9.53) 56,650   2·25

    Watermark St. Edward's Crown (Nos. S2, S14, S26)

E2 No date (issued 11.57) 7,180   6·00

These booklets were made up from vertical rows 1 and 2 from sheets and so
do not have inverted watermarks. "D" booklet machines were withdrawn in
November 1960.

Booklet Series "E"

Contents: $4 \times 1\frac{1}{2}$d., 4×1d., $4 \times \frac{1}{2}$d. in panes of four

II. WHITE PRINTED COVER AS TYPE B. Not interleaved. For use in "F1"
machines.
Watermark Tudor Crown (Nos. S1, S13, S25)

K1 No date (Back cover "MINIMUM FOREIGN LETTER RATE FOUR
    PENCE") (issued 22.7.54) 180,360   4·00
K1a No date (Back cover "MONEY BY POST") (issued 11.54) 572,900   4·00

    Watermark St. Edward's Crown (Nos. S2, S14, S26)

K2 No date (Back cover "£5 only"). (issued 5.7.56) 373,000   2·50
K2a No date (Back cover "£10 only". Inland letter rate $2\frac{1}{2}$d.) (issued 6.57) .. 532,000   2·50
K2b No date (Back cover "£10 only". Inland letter rate 3d.) (issued 8.58) .. 541,000   3·50

Watermark Crowns (Nos. S4, S16, S28)

K3 No date (Back cover "£10 only". Overseas letter rate 6d.) (issued 13.8.59)   623,500   3·00
K3a No date (Back cover "£10 only". Overseas letter rate 4d.) (issued 10.60)   250,000   4·50

1s. booklets continued to be available until 1964. The machines were then converted to issue the thicker 2s. booklets.

2s. BOOKLETS

Contents: 4 × 3d., 4 × 1½d., 4 × 1d., 4 × ½d. in panes of four

I. SALMON COVER AS TYPE B. Fully interleaved
Watermark St. Edward's Crown (Nos. S2, S14, S26, S68)

N1 No date (issued 22.4.59)	452,470	4·00

II. SALMON COVER AS TYPE C. Fully interleaved
Watermark Crowns (upright) (Nos. S4, S16, S28, S70)

N2 No date (issued 2.11.60)	300,500	3·75

III. LEMON COVER AS TYPE C. Fully interleaved
Watermark Crowns (upright) (Nos. S4, S16, S28, S70)

N3 No date (issued 9.2.61)	1,330,750	4·00

Watermark Crowns (sideways) (Nos. S4d or S5a, S16e or S17a, S28a or S29a, S70d or S71a) or blue phosphor (Nos. S10b or S11a, S21b or S22a, S33b or S34a, S75b or S76a)

N 4 APR 1961 (issued 26.5.61)	1,381,440	15·00
p. With blue phosphor bands (issued 14.7.61)	171,400	40·00
N 5 SEPT 1961	889,000	24·00
N 6 JAN 1962..	911,600	24·00
N 7 APR 1962	958,600	24·00
N 8 JULY 1962	935,600	24·00
p. With blue phosphor bands	51,600	45·00
N 9 NOV 1962	975,000	24·00
p. With blue phosphor bands	56,000	40·00
N10 JAN 1963..	1,105,400	24·00
p. With blue phosphor bands	58,390	50·00
N11 MAR 1963	1,090,800	24·00
N12 JUNE 1963	1,014,800	24·00
p. With blue phosphor bands	57,800	40·00
N13 AUG 1963	989,000	24·00
p. With blue phosphor bands	56,400	40·00
N14 OCT 1963	1,018,800	24·00
p. With blue phosphor bands	11,200	55·00
N15 FEB 1964	1,122,400	24·00
p. With blue phosphor bands	76,600	38·00
N16 JUNE 1964	386,570	24·00
p. With blue phosphor bands	63,400	55·00
N17 AUG 1964	122,300	24·00
p. With blue phosphor bands	58,800	55·00
N18 OCT 1964	1,179,800	26·00
p. With blue phosphor bands	94,200	40·00
N19 DEC 1964	109,170	24·00
p. With blue phosphor bands	34,000	40·00
N20 APR 1965	1,435,400	22·00
p. With blue phosphor bands	40,800	38·00

2s. booklets in this composition were withdrawn from sale on 31 August 1965

Contents changed: 4 × 4d. in pane of four, 2 × 1d. and 2 × 3d. in pane of four arranged *se-tenant* horizontally

ORANGE-YELLOW COVER AS TYPE C. Printed in black. Fully interleaved
Watermark Crowns (sideways) (Nos. S17a, S71a, S85d) and blue or violet phosphor with one band on 3d. (Nos. S22a, S23d, or S24b; S77b or S78c; S90c, S91b or S92b)

N21 JULY 1965 (issued 16.8.65)	2,671,800	1·50
p. With blue phosphor bands (issued 16.8.65)	109,600	13·00
N22 OCT 1965	1,852,800	1·50
p. (a) With blue phosphor bands .. .. ⎫	223,200	20·00
p. (b) With violet 8 mm. phosphor bands .. .. .. ⎭		11·00
N23 JAN 1966	1,633,200	2·50
p. (a) With blue phosphor bands .. .. ⎫	350,600	20·00
p. (b) With violet 8 mm. phosphor bands .. .. ⎭		12·00
N24 APR 1966	2,125,200	2·50
p. With violet 8 mm. phosphor bands	240,000	6·00
N25 JULY 1966	1,981,800	2·00
p. With violet 8 mm. phosphor bands	97,400	30·00

N26 OCT 1966			1,787,400	2·10
p. With violet 8 mm. phosphor bands			471,400	6·00
N27 JAN 1967			644,200	2·25
p. With violet 8 mm. phosphor bands			2,100,400	5·00
N28p APR 1967 .. .. (a) With violet 8 mm. phosphor bands .. ⎫			2,330,200	5·00
(b) With violet 9·5 mm. phosphor bands .. ⎭				
N29p JULY 1967. With violet 8 mm. phosphor bands			3,209,800	4·00
N30p OCT 1967 (issued 15.9.67) (a) With violet 8 mm. phosphor bands .. ⎫			3,924,600	4·00
(b) With violet 9·5 mm. phosphor bands .. ⎭				28·00

For illustration showing how the *se-tenant* stamps with one phosphor band on the 3d. are printed, see listing of No. SB36.

Watermark Crowns (sideways), 3d. with two violet phosphor bands (Nos. S23*d* or S24*b*; S78*c* or S80; S91*b* or S92*b*)

N31p JAN 1968 (issued early 11.67) .. .. .. (a) Violet 9·5 mm. ⎫				2·25
(b) 8 mm. bands				
on 4d. pane			1,864,800	15·00
(c) 8 mm. bands ⎬				
on *se-tenant*				
pane .. ⎭				15·00
N32p MAR 1968 (issued mid 1.68) .. .. (a) Violet 9·5 mm. ⎫				2·25
(b) 8 mm. bands				
on 4d. pane			3,078,800	15·00
(c) 8 mm. bands ⎬				
on *se-tenant*				
pane ⎭				15·00

Nos. N31p(*c*) and N32p(*c*) have one band on 3d.

2s. booklets were withdrawn on 11 February 1971 prior to decimalisation on 15 February.

2s. BOOKLETS FOR HOLIDAY RESORTS

Contents: 8 × 2½d. in panes of four and 3 × ½d. and 1 × 2½d. in pane of four arranged *se-tenant*

LEMON COVER AS TYPE C. Printed in red. Fully interleaved
Watermark Crowns. Chalky paper (Nos. S6, S58)

A. Black stitching
NR1 No date (issued 15.7.63) .. .. 415,000 2·50

B. White stitching
NR1a No date (issued 3.9.63) .. .. 50,000 3·00

Contents changed: 8 × ½d. and 8 × 2½d. in panes of four arranged sideways, vertically *se-tenant*

LEMON COVER AS TYPE C. Printed in red. Fully interleaved
Watermark Crowns (sideways) (No. S5*a/b*, S57*b/c*)

NR2 1964 (issued 1.7.64) .. .. 827,800 1·10
These replaced the normal 2s. booklets in the resort towns to which they were issued.

2s. BOOKLET FOR CHRISTMAS CARDS

Contents: 8 × 3d. in two panes of four arranged sideways
ORANGE-YELLOW COVER AS TYPE C. Printed in red. Fully interleaved
Watermark Crowns (sideways) (No. S71*a*)

NX1 1965 (issued 6.12.65) 1,208,000 55
The above was withdrawn on 3.1.66 but reissued on 16.5.66 as a holiday resort booklet.

2s.6d. BOOKLETS

Contents: 6 × 2½d., 6 × 1½d., 3 × 1d. (page completed by three perforated labels),
6 × ½d. in panes of six

LABELS.   The wording printed on the labels differs as follows:—
"PPR"="MINIMUM INLAND PRINTED PAPER RATE 1½d." Two types exist:
    (a) 17 mm. high. Printed in photogravure
    (b) 15 mm. high. Printed by typography
"SHORTHAND"="SHORTHAND IN 1 WEEK" (covering all three labels)
"POST EARLY"="PLEASE POST EARLY IN THE DAY"
"PAP"="PACK YOUR PARCELS SECURELY" (1st label), "ADDRESS YOUR
LETTERS CORRECTLY" (2nd label) "AND POST EARLY IN THE DAY" (3rd label)

I. Composite Booklets containing Stamps of King George VI and Queen Elizabeth II

A. GREEN COVER AS TYPE A. Not interleaved
    K.G. VI ½d. (No. Q3), 1d. (No. Q6) and Q.E. II 1½d. (No. S25), 2½d. (No. S51)

F 1 MAY 1953	PPR 17 mm.	2,272,000	10·00
b. Date error "MAY 195" for "MAY 1955"			
F 2 JUNE 1953	PPR 17 mm.	2,751,000	10·00
F 3 JULY 1953	PPR 17 mm.	2,199,000	15·00
F 4 AUG 1953	PPR 17 mm.	2,464,000	13·00

B. GREEN COVER AS TYPE A, but with the addition of two interleaving pages,
one at each end
    K.G. VI ½d. (No. Q3), 1d. (No. Q6) and Q.E. II 1½d. (No. S25), 2½d. (No. S51)

F 5 SEPT 1953	PPR 17 mm.	} 2,386,000	65·00
F 6 SEPT 1953	PPR 15 mm.		14·00

C. GREEN COVER AS TYPE B. Contents as Nos. F 5/6
    K.G. VI ½d. (No. Q3), 1d. (No. Q6) and Q.E. II 1½d. (No. S25), 2½d. (No. S51)

F 7 OCT 1953	PPR 17 mm. ...	} 2,532,000	15·00
F 8 OCT 1953	PPR 15 mm. ...		18·00
F 9 NOV 1953	PPR 17 mm. ...	} 4,308,000	15·00
F10 NOV 1953	PPR 15 mm. ...		60·00
F11 DEC 1953	PPR 17 mm. ...	2,918,000	15·00
F12 JAN 1954	SHORTHAND	2,199,000	20·00
F13 FEB 1954	SHORTHAND	2,202,000	15·00

D. GREEN COVER AS TYPE B with contents as Nos. F 5/6 but Q.E. II ½d. in place
of K.G. VI ½d.
    K.G. VI 1d. (No. Q6) and Q.E. II ½d. (No. S1), 1½d. (No. S25), 2½d. (No.S51)

F14 MAR 1954	PPR 17 mm. ...	139,000	£350

II. Booklets containing only Queen Elizabeth II Stamps

GREEN COVER AS TYPE B.
    Watermark Tudor Crown (Nos. S1, S13, S25, S51)

A. Two interleaving pages, one at each end

F15 MAR 1954	PPR 15 mm. ...	2,085,000	£150
F16 APR 1954	POST EARLY	3,176,000	15·00
F17 MAY 1954	POST EARLY	2,435,000	15·00
F18 JUNE 1954	POST EARLY	2,419,000	15·00
F19 JULY 1954	POST EARLY	2,876,000	16·00
F20 AUG 1954	POST EARLY	2,871,000	18·00
F21 SEPT 1954	POST EARLY	2,799,000	15·00
F22 OCT 1954	POST EARLY	2,803,000	15·00
F23 NOV 1954	POST EARLY	3,739,000	15·00
F24 DEC 1954	POST EARLY	2,813,000	15·00

B. Fully interleaved

F25	JAN 1955	POST EARLY	..	..	..	(a) (original setting) (b) (modified setting)	2,551,000	28·00 18·00
F26	JAN 1955	PAP..	..	..	..	.. ..	160,000	35·00
F27	FEB 1955	PAP..	..	..	..	.. ..	2,694,000	16·00
F28	MAR 1955	PAP..	..	..	..	.. ..	2,530,000	15·00
F29	APR 1955	PAP..	..	..	..	.. ..	2,522,000	17·00
F30	MAY 1955	PAP..	..	..	..	.. ..	2,530,000	17·00
F31	JUNE 1955	PAP..	..	..	..	.. ..	2,522,000	16·00
F32	JULY 1955	PAP..	..	..	..	.. ..	2,431,000	17·00
F33	AUG 1955	PAP..	..	..	..	(a) Combination TTET (b) Combination TEET	2,563,000	16·00

In the modified setting the distance between " IN THE " is 1 mm. and this is only found on the majority of the Jan. 1955 edition (Booklet F25). The normal spacing is 1½ mm.

> MIXED WATERMARKS.   Nos. F33/8 and F42/3 exist with mixed Tudor Crown and St. Edward's Crown watermarks.   The mixed watermarks are indicated by the code letters "T" (Tudor) and "E" (Edward) starting with the first pane of the booklet, i.e. 2½d., 1½d., 1d., ½d.   We only quote one price for each booklet and this is the minimum price.   Some combinations are scarcer and worth more.

Tudor Crown, St. Edward's Crown and mixed watermarks. All have PAP labels.

F34 SEPT 1955 (TTTT)	..	..	..	..	(a) Combination TTET (b) Combination TEET (c) Combination TEEE (d) Combination ETET (e) Combination EEET (f) Combination EEEE	2,275,000	12·00
F35 OCT 1955 (TTTT)	..	..	..	..	(a) Combination TTET (b) Combination EEET (c) Combination TEEE (d) Combination EEEE	2,289,000	15·00
F36 NOV 1955 (TTTT)	..	..	..	..	(a) Combination TEEE (b) Combination EEET (c) Combination EEEE	4,125,000	15·00

Watermark St. Edward's Crown (Nos. S2, S14, S26, S53). All have PAP labels

F37 DEC 1955 .. (a) Combination TEET (b) Combination EEET	2,789,000	15·00	F44 JULY 1956	..	..	2,279,400	15·00
			F45 AUG 1956	..	..	2,264,400	15·00
			F46 SEPT 1956	..	..	2,533,000	15·00
F38 JAN 1956 .. (a) Combination EEET	2,001,000	12·00	F47 OCT 1956	..	..	2,536,000	15·00
			F48 NOV 1956	..	..	4,165,800	14·00
F39 FEB 1956	2,031,000	15·00	F49 DEC 1956	..	..	2,724,600	14·00
F40 MAR 1956	2,289,000	15·00	F50 JAN 1957	..	..	2,212,800	16·00
F41 APR 1956	2,283,000	15·00	F51 FEB 1957	..	..	2,772,790	15·00
F42 MAY 1956 .. (a) Combination EEET (b) Combination TEEE	2,275,000	15·00	F52 MAR 1957	..	..	2,497,800	12·00
F43 JUNE 1956 .. (a) Combination EEET (b) Combination TEEE	2,293,000	15·00					

Contents changed: 6 × 2½d., 6 × 2d., 6 × ½d. in panes of six
Watermark St. Edward's Crown (Nos. S2, S38, S53)

F53 APR 1957	..	..	2,451,800	11·00	F58 SEPT 1957	 2,482,200	11·00
F54 MAY 1957	..	..	2,062,400	15·00	F59 OCT 1957	 2,505,600	10·00
F55 JUNE 1957	..	..	1,843,000	11·00	F60 NOV 1957	 3,085,600	10·00
F56 JULY 1957	..	..	2,305,000	11·00	F61 DEC 1957	 281,000	13·00
F57 AUG 1957	..	..	2,265,000	10·00			

The 2s.6d. booklets were withdrawn from sale on 27 July 1958.

3s. BOOKLETS

Contents: 6 × 3d., 6 × 1½d., 6 × 1d., 6 × ½d. in panes of six

I. RED COVER AS TYPE B. Fully interleaved
   Watermark St. Edward's Crown (Nos. S2, S14, S26, S68)

M1 JAN 1958	 1,815,000	10·00	M9 NOV 1958 ..	
M2 FEB 1958	 2,224,000	10·00	(a) Combination EEEC	
M3 MAR 1958	 2,271,000	10·00	(b) Combination EECE	
M4 APR 1958	 2,654,000	10·00	(c) Combination EECC	1,367,000 10·00
M5 MAY 1958	 2,146,000	10·00	(d) Combination CECE	
M6 JUNE 1958	 2,222,000	10·00	(e) Combination CCCE	
M7 JULY 1958	 885,000	10·00		
M8 AUG 1958	 896,000	10·00		

MIXED WATERMARKS. See notes above No. F34. The mixed watermarks
here are indicated by the code letters "E" (Edward) and "C" (Crowns) starting
with the first pane of the booklet, i.e. 3d., 1½d., 1d., ½d.

Watermark Crowns (Nos. S4, S16, S28, S70), or graphite lines (Nos. S7, S18,
S30, S72)

M10 DEC 1958 ..	(a) Combination ECEC		
	(b) Combination CEEE		
	(c) Combination CECE	886,000	13·00
	(d) Combination CEEC		
	(e) Combination CECC		
M11 JAN 1959 ..	(a) Combination CECC	1,145,000	13·00
M12 FEB 1959		1,125,000	13·00
M13 AUG 1959		1,038,000	13·00
g. With graphite lines (issued 4.8.59)		47,000	£120
M14 SEPT 1959		1,542,000	13·00
g. With graphite lines		74,000	£140

II. BRICK-RED COVER AS TYPE C. Fully interleaved
   Watermark Crowns (Nos. S4, S16, S28, S70), graphite lines (Nos. S7,
   S18, S30, S72) or green phosphor (Nos. S9, S20, S32, S74)

M15 OCT 1959	1,016,000	13·00
g. With graphite lines	74,000	£120
M16 NOV 1959	2,287,000	13·00
M17 DEC 1959	1,027,000	13·00
M18 JAN 1960	752,000	13·00
M19 FEB 1960	750,000	14·00
g. With graphite lines	37,600	£140
M20 MAR 1960	966,000	13·00
g. With graphite lines	39,600	£150
M21 APR 1960	941,000	14·00
g. With graphite lines	38,200	£140
M22 MAY 1960	911,000	14·00
M23 JUNE 1960	982,000	14·00
M24 JULY 1960	989,200	14·00
M25 AUG 1960	897,000	14·00
p. With green phosphor bands (issued 14.8.60)	39,800	27·00
M26 SEPT 1960	1,326,600	14·00
M27 OCT 1960	1,343,400	14·00
M28 NOV 1960	2,068,200	14·00
p. With green phosphor bands	11,900	32·00

III. BRICK-RED COVER AS TYPE D. Fully interleaved
   Watermark Crowns (Nos. S4 or S5, S16 or S17, S28 or S29, S70 or S71),
   green or blue phosphor (Nos. S9 or S10, S20 or S21, S32 or S33, S74 or S75)

M29 DEC 1960	905,200	14·00
p. With green phosphor bands	31,800	35·00
M30 JAN 1961	731,800	14·00
M31 FEB 1961	727,000	14·00
M32 MAR 1961	754,600	14·00
M33 APR 1961	760,800	14·00
p. With blue phosphor bands	142,600	24·00
M34 MAY 1961	738,000	14·00
M35 JUNE 1961	768,000	14·00
M36 JULY 1961	783,400	14·00
p. With blue phosphor bands	7,800	24·00

M37 AUG 1961	747,400	14·00
p. (a) With green phosphor bands	⎫ 32·00	
p. (b) With blue phosphor bands ..	⎬ 54,400 25·00	
M38 SEPT 1961	513,600	14·00
p. With blue phosphor bands	19,200	30·00
M39 OCT 1961	494,600	14·00
p. With blue phosphor bands	18,800	25·00
M40 NOV 1961	467,600	14·00
M41 DEC 1961	356,800	14·00
M42 JAN 1962	447,000	14·00
M43 FEB 1962	654,200	14·00
p. With blue phosphor bands	11,800	25·00
M44 MAR 1962	655,200	14·00
p. With blue phosphor bands	19,400	25·00
M45 APR 1962	569,600	14·00
p. With blue phosphor bands	19,600	25·00
M46 MAY 1962	475,000	14·00
p. With blue phosphor bands	27,000	25·00
M47 JUNE 1962	468,400	16·00
p. With blue phosphor bands	27,200	25·00
M48 JULY 1962	729,400	14·00
M49 AUG 1962	691,200	14·00
p. With blue phosphor bands	28,800	25·00
M50 SEPT 1962	687,400	14·00
p. With blue phosphor bands	11,800	25·00
M51 OCT 1962	864,600	14·00
p. With blue phosphor bands	35,200	25·00
M52 NOV 1962	1,125,600	14·00
p. With blue phosphor bands	51,800	25·00
M53 DEC 1962	1,035,000	14·00
p.With blue phosphor bands	19,200	25·00
M54 JAN 1963	499,400	16·00
M55 FEB 1963	462,400	14·00
p. With blue phosphor bands	39,400	25·00
M56 MAR 1963	512,800	14·00
p. With blue phosphor bands	39,200	25·00
M57 APR 1963	512,800	14·00
p. With blue phosphor bands	39,600	25·00
M58 MAY 1963	520,800	14·00
p. With blue phosphor bands	19,400	80·00
M59 JUNE 1963	532,400	14·00
p. With blue phosphor bands	19,800	23·00
M60 JULY 1963	712,000	14·00
p. With blue phosphor bands	17,800	25·00
M61 AUG 1963	698,600	14·00
p. With blue phosphor bands	19,800	25·00
M62 SEPT 1963	503,000	14·00
M63 OCT 1963	660,400	14·00
M64 NOV 1963	670,000	14·00
p. With blue phosphor bands	39,400	23·00
M65 DEC 1963	711,400	14·00
p. With blue phosphor bands	19,350	30·00
M66 JAN 1964	619,600	16·00
p. With blur phosphor bands	67,000	25·00
M67 MAR 1964	666,600	14·00
p. With blue phosphor bands	30,400	25·00
M68 MAY 1964	636,600	14·00
p. With blue phosphor bands	46,600	35·00
M69 JULY 1964	865,800	14·00
p. With blue phosphor bands	27,400	25·00
M70 SEPT 1964	915,600	14·00
p. With blue phosphor bands	39,800	25·00
M71 NOV 1964	2,157,600	14·00
p. With blue phosphor bands	99,200	23·00
M72 JAN 1965	1,009,800	14·00
p. With blue phosphor bands	50,000	23·00
M73 MAR 1965	944,600	10·00
p. With blue phosphor bands	38,200	23·00
M74 MAY 1965	765,600	10·00
p. With blue phosphor bands	58,200	25·00

3s. booklets were withdrawn from sale on 31 August 1965.

3s.9d. BOOKLETS

Contents: 18 × 2½d. in panes of six
RED COVER AS TYPE B.

A. Two interleaving pages, one at each end
  Watermark Tudor Crown (No. S51)

G1 NOV 1953	 1,446,000	14·00	G5 FEB 1955	 925,000	14·00
G2 JAN 1954	 1,572,000	16·00	G6 APR 1955	 1,112,000	15·00
G3 MAR 1954	 1,474,000	14·00	G7 JUNE 1955	 675,000	16·00
G4 DEC 1954	 1,477,000	14·00	G8 AUG 1955	 636,000	16·00

  Tudor Crown, St. Edward's Crown and mixed watermarks

G9 OCT 1955 (TTT)		
	(a) Combination TET	
	(b) Combination EET } 1,661,000	14·00
	(c) Combination EEE	
G10 DEC 1955 (TTT)		
	(a) Combination TET } 616,000	16·00
	(b) Combination EEE	

B. Fully interleaved
  Watermark St. Edward's Crown (No. S53)

G12 FEB 1956	 638,000	8·00	G17 DEC 1956	 1,065,800	8·00
G13 APR 1956	 642,000	8·00	G18 FEB 1957	 1,376,000	8·00
G14 JUNE 1956	 634,000	8·00	G19 APR 1957	 1,139,600	8·00
G15 AUG 1956	 747,200	8·00	G20 JUNE 1957	 1,115,200	6·00
G16 OCT 1956	 1,762,800	8·00	G21 AUG 1957	 39,600	14·00

3s.9d. booklets were withdrawn from sale on 30 September 1957.

4s.6d. BOOKLETS

Contents: 18 × 3d. in panes of six
I. PURPLE COVER AS TYPE B. Fully interleaved
  Watermark St. Edward's Crown (No. S68)

L1 OCT 1957	 2,249,000	8·00	L5 JUNE 1958	 1,096,000	10·00
L2 DEC 1957	 4,539,000	8·00	L6 OCT 1958	 1,796,000	10·00
L3 FEB 1958	 1,789,000	10·00	L7 DEC 1958	 1,808,000	10·00
L4 APR 1958	 2,691,000	8·00			

  Watermark Crowns (No. S70)

L8 DEC 1958	..	*(incl. above)*	32·00

II. PURPLE COVER AS TYPE C. Fully interleaved
  Watermark Crowns (No. S70) or graphite lines (No. S72)

L 9 FEB 1959 .. .. *(with L14)*	2,260,000	11·00
L10 JUNE 1959 .. .. *(with L16)*	2,195,000	11·00
L11 AUG 1959	1,710,000	11·00
g. With graphite lines	97,600	10·00
L12 OCT 1959	1,852,000	11·00
L13 DEC 1959 .. .. *(with L17)*	1,409,000	11·00

III. VIOLET COVER AS TYPE C. Fully interleaved
  Watermark Crowns (No. S70), graphite lines (No. S72) or green phosphor
  (No. S74)

L14 FEB 1959 .. .. *(incl in L9)*		12·00
L15 APR 1959..	2,137,000	11·00
g. With graphite lines	99,200	10·00
L16 JUNE 1959 .. .. *(incl. in L10)*		11·00
g. With graphite lines	99,400	10·00
L17 DEC 1959 .. .. *(incl. in L13)*		10·00
L18 FEB 1960	1,801,000	12·50
g. With graphite lines	79,600	11·00
L19 APR 1960..	1,730,000	12·50
g. With graphite lines	78,800	11·00
L20 JUNE 1960	1,832,000	12·50
L21 AUG 1960	1,771,600	13·00
p. With green phosphor bands	39,800	24·00
L22 OCT 1960	2,723,600	14·00

IV. VIOLET COVER AS TYPE D. Fully interleaved
Watermark Crowns (No. S70 or S71), green or blue phosphor (Nos. S74, S75 or S76)

L23	DEC 1960	1,772,000	15·00
L24	FEB 1961	1,982,200	16·00
	p. With green phosphor bands	27,200	18·00
L25	APR 1961	3,428,400	14·00
	p. With blue phosphor bands	297,400	18·00
L26	JUNE 1961	1,825,600	14·00
L27	AUG 1961	2,679,800	14·00
	p. (a) With green phosphor bands	} 63,120	32·00
	p. (b) With blue phosphor bands		18·00
L28	OCT 1961	3,061,000	14·00
	p. With blue phosphor bands	31,400	18·00
L29	DEC 1961	1,942,800	14·00
L30	FEB 1962	2,405,200	14·00
	p. With blue phosphor bands	43,600	18·00
L31	APR 1962	1,985,000	15·00
	p. With blue phosphor bands	75,400	18·00
L32	JUNE 1962	2,190,600	15·00
	p. With blue phosphor bands	74,000	26·00
L33	AUG 1962	2,533,800	15·00
	p. With blue phosphor bands	83,600	26·00
L34	OCT 1962	3,525,400	15·00
	p. With blue phosphor bands	83,200	90·00
L35	DEC 1962	1,822,000	15·00
	p. With blue phosphor bands	82,200	18·00
L36	FEB 1963	2,352,600	15·00
	p. With blue phosphor bands	117,000	18·00
L37	APR 1963	2,390,200	15·00
	p. With blue phosphor bands	119,000	18·00
L38	JUNE 1963	2,873,600	15·00
	p. With blue phosphor bands	178,600	20·00
L39	AUG 1963	2,474,200	15·00
	p. With blue phosphor bands	111,000	18·00
L40	OCT 1963	1,829,200	15·00
	p. With blue phosphor bands	99,400	18·00
L41	NOV 1963	1,821,000	15·00
	p. With blue phosphor bands	99,600	18·00
L42	DEC 1963	2,431,400	16·00
	p. With blue phosphor bands	46,400	80·00
L43	JAN 1964	1,043,800	15·00
L44	FEB 1964	1,069,000	15·00
	p. With blue phosphor bands	87,000	20·00
L45	MAR 1964	1,014,200	15·00
	p. With blue phosphor bands	82,800	26·00
L46	APR 1964	1,006,600	20·00
	p. With blue phosphor bands	62,400	18·00
L47	MAY 1964	1,028,800	15·00
	p. With blue phosphor bands	105,200	18·00
L48	JUNE 1964	1,067,400	15·00
	p. With blue phosphor bands	70,400	18·00
L49	JULY 1964	1,673,600	15·00
	p. With blue phosphor bands	56,200	18·00
L50	AUG 1964	1,622,600	20·00
	p. With blue phosphor bands	78,200	18·00
L51	SEPT 1964	1,561,200	15·00
	p. With blue phosphor bands	98,000	18·00
L52	OCT 1964	1,781,800	15·00
	p. With blue phosphor bands	197,800	20·00
L53	NOV 1964	1,686,000	15·00
	p. With blue phosphor bands	138,000	18·00
L54	DEC 1964	1,684,000	12·00
	p. With blue phosphor bands	119,200	18·00
L55	JAN 1965	1,519,200	12·00
	p. With blue phosphor bands	95,000	18·00
L56	FEB 1965	1,504,600	12·00
	p. With blue phosphor bands	94,200	18·00
L57	MAR 1965	1,479,600	12·00
	p. With blue phosphor bands	18,800	£120
L58	APR 1965	1,438,400	8·00

An edition dated MAY 1965 was prepared, but not issued. Advertisers' voucher copies are known (Price £50).

Contents changed: 12 × 4d., 6 × 1d. in panes of six

SLATE-BLUE COVER AS TYPE D

Watermark Crowns (Nos. S17, S85), blue or violet phosphor (Nos. S22, S23 or S24; S90, S91 or S92)

L59 JULY 1965 (issued 26.7.65)	2,191,600	8·00
p. With blue phosphor bands (issued 26.7.65)	75,400	15·00
L60 SEPT 1965	1,839,600	8·00
p. (a) With blue phosphor bands	} 200,800	16·00
p. (b) With violet 8 mm. phosphor bands		15·00
L61 NOV 1965	2,005,000	7·50
p. (a) With blue phosphor bands	} 165,800	17·00
p. (b) With violet 8 mm. phosphor bands		15·00
L62 JAN 1966	1,671,000	8·00
p. (a) With blue phosphor bands	} 334,600	17·00
p. (b) With violet 8 mm. phosphor bands		15·00
L63 MAR 1966	1,201,600	8·00
p. With violet 8 mm. phosphor bands	153,200	7·00
L64 JAN 1967	98,800	7·50
p. With violet 8 mm. phosphor bands	396,600	7·00
L65 MAR 1967	97,200	15·00
p. (a) With violet 8 mm. phosphor bands	} 255,400	8·00
p. (b) With violet 9·5 mm. phosphor bands		8·00

Watermark Crowns, violet 9·5mm. phosphor (Nos. S24, S92)

L66p MAY 1967	697,200	7·00
L67p JULY 1967	569,000	7·00
L68p SEPT 1967	750,800	6·00
L69p NOV 1967	1,802,600	5·50
L70p JAN 1968	729,400	5·50
L71p MAR 1968	729,400	5·50

5s. BOOKLETS

Contents: 12 × 2½d., 6 × 2d., 6 × 1½d., 6 × 1d., 6 × ½d. in panes of six

I. Composite Booklets containing Stamps of King George VI and Queen Elizabeth II

A. BUFF COVER AS TYPE A. Not interleaved

K.G. VI ½d. (No. Q3), 1d. (No. Q6), 2d. (No. Q12) and Q.E. II 1½d. (No. S25), 2½d. (No. S51)

H1 MAY 1953	..	1,309,000	17·00
H2 JULY 1953	..	1,716,000	17·00

B. BUFF COVER AS TYPE A but with the addition of two interleaving pages, one at each end

K.G. VI ½d. (No. Q3), 1d. (No. Q6), 2d. (No. Q12) and Q.E. II 1½d. (No. S25), 2½d. (No. S51)

H3 SEPT 1953	..	1,070,000	18·00

C. BUFF COVER AS TYPE B. Contents as No. H3

K.G. VI ½d. (No. Q3), 1d. (No. Q6), 2d. (No. Q12) and Q.E. II 1½d. (No. S25), 2½d. (No. S51)

H4 NOV 1953	..	2,126,000	18·00
H5 JAN 1954	..	692,000	20·00

D. BUFF COVER AS TYPE B. Contents as Nos. H 4/5 but ½d. Q.E. II in place of K.G. VI ½d.

K.G. VI 1d. (No. Q6), 2d. (No. Q12) and Q.E. II ½d. (No. S1), 1½d. (No. S25), 2½d. (No. S51)

H6 MAR 1954	..	16,000	£140

E. BUFF COVER AS TYPE B. Contents as No. H6 but 1d. Q.E. II in place of K.G. VI 1d.
K.G. VI 2d. (No. Q12) and Q.E. II ½d. (No. S1), 1d. (No. S13), 1½d. (No. S25), 2½d.
(No. S51)

H7 MAR 1954	..	..	160,000	65·00
a. Extra 1½d. pane	..	..		

II. Booklets containing only Queen Elizabeth II Stamps

A. BUFF COVER AS TYPE B
Watermark Tudor Crown (Nos. S1, S13, S25, S36, S51)

A. Two interleaving pages, one at each end

H 8 MAR 1954	..	..	1,092,000	55·00	H11 SEPT 1954	..	..	1,357,000	20·00
H 9 MAY 1954	..	..	1,884,000	18·00	H12 NOV 1954	..	..	2,309,000	20·00
H10 JULY 1954	..	..	1,351,000	27·00					

B. Fully interleaved

H13 JAN 1955	..	..	1,349,000	20·00	H15 MAY 1955	..	..	1,461,000	18·00
H14 MAR 1955	..	..	1,450,000	20·00	H16 JULY 1955	..	..	1,460,000	20·00

MIXED WATERMARKS. Nos. H17/19 and H21 exist with mixed Tudor
Crown and St. Edward's Crown watermarks. The mixed watermarks are
indicated by the code letters "T" (Tudor) and "E" (Edward), starting with
the first pane of the booklet, i.e. 2½d. (2), 2d., 1½d., 1d., ½d. We only quote one
price for each booklet and this is the minimum price. Some combinations are
scarcer and worth more.

H17 SEPT 1955	.. ..	.. ..		
	(*a*) Combination TTTETT			
	(*b*) Combination TTTEET			
	(*c*) Combination TTTETE			
	(*d*) Combination TTEETT			
	(*e*) Combination TTEEET			
	(*f*) Combination TTEEEE			
	(*g*) Combination TETETT			
	(*h*) Combination TETEET			
	(*i*) Combination TEEETT			
	(*j*) Combination TETETE			
	(*k*) Combination TEEETE			
	(*l*) Combination ETTETT			
	(*m*) Combination ETTEET	1,328,000	14·00
	(*n*) Combination ETEETT			
	(*o*) Combination ETEEET			
	(*p*) Combination EETETT			
	(*q*) Combination EETEET			
	(*r*) Combination EETETE			
	(*s*) Combination EETEEE			
	(*t*) Combination EEETTT			
	(*u*) Combination EEETET			
	(*v*) Combination EEETEE			
	(*w*) Combination EEEETT			
	(*x*) Combination EEEEET			
	(*y*) Combination EEEEEE			

Watermark St. Edward's Crown (Nos. S2, S14, S26, S37, S53)

H18 NOV 1955 ..			H20 MAR 1956	..	.. 1,403,000	20·00
(*a*) Combination TTEEEE			H21 MAY 1956 ..			
(*b*) Combination EETEEE			(*a*) Combination EETETT		1,572,000	20·00
(*c*) Combination TEEEEE	2,147,000	17·00	(*b*) Combination EEEEET			
(*d*) Combination EEEETE			H22 JULY 1956	..	.. 1,465,190	17·00
(*e*) Combination EEEEET			H23 SEPT 1956	..	.. 1,589,000	17·00
H19 JAN 1956 ..			H24 NOV 1956	..	.. 2,430,600	20·00
(*a*) Combination TTTEET			H25 JAN 1957	..	.. 100,000	22·00
(*b*) Combination EETETT	1,337,000	20·00				
(*c*) Combination EEEEET						

Introduction of 2d. light red-brown (No. S38) in place of No. S37

H26 JAN 1957	..	..	1,417,800	18·00	H29 JULY 1957	..	..	1,453,600	16·00
H27 MAR 1957	..	..	1,435,400	16·00	H30 SEPT 1957	..	..	2,104,600	16·00
H28 MAY 1957	..	..	1,375,200	16·00	H31 NOV 1957	..	..	1,708,400	16·00

Contents changed: 12 × 3d., 6 × 2½d., 6 × 1d., 6 × ½d. in panes of six
Watermark St. Edward's Crown (Nos. S2, S14, S53, S68)

H32 JAN 1958	1,528,000	16·00	
H33 MAR 1958	442,000	16·00	
H34 MAY 1958	795,000	14·00	

H35 JULY 1958 (11.58)
(a) Combination EEEEC ⎫
(b) Combination EEECE ⎬ 1,313,000   12·00
(c) Combination EEECC ⎭

H36 NOV 1958 ..
(a) Combination EEECE ⎫
(b) Combination EECEE ⎪
(c) Combination ECCEE ⎬ 1,235,000   12·00
(d) Combination CCBEE ⎪
(e) Combination CCCEE ⎭

> **MIXED WATERMARKS.** See notes above No. H17. The mixed watermarks
> here are indicated by the code letters "E" (Edward) and "C" (Crowns) starting
> with the first pane of the booklet, i.e. 3d. (2), 2½d., 1d., ½d.

II. BLUE COVER AS TYPE C. Fully interleaved
Watermark Crowns (Nos. S4, S16, S55, S70), graphite lines (Nos. S7, S18,
S59, S72) or green phosphor (Nos. S9, S20, S61, S74)

H37   JAN 1959   .. ..
(a) Combination CCCCE ⎫
(b) Combination CCCEC ⎬ 1,330,000   14·00
(c) Combination CCCEE ⎪
(d) Combination CCECC ⎭

H38 MAR 1959	895,000	16·00
H39 JULY 1959	1,122,000	16·00
g. With graphite lines (issued 21.8.59)	46,200	60·00
H40 SEPT 1959	1,541,000	16·00
H41 NOV 1959	1,340,000	16·00
H42 JAN 1960	1,092,000	16·00
H43 MAR 1960	1,042,000	16·00
g. With graphite lines	38,000	70·00
H44 MAY 1960	1,023,000	16·00
H45 JULY 1960	1,104,000	18·00
H46 SEPT 1960	1,158,800	18·00
g. With graphite lines	65,999	70·00
p. With green phosphor bands	39,600	38·00
H47 NOV 1960	1,308,400	18·00

III. BLUE COVER AS TYPE D. Fully interleaved
Watermark Crowns (Nos. S4, S16, S55, S70)
or blue phosphor with two bands on 2½d. (Nos. S10, S21, S62, S75)

H48 JAN 1961	1,344,600	18·00
H49 MAR 1961	2,382,600	18·00
p. With blue phosphor bands	97,400	45·00
H50 MAY 1961	1,219,200	18·00
H51 JULY 1961	1,148,200	18·00
p. With blue phosphor bands	7,200	45·00
H52 SEPT 1961	1,728,600	18·00
p. With blue phosphor bands	15,200	45·00
H53 NOV 1961	1,367,000	18·00
H54 JAN 1962	963,800	18·00
p. With blue phosphor bands	38,600	45·00

Watermark Crowns (Nos. S4 or S5, S16 or S17, S55 or S57, S70 or S71)
or blue phosphor with one phosphor band on 2½d. (Nos. S10 or S11, S21
or S22, S63 or S65, S75 or S76)

H55 MAR 1962	1,006,200	18·00
p. With blue phosphor bands	23,600	45·00
H56 MAY 1962	1,120,800	18·00
p. With blue phosphor bands	50,800	45·00
H57 JULY 1962	1,309,600	18·00
p. With blue phosphor bands	16,600	45·00
H58 SEPT 1962	1,523,800	18·00
p. With blue phosphor bands	49,800	45·00
H59 NOV 1962	1,543,200	18·00
p. With blue phosphor bands	51,000	45·00
H60 JAN 1963	1,024,600	18·00
p. With blue phosphor bands	38,800	£150
H61 MAR 1963	1,116,800	18·00
p. With blue phosphor bands	15,800	50·00
H62 MAY 1963	1,102,200	18·00
p. With blue phosphor bands	78,600	45·00
H63 JULY 1963	1,456,400	18·00
p. With blue phosphor bands	44,600	45·00
H64 SEPT 1963	1,402,200	18·00
p. With blue phosphor bands	36,200	50·00
H65 NOV 1963	1,400,000	18·00
p. With blue phosphor bands	78,800	45·00
H66 JAN 1964	831,600	18·00
p. With blue phosphor bands	43,000	45·00
H67 MAR 1964	760,200	18·00
p. With blue phosphor bands	55,800	45·00
H68 MAY 1964	760,200	18·00
p. With blue phosphor bands	66,000	50·00
H69 JULY 1964	1,647,200	18·00
p. With blue phosphor bands	29,400	45·00
H70 SEPT 1964	1,574,000	18·00
p. With blue phosphor bands	38,400	45·00
H71 NOV 1964	1,152,400	18·00
p. With blue phosphor bands	98,600	45·00
H72 JAN 1965	1,119,000	18·00
p. With blue phosphor bands	55,200	38·00
H73 MAR 1965	657,600	18·00
p. With blue phosphor bands	19,000	45·00
H74 MAY 1965	1,076,600	18·00
p. With blue phosphor bands	56,800	45·00

5s. booklets were withdrawn from sale on 31 August 1965.

6s. BOOKLETS

Contents: 18 × 4d. in panes of six

CLARET COVER AS TYPE D. Fully interleaved
Watermark Crowns (No. S85), blue or violet phosphor (Nos. S90, S91 or S92)

Q 1 JUNE 1965 (issued 21.6.65)	1,166,800	15·00
p. With blue phosphor bands (issued 21.6.65)	101,800	15·00
Q 2 JULY 1965	1,718,000	15·00
p. With blue phosphor bands	136,200	15·00
Q 3 AUG 1965	1,192,400	15·00
p. With blue phosphor bands	87,600	18·00
Q 4 SEPT 1965	1,907,800	15·00
p. (a) With blue phosphor bands .. .. }	244,400	18·00
p. (b) With violet 8 mm. phosphor bands .. .. .. }		18·00
Q 5 OCT 1965	1,889,600	15·00
p. (a) With blue phosphor bands .. .. }	263,600	18·00
p. (b) With violet 8 mm. phosphor bands .. .. .. }		18·00
Q 6 NOV 1965	1,788,800	15·00
p. (a) With blue phosphor bands .. .. }	98,200	18·00
p. (b) With violet 8 mm. phosphor bands .. .. .. }		18·00
Q 7 DEC 1965	1,662,000	15·00
p. (a) With blue phosphor bands .. .. }	93,000	18·00
p. (b) With violet 8 mm. phosphor bands .. .. .. }		18·00
Q 8 JAN 1966	1,114,800	15·00
p. (a) With blue phosphor bands .. .. }	349,200	18·00
p. (b) With violet 8 mm. phosphor bands .. .. .. }		18·00
Q 9 FEB 1966	1,448,600	15·00
p. With violet 8 mm. phosphor bands	116,800	18·00
Q10 MAR 1966	1,038,000	15·00
p. With violet 8 mm. phosphor bands	122,400	18·00

Q11 APR 1966		1,124,200	15·00
p. With violet 8 mm. phosphor bands		119,600	20·00
Q12 MAY 1966		1,099,000	15·00
p. With violet 8 mm. phosphor bands		121,000	18·00
Q13 JUNE 1966		1,070,400	15·00
p. With violet 8 mm. phosphor bands		121,000	18·00
Q14 JULY 1966		667,600	15·00
p. With violet 8 mm. phosphor bands		46,800	22·00
Q15 AUG 1966		1,503,200	15·00
p. With violet 8 mm. phosphor bands		42,400	45·00
Q16 SEPT 1966		1,402,400	15·00
p. With violet 8 mm. phosphor bands		227,200	18·00
Q17 OCT 1966		986,600	15·00
p. With violet 8 mm. phosphor bands		227,200	22·00
Q18 NOV 1966		1,078,000	15·00
p. With violet 8 mm. phosphor bands		271,200	16·00
Q19 DEC 1966		1,069,400	15·00
p. With violet 8 mm. phosphor bands		270,500	16·00
Q20 JAN 1967		231,400	18·00
p. With violet 8 mm. phosphor bands		622,400	18·00
Q21 FEB 1967		253,800	18·00
p. With violet 9·5 mm. phosphor bands		566,200	16·00
Q22 MAR 1967		395,000	15·00
p. With violet 9·5 mm. phosphor bands		580,800	15·00
Q23 APR 1967		395,400	16·00
p. With violet 9·5 mm. phosphor bands		632,200	15·00

Watermark Crowns, violet 9·5 mm. phosphor (No. S92)

Q24p MAY 1967		1,612,600	15·00
Q25p JUNE 1967		1,596,800	15·00
Q26p JULY 1967		776,600	15·00
Q27p AUG 1967		750,600	18·00

10s. BOOKLETS

Contents: 30 × 3d., 6 × 2d., 6 × 1½d., 6 × 1d., 6 × ½d. in panes of six
I. GREEN COVER AS TYPE D. Fully interleaved
Watermark Crowns (Nos. S4, S16, S28, S40, S70)

X1 No date (issued 10.4.61)		902,000	45·00
X2 OCT 1961	.. ..	483,200	45·00

Contents changed: 30 × 3d., 6 × 2½d., 6 × 1½d., 6 × 1d. in panes of six
Watermark Crowns (Nos. S17, S29, S57, S71)

X3 APR 1962	.. ..	524,680	35·00
X4 AUG 1962	.. ..	474,600	38·00
X5 MAR 1963	.. ..	493,200	35·00
X6 JULY 1963	.. ..	620,600	35·00
X7 DEC 1963	.. ..	606,600	35·00
X8 JULY 1964	.. ..	599,400	30·00
X9 DEC 1964	.. ..	415,200	50·00

10s. booklets in this composition were withdrawn from sale on 31 August 1965.

Contents changed: 24 × 4d., 6 × 3d., 6 × 1d. in panes of six
II. OCHRE COVER AS TYPE D. Fully interleaved
Watermarks Crowns (Nos. S17, S71, S85)

X10 AUG 1965 (issued 23.8.65)	.. ..	854,200	16·00
X11 DEC 1965	.. ..	658,800	18·00
X12 FEB 1966	.. ..	663,600	18·00
X13 AUG 1966	.. ..	686,800	14·00
X14 NOV 1966	.. ..	796,000	12·00

Watermark Crowns, violet phosphor with one side band on 3d. (Nos. S23 or S24, S78, S91 or S92)

X15p FEB 1967	.. .. (a) With violet 8 and 4 mm. phosphor bands ⎱	301,800	6·50
	(b) With violet 9·5 and 4 mm. phosphor bands ⎰		6·50

Watermark Crowns, violet 9·5 mm. phosphor with one centre 4 mm. band on 3d. (Nos. S24, S79, S92)

X16p AUG 1967	.. ..	1,488,800	6·00
X17p FEB 1968	.. ..	474,400	5·00

Section B.   Machin £.s.d. Issues with Violet Phosphor Bands

> NOTE. All booklets in this Section are fully interleaved

2s. BOOKLETS

Contents: 4 × 4d. in pane of four and 2 × 1d. and 2 × 3d. in pane of four arranged *se-tenant* horizontally

ORANGE-YELLOW COVER AS TYPE C
PVA gum (Nos. U2, U10, U12)

NP27 MAY 1968 (issued 6.4.68)	..	..	..	..	..	..	..	..	3,112,400	70
NP28 JULY 1968	..	..	..	..	..	..	..	..	1,971,685	70
NP29 AUG 1968	..	..	..	..	..	..	..	..		2·00

2s. booklets containing 3d. stamps were withdrawn on 14 September 1968.

Contents changed: 6 × 4d. in pane of four and in pane of two plus two printed labels *se-tenant* vertically

GREY COVER AS TYPE C
One centre phosphor band on *se-tenant* pane. PVA gum (Nos. U12, U13)

NP30 SEPT 1968 (issued 16.9.68)	..	..	..	..	..	..	..	2,497,400	55
NP31 JAN 1969	..	..	..	..	..	..	..	2,247,600	£100

Change to one centre phosphor band on 4 × 4d. pane. PVA gum (No. U13)

NP31a SEPT 1968 (issued 16.9.68)	..	..	..	..	..	..	*(incl. in* NP30)	£325
NP32 NOV 1968	..	..	..	..	..	..	..	2,397,400	55
NP33 JAN 1969	..	..	..	..	..	..	..	*(incl. in* NP31)	55

Change to 4d. bright vermilion with one centre phosphor band. PVA gum (No. U14)

NP34 MAR 1969 (issued 3.3.69)	..		90	NP39 JAN 1970 ..	.. 1,172,000	1·25
NP35 MAY 1969 ..	.. 2,092,000	1·10	NP40 MAR 1970 ..	.. 1,168,600	1·25
NP36 JULY 1969 ..	.. 436,000	1·40	NP41 MAY 1970 ..	.. 1,390,800	1·25
NP37 SEPT 1969 ..	.. 1,612,400	1·25	NP42 JULY 1970 ..	.. 1,023,800	1·25
NP38 NOV 1969 ..	.. 1,470,400	1·25	NP43 AUG 1970 ..	.. 1,037,800	1·25
b. Imprint error "HARRISOU" for "HARRISON"			NP44 OCT 1970 ..	.. 2,544,600	1·25
			NP45 DEC 1970 ..	.. 2,273,400	1·25

Where the first column for NP34 shows 1,952,000.

4s.6d. BOOKLETS

Contents: 12 × 4d., 6 × 1d. in panes of six
I. SLATE-BLUE COVER AS TYPE D
PVA gum (Nos. U2, U12)

LP45 MAY 1968 (issued 1.5.68)	..	..	..	..	..	..	..	742,600	4·00

Type E. With GPO Cypher   Type F. With Post Office Crown Symbol

(Des. Stuart Rose)

(In Types E/F the design subject is changed from time to time and this is indicated in brackets after the date)

II. BLUE COVER AS TYPE E showing Ships
PVA gum (Nos. U2, U12)

LP46 JULY 1968 *(Cutty Sark)* 427,600		1·25

Change to one centre phosphor band on 4d. PVA gum (Nos. U2, U13)

LP47 SEPT 1968 *(Golden Hind)* (issued 16.9.68) 1,052,800		1·25
LP48 NOV 1968 *(Discovery)* 1,009,000		1·25

Change to 4d. bright vermilion with one centre band. PVA gum (No. U14)

LP49 JAN 1969 *(Queen Elizabeth 2)* (issued 6.1.69) 775,200		1·25
LP50 MAR 1919 *(Sirius)* 1,105,800		1·25
LP51 MAY 1969 *(Sirius)* 993,200		1·60
LP52 JULY 1969 *(Dreadnought)* 932,000		2·25
LP53 SEPT 1969 *(Dreadnought)* 1,318,600		3·25
LP54 NOV 1969 *(Mauretania)* 1,469,400		2·50
LP55 JAN 1970 *(Mauretania)* 1,046,600		2·50
LP56 MAR 1970 *(Victory)* 872,400		2·50
LP57 MAY 1970 *(Victory)* 515,800		5·00

III. BLUE COVER AS TYPE F showing Ships
PVA gum (Nos. U2, U14)

LP58 AUG 1970 *(The Sovereign of the Seas)* 412,600		2·50
LP59 OCT 1970 *(The Sovereign of the Seas)* 746,600		4·75

5s. BOOKLETS

Type E. With GPO Cypher   Type F. With Post Office Crown Symbol

(Des. Stuart Rose)

Contents: 12 × 5d. in panes of six

I. CINNAMON COVER AS TYPE E showing English Homes
PVA gum (No. U17)

HP26 DEC 1968 (Ightham Mote) (issued 27.11.68) 978,000		1·10
HP27 FEB 1969 (Little Moreton Hall) 1,510,200		1·10
HP28 APR 1969 (Long Melford Hall) 1,963,200		1·10
HP29 JUNE 1969 (Long Melford Hall) 1,821,000		1·50
HP30 AUG 1969 (Long Melford Hall) 1,660,800		1·50

II. CINNAMON COVER AS TYPE F showing English Homes
PVA gum (No. U17)

HP31 OCT 1969 (Mompesson House) 2,251,200		1·50
HP32 DEC 1969 (Mompesson House) 960,200		2·40
HP33 FEB 1970 (Cumberland Terrace) 910,800		2·00

431

Type P
(Des. Peter Gauld)
Issued to publicise the " Philympia " International
Philatelic Exhibition, London, September 1970

III. CINNAMON COVER AS TYPE P. Stitched in red
PVA gum (No. U17)

HP34 (no date) (issued 3.3.70)	..	..	..	..	..	..	.. 1,019,800	1·00

IV. CINNAMON COVER AS TYPE F showing English Homes
PVA gum (No. U17)

HP35 JUNE 1970 (The Vineyard, Saffron Walden)	..	..	..	..	.. 1,814,400	2·00
HP36 AUG 1970 (The Vineyard, Saffron Walden)	..	..	..	..	.. 2,076,800	2·00
HP37 OCT 1970 (Mereworth Castle)	..	..	..	..	..	.. 3,301,400	2·25
HP38 DEC 1970 (Mereworth Castle)	..	..	..	..	..	.. 5,517,680	2·50

6s. BOOKLETS

Contents: 18 × 4d. in panes of six
I. CLARET COVER AS TYPE D
Gum arabic (No. U11 (1))

QP28 SEPT 1967 (issued 21.9.67) ..	..	..	..	..	..	..	.. 1,345,000	26·00
QP29 OCT 1967	..	..	..	..	..	..	..	.. 1,487,400	28·00
QP30 NOV 1967	..	..	..	..	..	..	..	.. 1,522,200	30·00
QP31 DEC 1967	..	..	..	..	..	..	..	.. 1,531,000	32·00
QP32 JAN 1968	..	..	..	..	..	..	..	.. 1,251,400	32·00

Change to 4d. deep olive-brown. Gum arabic (No. U11 (2))

QP33 FEB 1968	..	..	..	..	..	..	..	.. 1,314,400	32·00
QP34 MAR 1968	..	..	..	..	..	..	..	.. 1,090,600	26·00
QP35 APR 1968	..	..	..	..	..	..	..	.. 1,127,800	24·00
QP36 MAY 1968	..	..	..	..	..	..	..	.. 1,398,000	13·00

Change to PVA gum (No. U12 (2))

QP37 MAY 1968	..	..	..	..	..	..	..	.. (*incl. in* QP36)	£200

Type E. With GPO Cypher   Type F. With Post Office Crown Symbol
(Des. Stuart Rose)

II. ORANGE-RED COVER AS TYPE E showing Birds
PVA gum (No. U12 (2))

QP38 JUNE 1968 (Kingfisher) (issued 4.6.68)	..	..	..	..	..	1,212,000	1·25
QP39 JULY 1968 (Kingfisher)	..	..	..	..	..	1,195,000	5·00
QP40 AUG 1968 (Peregrine Falcon)	..	..	..	..	..	1,223,800	1·25

Change to one centre phosphor band. PVA gum (No. U13)

QP41 SEPT 1968 (Peregrine Falcon) (issued 16.9.68)	..	..	..	..	1,010,200	1·25
QP42 OCT 1968 (Pied Woodpecker)	..	..	..	..	..	1,277,800	1·50
QP43 NOV 1968 (Pied Woodpecker)	..	..	..	..	..	1,006,200	1·75
QP44 DEC 1968 (Great Crested Grebe)	..	..	..	..	..	975,600	1·75
QP45 JAN 1969 (Barn Owl)	..	..	..	..	..	1,017,000	1·75

Change to 4d. bright vermilion with one centre phosphor band. PVA gum (No. U14)

> MIXED GUMS. Nos. QP46/7 exist with gum arabic and PVA panes in the same booklet. The mixed gums are indicated by the code letters " G " (Gum arabic) and " P " (PVA), starting with the first pane of the booklet.

QP46 FEB 1969 (Barn Owl) (issued 20.2.69) (PPP) .. .. ..   1·75

(a) Combination GGP		95·00
(b) Combination GPG		95·00
(c) Combination GPP	1,035,200	50·00
(d) Combination PGG		95·00
(e) Combination PGP		50·00
(f) Combination PPG		50·00
(g) Combination GGG		£125

QP47 MAR 1969 (Jay) (PPP) .. ..   1·75

(a) Combination GGP		95·00
(b) Combination PGP	1,424,400	50·00
(c) Combination PPG		50·00
(d) Combination GPP		50·00
(e) Combination GPG		95·00

QP48 MAY 1969 (Jay)	..	..	..	..	..	533,800	2·00
QP49 JULY 1969 (Puffin)	..	..	..	..	..	498,400	2·00
QP50 SEPT 1969 (Puffin)	..	..	..	..	..	506,200	2·25

III. ORANGE-RED COVER AS TYPE F showing Birds
PVA gum (No. U14)

QP51 NOV 1969 (Cormorant)	..	..	..	..	..	472,600	2·25
QP52 JAN 1970 (Cormorant)	..	..	..	..	..	487,800	2·25
QP53 APR 1970 (Wren)	..	..	..	..	..	512,800	2·25
QP54 AUG 1970 (Golden Eagle)	..	..	..	..	..	570,600	2·50
QP55 OCT 1970 (Golden Eagle)	..	..	..	..	..	754,800	2·50

10s. BOOKLETS

Type E I   Type E II

Pictorial Cover with GPO Cypher

(Des. Stuart Rose)

Two types of Cypher:
Type I. GPO in clear letters. 10s. Booklets XP4/5
Type II. GPO in black letters. 10s. Booklets XP6/10

Contents: 24 × 4d., 6 × 3d., 6 × 1d. in panes of six
BRIGHT PURPLE COVER AS TYPE E I showing Explorers
  PVA gum (Nos. U2, U9, U12)

XP4 MAY 1968 (Livingstone) (issued 25.3.68)	..	..	..	..	..	..	713,200	3·50
XP5 AUG 1968 (Livingstone)	..	..	..	..	..	..	..	39,497	3·50

Contents changed: 12 × 5d., 14 × 4d., 4 × 1d., in panes of six and one horizontally *se-tenant* pane of 2 × 4d., and 4 × 1d.
YELLOW-GREEN COVER AS TYPE E II showing Explorers
  PVA gum (Nos. U3, U13, U17)

XP6 SEPT 1968 (Scott) (issued 16.9.68)	..	..	..	..	..	..	1,513,400	3·50

Change to 4d. bright vermilion but *se-tenant* pane comprises 1d. with two phosphor bands and 4d. with one left side phosphor band. PVA gum (Nos. U2, U14, U16, U17).   For booklets with mixed gum, see note above No. QP46

XP 7 FEB 1969 (Mary Kingsley) (issued 6.1.69)	..	..	..	..	2,338,200	2·25
XP 8 MAY 1969 (Mary Kingsley) (PPPPP)	..						3·50
			(a) Combination PPPGP	1,165,200	50·00
			(b) Combination PPGPP		£140
XP 9 AUG 1969 (Shackleton)	..	..	..	..	..	..	1,765,600	2·25
XP10 NOV 1969 (Shackleton)	..	..	..	..	..	..	1,176,000	5·00

Type F

(Des. Stuart Rose)

Pictorial Cover with Post Office
Corporation Crown Symbol

YELLOW-GREEN COVER AS TYPE F showing Explorers
  PVA gum (Nos. U2, U14, U16, U17)

XP11 FEB 1970 (Frobisher) (issued 2.2.70)	..	..	..	..	..	..	490,200	5·00
XP12 NOV 1970 (Captain Cook)	..	..	..	..	..	..	..	737,400	5·00

£1 BOOKLET ("STAMPS FOR COOKS")

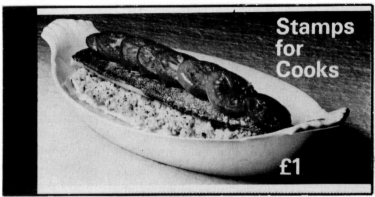

Type X

Contents: 18 × 5d., 36 × 4d., 6 × 1d., in panes of fifteen and one horizontally
se-tenant pane of 3 × 5d., 6 × 4d., and 6 × 1d. There are 12 recipes on interleaving pages and on *se-tenant* labels attached to each pane.

FULL COLOUR COVER AS TYPE X size 6 × 2⅞ in. showing "Baked Stuffed Haddock"

Pane of fifteen 5d. has two phosphor bands, panes of fifteen 4d. have one centre phosphor
band but *se-tenant* pane has two phosphor bands on 1d. and 5d. and one side band on 4d.
(three stamps with band at left and three stamps with band at right)

ZP1 (no date) (issued 1.12.69) (stapled)	10,848	65·00
ZP1a As last but booklet is sewn with thread	374,902	10·00
(s) Each stamp overprinted "Specimen". Stapled		£2000
(sa) Each stamp cancelled with Philatelic Bureau postmark of 8 June 1971. Stitched		£1800

Examples of this booklet are known with one or two colours omitted from the cover.

Examples of No. ZP1sa were issued as specimens to firms and organizations interested in
sponsoring similar booklets.

APPENDIX HB

Postage Rates

Postage rates from 1635 have been researched from official records and the following extract is reproduced with kind permission of the Post Office. The rates given apply only to the period covered by this Catalogue.

Letter Post
The Treasury was empowered to regulate rates of postage, and subsequent changes were made by Treasury Warrant.

Date	Rates of Charge		
1 May 1952	2oz	.. ..	2½d.
	4oz	.. ..	3d.
Then 1d. for each additional 2oz.			

Date	Rates of Charge		
1 January 1956	2oz	.. ..	2½d.
Then 1½d. for each additional 2oz.			

1 October 1957	1oz	.. ..	3d.
	2oz	.. ..	4½d.
Then 1½d. for each additional 2oz.			

Date	Rates of Charge		
17 May 1965	2oz	.. ..	4d.
Each additional 2oz. up to 1lb. 2d.			
Each additional 2oz. thereafter 3d.			

3 October 1966	2oz.	.. ..	4d.
Each additional 2oz up to 1lb. 2d.			
Each additional 2 oz. up to 1lb. 8oz. 3d.			
Over 1lb. 8oz. up to 2lb. 3s.6d.			
Each additional 1lb. 2s.			

Introduction of the first and second class services for letters and cards.

Date	Weight not exceeding	First Class	Second Class
16 September 1968	4oz... ..	5d.	4d.
	6oz... ..	9d.	6d.
	8oz... ..	1s. 0d.	8d.
	10oz... ..	1s. 3d.	10d.
	12oz... ..	1s. 6d.	1s. 0d.
	14oz... ..	1s. 9d.	1s. 2d.
	1lb. 0oz... ..	2s. 0d.	1s. 4d.
	1lb. 2oz... ..	2s. 3d.	1s. 6d.
	1lb. 4oz... ..	2s. 6d.	1s. 7d.
	1lb. 6oz... ..	2s. 9d.	1s. 8d.
	1lb. 8oz... ..	3s. 0d.	1s. 9d.
	2lb. 0oz... ..	4s. 0d.	Not admissible over 1½lbs.
Each additional 1lb. 2s.			

Postcards
From 1925 the maximum size allowed was 5⅞″ × 4⅛″ and the minimum size was 4″ × 2¾″.

Date	Charge		
1 May 1940	.. .. ..	2d.
1 October 1957	.. .. ..	2½d.
17 May 1965	.. .. ..	3d.

Printed Papers

Date	Rates of Charge		
1 June 1951	4oz.	.. ..	1½d.
Then ½d. for each additional 2oz. up to 2lb.			

| **1 January 1956** | 2oz | .. .. | 1½d. |
| Then 1d. for each additional 2oz. | | | |

| **1 June 1956** | 4oz. | .. .. | 2d. |
| Then 1d. for each additional 2oz. | | | |

1 October 1957	2oz.	.. ..	2d.
	4oz.	.. ..	4d.
Then 1d. for each additional 2oz.			

Date	Rates of Charge		
1 October 1961	2oz.	.. ..	2½d.
	4oz.	.. ..	4d.

17 May 1965			
Not over 2oz.	.. ..	3d.
Not over 4oz.	.. ..	5d.
Each additional 2oz.	.. ..	1d.

Newspaper Post

From 1870 the charge had been ½d. per copy irrespective of weight, but from 1 November 1915 the maximum weight permitted was 2lb.

Date	Charge Per Copy not exceeding			Date	Charge Per Copy not exceeding		
1 July 1940	4oz.	..	.. ..1½d.	**1 October 1961**	6oz.	..	.. .. 3d.

Then ½d. for each additional 4oz. · Then 1½d. for each additional 6oz.

Date	Charge Per Copy	Date	Charge Per Copy
1 June 1956	6oz. .. .. .. 2d.	**17 May 1965**	2oz. .. .. .. 3d.

Then 1d for each additional 6oz. · 4oz. .. .. .. 5d.

1 October 1957 6oz. .. .. ..2½d.
Then 1½d. for each 6oz.

Then 1d. for each additional 2oz. Per copy regulation abolished

Articles for the Blind

This service was made free of charge from 17 May 1965 (maximum weight 15lb.).

Date	Rates of Charge		Date	Rates of Charge	
1 July 1940	2lb.	½d.	**12 April 1954**	2lb.	½d.
	5lb.	1d.		5lb.	1d.
	8lb.	1½d.		8lb.	1½d.
	11lb.	2d.		11lb.	2d.
	15lb.	2½d.		15lb.	2½d.

Express Service

Service 1. Express by special messenger all the way.

Date	Charges	Notes
1934	6d. per mile plus cost of special conveyance if used. Weight fee (for packets over 1lb.) 3d.	Charge for additional articles 1d. per article after the first. Waiting fee 2d. for each 10 minutes after the first 10 minutes
1 January 1956	1s. per mile plus cost of special conveyance if used	Additional articles 2½d. for each item beyond the first. Waiting fee 4d. for each 10 minutes after the first 10 minutes
1 October 1957	As above	Additional articles 3d. for each item beyond the first
17 May 1965	3s. per mile plus cost of special conveyance if used	Each additional article 4d. for each item beyond the first. Waiting fee 1s. for each 10 minutes after the first 10 minutes

Service 2. Special Delivery at the request of the sender. Post Office messenger from the delivery office after transmission by post.

Date	Charges	Notes
1 January 1956	Full postage plus special fee of 1s. (from 1934 6d.).	If a special conveyance was used the actual cost, or if that was unknown, 1s. per mile
17 May 1965	Full postage plus special fee of 3s.	As above but 6s. per mile
16 September 1968	As above but only for first class service.	

There was also a Limited Sunday Special Delivery Service. Charges were as for Service 2 except the special fee was 1s.6d. in 1934; 3s. from 1 January 1956 and 9s. from 17 May 1965 in addition to full postage.
The service providing for the express delivery of a message received by telephone was withdrawn on 30 December 1955.

Service 3. Express delivery all the way at the request of the addressee. Charges were the same as for Service 1. Additional articles 2d. for every ten beyond the first (from 1934 1d.). From 17 May 1965 this charge was increased to 6d. for every ten after the first.

Railex

This service was introduced on 1 January 1934. It provided for the conveyance of a postal packet to a railway station by Post Office messenger for despatch on the first available train, and for its immediate delivery by Post Office messenger from the station of destination.

Date	Charge	
1 July 1940	Not exceeding 2oz.	3s. od.
	Over 2oz. and up to 1lb. ..	3s. 6d.
1 January 1956	Not over 2oz.	6s. od.
	Not over 1lb.	7s. od.
17 May 1965	Charge per packet	20s. od.
	(irrespective of weight but not exceeding 1lb.)	

Official Parcel Post
This service had first been introduced on 1 August 1883.

Date	Rates of Postage		Date	Rates of Postage	
31 March 1952	2lb. ..	11d.	**1 October 1961**	2lb. ..	2s. od.
	3lb. ..	1s. 1d.		3lb. ..	2s. 3d.
	4lb. ..	1s. 3d.		4lb. ..	2s. 6d.
	5lb. ..	1s. 5d.		5lb. ..	2s. 9d.
	6lb. ..	1s. 7d.		6lb. ..	3s. od.
	7lb. ..	1s. 9d.		7lb. ..	3s. 3d.
	8lb. ..	1s. 10d.		8lb. ..	3s. 6d.
	11lb. ..	1s. 11d.		11lb. ..	3s. 9d.
	15lb. ..	2s. od.		15lb. ..	4s. od.
7 April 1953	2lb. ..	1s. od.			
	3lb. ..	1s. 2d.	**29 April 1963**	2lb. ..	2s. od.
	4lb. ..	1s. 4d.		3lb. ..	2s. 3d.
	5lb. ..	1s. 6d.		4lb. ..	2s. 6d.
	6lb. ..	1s. 8d.		5lb. ..	2s. 9d.
	7lb. ..	1s. 10d.		6lb. ..	3s. od.
	8lb. ..	1s. 11d.		8lb. ..	3s. 6d.
	11lb. ..	2s. od,		10lb. ..	4s. od.
	15lb. ..	2s. 1d.		12lb. ..	4s. 6d.
12 April 1954	2lb. ..	1s. 1d.		15lb. ..	5s. od.
	3lb. ..	1s. 3d.		18lb. ..	5s. 9d.
	4lb. ..	1s. 6d.		22lb. ..	6s. 6d.
	5lb. ..	1s. 8d.	Increased weight limit of 22 lbs. introduced		
	6lb. ..	1s. 10d.	18 February 1963		
	7lb. ..	2s. od.			
	8lb. ..	2s. 1d.	**17 May 1965**	2lb. ..	2s. 9d.
	11lb. ..	2s. 3d.		3lb. ..	3s. od.
	15lb. ..	2s. 4d.		4lb. ..	3s. 3d.
				6lb. ..	3s. 6d.
1 January 1956	2lb. ..	1s. 3d.		8lb. ..	4s. od.
	3lb. ..	1s. 5d.		10lb. ..	4s. 6d.
	4lb. ..	1s. 8d.		14lb. ..	5s. 6d.
	5lb. ..	1s. 11d.		18lb. ..	6s. 6d.
	6lb. ..	2s. 1d.		22lb. ..	7s. 6d.
	7lb. ..	2s. 3d.			
	8lb. ..	2s. 6d.	**3 October 1966**	(Ordinary Rate)	
	11lb. ..	2s. 8d.		1½lb. ..	2s. 6d.
	15lb. ..	2s. 9d.		2lb. ..	3s. od.
1 June 1956	2lb. ..	1s. 4d.		6lb. ..	4s. 6d.
	3lb. ..	1s. 6d.		10lb. ..	6s. od.
	4lb. ..	1s. 9d.		14lb. ..	7s. 6d.
	5lb. ..	2s. od.		18lb. ..	9s. od.
	6lb. ..	2s. 3d.		22lb. ..	10s. 6d.
	7lb. ..	2s. 6d.	(Local delivery) As for ordinary less 1s.od.		
	8lb. ..	2s. 9d.	at each step.		
	15lb. ..	3s. od.			
			16 September 1968	(Ordinary Rate)	
1 October 1957	2lb. ..	1s. 6d.		1½lb. ..	2s. 6d.
	3lb. ..	1s. 9d.		2lb. ..	3s. od.
	4lb. ..	2s. od.		6lb. ..	4s. 6d.
	5lb. ..	2s. 3d.		10lb. ..	6s. od.
	6lb. ..	2s. 6d.		14lb. ..	7s. 6d.
	7lb. ..	2s. 9d.		18lb. ..	9s. od.
	8lb. ..	3s. od.		22lb. ..	10s. 6d.
	11lb. ..	3s. 3d.	(Local delivery) As for ordinary less 1s.od.		
	15lb. ..	3s. 6d.	at each step.		

Further Reading

The following list is representative of the major works relating to Queen Elizabeth II pre-decimal issues, stamp booklets, postmarks and postal history. It is culled in part from *A List of Books on the Postal History, and Adhesive Postage and Revenue Stamps of Great Britain*, compiled by Arnold M. Strange (2nd edition, 1971, Great Britain Philatelic Society, London). Later publications are also included.

STAMPS

Bater, Gerry and The Lord Spens. *The Queen Elizabeth II Waterlow "Castle" High Values, 1955–1958.* (1990. The G.B. Overprints Society.)

Hine, I. S. and Loveland, R. A. *Great Britain, Queen Elizabeth II. Check List of Photogravure Cylinder Numbers, 1952–1963.* (1964, A. L. Bert.)

J.L. *Shelley Simplified Catalogue of Varieties on Queen Elizabeth II Postage Stamps.* (11th Edn. 1968. Shelley Stamps, London. Supplement 1969/70.)

Langston, Colin M. *Catalogue of Flaws on Q.E. G.B. Sheet Stamps.* (1966. The Author, London.)

Langston, Colin M. *A Priced Catalogue and Guide to Collecting Queen Elizabeth Great Britain Stamp Booklets. March 1953 to December 1963.* (1964. The Author, London.)

Langston, Colin M. *The Complete List of Flaws on Queen Elizabeth Great Britain (1st Design) Stamps from Booklets and Coils.* (1969. The Author, London.)

Langston, Colin M. and Corliss, H. C. *Stamps of Great Britain Issued in Rolls and the Machines which Use Them. An Historical Survey including a Check List of the Rolls issued since 1938.* (1961. The Authors, London.)

Mackay, James A. *British Stamps.* (1985. Longman Group Ltd., London.)

Myall, D. G. A. *The Deegam Se-tenant Catalogue of G.B. Elizabethan Definitives.* (1979. The Author, Bridport, Dorset.)

Myall, D. G. A. *The Deegam Catalogue of Elizabethan Coil Leaders.* (1987. The Author, Bridport, Dorset.)

Potter, David. *British Elizabethan Stamps.* (1971. B.T. Batsford, London.)

Rigo de Righi, A. G. *The Stamps of Royalty; British Commemorative Issues for Royal Occasions, 1935–1972.* (1973. The National Postal Museum, London.)

Rose, Stuart. *Royal Mail Stamps—A Survey of British Stamp Design.* (1980. Phaidon Press, Oxford.)

The Shalan Catalogue. A Guide to the Missing Phosphor Lines Issues of Queen Elizabeth II Great Britain. (3rd. Edn. 1971. Shelley Stamps, and B. Alan Ltd., London.)

Wijman, J. J. *Postage Stamps of Great Britain and their History.* (1986. The Author, Netherlands.)

Williams, L. N. and M. *Commemorative Postage Stamps of Great Britain.* (1967. Arco Publications, London.)

POST OFFICE BOOKLETS OF STAMPS

Alexander, Jean and Newbery, Leonard F. *British Stamp Booklets. Part 1, Series 1; Part 2, Series 1/2; Part 3, Series 3/5; Part 4, Series 6, Part 5, Series 7; Part 6, Series 8/9, Part 7, Series 10/11* (1987–93 in seven parts. The Great Britain Philatelic Society, London.) Parts 4/7 contain information on booklets issued from 1951/70.

POSTAL HISTORY AND POSTMARKS

Awcock, P. G. *Automatic Letter Sorting in the United Kingdom.* (7th. Edn. 1985. The Author, Haywards Heath.)

Bennett, J. Bruce, Parsons, Cyril, R. H., and Pearson, G. R. *Current Machine Postmarks of the United Kingdom.* (1963. British Postmark Society, London.)

Dagnall, H. *The Mechanised Sorting of Mail.* (1976. The Author, Leicester.)

Daunton, M. J. *Royal Mail: The Post Office since 1840.* (1985. The Athlone Press, London.)

Farrugia, Jean. *A Guide to Post Office Archives.* (1986. The Post Office, London.)

Holland, F. C. *Introduction to British Postmark Collecting.* (1971.)

Langston, Colin M. *Surcharge and Explanatory Dies of Great Britain.* (1964. The Author.)

Mackay, James A. *The Parcel Post of the British Isles.* (1982. The Author, Dumfries.)

Mackay, James A. *Registered Mail of the British Isles.* (1983. The Author, Dumfries.)

Mackay James A. *Scottish Postmarks 1693–1978.* (1978. The Author, Dumfries.)

Mackay James A. *English and Welsh Postmarks since 1840.* (1980. The Author, Dumfries.)

Mackay, James A. *British Post Office Numbers 1924–1969.* (1981. The Author, Dumfries.)

Mackay, James A. *Surcharged Mail of the British Isles.* (1984. The Author, Dumfries.)

Mackay, James A. *Official Mail of the British Isles.* (1983. The Author, Dumfries.)

Mackay, James A. *Machine Cancellations of Scotland.* (1986). The Author, Dumfries.)

Mackay, James A. *Postal History Annual.* (From 1979. The Author, Dumfries.)

Muir, Douglas N. and Robinson Martin. *An Introduction to British Postal Mechanisation.* (1980). Postal Mechanisation Study Circle, Henley-on-Thames, Oxon. Supplements 1981, 1983 and 1992.)

Parsons, Cyril R. H., Peachey, Colin G. and Pearson, George R. *Local Publicity Slogan Postmarks 1963–1969.* (1981. 2nd edn. The Authors, Herts.)

Parsons, Cyril R. H., Peachey, Colin G. and Pearson, George R. *Slogan Postmarks of the Seventies.* (1980. The Authors, London.)

Parsons, Cyril R. H., Peachey, Colin G. and Pearson, George. *Collecting Slogan Postmarks 1917–69.* (1986. The Authors, Aylesbury.)

Pask, Brian and Peachey, Colin, G. *Twenty Years of First Day Postmarks.* (1983. British Postmark Society, Herts.)

Peach, Jack. *U.K. Machine Marks.* (1982. 2nd Edn. Vera Trinder Ltd., London.)

Pearson, George R. *Special Event Postmarks of the United Kingdom, Vol. II 1883–1983.* (1984. 3rd Edn. British Postmark Society, Herts.)

Pearson, George R. *Special Event Postmarks of the United Kingdom. Vol. I "The Early Years" 1851–1962* (1991 4th. Edn. British Postmark Society, Herts.)

Reynolds, Paul. *The Machine Cancellations of Wales 1905–1985.* (1985. Welsh Philatelic Society, Swansea.)

Swan, V. *British Slogan Cancellations, 1917–1960.* (1960. The Author, Alton.)

Wellsted, Hilary. *Express Service 1891–1971.* (1986. Postal History Society, Tonbridge.)

Whitney, Dr. J. T., Peachey, Colin G. and Crookes, V. Brian. *Collect British Postmarks.* (1993 6th Edn. British Postmark Society, Herts.)

COMPLETE YOUR SET

No stamp collector likes to have incomplete sets – whether you are talking about Tudor Crowns, St Edward Crowns or the Crown of the SG Catalogue range – the **Great Britain Specialised Catalogue.**

Volume 1	(item 0285)	**Queen Victoria**
Volume 2	(item 0286)	**King Edward VII to King George VI**
Volume 3	(item 2810)	**Queen Elizabeth II pre-decimal issues**
Volume 4	(item 2820)	**Queen Elizabeth II decimal definitive issues**
Volume 5	(item 2891)	**Queen Elizabeth II decimal special issues**

INTERESTED IN WILDINGS?

Then you need the Stanley Gibbons Uvitec Micro Ultra Violet Lamp.

As all GB collectors know, the 'Wilding' definitives went through quite a number of changes during their period of issue, with some of the combinations of paper and phosphor type being extremely hard to find.

Unfortunately not all of these desirable items can be spotted with the naked eye, many of them requiring the aid of a shortwave ultra violet lamp for positive identification.

Following exhaustive research and tests Stanley Gibbons believe that they have come up with the perfect answer to the 'Wilding' collectors prayer.

The Stanley Gibbons Uvitec Micro Short Wave Ultra Violet Lamp.
MODERN – designed for today's collector and produced by the leading manufacturer of UV lamps in Britain.
EFFECTIVE – detects phosphors, paper and ink variations, fakes, forgeries and repairs.
SAFE – the specially designed hood protects the eyes from direct UV light.
SMART and ROBUST – well designed plastic casing built to withstand regular use.
CONVENIENT – battery powered, ideal for taking to stamp shops and fairs.
EASY TO USE – simple press button, on-off operation.
SMALL and LIGHT – slips easily into the pocket. Weighs less than 6oz (with batteries) and therefore suitable for prolonged use.
VERSATILE – comes with its own detachable viewing hood allowing effective daylight use. Suitable for studying individual stamps or for 'sweeping'.
CLEAR INSTRUCTIONS – are provided with every lamp.
THE PRICE – not only one of the best ultra violet lamps on the market but also one of the least expensive.

COMPLETE YOUR SET

No stamp collector likes to have incomplete sets – whether you are talking about Tudor Crowns, St Edward Crowns or the Crown of the SG Catalogue range – the **Great Britain Specialised Catalogue.**

Volume 1   (item 0285)   **Queen Victoria**
Volume 2   (item 0286)   **King Edward VII to King George VI**
Volume 3   (item 2810)   **Queen Elizabeth II pre-decimal issues**
Volume 4   (item 2820)   **Queen Elizabeth II decimal definitive issues**
Volume 5   (item 2891)   **Queen Elizabeth II decimal special issues**

Volume 1 is available either case bound or paperback

HOW TO KEEP RIGHT UP TO DATE

A handbook-catalogue such as this volume can only be published every two or three years. For more simplified but up to date details of the current GB market it is wise to augment the information provided in the Great Britain Specialised Catalogue with

Collect British Stamps (item 0289) – published each November. The World's most successful Catalogue, published in full colour.

Great Britain CONCISE Stamp Catalogue (item 2887) – published each May. A one-volume Catalogue based on the GB listing in Part 1 with a host of additional information.

THE MAGAZINE FOR THE GB COLLECTOR

Each month **Gibbons Stamp Monthly** contains a 'British Stamps' section with regular coverage of new issues, Machins, varieties and books, including the supplements to the Great Britain Specialised Catalogue. Feature articles cover a variety of topics from Queen Victoria line-engraved to modern postal history and a varied selection of advertisements provide the very latest in market information.

Please send for a free specimen copy and subscription details to **Hugh Jefferies, Stanley Gibbons Magazines, Parkside, Ringwood, Hampshire BH24 3SH.**

Frequent articles on Great Britain stamps and postal history in